WINE of LIFE

By CHARLES GORHAM

WINE of LIFE

A novel about Balzac

by

CHARLES GORHAM

THE DIAL PRESS   1958   NEW YORK

DESIGNED BY WILLIAM R. MEINHARDT
PRINTED IN THE UNITED STATES OF AMERICA
BY THE HADDON CRAFTSMEN, SCRANTON, PENNA.

"It seems to me that Balzac is the greatest novelist the world has produced."
W. Somerset Maugham

The Revolutionary Wind . . .

IN PARIS, IN
Père-Lachaise, Honoré de Balzac sleeps, along with other famous
Frenchmen and several thousands of his worthy but less eminent
fellow-countrymen. Père-Lachaise is on a height that commands
a view of the city. Héloise and Abélard are buried there, with
Musset, Molière, Rachel, La Fontaine, Oscar Wilde, and scores
of others famous enough to be remembered by nothing more than
the last name. Here too, buried where they fell, are three hundred
Communards of 1870, shot down at the Mur des Fédérés by troops
from Versailles in white breeches. Each year, Paris workingmen
put scarlet roses on their common grave. Each year, some young
novelist puts flowers on the grave marked: BALZAC.

*"Paris can be a desert for the heart, but at certain moments,
from the heights of Père-Lachaise, there blows a revolutionary
wind that suddenly fills that desert with flags and fallen glories."*

So writes another Frenchman, Albert Camus.

Paris was often Balzac's desert, but it was his garden too, as
was all of France. When the Existentialist wind whistles down
from Père-Lachaise, part of the breath of life in it comes from
the bones of Balzac.

He was a man engaged in pursuit, sometimes frantic, sometimes
dogged, sometimes reckless, sometimes shrewd, but always he was
in pursuit, of love, fame, money, women, and always, in the end,
of truth. A strong man was Balzac, driven by a force he did not
comprehend and sometimes hated, at last consumed in the blaze
of his own talent.

What drove him, from cradle to grave?

What caused him to become a crucible in which masterpieces
were created?

Let us look at Balzac's childhood, beginning on the day after
it began, in Touraine, a century and a half ago. . . .

WINE of LIFE

Chapter 1

THE PARISH CLERK of the City of Tours read off the words he was entering into his brassbound record book, to the pages of which were committed the vital statistics of the town. The room was close and smelled musty. The scratching of the clerk's quill pen made a counterpoint to his voice, the monotonous, disenchanted voice of a petty official.

"Twenty-first of May, 1799," he read. "Second of Prairial, Seventh Year of the French Republic, there appeared before me, the citizen Bernard-François Balzac, Proprietor, dwelling in this commune, rue de l'Armée de l'Italie, Chardonnet Section, Number 25, to notify the proper authority of the birth of a son. Said child is legitimate and is to receive the name Honoré Balzac."

The clerk blew his nose with bureaucratic force and dusted the wet ink with sand.

"There you are, Monsieur Balzac," he said. "All official. Permanent record."

Bernard-François Balzac touched the record book and laughed.

"The French Republic is a marvel," he said. "Birth, death, marriage, murder, all made official in the same prose. I tell you, my friend, things will be different when Bonaparte takes command in Paris."

The clerk sniffed and returned the book to its shelf behind him.

"France is a republic, monsieur," he said. "In a republic, the people command, not a Corsican upstart. Besides, in any case, the records must be kept . . . under the King, the Republic, or Bonaparte. No matter what happens in Paris, the records must be kept, as they have always been kept."

"Evidently," said Bernard-François good-naturedly. "Pay no attention to me, my friend. When a man has a son at my age, he is entitled to a little joke."

3

He shook hands with the clerk, paid his fee, and departed, glad to be out of the stuffy office, which stank of petty officialdom. Bernard-François served the government too, but on a loftier echelon. He was Commissariat-General for the 22nd Infantry Division, army of the French Republic, the official in charge of military procurement for the City of Tours and the area around it. A big man, handsome and vital, he was dressed in accordance with his position as a member of the upper bourgeoisie of Tours. His blue frock coat was of excellent cut, faced with the best velvet. The standing collar was trimmed with gold braid. His fawn colored trousers were sleek and close-fitting. His linen was immaculate. He carried a slim gold-headed stick and moved with elegant self-confidence, the picture of a man in whom success has not destroyed the taste for living, or the talent for smiling at himself on occasion. He was fifty-one, but he moved with the verve of a man in his thirties. He was a ladies' man and looked it. The child born yesterday morning was the first to bear the Balzac name, but not the first to have sprung from the Balzac loins, nor would he be the last.

His carriage and driver waited for him in front of the City Hall and when he appeared, the driver began to climb down from his box. Bernard-François shook his head.

"It's a fine day. I'm going to stretch my legs for a bit," he said. "I've had a night of it, you know." The driver touched his cap, smiled, and prodded the horses with the butt of his whip.

"As you command, monsieur."

The carriage moved off, raising a cloud of cinnamon-colored dust. Bernard-François twirled his stick and stepped briskly over the cobbles. "I ought to go straight home," he said to himself. "But, Name of the Lord! I don't want to."

He paused for a moment, twirling his gold-headed stick. "After all," he cajoled himself. "A man doesn't have a son and heir every day in the week. He is entitled to enjoy the affair."

He crossed the square and turned into a narrow street that led to the bank of the River Loire. Workmen in blue smocks touched their caps respectfully, as they did in Tours to a gentleman, Republic or no Republic. Everyone knew that Bernard-François had done well under the King, that he did well now, under the Directory, that he would continue to do well, even if the Corsican took command when he returned from his wars in North Africa.

4

In Bernard-François they recognized a type to be admired and envied, the kind of man upon whom fortune insists on smiling, no matter what the political season.

Bernard-François agreed with them. He was proud of his status and enjoyed it all the more because it had been gained through his own efforts, without the advantages of birth or inherited wealth. He had been born in the south, in a poor village in Languedoc, the son of an ordinary farm laborer. Almost from birth, he had shown such quickness of mind that the parish priest had singled him out and given him the rudiments of an education, hoping to see him ordained. When he had learned to read and write, to do sums and offer a sampling of Latin, Bernard-François Balssa, for such was his name, had realized that his instincts were not for the cloth. The priestly vows of poverty made no appeal to his nature. The disappointed curé gave him a few francs from the parish funds, blessed him, and sent him on his way.

He went to Paris and made a place for himself in the fierce, dangerous and royal city, using his wits and his courage. There was no pomposity in him, but no false modesty either. He regarded himself with honest admiration. He had a mild literary flair, and this had prompted him to change his name from Balssa to that of the seventeenth century moralist, Louis Guez de Balzac, though modesty persuaded him to omit the particle "de."

Meditating, this pillar of the French Republic paused when he reached the bank of the Loire. He stood on the quay, leaning against the granite wall. A barge, propelled by an enormous, lazy sweep, was going upstream toward Orléans. On the stern the republican tricolor fluttered bravely in the light breeze. Whether because of the fine day, or the birth of his son, or merely because he was French, Bernard-François was oddly moved by the gallant bit of bunting. He lifted his hat and waved to the bargeman, who took his pipe from his mouth, stood up, and waved in return.

For a Frenchman, the times were propitious, in this Eighteen Hundreth Year of Our Lord. Bonaparte was in Egypt, making more French victories. The proud and various Italian kingdoms had been brought to their knees and most of Italy was a French province. Soon the arrogant milords on the other side of the Channel would learn that water was no defense against Frenchmen, when Frenchmen were led by Bonaparte. France was mounted on Europe's back; soon she would be astride the world, which, for its own good, mind you, would become civilized and French.

When the barge and its flag were out of sight, Bernard-François turned and walked along the bank of the Loire to the Café du Commerce, which had a paved terrace under awnings, facing the river. He was looking for company and he was in luck. Seated at a large round table were half a dozen friends and acquaintances: white-haired Senator de Ris, Baron de Pommereul, who had been a general in the army and fought the Royalist Rebels in the Vendée; Monsieur de Margonne, who owned the great estate of Saché; the Mayor of Tours, in a top hat. There was the Colonel of the 22nd, in full regimentals, wearing a sword. None of the men wore wigs or lace, for such finery was out of date, now that the shabby Corsican was becoming the first citizen of France, but all were well-dressed, well-fed, well-groomed, men of substance, like Bernard-François himself.

Bernard-François was a favorite here. Everyone greeted him heartily and there was a shuffling of chairs as a place was made at the common table. Before he sat down, he raised his cane like a marshal's baton and called for attention.

"Gentlemen, I have an announcement," he said, in the tones of an orator. "Yesterday, at eleven o'clock, the population of Tours was increased by one. His name is Honoré Balzac, and while at the moment he is no beauty, I promise you that one day the world will be aware of his presence."

Baron de Pommereul pounded on the table and cried, "Bravo!" The others cheered. The commandant of the 22nd drew his sword and made a parade-ground salute. The mayor shouted "Garçon! Garçon! Take away this wine and bring brandy for all, in honor of Honoré Balzac, aged one day, four hours."

The waiter brought thin glasses and a dusty bottle of the best brandy. Bernard-François stood, while the others drank his health. When the health of his son was proposed, he drained his glass at a gulp. The brandy was smooth as silk. Instantly it reached his stomach, it began to radiate warmth and well-being through his body. He sat down, wiping his lips. The Mayor refilled his glass.

"How is madame?" asked Margonne.

Bernard-François shrugged and said, "As well as one can expect, old boy. After all, it's a first child. She will be splendid to-

6

morrow, I'm sure of that. Name of the Lord, why shouldn't she be? She has a son!"

Baron de Pommereul smiled, inclining his long, aristocratic head. "You seem confident of the boy's future, Balzac, even in these troubled times, when only God has any idea what the next year will bring to France."

"Why shouldn't I be confident?" Bernard-François demanded. "He is my son, after all. You know, I came from nothing. From a muddy village in Languedoc. I have managed. He will manage."

Baron de Pommereul smiled again. "I envy you, my friend!" he said. "You are pleased not only with yourself, but with the world in general."

"Why not?" asked Bernard-François. "I have been good to the world in general, and the world in general has been good to me. I have never had a doctor in my life. I enjoy food, wine and love. I expect to live to be a hundred, if only for the purpose of collecting the lion's share of the tontine Lafarge. I ask you, gentlemen, when a man has luck like mine, does he have any right to be less than pleased—with himself and the world in general?" He rapped on the table with his cane and called: "Garçon! Another bottle. Brandy for all!"

It was after dark when Bernard-François left the café and rode home in a hackney carriage. His mood was lofty. He felt like a prince. He was not drunk; indeed, he had never been drunk in his life, but the brandy had made him mellow and he had been warmed by the companionship of his friends, good fellows all. He felt at ease with the world and with himself.

Then, as the carriage turned into the Chardonnet section, where he lived, he began to return to reality, aware of a pang of something that was not quite guilt, but related to it. It was the way he felt these days, whenever he thought of his wife.

He entered the house quietly, leaving his hat and stick in the hall, going up a narrow, carpeted staircase to the room where his wife lay in childbed. The house smelled of furniture wax and of some strong soap the midwife had used. Bernard-François wrinkled his nose, standing in front of his wife's door. The café had smelt better and so had the spring breeze from the river. He opened the door quietly and stepped into his wife's bedroom, which was hung with heavy red velvet intended to deaden the noise from the street. The effect was that of an airless but quite luxurious cave. On a canopied bed, supported by an arrangement of cushions, rested Anne-Charlotte-Laure Balzac, née Sallambier. She was thirty-two years younger than her husband, beautiful, vain, intelligent and embittered. She turned her head on the pillows, and looked at her husband with disapproval.

"Do you think it correct to abandon me in my hour of pain, monsieur?" she asked.

Bernard-François sighed gently. He had taught himself not to permit his wife's disposition to curdle his own enjoyment of life.

"I went to the City Hall, my dear, to register the child's birth," he said. "A formality, but one that the State requires."

"And then you went to the café, to parade like a peacock," she said. "As if you had produced the child, not I."

"You are depressed," said Bernard-François. "It is only natural, after the birth of a child. It will pass."

"What do you know about it?" she demanded angrily. "Your part of the affair is done within a few seconds." She made a face to indicate that these seconds had not been enjoyed. "I am the one who had to suffer for nine long months. And the pain! The pain!"

"The thing has been done before, madame," observed her husband mildly. "I assure you, Anne-Charlotte, you will recover."

She looked at him with hatred.

"Recover?" she said. "You understand nothing, monsieur. Nothing. I shall never recover. I am condemned."

Bernard-François went into the next room, where his infant son slept in a walnut cradle. He picked up the child, trying not to wake him, and carried him into his wife's room.

"Here is your son, madame," he said. "Our son."

He came closer to her, the baby in his arms. She smelt the brandy on his breath, the stale tobacco on his clothes. She was filled with loathing, for the child as well as its father. She wanted to vomit.

"Take him away!" she shrieked. "He is loathsome. I detest him. Take him away!"

"Madame, he is your son," Bernard-François said calmly.

The child had been wakened by his mother's voice. Now he began to wail piteously, as if he had understood her words. Bernard-François rocked him gently.

8

"Take him away!" screamed Anne-Charlotte, beating on the mattress with her clenched fists. "He is dark and ugly. He disgusts me. Take him out of the house at once."

Bernard-François said nothing. He took Honoré back to his cradle, then returned to his wife's room.

"You will change your mind in the morning," he said, bending to arrange her coverlet. "Get some rest, my dear. You will feel better."

"Leave me alone!" she cried, striking out at him. "Get out! Get out!"

She refused to nurse the child, then firmly refused to see him.

"I detest him," she said cold-bloodedly. "Take him out of my sight."

On the third day of the boy's life, Bernard-François had a talk with Nacquart, his wife's physician.

"I tell you, it's unnatural," Bernard-François complained. "She is bursting with milk. She refuses to feed him, but squeezes the stuff into a bottle and throws it away."

Nacquart was a young man, friend as well as physician. He shrugged his shoulders and made a helpless gesture with his thin, exceptionally clean fingers.

"Sometimes it happens," he said. "One hopes it will pass, as a fever passes, or a nightmare. In the meantime, the child needs care. It might be best to find someone to look after him. Outside the house, I mean."

"Outside the house!" said Bernard-François. "You mean I'm to put him out to board? My own son?"

"For the time being, it might be best," Nacquart said carefully. "Later, when she is rested, more herself, we shall see."

"But to turn him out, like a stray cat. I tell you, Nacquart, it's not natural." He looked steadily at the physician. "You've treated my wife, Nacquart," he said. "Do you think she is mad? Do you think she has lost her reason?"

Nacquart put a hand on his shoulder. "In my judgment, she is not mad, but merely malicious," he said quietly.

After Nacquart had gone, Bernard-François sat down in a comfortable chair in the front sitting room. The weather had turned cool, and a small fire burned in the hearth behind a polished brass fender. It was a neat, silent room, filled with polished furniture. Bernard-François stared at a spot on the gleaming brass where the firelight struck it, staring at the point of light until it had an hypnotic effect.

No one in Tours, besides himself, knew that the baby upstairs was not Anne-Charlotte's first child. The first child had been born a few months after she married Bernard-François, and had lived only a few days. Bernard-François had not been the father. The father had been the rich Parisian banker Doumerc, in whose household Anne-Charlotte had served as governess and from whom she had received the handsome dowry she brought to her marriage.

Bernard-François knew his wife. Her nobility, her austerity, the virtue she was proud of—all were a mask for the obsessive bitterness with which she viewed a world that had played her a trick and forced her into an unnecessary marriage.

"She is not mad, merely malicious."

That was what Nacquart had said, and Nacquart was no fool. Yet isn't maliciousness, carried to extremes, a form of madness? he asked himself, staring at the fire. He was a kindly man, an admirer of Rousseau. To turn his son out of the house almost before he had drawn breath seemed to him diabolical. Yet he knew Anne-Charlotte. If I insist the child remain at home, she will destroy him systematically, he thought. She has taken her stand. She will not relent.

If I were thirty, even forty, he thought, I would slap her face and order her to put the boy on her breast. But I am fifty-two. I am too old to live in a house at war with a woman. I need peace. Peace and quiet.

Reluctantly, he concluded that Nacquart was right. The boy must go—for six months or a year at least. It was too bad, but there it was, nothing to be done. His mind made up, Bernard-François relaxed and became more cheerful. He rang for his carriage and ordered the driver to take him to the café.

The next morning, Nacquart found a woman willing to serve as young Honoré's wet nurse.

"She's a good soul," the doctor said. "Wife of the gendarme, Poussinet, a friendly woman with more milk in her big breasts than her own child can drink. She won't charge much, and you can trust her to look after the boy."

The gendarme, Poussinet, lived in a thatched roof cottage, on

10

the highroad to Paris, half a mile outside the walls of Tours. With Nacquart, Bernard-François drove there in a closed carriage, Honoré on his lap. The movement of the vehicle seemed to exert a calming effect on the infant and he slept through most of the journey, but as the carriage pulled up in front of the cottage, he awakened and began to cry.

"Let me have him, monsieur," Madame Poussinet said gently. She was a good-looking woman in her twenties, with a broad, tanned peasant's face. Bernard-François handed over his son, feeling a burst of confidence in her. Without hesitation, ignoring the men, she undid her bodice and laid bare a breast, guiding the baby's mouth, murmuring to him in some strange maternal patois. Greedily, young Honoré took the hired breast.

"Don't you worry about him, monsieur," Madame Poussinet said firmly. "We'll take good care of him here and he won't go hungry, I promise you that."

Bernard-François was embarrassed to discover that his eyes were filled with tears. He blew his nose loudly then dabbed at the corners of his eyes.

"Touch of a cold," he said brusquely. "Take good care of the boy, madame. I will come and fetch him on Sundays, for a visit home."

"His mother is very ill?" Madame Poussinet asked innocently. Nacquart had told her that was the reason the child was being boarded out.

Bernard-François hesitated, then nodded slowly and said, "Very ill, madame. Very ill indeed."

During the ride back into Tours, Bernard-François was silent. He stared through the window at the small farms along the road. When the carriage pulled up in front of his house, he turned impulsively and seized his companion's hand. "You are a good friend, Nacquart," he said with some emotion. "A good friend." He got down from the carriage. Nacquart spoke to him through the window, saying, "Try to remember, François, that God decides these things. Try not to blame yourself too much. Or your wife."

The carriage moved away. In front of his house, Bernard-François stood motionless for a full minute. "I feel like a Judas," he said to himself. Then he went into the well-kept house, unwillingly, as if he entered a prison.

Chapter 2

OVER THE FLAT, rich countryside passed the voice of the bells of St. Gatien Cathedral, solemn and slow, ringing to mass in the center of Tours, half a mile away. It was a Sunday morning in Spring, in the fourth year of the new century. The sun that rose over Touraine was no longer a Republican sun. A few days earlier, in Paris, Bonaparte had announced that he was henceforth Emperor of the French.

From the window of his room in the Poussinet cottage, five year old Honoré Balzac looked toward the city. As the bells rang, his heart rang with them.

"Come to Mass! Come to Mass!" the bells were saying.

"It is Sunday! It is Sunday!" his heart was saying. "The day I go home! The day I go home!"

He was a sturdy, valiant child, with brown hair in ringlets and deep-set, passionate eyes. Dressed in his Sunday clothes—a brown silk jumper with a blue belt—he made a fine appearance. A stranger would have refused to believe that such a lad could be rejected by any mother in her right mind.

He turned away from the window and went next door to the room occupied by his sister, Laure, a year younger than himself, and a fellow exile from the Balzac home, an exile sharpened by the fact that two younger children, a sister, Laurence and a brother, Henri, were not only kept at home, but given every attention.

Honoré pounded on his sister's door. "Laure! Laure!" he shouted. "Get dressed! It's Sunday morning."

"I am dressed," she answered.

Honoré opened the door and cried, "Well come then! It's Sunday, you idiot. We're going home!"

Laure was dressed in pale blue velvet. She was a beautiful, solemn child with a gentle disposition. "It is early," she said. "Papa won't come for a long time."

12

Honoré seized her hand and pulled her along with him. "He might be early," he said. "Come on! Come on!"

They clattered down a narrow staircase that led from the attic rooms to the kitchen. In front of a great black stove stood Madame Poussinet, stirring something that cooked in a polished copper kettle. In her free arm she held a three months' old baby. She had a new one every year, but child-bearing seemed to have no effect on her figure or her temperament.

"Madame! Madame! cried Honoré. "It's Sunday!"

"It's Sunday," Laure said, echoing him as she often did.

Madame Poussinet laughed and put the baby in his cradle, then kissed the two Balzacs.

"I know it's Sunday, you foolish children," she said. "Do you think that merely because I can't read that I don't know the day of the week? Besides, I have ears. I can hear the bells. Sit down there, now, and I'll give you some breakfast."

They sat down at the kitchen table, which was spread with a red checked cloth. Madame Poussinet gave them each a bowl of chocolate and a crescent roll.

"My father says the Emperor will see to it that everyone in France learns to read," said Honoré solemnly.

Madame Poussinet laughed and pointed to the baby.

"That little fellow, perhaps," she said. "If Bonaparte wants me to read, he'll have to come teach me himself."

Laure burst into laughter but Honoré frowned.

"He is not to be called Bonaparte any longer," he informed Madame Poussinet. "He is the Emperor."

"What is an emperor?" Laure asked. "Is he like a king?"

"More than a king," Honoré answered. "But Papa says that a king is better. I don't altogether understand."

"What!" exclaimed Madame Poussinet. "Something *you* don't understand? Is this Honoré Balzac? Are you ill?"

"I can read," Honoré said stubbornly. "You know it's true. I can read."

It was true. Once a week, Dr. Nacquart drove out to the Poussinet cottage in his carriage to see to the children's health. This year and last, as a joke at first, he had taught Honoré his letters. The boy's progress astonished him. Nacquart was a doctor, but he was also a student of human nature. In the process of teaching the A B C's, Nacquart discovered something that was to escape

13

schoolmasters and others for a long time to come . . . the fact that in dealing with Honoré Balzac, age five, he was confronted with genius, face to face with one of those extraordinary souls that God has been pleased to endow with the ability to create a world modeled after His own—a world made with paint or words or musical sounds or pure idea.

Honoré, at five, could read. He could not add or take away. He could not spell or play games. He knew no Latin, no history, no science. But he could read French. From the first, he had embraced the language with the ardent certainty with which he often yearned to embrace his mother.

"Come on, Laure, let's go outside and wait," he said.

Obediently, Laure followed him. In five years, Bernard-François had never arrived before half-past eleven, but every Sunday for three years now, Honoré had waited at the gate of the cottage from nine o'clock until he came. When it was raining or snowing, he might be persuaded to take shelter in the overhang of the thatched roof, but rain or shine, in heat or cold, he was at his post by nine o'clock, meeting every protest by saying, "He might come early, this time. He might come early, for all one knows."

This Sunday, as on all Sundays, Bernard-François reached the Poussinet cottage at a little after half-past eleven. Honoré saw the dust of his carriage far off down the road and his grip on the gate post tightened. Once he had raced out to meet the carriage and nearly been trampled to death under the horses' hooves, so that now he was forbidden to pass the gate. He stood motionless as a guardsman until the carriage rolled to a stop and Bernard-François climbed down, then flung himself forward and hugged his father's knees. After a moment, Bernard-François disengaged himself, kissed both his children and said, "Into the carriage with you both. We mustn't be late for dinner, you know. It makes your mother very cross."

In the carriage, Honoré picked up his father's gold-knobbed cane, holding it between his legs, hands folded over the gold ball, as he had seen his father do. It didn't matter that Laure, being younger, sat on his father's lap. He had his father's cane in his hands, and to Honoré the cane seemed to be a part of his father's body, almost a living thing.

After the birth of Henri, a few months earlier, Bernard-François had moved his family to a larger house. His fortunes had im-

14

proved during the years when Bonaparte had been First Consul. Now, in addition to the Commissariat, he was Director of Hospitals for Touraine, a prominent figure not only in Tours, but throughout the province. The Mayor of Tours was his intimate friend and already people whispered that the brilliant, eccentric Monsieur Balzac might be just the man for mayor, should the present incumbent, as he expected, move on to bigger things in Paris.

The new house was one that suited Bernard-François' position, much larger than the old one, and grander, though Honoré preferred the old, a fact that he kept to himself.

The dining room was furnished in the style of Louis XIV. There was a high, gilded ceiling with intricate plaster work. The table could be extended to accommodate forty people at dinner. There was an oak sideboard on which was displayed an impressive assortment of silver and glassware. Arranged on shelves in a glass-doored cabinet was a tea service of eggshell china, made to order in Limoges. The cabinet was always locked. More than once, Honoré had been thrashed merely for pressing his nose to the glass in order to admire the pretty cups that it seemed, were never used.

At the head of his table, a servant behind him, sat the prospective Mayor of Tours, a commanding figure, filled with authority, every inch the master in appearance, though in this house, as in many others, the true master sat at the foot of the table.

Looking at his mother, Honoré thought she was the most beautiful creature he had ever seen. She *was* beautiful, Anne-Charlotte, proud as a queen, with a heart-shaped face, a small but full-lipped mouth, red-gold hair brushed 'til it was silky, skin delicate as the tea-cups he had been thrashed for looking at. She loved clothes and dressed herself in the height of the mode, favoring gowns that were often somewhat daring for a provincial town like Tours. Today she wore a dress of fawn-colored velvet with an underglow of pink that showed in the light. The bodice was tight, the neck low. Her throat and the upper part of her breasts were covered by a light fall of transparent lace. Compared to Madame Poussinet and the rough-handed peasant women Honoré saw on week-days she looked like a goddess from heaven. He stared at her, enchanted, a lump rising in his throat. Then he could not contain himself and blurted out, "Mother, you are beautiful!"

Anne-Charlotte had been talking to a young lieutenant of infantry seated on her right. She stiffened at the sound of Honoré's voice. A dead silence controlled the room. Laure bit her lip. Behind Honoré, a nervous servant dropped a spoon. The clock ticked like a human heart. The blood rose to Honoré's face, making his cheeks burn as if he stood by an open fire. Everyone waited, scarcely drawing breath. The young officer was embarrassed. Then Anne-Charlotte addressed her husband.

"Monsieur! Your son forgets himself. Please remind him of his manners."

Bernard-François coughed and flushed, then said awkwardly, "Mustn't interrupt, my boy. Mother was talking, you see, to the lieutenant."

With his hands held under the table, Honoré clenched his fists until the nails bit into the palms. He fought back the welling tears, keeping his eyes fixed on his plate. Then he raised his head and said, "I'm sorry, mother."

Anne-Charlotte nodded coldly and the meal was resumed. When the sweet was served, she said to the servant, "None for Master Honoré, please. He prefers interruptions to dessert."

Honoré sat in his place while the others ate dessert. His mouth was firm. Inside his head, keeping time with the ticking clock and the rhythmic sound of the dessert spoons, a voice was saying, "I will not cry. I will not cry." He raised his head and looked at his mother, watching her consume the sweet with precise, elegant movements. He felt no anger, no resentment, but only a sense of bafflement and of overwhelming love for this creature, who seemed more than ever both beautiful and good, and a feeling that he must be monstrously evil, detestable, in some way cursed, since his mother rejected him. He blamed himself, never his mother.

"She was quite right, you know," he said to Laure, when they were back at the Poussinets. "I was the one who interrupted, and that is very rude."

Such were Honoré's Sundays at home, always begun on a note of hope, always ending in disgrace. His mother was implacable. Never did her icy contempt falter, never did she disclose a crack in her armor. From the day she had lain in childbed and ordered him out of the house, she had never faltered.

Honoré blamed himself. In bed at night, he stared at the stars through his window and asked himself again and again what was the flaw in his character that made his mother despise him.

For her own part, Anne-Charlotte probably had no idea of the source of her harshness and cruelty. She was an odd mixture of Puritan mysticism, snobbery, and intolerable, gnawing lust. The banker Doumerc, when he seduced her in a servant's room, had opened a wound in her nature. She hated her own sexuality, yet she was enslaved by it and sometimes could not keep it under control. Lately, she had begun to study the Scandinavian mystic, Swedenborg, who was enjoying a vogue among advanced thinkers in France. Swedenborg is strong medicine, even for the best balanced mind. For Anne-Charlotte to read him was like taking a journey to the pits of hell.

"Give up that northern maniac," Bernard-François argued, offering her his own copy of Rousseau's CONFESSIONS. "If you must wallow in ideas, at least wallow in French ideas."

She seized the book and flung it across the room.

"Filth!" she shouted. "Licentious trash! Is it from Rousseau that you have acquired your taste for servant girls, monsieur?"

In rage, her face became hideous, her eyes blazing fanatically, her mouth contorted, her teeth bared like those of an animal.

Bernard-François picked up his book, giving it an affectionate pat. It was true that he sought comfort with serving wenches and peasant girls. He wasn't ashamed of it.

"After all," he told Nacquart, "a man is a man, is he not?"

Nacquart served as counselor to husband, wife and children. For some reason, Anne-Charlotte trusted him, and it was Nacquart who finally persuaded her to bring the older children home. He was too shrewd to appeal to her motherhood. He worked on her inbred snobbery and petit-bourgeois sense of caste.

"You must consider the fact that people will talk, madame," he said. "To put them out to a wet nurse is one thing, and perhaps not too unusual. But they are far beyond that now."

"I have no time," argued Anne-Charlotte.

"With the right governess, they will be no trouble to you," he suggested.

Nacquart was persuasive. Skillfully, he brought her around to agreement with his point of view. A few days later, Honoré and his sister came home to stay.

Packing his things, Honoré trembled with excitement. Madame

Poussinet, helping him, laughed at the boy's agitation. Then she sank to her knees beside him and drew his head to her breast.

"Honoré, child, don't expect too much," she said quietly. "Please. You must not expect too much! You are going home, child, to your mother. You are not going to heaven."

Anne-Charlotte received them in her new front sitting room, the walls of which were covered with cool grey damask. It was a chill, formal room, immaculate and forbidden. Before today, neither Honoré nor Laure had ever set foot inside it, but only peered in through the door. Even Bernard-François was encouraged to avoid it; the room was madame's private domain.

She sat on a straight-backed chair, dressed in satin of a cool grey, like the grey of the walls. Beside her stood a hawk-faced creature in dull black, a servant, thought Honoré, yet not quite a servant.

"This is Mademoiselle Delahaye," Anne-Charlotte told them. "She will be your governess. You are to obey her, as you would obey me, is that understood?"

Honoré stood silently, staring at this formidable stranger who was henceforth to rule his life.

"Well, Honoré, have you lost your tongue?" his mother demanded. "Is it understood that you are to obey?"

"Yes, mama," he said.

"Say 'Yes, madame' if you please," Anne-Charlotte demanded sharply. "You know I detest familiarity."

"Yes, madame," Honoré said mechanically.

"Yes, madame," repeated Laura.

"Very well," said Anne-Charlotte. "Mademoiselle, you may take them to their rooms."

Mademoiselle Delahaye smoothed her long black skirt. She was nearly as tall as Bernard-François himself. Her hands had long, bony fingers, the knuckles of which cracked when she flexed them.

"Come children, quickly," she said, in a harsh, northern accent. "Quickly. Quickly. Vite! Vite!"

The children bowed to Anne-Charlotte and followed the governess out of the room.

"Quickly, quickly," she was saying. "There is to be no dawdling."

Mademoiselle Delahaye had been trained in England. She be-

18

lieved that hardship was the best teacher and it was this that prompted Anne-Charlotte to select her from among the dozen applicants she had interviewed.

"You will have a free hand," Anne-Charlotte had promised. "But I warn you, I expect discipline. These children have been living with a gendarme's wife, a good enough sort, but common. Their manners are atrocious. You must remedy that."

"Of course, madame," the governess had answered.

They had understood each other from the first, Mademoiselle Delehaye and her new mistress. They were out of the same mold—women who resented the world because it had failed to pay proper tribute to their virtues.

"Quickly! Quickly!" crackled the voice of Mademoiselle Delehaye, herding them upstairs and through a dark corridor in the west wing, where rooms had been made ready for them.

"This is your room, Honoré. This is yours, Laure."

A firm hand on the shoulder guided each child to his room. Their bags had already been brought upstairs by the coachman and they were commanded to unpack.

"Carefully mind you. Hang everything up properly. And quickly! Quickly! No dawdling!"

Such were the circumstances under which Honoré Balzac returned to the parental roof. It is a key to his character that he was glad to be home, even on his mother's terms. He would have lived like a silent Trappist for the sake of being home.

That night, after he and Laure had been put to bed, he waited until the house was silent. Then he crept to the window and sat on the sill, regarding the gabled roofs of Tours, silhouetted against the night sky. There was a pale, chill moon. Honoré sighed. He had been given his supper in the kitchen, with Laure, and then sent up to bed. He was alone now, and forgotten by everyone but Laure, asleep in the next room. But he was happy. He was under his mother's roof.

Through most of the night, he sat at his window, watching the shifting silvery light, until the moon set, then counting the stars of Touraine. These last months, he and Nacquart had been reading the Bible. There was a verse he had memorized. He said it now to himself, under his breath, his eyes on the stars . . .

"Yahweh est mon pasteur; je ne manquerai de rien. Il me fait

*reposer dans des verts pâturages, il me mène près des eaux re-
fraîchissantes, il restaure mon âme."*

When first Nacquart had read these words, Honorè's blood had
tingled. "It is beautiful!" he had exclaimed. Then he had frowned
and said, "Is it true? The Lord is my Shepherd?"

Nacquart had nodded soberly and assured him, "Yes, it is true
enough, my child, if one believes it."

Honoré learned the lines by heart, decided that he believed
them and that therefore they were true. He climbed down from the
window sill and crept into his bed. Cheek on the pillow, he murmured the words to himself again: *"Yahweh est mon pasteur; je
ne manquerai de rien."*

Balzac senior was a busy man. When not engaged in official
duties or with private literary labors, he was at the café, unless he
was keeping an assignation with some country girl or other in the
back room of a rural inn. A man of affairs, his days were filled,
and it isn't surprising that several weeks passed before it occurred to him that his son might profit by being sent to school.
Once the matter was decided, however, he enrolled the boy in the
best school in Tours—the Institut Léguay, an establishment noted
for its severity.

On a Monday morning, Honorè and his father set out for
school.

"You'll find it simple enough," said Bernard-François, who had
not been to school for as much as a day. "After all, you're my son.
You must have a good set of brains in your head."

Reinforced by these words, Honoré began his academic career.
After the first few weeks, he began to wonder whether, after all,
he was actually his father's son. Arithmetic baffled him. Latin was
hopeless. Geography meant nothing to him. Day after day, the
master roared: "Balzac, you are a dunce! Your father might better save his money and put you to work on a farm."

Stubbornly, Honoré insisted, "I can read, monsieur. I can
read."

"Oh, yes. We can read," said the master, mocking him. "But
can we read what we're asked to read? Oh no! Only what pleases
his lordship."

At recess, the boys were turned out into a paved yard behind the
school and allowed to play as they pleased. It was in this yard

20

that Honoré learned to utter his first bad words, here that he heard from older boys strange tales about men and women, and here that he had his first fight.

His opponent was two years older than he and the point at issue was his mother's honor.

"Hey, Balzac," the boy had demanded, "Is it true your mother sleeps with the officers from the 22nd?"

The blood rose in Honoré's head. Literally blinded with rage, he flung himself at the offender, threw him to the ground, grasped his throat, and smashed his head against the pavement. His purpose was murder. Three boys and a master pulled him off and held him. The older boy got to his feet, shook his head and moved away.

That night when he got home, his clothes torn, his lips bleeding, Honoré was sent to bed without supper. At the risk of being punished herself, Laure hid a roll and a piece of sausage under her apron and brought them to him, after the governess had turned out the lights and gone. Honorè put the food on his bed. He took Laure in his arms and kissed her. "I love you," he whispered.

"I love you too," she said.

Clinging together in the dark, the two children began to weep silently. They were afraid to cry out loud, for fear the governess would hear them. Crying was forbidden.

A few days later, at the café, Honoré's father heard of his son's victory from one of the Institut Léguay masters who had seen the fight.

"I tell you, Balzac, the lad was like a tiger," said the schoolmaster with some admiration. "If we hadn't pulled him off, I think he'd have killed the other boy."

Bernard-François was delighted. . . . That night he came to Honoré's room, clapped the boy on the back, congratulated him and said, "I want to buy you a present, my boy. What would you like?"

"A violin," replied Honoré without hesitation.

Bernard-François was astonished. "A violin?" he said. "Can you play the violin?"

"I can learn," was the answer.

Bernard-François found a cheap violin and Honoré, with Nacquart's help, learned to play simple tunes and to read simple music. Not long after this, he was struck by a conviction that

21

would have seemed absurd to anyone but Laure, to whom he confided it one evening while they sat in the kitchen having supper. His broad forehead was furrowed. His deep-set eyes stared intently at the rim of his plate. Then he said quite soberly, "Laure, do you realize that one day I am going to be famous?"

She nodded sagely and agreed with him. They went on with their dinner. That night, in his bed, Honoré thought of what he had said. He was absolutely certain that he was going to be famous, but he wasn't at all certain about the vehicle of his glory. He thought of being a soldier, like the Emperor. He thought of the mayor, with his chain and sash. He thought of his father, tall and straight, with his braided collar, his splendid coat, swinging his gold-headed cane.

He went to sleep.

The next evening, after supper, he took the cane from its rack in the hall and marched up and down with it, swinging the stick as he had seen his father do. There was a vase of flowers in the hallway, resting on a small table. After a moment, there was a crash, and not much later there was Anne-Charlotte, towering with rage. She snatched the stick from his hands and slashed out with it at his face, cutting his cheek and his lip. She brought it down on his shoulders and thrashed him up the stairs to his room.

Laure bathed his cut face and brought cold rags for his bruised shoulders.

"I hate Mama," she said, without passion, as she might have said she hated boiled squash. "I hate her."

"You must not say that," he protested.

"Why? She hates us," Laure said.

"She is our mother," Honoré said. "She loves us."

During those years, nothing would budge him. Each day he woke up, hoping that this would be the day on which his punishment would come to an end. He loved his mother with such passion that it was impossible for him to believe that underneath she did not love him back. He was too young to realize that love is never returned in kind, and sometimes not at all.

He and Laure were allies. The other two children, Henri and Laurence were treated almost as if they were members of another family. Henri was the favorite. With him Anne-Charlotte was indulgent as she was with no one else. She seemed determined to spoil him and there was nothing he wanted that he did not get. Honoré tried to ignore Henri, though sometimes he would look at his brother and wonder what hidden virtue appealed to his mother.

Laurence, his younger sister, was sickly and slow to learn. Honoré rather liked her and called her Milady Plum Pudding. Not until many years later did it occur to him that Bernard-François might not be the father of the two younger children.

Chapter 3

BEFORE THE REVolution, under various Kings, the Collège de Vendôme had prepared cadets for commissions in the French army. Now, under the Empire, the military function of the school was gone, but a certain martial flavor remained, a kind of barracks odor left over from earlier days. Situated in the heart of the town of Vendôme, thirty-five miles from Tours, facing the little River Loir, the school with its grim grey walls, its towers and barred windows, looked more like an arsenal or a prison than a place for boys to study.

"You'll get a good education at Vendôme," Honoré's father had promised. "They'll get you ready for the Polytechnic."

"Why must I be an engineer, father?" the boy asked.

"It's the thing of the future," Bernard-François explained. "Under the Emperor, France leads the world. First we will rebuild France, then the world, just the way the Romans did. I tell you, my boy, the engineer, the technical man, he is the prince of the future."

Honoré nodded soberly. He was eight years old. The winter before he had had smallpox, and his illness had been such a nuisance in the house that his mother insisted he be sent away to boarding school. Vendôme was chosen because it was cheap and because the boys were not permitted home visits on weekends or holidays, and also because it was famous for the severity of its discipline.

At his day school in Tours, Honoré had not been a success. Hopeless in mathematics, indifferent in Latin and Greek, desultory in history, he was marked down as lazy and rather stupid. His schoolmates respected his physical strength, but regarded him as a queer fish because of his habit of going into what seemed to be a kind of trance. Actually, what he was doing was memorizing something he had read. His memory was phenomenal, his ability to read extraordinary. His eye took in six or seven lines of type at a glance, sometimes nearly a page.

It was on a pleasant June day that he passed through the gates of the Collège de Vendôme, his father beside him. Outside, the sun was shining, but the high wall that surrounded the school cut off the light once the gate was behind them. The main building, through the corridors of which he walked with his father, was dank in spite of the warmth of the day. There was a thick, disgusting odor that made him gag, a smell produced by filth, spoilt food, dampness, and the body odors of three hundred unwashed boys.

The headmaster, Monsieur Mareschal, looked critically at the new boy.

"Do as you're told, my boy, and work, and you'll get on very well," he said. "We try to teach discipline here you see, as well as Latin and Greek."

When his father had gone, Honoré was given a school uniform, made of prickly grey flannel, then led to his classroom by a priest dressed in a sour smelling cassock. The school was under secular administration, but most of the teachers were priests of the Oratorian order.

There were eighty boys in the classroom, all more or less Honoré's age, seated on wooden forms, facing the master, who was enthroned on a dais, in front of a large map of France. On the wall over the map there hung a Christus and Crucifix of terrifying realism. When Honoré entered the room with his guide, eighty heads were turned. With one hundred and sixty eyes upon him, he felt a rush of panic and turned instinctively to flee. The priest's hand caught his arm. The form master, Father Haugoult, looked at him with sick eyes, then indicated with his pointer a few inches of space on one of the forms near the back of the room. Honoré sat down. Father Haugoult went on with the lesson. One by one, in alphabetical order, the boys rose, translated a line of Latin, then sat down and relapsed into boredom.

Honoré sat in his place, numb with fear at the strangeness. Suddenly, his neighbor nudged him and asked in a whisper, "Do you have any pigeons?"

Honoré shook his head.

"I have six," the boy said. "You can fly one of mine, if you like."

Honoré was about to answer, when Father Haugoult's voice burst on his ears like a cannon shot.

"Balzac!"

Honoré rose.

"Come here!"

He walked to the front of the room and faced the priest.

"Hold your hands out, palms up!"

Honoré extended his hands. Father Haugoult lifted the punishment strap, then brought it down on Honoré's hands, first left, then right, two strokes to each hand. The pain was sudden and intense. Tears rose in Honoré's eyes but he fought them back.

"We do not talk in class, Balzac," said Father Haugoult. "Go back to your seat."

Honoré returned to his seat. The class tittered. Father Haugoult resumed the lesson.

It was a spiritual prison house to which young Balzac had been sent. The school was almost independent of the outside world. Inside the walls were a chapel, infirmary, bakery, slaughter-house, vegetable garden, water supply, cobbler's and tailor's shop. The three hundred scholars were cut off from normal society as effectively as if they had been confined in the old Bastille.

Discipline was harsh as that of a prison. The rules were enforced by a system of punishments originally invented by the Jesuits, with whom the Oratorians had some connection. Everything bore the stamp of monastic rule. The great sin was idleness, and to the Oratorian temperament, contemplation was a form of idleness.

"Balzac, you are idling!"

"Balzac, you are doing nothing!"

"Balzac, you will get the strap!"

During his years at Vendôme, these phrases were burned into Honoré's mind.

At first, as a new boy, he was teased and bullied by his companions as well as the priests. Then one day in the classroom when Father Haugoult was absent for a moment, he decided to put an end to the teasing. He lifted one of the heavy oak tables with both hands, steadied it, then looked at the others and said, "Now ten of you try to move it."

Ten good-sized lads seized the table and pulled. The veins stood out on Honoré's forehead and his heart pounded, but he hung on. The table could not be budged. The boys looked at Honoré with amazement and schoolboy respect. He wiped the sweat from his forehead and went on with the book he was reading.

26

At the end of a month his newness had worn off and he was accepted by the other boys as a mediocre student who preferred to be left to himself. The only diversions the school offered were fighting, flying pigeons from the roof, and masturbation, practised privately or en masse. None of these appealed to young Balzac. He kept his distance and his counsel.

The masters, especially Father Haugoult, sensed from the first that there was something in his temperament that resisted their authority. They resented him, as schoolmasters often resent a pupil whose nature obliges him to make progress in a manner different from the ordinary. He was beaten, bullied and ridiculed; the priests were determined to break his spirit.

Except for one thing, they might have succeeded. In his eagerness to make sure that Honoré got into the engineering school, Bernard-François had arranged for him to be specially tutored in mathematics. During the recreation period, when the other boys were at play in the courtyard, Honoré went to the library instead. Here old Father Guizot was supposed to drill him in mathematics.

Father Guizot was as much a misfit at Vendôme as was Honoré himself. A timid priest, incapable of maintaining order in class, disinclined to inflict pain, he had been made librarian in desperation, simply to get him out of the way.

After the first few sessions, he said quietly, "You don't care very much for numbers, do you, Balzac?"

Honoré shook his head.

"Neither do I," the priest confessed. "What do you like?"

"To read," said Honoré.

"So do I," said Father Guizot with a shy smile. "Let us make a bargain, boy. If you don't complain about not learning to add and subtract, we can use the time for reading, you and I."

Honoré's eyes swept around the room. The stone walls were lined with books, hundreds of books, thousands, perhaps. The boy felt a sensation akin to hunger.

"Can I read whatever I like?" he asked.

"Certainly," the priest replied. "I am the same way myself. I only read what I like, you know."

So the two misfits, boy and priest, passed their afternoons together, hidden away from the rest of the school. From the courtyard came the sounds of the other lads at play. Honoré scarcely heard them. He was immersed in the world of his book, whatever

27

it was. His life in the classroom, the chapel, the dormitory, faded into the background. His real life was here, in the books he read. When he entered the silent library, he entered another world. He developed a thirst for information that would not be quenched. He read books on every subject: theology, history, philosophy, science, politics. What he read was digested by some mysterious process unrelated to scholarship. Myriad facts and details were stored up in his mind. He became a kind of miser of knowledge. His ability to assimilate ideas began to reach phenomenal proportions. Sometimes he seemed to anticipate the writer, and a single word was enough to give him the meaning of a whole sentence. He developed the ability to form conceptions from what he had read more real than things actually experienced. When he read a description of the Battle of Austerlitz, it was as if he were in the middle of the fighting. The rolling salvos of the French guns rang in his ears. He heard the shouting and cursing of the soldiers, the shrieks of the wounded, the prayers of the dying, the mad, terrifying protests of the horses. He smelled the smoke of battle and the awful sounds of imagined war were more real to him than the actual shouts of his classmates, rising from the courtyard below. Immersed in a book, he left time and space behind him.

His memory, which should have been an asset in school, more than once got him into trouble. He had only to hear the lesson once in order to be able to repeat it, and since he was ninth in the alphabetical listing, he seldom bothered to prepare for class. Unfortunately, sometimes Father Haugoult changed the sequence of recitation without warning. Called on first, Honoré always performed like a stammering dolt.

"Again, Balzac?" the priest would say. "Come up to the front and be punished then."

As he stoked the fires of his own mind with book after book, Honoré came to realize that the masters in whose classes he sat knew nothing. At first he was furious with them. Then he became contemptuous, then indifferent. He developed a way of looking at Father Haugoult that drove the priest into a rage.

"If you look at me like that again, Balzac, you will get the strap, I promise you," the master would shout, his long, damp fingers trembling with anger.

"I cannot help the way I look, Father," Honorè would reply calmly. "That is something God decided for me."

28

"Come to the front! Come to the front!" the unhappy priest would scream, reaching for the strap. Indifferently, Honoré would rise and go forward to be punished.

The dormitories, which had once been barracks, were partitioned off into cubicles six feet by four. The floors and the outer walls were stone, damp and slimy to the touch. The inner walls were plaster to a height of five feet, with bars above. The doors were fitted with gratings and kept locked at night, to prevent visiting between cubicles. As punishment for persistent disobedience, a boy was sometimes locked in his cubicle for as long as a month, living on half rations, permitted neither reading matter nor companionship.

Young Balzac, naturally, was frequently locked in his cell. It was during one of these periods of confinement (again he had *"looked"* at Father Haugoult in a certain way) that he conceived the idea for his first piece of original writing. It was to be a treatise on the human will, an investigation of man's independence of spirit.

For a month of solitary confinement, he lay on his straw pallet or stood on a bench, staring through his barred window at the sluggish River Loir which passed beneath the college walls. Out of the hotchpotch of his reading, he put together a theory. It seemed to him that the human will was central . . . that ideas were actually achieved in the mind, before attaining existence in what is called the real world. He echoed the Greeks and others, but in the echo there was the hint of a new and famous accent.

When his month of confinement ended, he returned to the classroom. Whenever he had a spare moment, or could steal one, he wrote down parts of his treatise, as he remembered it from the oddly isolated period when he had been alone in his cell. At other times, he sat in class, lost in thought, gazing at a scar on the surface of the desk, marshaling his ideas and casting them into words, to be aroused by Father Haugoult's bellow: "Balzac! You are doing nothing!" and the inevitable cut of the strap on his hands.

As time passed, a relentless feud developed between young Balzac and the baffled, frustrated priest. Father Haugoult hated the boy and realized that his very existence was a challenge to his authority. Honoré did not hate the priest. There was very little hatred in his nature. But he accepted the fact that in order to survive, he must evade Father Haugoult's interference.

In every field but the physical, the battle was on unequal terms, with the advantage on Honoré's side. He was more than a match for the tired priest. In debate, he was always able to maneuvre Father Haugoult into a corner. When it came to a question of fact, he always had the answer. After the first two years, even on questions of religious doctrine Honoré sometimes put his opponent—an ordained priest—at a disadvantage. He was not irreligious. He was simply defending himself with the weapons he had. Besides, in the long run, Father Haugoult had the strap, the solitary cells, or even the dreaded coulotte de bois, the medieval stocks that were used in extreme cases.

One day, while the class was doing Latin, Honoré was called on to recite. He had done his own free translation, as well as the literal rendering required in class, but when he rose to recite, his mind was wandering and he forgot himself. He read the Latin: *"Caius Gracchus vir nobilis,"* then gave his own translation: "Caius Gracchus had a noble heart."

By the book, he was clearly wrong. Father Haugoult's pointer came down sharply, making a sound like a pistol shot.

"Where do you find heart in *nobilis?*" he demanded. "Where, I ask you? Where? Where? Where?"

With each *"Where?"* the pointer came down and struck the desk top with force. Honoré knew that he had blundered, but something prompted him to stand his ground. "Caius Gracchus had a noble heart," he repeated slowly, savoring the words on his tongue.

The pointer flashed in the air like a blade, then struck the top of the desk with such force that the desk shuddered.

"Nobilis!" Father Haugoult shouted. "Of noble family. Of patrician rank. Where do you find heart in that?"

"In my imagination," answered Honoré calmly.

"I am here to teach you Latin, Balzac, not to encourage your imagination," said Father Haugoult.

Honoré forgot himself. "That is fortunate, mon père, for my imagination," he said.

Instead of bursting into rage, Father Haugoult turned cold. He walked to the front of the room, put down his pointer, and stood with his hands on his hips, looking at young Balzac, saying nothing, revealing nothing. The other boys became silent. They were used to the priest's rages, but none of them had ever seen him as he

30

was now, chill as an executioner ready to drop the knife. Through a high window came a shaft of sunlight. Honorè stared at the dust particles dancing in the beam, waiting for the priest to speak. At last Father Haugoult said calmly, "This time, Balzac, you have gone too far. You will come with me."

There was a gasp from the shocked boys.

"The lash!" they whispered, one to the other. "Balzac is getting the lash!"

The dreaded cat-o-nine-tails was not much used at Vendôme. Most masters preferred the simple strap, but it was a priest's privilege to use the tawse, if he thought the offence was serious enough.

Honoré followed Father Haugoult down a long corridor, up a staircase, through another corridor, to the priest's private study, a room with windows shaped like arrowheads, the corners deep in murky shadow. The air was stale and somewhat damp. Through the badly worn soles of his shoes, Honoré felt the chill of the naked stone floor. He was afraid. Heretofore, when he had been beaten, it had been done in the presence of his schoolmates, and he had drawn courage from the fact that others were watching. Now he was alone with Father Haugoult, in a strange room, in a strange part of the school, at the priest's mercy. He wanted to stammer some apology, to cry out for mercy. He could not do it. His own will was stronger than the fear that made his heart pound and his fingers tremble.

"Well, Balzac, this time you have really gone too far," said Father Haugoult. "This time you have insulted me personally. Me. A priest. Do you know what that means, Balzac? You have insulted God Himself. You must be punished, and severely."

"If you say so, Father," Honoré said mechanically.

"I do. I do say so, indeed," said Father Haugoult.

He went to a cabinet on the wall and took out the lash, a series of knotted thongs fastened to a stout wooden handle, the kind of instrument used in the prison galleys for the punishment of hardened criminals. The priest made a pass in the air and the weighted thongs seemed to sing.

"Take down your trousers and drawers, Balzac," he said. "Put your hands on the desk, and lean forward."

Honoré undid his belt and let down his pants, then pulled down his underdrawers, and took his place by the desk. He felt the cold

31

on his bare legs and buttocks and shuddered. Then he heard the hissing sound of the lash as it was raised in the air, high above Father Haugoult's head. The lash fell, and he felt the first blow on his buttocks and heard the priest grunt with satisfaction. His head was bent forward so that his nose nearly touched the desk and he smelt the oil that had been used on the wood. A second blow fell, a third. Honoré's teeth were jammed together, biting his tongue. He kept his grip on the edge of the desk, fighting back the tears. With the fourth blow, the skin was broken. He felt the warmth of his blood trickling down his thighs to the floor.

He took a dozen lashes before the priest was satisfied. For a moment, Father Haugoult stood behind him, holding the lash that now dripped blood, looking at the lacerated skin. Then he said dispassionately, "Very well, Balzac. Pull up your clothes."

Honoré stood erect. His buttocks and thighs were so numbed that he felt no pain. Pain would come later, he knew that, when the numbness had worn off. It was that way with soldiers, he had read. Sometimes they were wounded in battle and felt nothing until later, when the shock had worn off. As he adjusted his clothing, he felt blood on his hands. When his trousers were fastened he faced the priest, proud of the fact that he had not cried.

"Is that all, Father?"

"For the present," said Father Haugoult. "In the future, Balzac, please try to remember that preparation means preparation. P-R-E-P-A-R-A-T-I-O-N." He spelled the word out slowly, pausing between each letter, as he had paused between each blow of the lash.

"Yes, Father," said Honoré.

He made his way through the corridors and entered his dormitory cell, falling heavily onto the straw mattress of his cot. The numbness was gone now and there was searing pain in his buttocks. He moved slightly, causing the blood to flow. It was wet and warm and he felt as though he had urinated in his trousers. He sobbed once, in the empty cubicle, then put his fist in his mouth to stop the sound. For an hour he lay on his cot, silent after the single sob. Then he got up, his thighs stiff, and with some difficulty walked to the washroom at the end of the double row of cubicles. There was a tub of water, used by twenty boys. He washed the blood from his legs, allowing his skin to dry in the air. Then he dressed himself and went to the Refectory for the midday meal. As he took

32

his place at the long table, his fellow students glanced at him, then went on eating. The meal was a good one, a rich stew made of lentils and sausages. He spooned up a mouthful and ate it, enjoying the warmth in his stomach.

One of the sources of his strength was the ability to thrust from his mind whatever did not seem to serve him. Already, he had half-forgotten the beating in Father Haugoult's study. The pain was there, but it was blurred, for his mind was moving forward to the book he intended to read this afternoon, during the two hours set aside for his instruction in "mathematics."

Though the boys at Vendôme were not permitted to visit their homes at Easter time, parents were allowed to come to the school. Honoré had few visitors. Nacquart and Laure came once. One year, no one had come. Last year, his father had stayed for an hour. This year, he expected no one and was prepared to be alone. But as he passed through the corridor, a boy touched his arm and said, "Balzac, you better go downstairs. Your mother's waiting for you."

Honoré caught the boy's arm.

"What did you say?" he demanded.

The boy pulled his arm free.

"I said your mother's downstairs. Don't you know it's visitors' day?"

He walked off, shaking his head. Honoré stood in the corridor, bumped and pushed by hurrying boys. Slowly, almost unwillingly, he went down the stone staircase to the main hall, ordinarily empty, today crowded with boys and their parents.

Alone, with a little space around her, stood his mother.

He paused on the staircase, staring at her. He had not seen her for five years, and he was stunned by her beauty, which he had remembered with the eyes of an eight year old. Now he was thirteen and the impact was different. She was no longer a fairy princess, but a woman of flesh and blood. She was real—a woman of thirty-three, at the height of her beauty. The mother in his mind was a fantasy, created to suit his own needs. She was good, kind, innocent, and she loved him, not because he was brilliant or strong or first-born, but simply because he was her son. It was an image made to be smashed, and he knew that the moment to smash it had come.

He moved toward her, his heart pounding. They did not kiss. She looked at him, her eyes taking in the ill-fitting, ragged grey uniform, the shapeless clogs on his feet, his unbrushed hair. Her face betrayed nothing, neither love nor hate. She might have been looking at the scullery maid in somebody else's kitchen. Honoré looked at her. They were strangers, he and this beautiful woman in pearl grey silk. Yet she was his mother. He was her son. He himself, Honoré Balzac, had inhabited that body. Milk that God had intended for him had swelled in those breasts.

"I have been waiting for fifteen minutes," she said. "Where have you been? You were sent for."

"I'm sorry, mother."

"Of course. You are always sorry," she said. "Being sorry doesn't help."

They went to a restaurant in the town, an old half-timbered house with a low-ceilinged dining room. Ashamed of his shabby uniform and chilblained hands, Honoré was awkward at table. Halfway through the meal, he knocked over his wine-glass.

"Must you be such a boor!" his mother exploded.

He apologized, and sat back in his chair while a servant girl mopped up the spilt wine. Then he said in a calm voice, "Why did you come, mother?"

His mother looked at him, startled, and for an instant nearly lost her mask. Beneath the varnished elegance was a human being in agony. The mask did not break. She said coldly, "One is obliged to see to your health and so on. Your father is occupied these days." She lifted her nose contemptuously. "He is writing another book."

"What is it about?" he asked, eager for news of his father.

"What does it matter?" she said. "Your father's books are read by only three people, the printer, Dr. Nacquart, and your father himself."

"Have you never read one?"

"I have no time for such nonsense," she said. "Finish your sweet. It is time to get back to the school."

An hour later, she was gone. She had not even troubled to ask for a conference with the head master.

She brought him a little notoriety. Most of the mothers were in their forties, solid, middle-class women, stodgily dressed and going to fat. Everyone had noticed Anne-Charlotte.

34

"Was that really your mother, Balzac?" a boy from the form above called out, that night at dinner. "She had all the priests in a regular sweat."

There was a leer on the boy's face and a nasty undertone in his voice. Honoré ignored it. More and more, these days, he drew into himself, not precisely avoiding companionship, but never seeking it out.

Throughout the year, Honoré continued to work on his treatise, doing the reading in the library and most of the writing, secretly, in Father Haugoult's classroom. The book was the center of his life; he was infatuated with his own brilliance.

A few months after his mother's visit, at the beginning of his sixth year at Vendôme, his world exploded. He was in class. Having just recited, he did not expect to be called on again until Haugoult had gone through the roster. Quietly, behind a book, he drew out the sheets of his manuscript and began to work. There were nearly sixty pages, closely covered in his thin, rather spidery hand—about half of the projected essay that was to incorporate his entire view of life.

He was so absorbed in his work that he did not hear Father Haugoult coming up behind him, pointer in hand. For several seconds, the priest stood behind him, watching the pen fly over the paper. The class became silent. Everyone stared at the master and his victim. Honoré went on writing, unaware of his predicament. Then Father Haugoult touched the manuscript with the tip of his pointer.

"So, Balzac, you are writing, while the rest of us are doing Latin," he said in a silky voice. "What is it? A letter? Let me see."

He touched the sheet beneath Honoré's hand. Honoré snatched the paper away. Father Haugoult reached for the rest of the manuscript and the boy went blind with rage. He struck out with his fist and the priest staggerd backward, dropping his pointer.

"No!" Honoré shouted, on his feet. "No! No!"

For a moment the class was too stunned to move. To strike a priest was unheard of, a thing that had never been done in the history of the school. Then half a dozen boys came to Father Haugoult's assistance, seizing Honoré by the arms.

"He's gone crazy!" someone yelled. "Balzac has gone mad!"

"He hit the priest. He hit the priest."

35

"He's gone crazy."

Honoré fought against the boys who held him, but two big fellows pinioned his arms, and two others held his legs. He could not move. Father Haugoult picked up the treatise and began to read. Then he gave a short, bitter laugh.

"So it is for nonsense like this that you neglect your lessons, Balzac?" he said. "A TREATISE ON THE HUMAN WILL, indeed." He ruffled the papers. "Here is what I think of your will, Balzac."

The room was warmed by a charcoal brazier. Father Haugoult lifted the lid and dropped the manuscript into the fire. The paper flared up quickly. Honoré shrieked as if he had been stabbed, and fought madly against his captors. The flame died down.

"You monster!" Honoré screamed. "You monster!"

For the crime of striking a priest of God, Honoré was sentenced to the most severe of all the punishments used at the College de Vendôme—a week in the medieval stocks that were reserved for extraordinary offences.

Day and night, for seven days, his arms, legs and neck were confined by holes in a wooden board. Once a day he was fed a meal of bread and water. The cell was dark and damp. From time to time, a rat ran across his face. Water dripped from the stone walls and fell with a maddening rhythm.

At the end of the week, when he was brought up into the light, he gave a single scream and collapsed. He lay on the floor, writhing. He could not speak. He could scarcely stand. His eyes were like those of a terrified deer.

After two days, the director, Monsieur Mareschal, was sent for. He looked at Balzac and shook his head.

"He has had a breakdown, this one," he said. "We cannot keep him here. His mother must come and take him away."

Dr. Nacquart came for him and drove him home in his carriage. During the week he had been in the stocks, his nerves had broken. He was pale and emaciated. His expression was vacant and strange, like that of a sleepwalker. He had lost the power of speech. When addressed, he merely nodded, or made a throaty animal sound.

"Has he lost his reason?" demanded his mother. "Will he recover?"

Nacquart had served in the army and seen soldiers reduced to similar condition by the shock of battle.

36

"I don't think his reason has been affected," he told Anne-Charlotte. "It is his nerves. They have suffered a kind of breakdown, do you understand?"

"What must be done?" she demanded.

"He needs rest," said Nacquart. "Absolute rest. Plenty of food. Sun. Fresh air. And time. It will take time, madame, I remind you."

Honoré's mother gave orders that Nacquart's instructions were to be followed, not out of concern for her son, but because she could not bear the disgrace of having an idiot in the family.

For three months the boy remained almost completely silent. He seemed uncertain of his whereabouts. He stared off into space, his eyes empty and baffled. For several weeks, he recognized no one and it was necessary to feed him as a child is fed. He displayed no emotion, neither fear nor aggression, but passed his time placidly in a chair near his bedroom window, where he sat and stared at the sky.

Each morning, on the way to his office at the hospital, Bernard-François looked in on the boy, shook his head sadly, and went about his affairs. Anne-Charlotte refused to see him.

"He makes me nervous," she objected. "The way he stares at nothing. No, I prefer not to see him."

It was Laure who drew him out of the shell. The first word he uttered after his attack was his sister's name.

"Laure," he said, one morning when she came to give him his bowl of chocolate. "Laure," he repeated, feeling for the word.

"You are better!" she exclaimed, kissing his cheek.

"Laure," he said again, looking at her with wonderment.

The next morning, when she brought his breakfast, he caught her hand and said, "How is the Emperor?"

"The Emperor?"

"Napoleon," he said, in an odd, stilted voice. "How does he fare?"

Laure shrugged. "They say there are victories in the east," she said inconclusively. "At Leipsig. Dresden. Places one never has heard of."

Honoré shook his head. "It was a mistake to attack the Russians," he said soberly. "Russia is a swamp. Battles cannot be fought in swamps."

Laure laughed at him and said, "What do you know about Russia? You haven't come from Russia, but from Vendôme."

37

"Vendôme," he said, looking up at her. "Do you know that Vendôme is a prison? The Bastille could not have been worse."

She knelt beside his chair and held his hand. "You are home," she assured him. "You musn't think about Vendôme. You must get well."

"Home," he said doubtfully. "Yes, I suppose I am home."

In the end, the peasant vitality inherited from his father came to Honoré's rescue. The lethargy passed. He began to read again, then to take long walks, first with Laure or Nacquart, then by himself. He came to know every back alley in the ancient city of Tours, to know the history and romance attached to every ancient house. Sometimes his father's friend, Monsieur de Margonne, asked him to come and stay at the Chateau of Saché for a few days. Honoré loved the countryside of Touraine, the garden of France. Saché, with its vineyards and winding streams, became almost a second home to him.

Chapter 4

A YEAR AFTER
Honoré left Vendôme, his father came home one evening, bristling with excitement.

"I have been transferred to Paris!" he exclaimed. "Head of the Military Commissariat for the District of the Seine!"

"Paris?" Honoré gulped.

"Paris, my boy!" his father assured him. "Now we shall really begin to live."

"Will we see the Emperor?" Honoré asked.

"Of course. The Emperor, the Empress, the lot," said Bernard-François. "I tell you, my boy, Paris is the center of the world."

For Honoré, the center of the world turned out to be a slant-topped desk at Monsieur Lepître's school, where he was sent as a day boy, to prepare for the Sorbonne. Bernard-François found a house in the rather gloomy Marais District and for a year Honoré inhabited a room on the top floor. Then the family moved to Villeparisis, a few miles outside of Paris, and again he became a boarder at school.

After Vendôme, Lepître's was heaven, but even so, Honoré did not distinguish himself as a scholar, being content to pass, and nothing more. He was bored with school, but fascinated by the great city, by the sense of being at the center of things, in the midst of great affairs.

Then came 1814, a fateful year for France. The Imperial sun was beginning to set. Like a helpless woman, Paris cowered, waiting to be taken. With the other lads from Lepître's school, Honoré went into the streets, joining the anxious crowds. The Allies were on French soil and the Emperor, who had seemed to be in the confidence of Destiny, now knew the bitter taste of defeat, not on the frozen Russian steppes, far from France, but on the proud, fresh fields just north of Paris. English and German troopers rode

39

through the pleasant valleys of France. It was said that the Cossacks were behind them.

Paris waited.

One afternoon in March, a grey day, Honoré stood in the midst of the crowd that had gathered in the Tuileries Gardens, waiting for news, any news. Ragged, wounded French infantry trickled into the city, their eyes filled with defeat.

"The Allies are closing in on Paris," they told the crowds in the streets. "The Emperor has been beaten."

The common people wept. The Royalist aristocrats smiled quietly. In April, Bonaparte abdicated, at Fontainebleau. The Allied armies entered Paris. Honoré watched the British dragoons riding down the Champs Elysées; like thousands of others, he wept for France. He was stunned. He had worshipped the Emperor and regarded him as invincible.

In May, the King, Louis XVIII, rode into the capital in a gilded carriage drawn by eight white horses, behind an honor guard of enemy cavalry. Now came the dreaded Cossacks, bearded horsemen with fierce sabres, from whom a terrified citizenry hid their valuables and young daughters. Paris kept her shutters closed for a time. The Cossacks turned out to be men, like other men, soldiers, like other soldiers. The shutters were opened.

Then there was peace.

The new King sat in Versailles. The Emperor was at Elba, a prisoner of the British.

A year passed.

Then the word sped through France like an electric current: "Bonaparte has escaped from Elba! The Emperor is on the march!"

The Hundred Days passed too, and again the Emperor departed, this time for good. The crowds in the streets disappeared. The King relaxed. Paris returned to normal. At Lepître's school, the boys returned to their Greek and Latin, baffled but exhilarated. Honoré neglected his Latin to pore over the published accounts of the great battle at Waterloo, where the Emperor had met his final defeat, trying to understand where things had gone wrong. His school reports were bad. His mother wrote him scorching letters and hinted that he was already a failure, at the age of sixteen.

40

To his mother's surprise, he qualified for entrance to the University.

"Well, my boy, you must study law, that much is clear," his father told him.

"Law?" said Honoré. "I had thought of literature or philosophy."

"Philosophy doesn't pay," said Bernard-François. "As for literature, that is something one does on the side, as I do myself. No, the law is the profession for you, take my word for it. You see, France is in a state of flux. In my time, we've had the King, then the Republic, then the Directory, then the Consulate, the Empire, and now the King again. Things are confused in France, my boy. There will be work for lawyers in this country for a hundred years to come. It is the profession of the future. Besides, I have a friend who has agreed to take you into his office while you are working for your degree—even before you are qualified. You won't regret it, my boy. I promise you that. Lawyers will be the princes of the future."

If Honoré had regrets, he kept them to himself, at least for the time being, and applied his energies to the task of mastering the legal code that Bonaparte had bequeathed to France, along with the defeat at Waterloo.

The law has been described as a profession that sharpens the mind by narrowing it, and perhaps this is especially true of French law, where everything is written down and justice is reduced to questions of fact. It would be difficult to imagine a mind less suited to the Code Napoléon than the mind of Honoré Balzac, which had always refused to be harnessed to anything except his own imagination.

His masters were good men. First he served as the law clerk to the Advocate, Guyonnet de Merville, a man of intelligence and kindness, who liked him and respected his idiosyncracies. Then, after two years, he entered the office of the Notary, Passez, another old friend of his father's, who had a prosperous practice.

"My boy, your future is assured," Bernard-François told him, when he went to Passez's office. "You won't have to fight your way to the top, as I did. All you have to do, lad, is take your bachelor's degree in law. In good time, Passez will be ready to retire and you will take charge. Then you can marry, and marry well. Any number of girls from good families, girls with money in the bank,

41

mind you, will be glad to get their hands on a young lawyer with a bright future."

Honoré nodded absently. He was sitting in the garden at Ville-parisis, a book on his lap. His father leaned forward and glanced at the title.

"Rabelais!" he said. "Marvelous! What art! What precision! What understanding of life!"

Honoré agreed with his father. He was infatuated with Rabelais, the great teller of tales, who, like himself, had been born in Touraine.

Bernard-François glanced at his son, then said shyly, "I have just published a book of my own, my lad. It's nothing much, of course, but all the same, if you'd like to look at it . . ."

"I should be grateful," said Honoré politely.

Bernard-François went into the house, returning a few moments later with a slim volume in his hand. He gave it to Honoré, who read the title page aloud: "A NOTE ON THE SCANDALS CAUSED BY DEGRADED AND ABANDONED WOMEN."

"The title is a little long," his father said defensively. "Of course, it's a scientific work. All fact, you see. Nothing made up."

"I will read it with pleasure," promised Honoré.

Bernard-François leaned forward confidentially, glanced at the house, and lowered his voice to a conspiratorial level, "My boy, you are nearly seventeen. I'm no fool, you know. I understand how it is with lads your age. If you ever need advice, my boy, don't hesitate to come to me. I'll put you right, whatever it is."

Honoré agreed that when such problems were encountered they would be brought to Bernard-François for solution. The fact is, at seventeen he was an odd combination of innocence and sophistication. He read whatever came to his hand, and books had taught him that love was complex, terrifying, dangerous, and exceedingly enjoyable. Of actual experience, he had none. The schoolboy smut at Vendôme had embarrassed and sickened him. The crude street talk of Paris made his ears burn with embarrassment. When he was approached by a prostitute, he found it impossible to joke with the girl, the way other students did. When his classmates invited him to come along to some brothel or other, he always begged off with a lame excuse.

Yet he was curious and uncomfortable. Not long ago, by accident, he had seen his mother in corset and stockings, her hair

42

in a tumble down her back, her pale arms and shoulders bare. He had been paralyzed with fear staring at his mother's naked thighs, his heart thumping, his mouth dry. His mother seemed enormously wicked, enormously beautiful, above all, enormously forbidden. She was the woman whose love he wanted, and she had no love for him. Desperately, he wanted to please her, to win some prize to place at her feet.

The Sorbonne became the fountain of his youth. He haunted the old stone fortress of learning, attending the lectures of Cousin and Villemain—superb lectures in ancient halls, delivered to ardent young men. Cousin was prophetic and daring, a thinker who taught that man was a product of his environment. Villemain, a professor at twenty-eight, was eloquent, enthusiastic, alive with the passion for greatness.

"The Empire of politics has passed," said Villemain. "The Empire of Letters will never fall."

Honoré scribbled these words into the ragged copybook that held his notes on the Law.

"The Empire of Letters!"

The idea thrilled him. There were still worlds to conquer, in the wild country of literature.

As he passed through the courtyard of the Sorbonne into the bright spring sunshine, he was thrilled with life, infatuated with ideas of greatness. He turned into the Boulevard Saint-Michel and walked slowly through the Latin Quarter, downhill toward the Seine. The trees were coming into leaf and the air was fragrant. Paris was a tract of quivering grey. When he reached the river, he stopped, leaning against the stone guard rail, looking at the Ile de la Cité and the Cathedral de Notre-Dame.

His brain was racing. Beaumarchais! Shakespeare! Racine! Molière! Corneille!

His imagination was on fire. He stood by the river, watching the current, filled with a sense of the past and a longing for the future. Around him were the grey tides of Paris. Then a clock struck the hour, breaking into his revery. He stood erect, shook himself, and walked slowly toward the office of Monsieur Passez, the notary, where his desk and stool were waiting for him.

During these years while he was reading law and going to lectures at the Sorbonne his only confidante was Laure, whom he saw on weekends, when he went home to Villeparisis. With Laure, he was never embarrassed. He trusted her with his deepest secrets, and to her alone confided his aspirations to greatness.

On fine Sundays, after Mass, they liked to walk together along the back roads in the country behind Villeparisis, idling along, sometimes sitting by the road for an hour, talking or simply admiring the rich, rolling fields. One Sunday, just before he was eighteen, young Balzac said to his sister, "Some day, Laure, I will be famous. As famous as Bonaparte, perhaps."

Anyone else would have laughed at him. His mother would have responded with scorn. Laure believed him. She always believed him.

He knew in his heart that he would be famous, but how was it to be done? The army was meaningless, now that the Emperor was gone. Sometimes he thought of politics. The law could serve as a bridge to the world of politics. Finance was another thing. Sometimes he would stand in the Place de la Bourse, watching the stockbrokers passing in and out of the fake Roman temple that was the stock exchange. Something about the men of the Bourse repelled him. Most of them were new rich, men who had risen during the revolution and pushed the old aristocracy to one side.

The aristocracy fascinated him and so did the fashionable women of Paris. He would stand near the Palais-Royal or in the Champs-Élysées, watching the women, intrigued by their jewels, their fantastic coiffures, their elegant gowns, the blanket of scent they left in their wake.

Who owns these terrifying creatures? he wondered.

He went to the theatre when he could afford it, sitting in one of the cheapest seats, carried out of himself and away from the mundane study of law, into the marvelously contrived world of Molière or Racine.

Curiously though, it was not a Frenchman who revealed Balzac's destiny, but a foreigner, and an enemy at that. One night in his room at Villeparisis, he was reading a translation of IVANHOE. Reading, perhaps, is the wrong word. He was immersed in the book so completely that his own identity seemed to disappear. He became the Author of Waverly. As he read, he felt an enormous power that seemed to rise from the depths of his soul. This mighty nameless author was a kind of emperor, the master of a created world.

44

He put the book down and went to his window. There was a pale moon that bathed the countryside with mysterious, heatless light. I will be a writer, Balzac thought. A great writer. As great as the Author of Waverly.

In France, as elsewhere, the only writers worthy of respect from decent people were those who were dead and safely buried. Honoré's family was shocked, then outraged by his announcement that he intended to abandon the law for literature.

His mother merely sneered at first, then plunged into a rage.

"A writer indeed!" she said contemptuously. "Why not become the King of Sweden? You have never been a student. You were a failure at Vendôme. They sent you away. At Monsieur Lepître's school you were thirty-second in a class of thirty-five. Shocking! A son of mine, at the bottom of his class!"

For the first time in his life, he stood his ground against his mother. "I will not fail as a writer," he said calmly.

Diplomatically, Bernard-François intervened.

"Look here, my boy," he said. "I know something about writing, from the inside, you might say. It's all right as a pastime, but as for making it a career, that's another matter. There is no middle ground in literature. A man is either a king or he is nothing."

"Then I shall be a king," said Balzac boldly.

His mother laughed scornfully. "A king! You are soft in the head, my boy. You suffer from delusions of grandeur." She paused, dabbing at her mouth with a bit of perfumed lace, then went on. "A writer! After all we've done for him—school, university, everything. This is the way he thanks us. He wants to be a writer. My own son. A writer!"

Balzac smiled. He looked at his mother without fear. His conviction of destiny served as armor against her.

"Mother, you act as if I had just announced that I was going to become a burglar," he said calmly. "I intend to be a writer. A great writer."

"Greatness is not gotten by wishing," Anne-Charlotte said smugly.

"You are wrong," said Balzac. "It is gotten only by wishing. And by work."

"He speaks from a height already," said his mother. "I tell you, his dreaming has gone to his head. He needs a doctor."

45

Rage, ridicule, contempt having failed, Balzac's mother turned to tears. She wept, she cried aloud. She buried her head in the arm of her chair and sobbed as if she were mortally stricken. Bernard-François coughed nervously and brought her a glass of water. Her younger son, Henri, joined her weeping. Laure fled.

His mother's tears had no effect on young Balzac, the ingrate. He assumed the pose that was later to become world famous—arms folded across his chest, head high, looking proud as a lion—and waited until his mother had exhausted herself with false hysterics.

When her sobbing ceased and she sat sniffing at a bottle of lavender salts, he said quietly, "I don't want much, you know. An attic room. A few francs a week for food. Paper and ink." He paused. "And time. I shall want some time."

"An attic room," his mother said, coughing over her smelling salts. "Do you realize what you are saying, you foolish boy? You have a future certain as the seasons, thanks to your parents' foresight. All you need do is attend to your affairs—sit, in effect—and when a few years have passed, you will succeed Monsieur Passez. There is money in law, security, prestige. You could be a credit to your family. And you want to trade all this for a filthy attic and a life of debauchery with some street girl."

"No one mentioned debauchery," said Balzac calmly. "No one mentioned a companion. Only the attic."

"Everyone knows what writers are," his mother responded. "Free livers who care nothing for the rules, nothing for the opinions of decent society. They are rogues, the lot of them. It is common knowledge."

Balzac laughed. "I give you my word, mother, that I will postpone my loose-living until I have achieved fame and an income," he said.

"Do not be insolent," his mother said. "Please remember we are your parents."

"And I am your son," said Honoré softly. "I love you, mother. I have always loved you. You know that."

"You show your love in a strange way," she said.

Bernard-François got out of his chair, toying importantly with his watch chain.

"We must talk this over," he said. "It must be discussed. It is not the kind of thing one decides in an instant. After all, the boy's future, his whole life. . . ."

46

The family battle raged for a week. Anne-Charlotte pleaded, threatened, wept and stormed. Balzac refused to budge. Bernard-François pondered the matter, offered sage advice and dire warnings.

Balzac was unmoved.

"If we refuse you?" his mother demanded.

"I shall give up the Law, in any case, and look for work in Paris," he said. "Any kind of job that will put food into my mouth. I thought of being a food porter at Les Halles. It's hard work, but one is sure to eat."

At the end of a week, Anne-Charlotte changed her tactics. Since he was stubborn, he must have his way, but things must be so arranged that he brought about his own defeat. It was decided that he be given a hundred and twenty francs a month, for a period of two years, during which time he was to prove his talent or give up the effort.

"It will be enough to live on," Anne-Charlotte said. "But not enough for debauchery."

"It will be enough," said Balzac.

He would have tried on half the amount, or on nothing, if they had forced him to the wall.

Chapter 5

Even though the rent had been reduced to a token, no one wanted to live in the garret of the ancient house at No. 9, rue Lesdiguières, a dark street, narrow as a knife, near the Place de la Bastille.

The house itself was a dank ruin, the garret in such condition that no self-respecting peasant would have used it for a sty. One reached this palace by ascending five flights of perilous stairs that sagged and uttered ghostly creaks. The door was the kind found on a shed—three rough boards, nailed together with a diagonal fourth. The pitch of the roof was steep, so that on the north side floor and ceiling nearly met, giving the place the character of a lean-to. In thirty years, the roof tiles had not been renewed; patches of sky could be seen between them.

"A furnace in the summer time. Colder than the Seine itself in winter. Smells like an out-house. But it's cheap. You won't find a cheaper place in Paris, unless you want to sleep under the bridges."

So they had told him at the café on the corner, where he had inquired for lodgings.

"If it's cheap, it's what I want," he had said cheerfully.

Now he stood in the garret, the landlady beside him. It was mid-August, a sweltering day, and the room was the furnace he had been promised. There was a dormer window cut into the north wall. He stepped forward and peered through the dirty glass. There was a view of the public square and the well that served the district.

"Five francs a month, you say?" asked Balzac, turning.

The landlady nodded.

"I'll take it," Balzac decided.

He counted five francs into the calloused hand. The old woman looked at him and smiled. She was sixty, a wrinkled woman with kind eyes.

"You are an artist, monsieur? A painter, perhaps?" she asked.

Balzac shook his head. "An artist with words, I hope, madame,"

48

he said. "I am a writer." He tapped his forehead. "My paints are in my head."

"A writer. I hope the room brings you luck, monsieur," the landlady said, stowing away the five francs in a cracked purse that she carried in her bosom.

"Thank you, madame," said Balzac, with a little bow.

He stood in the center of the room, listening to the sound of the old woman's clogs on the stairs as she descended. Then there was the odd, conclusive silence one feels on the top floor of a house. Balzac had a glorious awareness of freedom. He was alone, in his own place. He went back to the window and pushed it open. The sounds of the city rose to greet him. Somewhere down the street, a man was berating his wife. Balzac gazed at the rooftops, at the hundreds of chimney pots. His heart pounded with excitement. Paris! And he was free! Free of the law. Free of his mother. Free to create his own destiny in this anonymous attic room.

He turned away from the window, looking at the dirty, mustard-colored walls, water-stained and cracked, then at the unreliable roof. He knew that his mother depended on discomfort and poverty to break his will, but he was determined to live without complaint on the pittance he had agreed to take.

During the next few days he patched up the chinks in the roof, stopped the worst cracks in the plaster, and whitewashed the walls. The weather was hot and he was soaked with sweat, but he enjoyed the work. When he was finished, his garret was no palace but it was clean. After being whitewashed, it suggested a monk's cell, and he thought this was appropriate, for he intended to live like a monk while he served his apprenticeship to literature.

He could not have lived much more cheaply. His lodging cost three sous a day. The oil he burned in his lamp at night, another three sous. He wore flannel shirts to save the cost of laundry. Each morning, he carried his own water from the fountain in the Place Saint-Michel. When the cold weather came, he nursed the fire in his coal grate.

To be poor successfully is an art, and Balzac learned the secret during his first months in the rue Lesdiguières. He had a bed to sleep on, a chair to sit on, a table at which to work, a lamp when it was dark, a token fire when the cold was extreme. Nearby was the Arsenal Library, to supply him with the books he needed.

49

Outside was all of Paris, to provide him with entertainment, instruction, and exercise in the form of walking.

It was enough.

During the summer and early autumn, he read passionately, seeking the thread of his own genius in the pages of acknowledged masters. Voltaire's brilliance filled him with terror. Corneille transported him. Racine made him throw down his pen in despair. One day he was filled with hope, the next with confusion.

During this period, a single attraction drew him from his garret. He began to observe the life of the Faubourg Saint-Antoine, the working-class district in which he lived. Dressed almost like a workman, he moved with ease through the crowded thoroughfares of the poor, joining groups at street corners or at the zinc bar in a cheap café, listening to the talk of the people.

These expeditions became a part of his studies, related to the hours passed in his room, in the world of books. He looked into the souls of the people, and came to understand their ways. He felt their rags on his own shoulders, his own feet in their tattered shoes. He shared the indignation they felt toward employers who mistreated them, and their outrage at a system that cheated them out of their labor. Here in the Faubourg, among the common people, was the dark soul of France. The teeming, vibrant slum was a seminary of revolution. In the streets and alleys of the Faubourg, Balzac saw beautiful and terrible things, life and death and love.

Sometimes he climbed the long hill from the Place de la Bastille to Père-Lachaise. He would wander through the cemetery, gazing at the stones of Molière, and La Fontaine, then go to the edge of the cliff and look down at the city, spread beneath him like a map. His heart stirred with wonder as he looked at the network of streets and alleys, avenues, boulevards and parks. Paris! The center of the universe. It was his battleground. He regarded it with awe, but without fear.

Balzac's Paris was not Baron Haussmann's modern miracle of boulevards and illuminated fountains. It was a medieval town, after dark not too much changed from the Paris of François Villon. The streets were narrow and paved with cobbles, where they were paved at all. There were few sidewalks. In wet weather, the city became a vast, foul-smelling mud puddle and the back streets were ditches where a man could sink to his knees in the mire.

50

By night it was a city full of shadows, dangerous and dark. Cutthroats lurked in the damp alleys, ready to murder a passerby for the sake of a few francs. When they left the main thoroughfares, pedestrians carried torches in their hands, and it was not unusual to go abroad armed with a pistol or dagger.

By day, central Paris was like an oriental bazaar. Peddlers swarmed along the quays of the Seine, dressed in smelly rags, hawking and singing their various wares. Pretty girls with bold eyes offered cakes of Nanterre. Old women sold patent matches. One could buy theater tickets from dubious agents near the river. Through the crowd, pointing with dirty fingers, wandered hundreds of décrotteurs—bootblacks who also brushed the mud from one's trousers. On the corners, street singers bawled popular ballads. Along the banks of the river, dentists set up their tables and pulled teeth with rusty forceps. On both sides of the Pont-Neuf, scores of pimps agitated boldly, trafficking in human flesh. Levantines with enormous trays offered love philtres, aphrodisiacs, and vile-smelling mixtures guaranteed to cure any ailment known to man.

It was a dangerous, unsanitary city, but it was Paris—center of the world—and Balzac worshipped every stone of it.

Near the Quai des Celestins, walls frowning upon the river, was the grim stone fortress called the Arsenal, which had been turned into a library. The most important rooms in the building were those used as living quarters by the librarian, Charles Nodier. Nodier's apartment was a gathering place for the young writers of Paris, and Nodier's "evenings" were a kind of postgraduate course in literature for the aspiring novelist, poet or playwright.

Balzac went one evening and was presented to his contemporaries. There was Victor Hugo, a stocky powerful youth, three years younger than Balzac, precocious, already famous for his verse. Alexandre Dumas, half-Negro, arrogant, totally sure of himself, towered over the others. Alphonse Lamartine, older than the rest of them, and serious minded, brooded over politics and writing. Alfred de Vigny, the dandy, was there. So was Boulanger, the painter.

Nodier made them all welcome.

He made Balzac welcome too, but some shyness in Balzac's nature obliged him to draw back from his fellows. He respected Hugo and Lamartine, detested Dumas, was baffled by de Vigny.

51

None of them became his friend. He was terrified of being laughed at. His mother's inveterate cruelty had made him suspicious of strangers. He could not relax and enjoy himself, as Dumas did or even Hugo. The other writers thought him sullen, a queer fish. He yearned to be part of the group at Nodier's, but he could not do it.

He kept to himself, as he had done at Vendôme and at Monsieur Lepître's school.

Balzac had only one real friend while he lived in his garret in the rue Lesdiguières. That was Père Dablin, so-called in spite of the fact that he was not yet forty, because of some indefinable quality that gave him the aspect of age. Dablin was an ironmonger, well-to-do, generous, and a friend of Bernard-François, at whose suggestion he had first looked Balzac up. Somewhere, perhaps during his revoluntionary days, Dablin has acquired a profound respect for books and for writers. Instead of becoming a kind of spy for Balzac's parents, he became Balzac's first supporter.

On Saturday evenings, Dablin would call at the rue Lesdiguières, and carry Balzac off for a good meal and a bottle of wine. They would sit through the evening in the restaurant, always a modest, quiet place, and talk about literature.

"Ah, my boy, I envy you," the little merchant would say, his black eyes glittering with excitement. "You have the world at your feet."

"I'd rather have it by the throat," said Balzac.

"Write comedy, my boy," urged Dablin. "That's what goes, nowadays. The people of France have been through strenuous times. They went to laugh. Make them laugh, even a little, and they will make you rich."

"Making people laugh is a job for clowns," said Balzac, with the haughtiness of youth. "I am not a clown, Père Dablin, but a writer."

Dablin was hurt. Balzac had spoken more harshly than he intended. He touched the ironmonger's hand and said, "It's not that I have anything against comedy, my friend. It's just that I have other fish to fry, at the moment."

"A tragedy?" said Dablin eagerly. "Something big? That's even better."

"Perhaps," said Balzac mysteriously.

"Have another glass of wine," Dablin insisted. "A tragedy. That's splendid! That's splendid!"

52

Afterward, Balzac walked home through the night, his stomach filled, his brain pleasantly mulled by the wine. He knew that his parents had asked Dablin to keep tabs on him, but he liked Dablin in spite of it. Besides, it was pleasant, once a week, to have a change from his usual diet of bread, cheese and coffee.

His mind hungered for a subject, a big subject, something he could get his teeth into. Toward the end of autumn, he was reading a two volume work on Cromwell that had been written by Villemain, his old teacher at the Sorbonne. As the life of the great Puritan unfolded on Villemain's pages, Balzac's pulse quickened. This was superb history that Villemain had written, but Balzac saw that there was more to Cromwell than history. There was the ebb and flow of drama, the surge of tragedy. In fact, the subject for a play!

He sat down at his table with Villemain's book at his elbow, and drew a foolscap pad toward him, testing the nib of his quill with his thumb, then beginning to write. As he scribbled the outline, he could see it all in his mind's eye. He heard the cadences of the as yet unwritten verse, saw the actors reading his lines on the stage of the Comédie Française, the national home of French drama.

The story seemed made to order. Balzac saw the unhappy queen, disguised in rags, entering Westminster, where the king was awaiting trial. He saw Cromwell himself, unyielding as rock, Stafford, the unfortunate Charles. Feverishly, he worked through the night, composing the outline of a five act tragedy. When he finished, dawn was breaking over the rooftops of Paris. He was exhausted and his feet were numb with cold, but he felt the sublime exhilaration that follows a strenuous bout of creative effort, a heady sense of kinship with the gods.

He stretched himself, chafed his tired wrist, stamped his feet and yawned. The sensible thing would be to get some sleep, but sleep was the last thing he wanted. He put on his overcoat and hat and went down the steep staircase on tiptoes, into the bitter winter morning. He turned toward Père-Lachaise, climbing the hill, intending to watch the sun rise over Paris.

The next day, he began work on the first act of his tragedy, which was to be written in verse. Balzac sweated over every line. If he had lived like a monk before, now he lived like a Trappist. He was at his work table day and night. Sometimes three or four days passed and he did not leave his garret, living on stale bread and cheese and lots of strong, black coffee. As the weather grew colder, he dressed for work in a knitted cap that covered his ears and an old overcoat that had been his father's. He no longer went to the Arsenal Library, to walk in the Faubourg, or to Père-Lachaise. The only break in routine he permitted was the weekly evening with Père Dablin.

Dablin was fond of Balzac but he was no judge of poetry. To be able to write verse at all seemed to Dablin a magnificent thing. He praised Balzac's first act, took him to dinner and then to the Comédie-Française, where they were playing Racine.

On the way home, Balzac was silent, almost sullen.

"What's wrong, my boy?" demanded Dablin. "Didn't Racine please you tonight?"

"He pleased me too much," Balzac said. "He makes me see that my own work is no good at all. It is nothing. Not even good imitation."

"Don't be discouraged," said Dablin eagerly. "Remember, Racine worked for two years before he was satisfied with Phèdre."

"Two years!" Balzac exploded. "Perhaps. But he didn't have a mother like mine."

Dablin laughed sympathetically; he knew Anne-Charlotte. "You have a point, my boy," he said. "I grant you that. Still, you must give yourself time."

The next morning Balzac gulped his coffee, standing by the spirit stove, then put on his overcoat and knitted cap and plunged into his Cromwell, tearing the first act to pieces, trying to achieve some of the grace that shaped the play he had seen the night before. He worked for a week, without rest, not getting into bed at all, but dozing in his chair. Then he slept the clock around in the heavy, drugged sleep of exhaustion.

In the middle of the morning, he was at work. He had not troubled to shave or comb his hair. He looked like a vagabond from the banks of the Seine. His concentration was interrupted by the sound of footsteps on the garret stairs.

"Who can it be?" he asked himself. "No one ever comes here but Père Dablin, and he never comes on a weekday."

"Monsieur Balzac! Monsieur Balzac!" It was the landlady, calling him. "You have a visitor, monsieur. A lady."

54

Balzac leaped from his chair, wondering what lady knew him well enough to climb that hazardous stairway for the sake of paying him a visit.

It was Laure, dressed in a coat with a high fur collar, her cheeks brilliant with the cold, her eyes flashing. He was too surprised to speak. He simply stood and stared at her. She laughed.

"Well, Honoré, aren't you going to kiss me?" she asked.

They embraced. He held her for a moment, then drew back, staring at her again. "Laure, you are beautiful," he said. "Magnificent."

She looked around the room, seeking a chair. Embarrassed, Balzac dusted off the one he used for work, and offered it to her. She sat down and he leaned against the wall, staring at her. She smiled at him slyly, as if she had a secret.

"Honoré! I am going to be married," she said.

"Married!" He felt as though a gulf had opened at his feet. "But you're only a child!"

"My dear brother, I am nineteen," she said.

Balzac sat on the edge of his cot. "I can't believe it," he said, trying to fight back the blind jealousy he felt. "Who is the fortunate gentleman?"

"His name is de Surville," she told him. "An engineer. Very handsome. Very sympathetic. Quite intelligent. You will like him, Honoré."

"How can I like a man who steals my baby sister?" he complained, trying to sound as if he were joking.

Laure was not a fool. She and Balzac were bound by the childhood alliance. She understood that her marriage must seem a form of desertion, almost a kind of treachery. She kissed his cheek and said, "Be happy for me, Honoré. Please?"

He caught her hand and held it. My God, he thought, I am jealous of my own sister. It is monstrous, unnatural. Aloud, he said, "I wish you every happiness. If I seem strange, it's only because I'm surprised. It comes as a shock."

She looked around his room and made a face. The bed was unmade, the floor dusty. There were dirty cups on the shelf.

"You really aren't very neat," she said. "Mother will be appalled. Let me make up the bed, at least."

She shooed him off the bed and began to shake out the wrinkled quilts with a great show of feminine efficiency.

55

"Mother?" he said. "Is she with you in Paris?"

"Of course," said Laure. "Do you think she'd let me come to Paris alone, even though I *am* engaged? You know our mother better than that."

"Where is she?" he asked.

"She had an errand. She is meeting me here in half an hour," said Laure, smoothing the bed.

Balzac's first impulse was to flee. The last person on earth he wanted to see was his mother. "How is she?" he asked.

"As ever," said Laure. "She doesn't change."

"And father?"

"He is still the cavalier of Villeparisis," said Laure. "One should be ashamed of his escapades, I suppose. Still, he has charm, you know. Imagine it, Honoré, at seventy!"

"Seventy-two," Balzac said mechanically.

"And you, Honoré, what about you?" Laure said, teasing him. "Don't you take after our father at all? Don't you have a girl? A 'little friend'? After all, a young man, alone in Paris."

"You sound like mother," Balzac said. He shook his head. "No, Laure. I have no girl." He went to his work table and picked up a sheaf of manuscript. "This is my mistress, Laure," he said. "Paper, ink, black coffee."

"What is it?" she said, touching the manuscript. "A novel?"

He shook his head. "A play," he said vaguely. "A tragedy."

"May I read it?"

"When it's finished," he said, arranging the sheets carefully and putting them out of sight in the drawer of his table.

Laure went to the window. "Your room is dreadful," she said. "But your view is quite nice."

Balzac looked around the room. He was used to the squalor now. It meant nothing to him. A cockroach scuttled across the floor. Mechanically, he stepped on it and kicked the corpse under his bed.

"Uggh!" said Laure, with a shudder. "How can you bear it?"

He laughed. "Some day this old house will have a bronze placque on it," he said. "Balzac lived here."

There was a sound in the stairwell. Balzac stiffened. The landlady's voice rose to warn him.

"Monsieur Balzac! Monsieur Balzac!"

"It's mother," said Laure. "Honoré, quickly, comb your hair."

Balzac ran a comb through his hair and straightened the collar of his flannel shirt. In the fly-specked glass, he looked at his image with distaste.

"Well, Honoré, is this the way you greet your mother?"

He turned. His mother stood in the doorway, clad in a coat of soft brown fur. The color was flattering. At forty, she was filled with superb feminine arrogance. Only the eyes, which were nervous and quick, betrayed the torturing confusion within. Balzac stepped forward, bowed, and kissed her hand.

"You are thin," she said. "And not very clean." She looked around his room, her eyes pausing at the bed. "I suppose Laure made that for you, not ten minutes ago. Certainly no man did it that neatly."

He gave her the one chair in the room. He and Laure remained standing, somehow unwilling to sit on the bed.

"So this is your hovel," said Anne-Charlotte. "For this, you gave up a good home and a career."

"I have a career, mother," he said. "And a home too, I hope."

"Have you written anything?" she demanded.

"I am writing a tragedy," he said. "I'm half finished."

"And when will this masterpiece be completed?"

"In time for Laure's wedding," he said cheerfully.

She shook her head. "I had hoped that a winter in Paris would cure you," she said. "But apparently your illness is the stubborn kind."

"Quite stubborn," he agreed. "Congenital. Incurable."

Anne-Charlotte rose, drawing her furs closely about her.

"I didn't come to admire your hovel," she said, "but to tell you that I've taken the trouble to talk with Monsieur Passez. He will take you back, if you return now, and he won't hold this madness against you."

Balzac shook his head. "The law doesn't suit me," he said.

"Passez thinks differently," Anne-Charlotte said. "He assures me that you have the makings of a first-rate lawyer."

"He is mistaken," Balzac said.

Anne-Charlotte shrugged. "Very well, dig your own grave if you must," she said sharply.

When they had gone, Balzac sat on the chair his mother had used, gazing at the embers of his tiny fire. The room was heavy with the smell of her perfume, and the unfamiliar scent went to his head, having a strong, erotic effect.

"I am twenty-one," he thought morosely. "Twenty-one, a Frenchman, and a writer, living alone in Paris. And I have never had a woman. It is grotesque."

It was a thing that troubled him, yet he could do nothing about it. He was shy with girls, and even if he could have found the girl and the courage, he didn't have enough money for a part-time mistress of the kind students and artists liked. Prostitutes made him sick at his stomach, even when they were young and attractive.

Old Père Dablin had urged him to visit a brothel on the edge of the Faubourg.

"It's not natural, the way you live," the ironmonger insisted. "It's not hygienic. Sours the spirit. It's bad for your work."

"Wasting time is bad for my work," Balzac replied angrily.

"A man needs a woman once in a while, even if she's only a whore," Dablin said stubbornly. "Come along, my boy. It won't cost you anything. I'll pay."

"Mind your business," Balzac shouted. "Go to your whores, if you like. I am going back to my work."

And he had stormed out of the little restaurant, his dinner half-eaten, leaving Dablin alone at the table.

Chapter 6

BALZAC HAD BEEN
prepared to dislike Laure's fiancé, even to hate him, but once he
set eyes on Eugène de Surville, his prejudice dissolved. The young
engineer (he was a few years older than Balzac himself) was so
evidently sincere that it was impossible to dislike him. Twenty
minutes after they met, he and Balzac were friends. They sat in
the garden at Villeparisis, enjoying an apéritif with Bernard-
François. It was a fine spring evening, warm, but with a lift in
the air. The three men were at their ease, the women of the household being occupied indoors.

At seventy-two, Bernard-François was still very much the dandy.
Though his income had been somewhat reduced since the restoration of the monarchy, he still went to the best tailors and never
quarreled about price. He wore a plum-colored coat with flared
cuffs, an elegant collar, a cravat of pale grey silk, impeccably
folded and held in place by a pin with a fine black pearl. The
gold-headed stick was beside him, resting against the arm of his
chair.

"You don't change, father," Balzac said, sipping his absinthe
frappé, enjoying the suggestive flavor of wormwood.

"I change for the better," the old man said heartily. "Everyone
in France knows that I intend to live to be a hundred. It's a pity,
my boy, that you were born in Touraine instead of in Languedoc,
like me. There is something about the air in the south that puts
long life into the bones. Or perhaps it's the water. I'm thinking of
writing a pamphlet about it."

He lifted his glass and squinted at the contents. He was drinking white wine diluted with water. His latest theory held that
strong drink shortened life and he had given up spirits and red
wine.

Slyly, de Surville made a reference to a local celebrity, an old
peasant of the village who had recently achieved the great age
of one hundred and ten.

59

"There's a man who has lived wisely," Bernard-François observed, admiring his glass of watered wine. "Depend upon it, he hasn't abused himself, that fellow. No excesses. Moderation."

"That's the extraordinary thing about it, sir," said de Surville, with a wink for Balzac. "They say he's a notorious drunkard. Guzzles cheap brandy by the bottle. As for smoking, he's a regular furnace. Ten or fifteen cheroots a day. And he still has an eye for the girls."

Bernard-François was caught off guard. He thought for a moment, then coughed and said, "Well, he has shortened his life, that fellow, no doubt about it. He's squandered a few good years."

The two young men roared with laughter. After a moment, Bernard-François laughed too. He was never above a joke on himself. The sound of the men's laughter brought Anne-Charlotte to the side door of the house. The three men got up.

"I should think you'd be putting the finishing touches on your play," she said to Balzac. "After all, you are going to read it this evening."

The finishing touches had long since been put on Balzac's Cromwell. It had been buffed, polished and manicured, all but fumigated. Nevertheless, he nodded and said, "You are quite right, mother."

He went upstairs and glanced at the pages of his manuscript. He hated it now. All the hope that had sustained him while he was scourging himself in his garret seemed to have abandoned him. He tested the weight of the pages in his hand, resisting an impulse to tear them to bits. His heart turned to lead as he read a few lines at random. They were lifeless and dull, when they were not pretentious. Ah, well, there's no help for it now, he thought despairingly. I'll have to read it, no matter how bad it is.

As if with malicious intent, Anne-Charlotte served a heavy meal to the family members and guests who had assembled to hear young Balzac read his play. By the time a move to the garden was made, everyone was stuffed with food, much more ready for a nap than a five act tragedy in verse.

Dr. Nacquart was on hand, with Monsieur de Margonne, from Saché. Baron de Pommereul and his lady had come. So had Père Dablin. And so had a new neighbor of the Balzacs, introduced to the young playwright as Madame de Berny. She was past her youth, this stranger, but a beautiful woman, with a splendid aristocratic head and a magnificent bearing. Balzac was instantly taken with her. During dinner, he had caught himself staring at her on occasion, and been aware of a reproving glance from his mother.

Now, as everyone settled in the garden to hear him read, he forced his eyes away from the stranger and fixed them firmly on the face of his sister Laure, who sat beside her fiancé in the little semicircle of people arranged in the garden. He had heard somewhere that it was easier to read in public if you pretended to be reading to one person. He stood facing them, manuscript in hand. He trembled, so that the pages rustled. His mouth was dry and he wished he had not eaten a second helping of duck.

"Very well, Honoré, you may begin," said Anne-Charlotte.

He swallowed once or twice, then began to read his lines in a high, unnatural voice. Bernard-François stirred, snorted, then blew his nose. Anne-Charlotte frowned. Laure smiled. Balzac went on, pausing from time to time to take a sip of wine. After the first few pages, his voice returned to its normal register. For a scene or two, he read with force. Then he became bored with his own lines, and mouthed them monotonously as a schoolboy giving a recitation in class.

At the end of Act Three, Bernard-François was fast asleep. From time to time, he snored comfortably. Baron de Pommereul looked worried. Nacquart and de Surville made an effort to give the impression of interest. Anne-Charlotte was annoyed. Laure was heartbroken. Madame de Berny, the stranger, leaned forward in her chair, frowning, sometimes making an impatient gesture.

Balzac stumbled through Act Five and reached the curtain speech. He cleared his throat and tried to put some vigor into these lines, that had seemed so magnificent when he put them on paper:

> Take up thy banners, France, my native lair
> And while avenging me, hear thou my prayer:
> As Carthage fell beneath a righteous wrath
> Who dared to stand across her glorious path!

He finished lamely. There was silence. Bernard-François snored happily. Then Laure collected herself and applauded. The others, except for Anne-Charlotte and Madame de Berny, followed her example. Bernard-François, rudely awakened, sat up, blinked, belched, then stared at his son.

"Well then, that's it," Balzac said lamely. "Of course, it will be a different matter with actors, costumes. . . ."

Anne-Charlotte stood up. "Actors, costumes!" she said. "Honoré, you have wasted your time and our money." She touched the manuscript. "For this trash, you gave up a career. It is absurd." She turned to her husband. "Come, monsieur, you have slept enough."

She stormed into the house. Sheepishly, still half asleep, Bernard-François followed her.

Laure kissed Balzac on the cheek and started to say something, then changed her mind and ran into the house. Nacquart and the others muttered compliments. Soon, Balzac was alone in the garden, with Madame de Berny. She smiled at him and said, "Sit down. You must be tired of standing."

The evening light was generous. Madame de Berny looked beautiful and much younger than her age, which was close to that of Anne-Charlotte. Balzac sat down, facing her.

"Your first play?" she said.

He nodded morosely. "And my last, I shouldn't wonder," he said.

"Nonsense. You are a born writer," she told him.

"You liked it?" he said eagerly.

She shook her head. "It is a dreadful play, but there is talent, underneath the badness. You are a born writer. A fool could see it."

"Are you joking with me?" he said suspiciously.

"Of course not," she said. "One may joke about politics or clothes or food. Even about love. But not about literature. You are a writer. It is a thing one feels."

"Tell me, madame, what is wrong with my Cromwell?" he asked, suddenly moved to trust this stranger, whom he had known only a few hours. "The subject's a good one. God knows I worked. But my thoughts seemed to die between my brain and the tip of my pen."

"I am not a critic, monsieur," she said cautiously. "But I cannot help wondering whether verse is your happiest medium. Have you tried prose? A novel?"

He shook his head. The French novel, in those days, was not quite respectable. He had been aiming higher.

"Of course you know nothing about women," Madame de Berny said. "In a novelist, this would be a serious fault, but it can be remedied."

"You are pleased to make fun of me," he said stiffly.

"Not at all," she said. "I am simply making an observation. It was not intended to be personal."

Balzac looked at her in the fading light. She was twenty years his senior and more. She was the product of another world. Yet he felt immediate kinship with her. Abruptly, almost rudely, he said, "Madame, tell me something. Are you happy?"

Startled, she was silent for a moment. Then she laughed and said, "What a question. Happiness is for the young. I am left over from the old regime."

"May I come and see you?" he asked. "I have written other things. Perhaps you would read them, advise me."

She glanced at the house. "I don't think your mother would approve," she said.

"I am not a child," said Balzac.

She stood up, tall and straight, looking like the portrait of an aristocrat.

"Please. May I come?" he asked.

"Very well," she said. "Come on Thursday, in the afternoon. I will give you China tea and you can give me the gossip from Paris."

When she had gone, he stood alone in the garden. It was dark now and the stars were out. The smell of the early flowers was heavy, and there was the smell of turned earth from the beds that were just being put in.

"It is extraordinary," he said to himself. "I am in love."

Except for Laure and old Dablin, everyone had a dismal opinion of Balzac's future. His mother took the failure of his Cromwell as conclusive.

"You must return to your profession while there is still time," she insisted. "It is senseless to spoil a good lawyer in order to make a poor writer."

"Write something popular," advised his father. "A handbook on marriage, now. That would sell. Perhaps I could help you."

Laure's fiancé offered to have the play read by an acquaintance who lectured at the Collège de France. "He is a professor, after all. His judgment should be worth something."

Anne-Charlotte insisted that this be done. The professor read Cromwell and delivered an opinion:

> It is far from my desire to discourage your son, Madame, but I am forced to give it as my opinion that he could employ his time to better advantage than in writing tragedies and comedies. If he will give me the pleasure of calling on me, I will be happy to explain to him how belles-lettres should be studied and the benefits that can be derived from them, without adopting literature as a profession.

When he was shown the professor's letter, Balzac bristled with anger.

"You forget that I was a student at the Sorbonne," he said. "As far as writing is concerned, the academic hand is a dead hand. I am a writer, a creator, concerned with life."

"You have failed with a play," his mother said. "A year wasted. What do you propose to do now?"

"Write novels!" said Balzac recklessly.

Bernard-François looked up.

"Novels?" he said. "Piffle for shopgirls and tired ladies. Write philosophy. Something with meat to it."

"If you had read Waverly you would not call novels piffle," said Balzac.

"So you mean to continue," said his mother.

"You agreed that I was to have two years," Balzac said calmly. "I haven't used up half the time. Yes. I mean to continue."

"A bargain is a bargain," said Bernard-François. "The boy has his rights."

"He will suck us dry," said Anne-Charlotte.

Nacquart, who had been Balzac's friend and ally since childhood, advised him to compromise with his mother.

"It might make things easier if you took a job," he suggested. "You could write in your spare time."

"If I take a job, I am lost," Balzac said desperately. "I would become a clerk, a machine, a circus horse, with prescribed hours for doing my thirty or forty laps in the ring, drinking, eating and sleeping. I would rather be dead. I am a writer or I am nothing."

It was Madame de Berny who really put the iron into Balzac's blood. She received him in her sitting room, the paneling painted a delicate grey, the curtains at the long windows made of grey silk with a pink undercast. The furniture was elegant, graceful, decadent. Everything in the room had been selected as part of the background for the woman who used it. The room suited Madame de Berny as a good frame suits a picture.

She gave him delicious Chinese tea and talked about books in a way that was new to him. She was the first cultivated woman he had met and he was enchanted.

"Laure, she is marvelous," he told his sister.

"She is also something over forty," said Laure doubtfully.

"What does age matter!" he said. "She's worth a dozen fresh faced girls, with half-formed breasts and nothing on their minds. She has lived, Laure, really lived. Her past is exciting as a novel. Did you know that she was born in the palace at Versailles, that her god-parents were the king and queen of France?"

"I believe she is married," said Laure dryly.

"To an old man, an invalid!" cried Balzac. "Besides, she was married at fifteen. What an outrage!"

Balzac had agreed to remain at Villeparisis until after Laure was married. On the pretext of tutoring one of the de Berny children, the oldest boy Alexandre, he managed to pass more time at the de Bernys than at home. After an hour with his pupil, he was free to devote himself to the mistress of the house.

From the first, she delighted him. He could talk to her without feeling like a fool. In Paris, he had not been able to take part in the free and easy life that centered on the cafés frequented by young artists, writers and musicians and their female companions. He had no gift for flirtation. Clever phrases died on his lips. He was blunt when he meant to be gallant, rude when he intended to be pleasant.

Now he found himself almost daily in the presence of a woman who treated him as a man of importance, recognized in him the strain of genius that he knew in his heart was there. He had read his Rousseau. Almost from the first, he recognized in Madame de Berny that rare and marvelous amalgam of mother and mistress that many a young artist demands and few are lucky enough to find. For a long time, he lacked the courage to do more than kiss her hand. For her own part, though she found Balzac refreshing, Madame de Berny held herself in check.

So they sat in her grey drawing room, sipping aromatic tea, occupied with talk of books, plays, famous men, infamous women. They talked of Racine, Molière, Voltaire, and of the corrupt, gorgeous court at Versailles.

"It was depraved, of course, but all the same, it was gallant, you know," she said. "And when the time came, the best of them died the way they had lived, gallantly, with courage."

Subtly, Madame de Berny began to polish Balzac's rough edges. He had never been much concerned with his appearance, and was satisfied to wear suits that his father had discarded, after these had been cut down and refitted by a local tailor. He had never learnt the proper way to tie a cravat. His fingernails were often dirty, his hair unkempt. He had no idea of how to behave in a drawing room.

Madame de Berny tried to teach him.

"Honoré, my dear boy, you come into a room with all the grace of a young bull turned into the enclosure with a cow," she complained. "There is plenty of time. Hesitate for a moment at the door, like this." She pretended to be a young man, entering a fashionable salon. "Select the people of importance. Look with arch disdain at the others. Then advance slowly, like this, making the most of your entrance."

"I am a simple fellow," he said. "Crude. All thumbs. Two left feet." He laughed and wiped his forehead, then told her how he had once gone to dance at the Odéon, during his student days in Paris. "I was rigged out in a dress suit, borrowed of course, with a flower in my buttonhole. I finally found a girl without a partner—a fat one that no one wanted. I steered her out to the dance floor."

"Well?"

"I hadn't taken three steps before I slipped on the polished floor and fell on my . . . fell down. Everyone laughed. I haven't tried to dance since, I can tell you that."

She patted his cheek. "I will teach you to dance, my child," she said. "If I hadn't happened to marry well, I should probably be one of several thousand ladies in 'reduced circumstances' giving lessons in deportment to the offspring of the new rich—meaning no offence to your parents, of course."

"I curse the day you were married!" said Balzac, forgetting himself.

"Honoré, please . . ." she said.

66

"Why do we pretend?" he demanded. "You know what I feel."

"I forbid you to speak!"

She was angry now, and hurt.

He went on, blindly.

"Your husband is an old man. An invalid. Almost a cripple. He keeps you buried here like a prisoner. It is wrong, I tell you. You are filled with life. You belong to the world. You should be free."

"If you continue, I shall be obliged to send you away," she said.

"No!"

She touched her lips with a finger. "Honoré, there are children and servants in the house. And, as you seem to have forgotten, a husband. Old perhaps. Ill, certainly. But still very much in possession."

He fell to his knees and seized her hand. His face betrayed his agony. "I love you," he said. "You cannot expect me to hide it. I adore you."

"Get to your feet this instant," she commanded. "You are making yourself ridiculous."

Sullenly, he rose to his feet, his vanity wounded. He walked to the window and said stiffly, "I beg your pardon."

"Don't turn your back to me," she said. "It's rude. Face about and hear what I have to say."

Grudgingly, he turned. Her eyes were filled with tears. He moved toward her, but she raised a hand and stopped him.

"I am fond of you, Honoré," she said. "More than I should be, perhaps. But there can be nothing more between us. I am a wife, a mother. Where that kind of thing is concerned, my life is over."

"No!" he said savagely.

"It is true," she said. "My life, my true life, belonged to a world that is finished forever. In this world, your world, I am only a timeserver. I go on living simply because I was unfortunate enough to have survived."

"I could not bear not seeing you," he said.

"Then you must stop saying things that disturb me," she said. "I believe in you. I want you as a friend, but that must be the end of it."

For a time, he kept his distance. He was terrified that she would send him away. But there were forces at work inside him that were getting beyond his control. The very room that she inhabited was aphrodisiac to his senses. He could not get her out of his mind, even for an instant. When he was with her, he longed to touch her, to cover her face with kisses. When he was alone, he was pursued by erotic imaginations that gave him no peace.

Madame de Berny was sorry for him. She was not a Puritan, and it was not prudery that inspired her to keep him at arm's length, but prudence. Prudence is a commodity that weakens by attrition. Despite her earlier resolutions, as the weeks passed, she found herself becoming more and more aware of young Balzac's physical presence. He was bursting with youth, with vitality, with unfulfilled desire. She was human. Her husband was ill and incompetent. For five years, she had not been granted the physical release of love. Against her judgment, almost against her will, she found herself drawn toward the inevitable, yet she could not bring herself to the point of sending Balzac away.

One hot night in August, they sat together in the rather ambitious garden of the de Berny château. They had eaten a light supper in the open air and afterward finished a second bottle of iced Alsatian wine. Madame de Berny was dressed in a gown made of white tulle, with a fitted bodice and a long, flowing skirt. As the evening light dwindled, she looked unreal as a ghost.

The heat was intense and a fathomless silence covered the night landscape like a blanket. The wall of the house loomed beside them. The windows were dark, except for a feeble light in the servants' quarters. The children were long since in bed. Monsieur de Berny, enjoying a period of comparative good health, had gone to Paris to see to his affairs.

"Only the last love of a woman can possibly satisfy the first love of a man."

This was a line Balzac was to write, later on. For him, on that August night, it was blindingly true. He moved toward her and for a few seconds they stood in the hot darkness, not moving, intoxicated by each other's presence. Then he took her in his arms and kissed her. For a few seconds, her lips remained closed, then they parted, and she seemed to melt. She touched the nape of his neck with her fingers. He shuddered. They drew apart, then kissed again. He touched her breast, clumsily.

"I can fight no longer," she said. "I have no more strength to fight with."

She took his hand and led him through a back door, up the

68

stairs to her bed-chamber. It was a large room, the walls covered with oyster white damask. There was a great bed with a canopy, a chaise-longue, an enormous mirror with a gilt frame, an armoire, a dressing table, a thick, pale Aubusson rug. All this Balzac saw in the soft moonlight that came in a liquid shaft through the high double windows curtained with net.

The room was filled with her perfume. They kissed again, clinging together, then parted. "I adore you," she whispered, her breath close to his ear. His hands fumbled in the darkness. He had never undressed a woman before. Gently, she moved his hands away.

"Silly," she said. "Let me do it."

She undid his cravat and opened his shirt. Then her hand was against his flesh. He buried his mouth at her throat.

"Be patient," she whispered. "There is time. There is lots of time."

In the wet, heavy moonlight, he heard a swish of silk as her petticoats fell away. He saw her for an instant in her white stays, then turned away, struggling with his own clothing.

Soundlessly, they moved together. Their mouths met and blended. Gently, she guided him to the bed. The silk sheets were cool to the touch, fragrant with perfume. She was kind to him, a gentle teacher.

For a long time they lay in silence on the broad soft bed, uncovered, exposed to the moonlight and to the warm, silken summer breeze, enjoying delicious, sensual fatigue. Somewhere off in the night, an owl hooted mysteriously. Madame de Berny laughed.

"Hoo! Hoo!" she said, imitating the bird. "A pompous bird, the owl."

It broke the spell. From that instant, there was no reserve of guilt between them. They accepted their love as inevitable, as beautiful, as correct. She raised herself on an elbow and looked down into his face, then took his chin in her hand and kissed him. "So now you are truly a writer," she said, smiling at him. "You have a mistress."

"Yes, I have a mistress," he said lazily, drawing her down to him.

It was nearly dawn when he dressed and slipped out of the house through the back door, passing quickly through the silent garden, making his way homeward by a short-cut, through a field

69

of high grass that was wet with dew, so that his trouser legs were soaked. His mouth was filled with the taste of love. His lips were bruised and his thighs ached. He was light-headed as if he had drunk a quantity of champagne. He was happy. He loved, with all his heart, soul and body. His love was returned. It was a miracle.

Villeparisis was a small town, not much more than a village, really, and in a village there are no secrets. Very soon, the gossip began. When Balzac went into the village square for a bottle of ink or a tablet of cheap paper, people glanced at him and smiled. One day a drayman, sitting on his box, winked and made an obscene gesture of the kind soldiers use. Instead of being ashamed or embarrassed, Balzac was rather pleased.

"Honoré, we must be careful," Madame de Berny warned him. "People talk."

"Let them talk!" he said defiantly. "As for me, I have no time to waste in idle gossip." He pulled her toward him. She pushed him away, laughing. They were in the de Berny sitting room.

"It's all very well for you," she said. "But seriously, we must be careful, I have a husband and children, remember. I don't want to hurt them."

"Of course, you are right," he said. "We must be careful. No more love making in the city hall. No more kissing in the public square."

"You are impossible," she said, unable to be angry with him. "If you care nothing for my reputation, dear boy, think of your own security. Your mother would be delighted to have an excuse for stopping your allowance. And what an excuse! *Mon Dieu!*"

"My famous allowance," he said. "We have argued, in my family, over fifteen hundred francs a year, as if we were debating the budget for the Royal Household." He clenched his fist and drove it into the palm of the other hand. "I've got to make some money," he said. "My own money."

"When you find yourself as a writer, you will have all the money you want," she said. She was like most people who have always had money; it was difficult for her to think of it, except in large terms.

"I need it now," he said harshly. "And I mean to get it."

A small muscle in his jaw seemed to knot as his mouth was set.

70

She looked at him, aware of the surging power in him. "Sometimes you frighten me," she said. "There is a devil inside you, fighting to get out."

It was true. Especially since they had become lovers, there had been a force inside him, fighting for release, a will to freedom, to independence.

"There are dangerous fires in you," she said. "They mustn't destroy you."

"I am fireproof," he said.

He made no real effort to conceal the situation from his mother; in fact, one part of his being insisted that she know the truth. At first she pretended to be unaware of what was going on, ignoring his visits to the de Berny house, but after awhile it became impossible to ignore what her own servants gossiped about. She challenged him with it. He refused to discuss it.

"Have you no respect for your family?" she demanded. "Balzac is an honorable name."

He laughed at her.

"Balzac, Balssa, what you will," he said. "It has survived all sorts of scandal. I believe that one of my uncles was hanged for slitting a half-witted girl's throat, after he had ravaged her. If the name has survived him, it can stand me."

The fact that Bernard-François' brother had gone to the gallows was never mentioned in the Balzac household. Anne-Charlotte was outraged. Her right arm stiffened, then flashed out, and she slapped his face.

"Insolence!" she cried.

"Truth," he said, taking no notice of the blow.

"That woman has bewitched you," his mother said. "She has stolen my son."

Balzac laughed.

There is nothing more engrossing than love, and his affair with Madame de Berny had, for the time being, freed him of his mother's shackles. Anne-Charlotte realized this and a desperate jealousy gnawed at her. She had turned her back on her son, but she could not bear the idea that anyone else should have him.

She put out tentacles, trying to draw him back into the sphere of her domination. Up until now, she had never expressed anything but contempt for his efforts at writing. She began to ask

71

about his work, to hint that she would be pleased if he showed her his manuscripts.

"Perhaps I can help you," she said. "Another opinion. . . ."

"I don't need any help, thank you," he answered brightly.

"Are you so sure of yourself then?" she asked.

"Quite."

She lost her temper and exclaimed, "What arrogance! You have published nothing, and you talk as though you had just been elected to the French Academy."

"That comes later," he said. "One needs a beard."

He strolled away, whistling a tune. It was not arrogance. It was merely health. He was beginning to recover from his childhood, and the process was much like recovering from a long and presumptively hopeless illness. The rejection, hardship and exile that he and Laure had shared became dulled, and for the time being seemed unimportant. The wound of childhood closed. Under the sore, the flesh still festered, but now he did not feel pain.

Chapter 7

IN AUGUST, LAURE was married, and went to live in Bayeux, where de Surville had been assigned as a district engineer for the government. There was no longer any excuse for Balzac to hang about Villeparisis. Besides, in a few weeks, the de Bernys would take up residence in Paris for the winter. He returned to Paris in September and found lodgings in Saint-Sulpice, better than what he had had in the rue Lesdiguières, but a long way from the luxury he wanted.

"I am going to earn money and I am going to earn it with my pen," he told Madame de Berny when they parted. "I will write anything, even notices to be pasted on walls, but I will not do anything other than writing."

But who would pay cash for what he could write?

The question was answered for him one night at Mother Lagatta's Brasserie, an eating house not far from his lodgings. Lagatta's was a popular rendezvous for young writers, artists, and actors, because it was cheap, informal, and generous with its portions of cassoulet Toulousain, a delicious concoction of white beans, sausage and conserve of duck; hearty, unladylike fare, a plate of which would keep a man going through the day.

Among the regulars at Lagatta's was a young writer who bore the magnificent name of Auguste le Poitevin de l'Egreville. He was the son of a provincial actor originally named Durand, and he had learnt from his father that most people are more impressed by appearance and manner than by such mundane virtues as talent, honor or industry. Le Poitevin had savoir-faire. His clothes were made by a good tailor and he wore them with dash and assurance. In Lagatta's he had recently become something of a celebrity, because he had already found a publisher for his novel, THE TWO HECTORS, a masterpiece as yet unwritten, except for the first three chapters.

One evening, he and Balzac sat at a small table, each with a plate of cassoulet in front of him, crusty on top, still sizzling from the oven, giving off a splendid aroma. They knew one another only casually, but after all they were both writers, and that gave them a common bond.

"I tell you, Balzac, art is all very well in its way, but it won't buy beans the way trash will," le Poitevin said. He brandished a forkful of beans, then popped them into his mouth. "You write a play in verse. Maybe it's good. I don't know. But what did it get you? Nothing. My novel is not in Alexandrines. In fact, I'm not sure it's in French. But I've already got eight hundred francs for it."

"You make it sound very simple," said Balzac.

He was not impressed by le Poitevin's mind, but he was very much impressed by the eight hundred francs le Poitevin had got from a publisher.

"What could be simpler than writing a novel?" le Poitevin asked innocently. "It is merely a matter of cribbing a story, something historical, for preference, since that's what the public wants these days. Change the names, change the setting, and there you are." He stabbed at Balzac with his fork. "Have you ever heard of Ann Radcliffe?" he demanded, as if he were making an accusation.

"Never," said Balzac.

"Oh, my dear fellow, my dear fellow. You may be a genius. I wouldn't know. As a hack, you're a rank amateur. Ann Radcliffe, now. You should know her. She's English, of course. The English are much better at literary prostitution than we French. Perhaps it's because there's no such thing as an Academy in England. At any rate, Ann Radcliffe is a gold mine of plots, a bonanza, an eldorado. I got my TWO HECTORS from her, of course."

Balzac was honestly shocked.

"You mean you *stole* the story?" he said.

Le Poitevin raised an admonitory hand. "Please, Balzac! One doesn't steal. He borrows. He adapts. He interprets. He finds inspiration. When he borrows from Ann Radcliffe it is mainly a matter of making the love scenes logical, conclusive and French, instead of blurred, sentimental and British. Do that and presto! You have something for which a publisher is delighted to pay eight hundred lovely francs."

Balzac sat back in his chair and laughed until tears rolled down his cheeks.

74

"You are not serious?" he said finally.

"Of course I'm serious," said le Poitevin. "Come along to my rooms when we've finished eating and I'll show you how it's done."

Yvette, Lagatta's serving girl, brought them coffee. She was a well-built country wench, seventeen or eighteen, with a full bosom and a clear skin. Balzac could not help staring at her breasts as she bent over to serve the coffee. When she had gone, le Poitevin shook his head.

"Nothing doing there, old man, I'm afraid," he said. "I've tried."

His tone implied that if he had tried to seduce her and failed, that the King of France himself would have no better luck.

Balzac shrugged.

"It is a matter of indifference to me," he said, just a little stuffily.

Le Poitevin laughed and stood up. "Come along to my digs, old fellow. I'll show you how to sell your soul."

He had a pair of rooms not far from the Brasserie Lagatta, modest enough, but far more ambitious than Balzac's quarters. There was a dark bed-chamber, suggestive of assignations, and a pleasant, English-looking sitting room with a handsome brass-bound grate. There were some deep leather chairs and a long, comfortable, crimson sofa. There were hunting prints on the walls and over the fireplace was a fencer's mask and a pair of crossed foils. They were the kind of rooms inhabited by young bachelors in books. Balzac was impressed.

If I had something like this, he thought, looking around him, I could entertain *her* properly, instead of sneaking into the house like a thief. *Her,* of course, was Madame de Berny, now in Paris for the winter season. The Paris ménage was a busy one and he saw her with difficulty.

"Have a chair," said his host. "I'll show you the tricks of the trade."

Balzac sat down and le Poitevin gave him a four-decker novel, translated from the English, miserably printed and cheaply bound. Balzac leafed through the first volume. Le Poitevin watched him with shrewd eyes.

"Here are the opening chapters of my book," he said matter-of-factly, handing Balzac a thin sheaf of manuscript, inscribed in a rather pretty hand.

Balzac ran through the pages quickly, then burst into slightly incredulous laughter. The action of Ann Radcliffe's novel took

75

place in an isolated country house, situated on a lonely English moor. Le Poitevin's story began in an isolated château, situated in a lonely part of Brittany. The plots were the same.

"But why haven't you finished it up?" asked Balzac curiously. "It's all here. A few days writing and you're done, ready for the next one."

Le Poitevin shrugged. "That's my trouble, comrade. I'm clever, but I'm lazy. An inherited fault, you see. My father was an actor."

He opened a bottle of red wine, filled two glasses, offered one to Balzac and drained his own at a gulp.

"You enjoy composition, old man," he said. "Why don't you finish it up for me?"

"I? Finish it? But it's your book, man," Balzac protested.

"It's Ann Radcliffe's book," said le Poitevin dryly. "Or perhaps it is no one's by now, since she probably cribbed it too. In any case, it's to be published under a pseudonym, so what does it matter who does the writing? What do you say, Balzac. Write it for me and I'll give you two hundred francs. That's fair enough, isn't it?"

"Fair enough," said Balzac. He looked at the manuscript in his hand, wondering if le Poitevin knew just how badly he needed two hundred francs. "I might have a go at it at that," he said tentatively.

"Good!" said le Poitevin. "Then it's agreed. We'll drink on it."

He poured more wine. They touched glasses and drank, then le Poitevin glanced at his watch, a handsome affair in a hunting case.

"Look here, old man, this is a bit awkward," he said. "I don't mean to hurry you on your way, but the fact is . . . well, damn it, you're a man of the world. The fact is, I'm rather expecting someone, d'you see?"

Balzac rose at once, rather hurt at being dismissed but trying not to show it. Le Poitevin offered him the Radcliffe novel and his own manuscript, saying, "Don't forget these, old man. Remember, we're in business together."

Balzac went down the stairs with the books and papers under his arm. In the dimly lighted hallway he nearly bumped into a young woman who glanced at him nervously, turned away, and hurried up the stairway toward le Poitevin's flat. She looked familiar. Balzac stood in the hallway, trying to place her. He heard

76

le Poitevin's voice saying, "Ah, my dear, I've been waiting for you."

Balzac was nearly home before he realized that the girl in the hallway had been Yvette, the serving girl from Lagatta's, looking rather unfamiliar in street clothes and a kerchief around her head. He laughed at himself. He's a clever dog, that le Poitevin. A clever dog. "Nothing doing there," says he. "I've tried, old boy," says he.

He threw off his coat and loosened his collar, rubbed his hands together, then sat down at his writing table with le Poitevin's manuscript in front of him. He pushed it aside and took up the Radcliffe novel. He went through it quickly, making notes, devouring the story as a brush fire devours dry undergrowth. When he finished he sat back in his chair, eyes narrowed, his mind working like an engine.

"Perhaps that idiot le Poitevin has taught me something after all," he said quietly. He recalled his promise to Madame de Berny, and smiled. "After all, my darling," he said, "this is better than writing things to be pasted on walls."

He picked up a quill and sharpened it, dipped it into the ink, drew his paper toward him and began. A page, two, three, four— the words dripped from his brow like sweat. When darkness came, he lit a candle, brewed coffee, and resumed his work. He had ignored le Poitevin's few pages and started at the beginning, making changes in depth, so that what he had was not quite the crude copy that le Poitevin had suggested. It was plagiarism, but it was skillful plagiarism. And it was an improvement on the original, which le Poitevin's pages had not been.

He worked through the night and the next day, then into the following night. At a little more than an hour after dawn, he came to the end of the story. He put a weight on top of the pages, yawned heavily, stretched himself, and fell on his bed, fully dressed. When he woke up, the street sounds told him it was past noon. He splashed some water on his face, ran a comb through his hair, tucked the manuscript under his arm, and whistled a tune as he went downstairs. The grueling session had exhilarated him. He felt as if he could conquer the world, or at least conquer the Brasserie Lagatta.

He found le Poitevin in the Brasserie, seated at his usual table. The restaurant was crowded, but most people had finished eating and were sitting over their coffee, talking and smoking black cheroots, making the atmosphere heavy with thick blue fumes. The waitress, Yvette, lounged against a wall. When she saw Balzac, she straightened up and blushed, then turned and pretended to be busy with something at the counter.

"Well, Balzac, old boy," said le Poitevin cheerfully. "Don't tell me you've finished a chapter already."

Balzac nodded, sitting opposite his partner. "Yes, I've finished a chapter," he said, pretending to be bored. He lifted a hand and called Yvette. She hesitated, then came to the table.

"M'sieu?"

"Soup of lentils," said Balzac. "Plenty of bread. Then a slice of ham. And coffee, Yvette. A large pot. Strong and hot."

"M'sieu."

She went off to get his food. Balzac grinned.

"Nothing doing there, eh?" he said. "I suppose she comes to do your washing."

Le Poitevin winked and reached for the pages Balzac had put on the table. He read a few lines and complained, "My God, what a handwriting. It looks as if a bug fell in the ink, then crawled over the page."

"I write fast," said Balzac, shrugging. "Besides, most people will read it in type."

"One gets used to it," le Poitevin admitted, already on the third page.

Yvette brought Balzac his soup, a thick, rich brew of lentils with sections of sausage swimming in it. At his left hand she placed a basket of fresh crunchy bread. There was nearly a loaf, more than his share, slashed halfway through in three or four places. Balzac realized he was being favored. He smiled at Yvette, who glanced at le Poitevin, then smiled back.

Balzac took a mouthful of soup and nodded with satisfaction. It was the first hot food he had taken since beginning the Radcliffe novel.

"Good peasant food," he said. "Just what I need."

"Be quiet!" le Poitevin commanded. "How can I read when you are jabbering. Eat your food and be still. Yvette, go away!"

Yvette busied herself at an adjoining table, from time to time glancing at Balzac. Balzac finished his soup and started on his slice of ham. By the time his coffee was brought, le Poitevin had leafed through to the end.

78

"My God, Balzac, you are inhuman," he said. "All this in a couple of days. I tell you, it's staggering."

Balzac thought so too, but he merely shrugged and said, "After all, I am a writer. It is simply a job of work."

Le Poitevin leaned forward, elbows on the table, his eyes bright with excitement. "Look here, Balzac, we can make a small fortune if we work together, as a team. I'll sell the stuff to the publishers, the fellows who peddle the books in the Palais-Royal. We can hash out the plots together . . . you and I and Ann Radcliffe. You do the writing. What could be better, my friend?"

Balzac took a mouthful of coffee and rolled it against his tongue, enjoying the bitter taste. He tapped the manuscript of THE TWO HECTORS.

"We aren't quite finished with this one yet," he said. "There is a little matter of two hundred francs. After all, you've been paid already."

Le Poitevin took an English purse out of his pocket and counted out two hundred francs. He hesitated, frowning, then counted out another hundred, handing the money to Balzac.

"Maybe this would be fairer," he said. "You have done all the writing."

Balzac took the extra hundred francs without argument. There was no false modesty in him, and he felt he had earned the money. He held the coins in his hand, staring at them. It was the first money he had earned with his pen—three hundred francs—nearly a fourth of the yearly allowance he had taken from his parents.

"What do you say to it, Balzac?" asked le Poitevin. "Shall we make a team of it, the two of us?"

Balzac frowned, staring at a bright spot on the rim of the copper coffee pot that stood on the table. He had come to Paris to write great books, to challenge Racine, to become immortal. Le Poitevin was a hack, without scruples, artistic or otherwise. To become le Poitevin's partner meant putting his own artistic conscience on the shelf. Perhaps I will destroy my talent, he thought, turning out trash to be sold in the booths in the Palais-Royal, blood, thunder, sex and faked Gothic terror, mixed like a salad and served up, so many pages a volume, so many volumes a book.

Yet what is the alternative? he asked himself. If I fail to make a living by writing, I will be forced to take a job in Paris, or to go crawling back to Villeparisis, to beg from the family.

Either would be disastrous for him, he knew. A job would steal time and energy needed for writing. To live under his mother's eye, now that he had found Madame de Berny, that was unthinkable. Much better to make a bargain with the devil, especially when the devil was as amiable as le Poitevin.

"All right, it's a bargain," he said, putting a hand across the table.

"Agreed!" said le Poitevin. "You won't regret it, Balzac, I promise you that. We'll make a fortune together."

Balzac nodded.

So was born the fiction factory of Horace de Saint Aubin and Company. Horace de Saint Aubin was the pen name the partners used most frequently. Another pseudonym, catering to the fashionable Anglophilism of the day, was Lord R'hoone, an anagram concocted from the letters of Balzac's real name. A third was A. de Veillerglé, derived from a part of le Poitevin's impressive designation.

The books that Balzac wrote that winter, modeled after those of Ann Radcliffe and others, were probably very bad books indeed, but they were gobbled up by the members of that part of Paris society that had its hub in the Palais-Royal, the beautiful, wicked, arcaded square off the rue de Rivoli. The Palais-Royal was the center of costly vice, haunt of gamblers, courtesans, rakes, and dandies, magnet for wealthy provincials and adventurous foreigners. The men and women of the Palais-Royal were not given to heavy thinking. They did not want books that asked them questions, or stories that were "true to life." They wanted novels that would shock them if possible, make them laugh, or titillate their weary senses, already jaded with gambling, alcohol and sex in all its varieties.

Balzac, as Lord R'hoone, gave them exactly what they wanted. He carried the method of his competitors a few steps forward. They were simply plagiarists; Balzac was an adaptor. Ann Radcliffe's plots were fine, but her treatment was much too tepid for the French taste. Balzac remedied that. Ann Radcliffe's women had limbs and bosoms; Balzac's had legs and breasts. When he described the bed upon which illicit love had taken place, you could smell the sheets, fouled with copulation. He was writing trash, but in spite of himself some of his true power came through, and it was this driving energy, felt even on the tawdry,

80

pseudonymous pages, that made the productions of Lord R'hoone so much in demand.

For a long time, Balzac put off telling Madame de Berny the truth about the way he was earning his living. During the first few months, when he and le Poitevin were getting the fiction factory organized, he made vague references to a novel he was writing, intimating that he was half-finished, that it went well or went badly, that it was a masterpiece, that it was trash. He hinted at "editorial work." He talked of "research" that he planned to do.

Actually, during this period, he wrote thirteen novels, all of which were eagerly purchased by the hole-in-the-wall publishers with whom le Poitevin did business. Balzac waited until he had written a Lord R'hoone that seemed better than the others, a four-decker romance entitled JEAN LOUIS, or THE RUIN OF A YOUNG GIRL. The four slim volumes were sloppily bound and printed on the cheapest paper. As soon as they were off the press, Balzac carried a set to Madame de Berny's house.

She looked at the books and laughed. "Is this a joke?" she demanded. "Why have you brought me this?"

They were in the library of the de Berny mansion in Paris, a magnificent room lined with shelves that held copies of the French classics bound in red, green and russet leather, gilt stamped with the de Berny coat of arms, exquisite volumes that gave pleasure when simply held in the hand, as objects. Lord R'hoone's novel, with its shabby covers, was out of place in this room as would have been a chimney sweep. Nevertheless, Balzac thrust the books into the hands of his mistress.

"I want you to read it," he said stubbornly.

"To read it?" she looked at him in surprise. "But you know I never read this kind of thing."

"Read it. As a service to me," he said bluntly.

She shrugged her shoulders, wondering what was in his mind, then said, "Very well, I'll read it, if you insist. But you may be sure that I'll keep it out of sight. I shouldn't want the children to see it. Or the servants. Children and servants both insist on the highest literary standards, you know."

Balzac smiled and sat down. This woman of mine is a marvel, he thought. She puts me at ease with a word, with a glance. I may be in the blackest pool of despair, ready to throw myself into the

81

Seine. Five minutes with her and she makes me feel that I am the most brilliant, the most charming, the most desirable man in Paris, in France, in the world.

"Come sit beside me," she said. "Hold my hand. Tell me what you have done with yourself during the three days since I've seen you."

He sat beside her on a satin covered love seat, taking her left hand in his right. Her hands were small, beautifully tended, the skin delicate as that of a girl.

"I have been writing, writing, writing," he said. "Eating cassoulet at Lagatta's, walking in the Faubourg, thinking of you."

"No affairs of the heart? No pretty girls? No adventures with a woman who isn't old enough to be your mother?"

She joked about the difference in their ages, but she never forgot it.

He smiled, kissing her hand. "Dozens of women," he said. "A different one every night. I have the pick of the Palais-Royal. They run after me in the Faubourg. I find them waiting on my doorstep at night, being glared at by the concierge."

"Then I shall be rid of you soon, thank heavens," she laughed.

There was an undercurrent of fear in her voice that she could not quite conceal. The twenty-odd years that stood between them could not be laughed away, but only pushed aside a little, so that their shadow was less emphatic.

Chapter 8

THAT NIGHT, IN-
stead of working on the latest Lord R'hoone title that was half-
finished, on his desk, (he had now settled down to doing more or
less a volume a week) Balzac went out into the city, drifting from
one café to the next, sometimes nodding to an acquaintance, more
often sitting alone with a coffee or marching along the pavement,
hands in his pockets, head thrust forward, looking rather like a
mastiff following a scent. It was quite cold and the cafés were
warmed by charcoal braziers that gave off a pleasant smell and
glowed cherry red in the feeble lamp light. Paris is like a woman,
he thought. She has a special attitude for every change of light or
shift in the temperature, and it is always a change that heightens
her charms and obscures her flaws. He loved the city, every stone
of it. He turned up the collar of his overcoat and walked through
the streets of the Marais. He was restless and uncertain, worried
about what Madame de Berny would say when she learned that he
was Lord R'hoone. More than anything else, he wanted her approval. He worried now, waiting for her judgment, as a student
worries while he waits for the results of an examination.

He fell into a familiar mood of dissatisfaction with himself.
Sometimes he regarded with amazement people like le Poitevin, to
whom everything seemed to come without effort, and who always
seemed to be so deliciously satisfied with themselves. Yet he was
not really jealous of le Poitevin. Not for all the money in the Bank
of France would he have changed places with his co-conspirator.
He and le Poitevin were different types, and he preferred his own.
In a war, a man like me would somehow have to be at the front,
with troops, in the mud and under fire, he thought, while a
man like le Poitevin would automatically turn up in white
breeches, as a member of somebody's staff.

Yet he often envied le Poitevin's self-assurance, his elegance in
dress, his ease with girls. He knew that on his own shoulders le

Poitevin's clothes would be not fashionable but absurd, that on his lips the phrases that suited le Poitevin would be merely silly. Yet sometimes he longed to behave like le Poitevin, if only for a night, to be a dandy, a minor rake, a devil with the serving girls.

He turned into the rue St. Sulpice, deciding to have a vin chaud at Lagatta's before going up to his room. Take the chill out of my bones, he thought, stamping his feet on the cobbles to get the blood going in them.

Lagatta's was nearly empty. Le Poitevin was not in the room, nor was anyone else Balzac knew. A pair of drabs, middle-aged and tired, sat moodily in a corner, waiting for nothing. In their wilted finery, they looked like ornaments discarded by a cheap carnival. Madame Lagatta, behind the till, dozed on her high stool. An aspirant poet with an aspirant beard struggled over his rhyme scheme, an empty coffee pot beside him. Yvette leaned against the serving counter, a limp towel in her hand. She came forward and mopped the table.

"M'sieu?"

"Good evening, little one," said Balzac cheerfully, half-consciously imitating le Poitevin's manner with her. "Cold enough for a hot wine, don't you think?"

"You are going to drink it, m'sieu, so it's your opinion that matters," she said.

"In that case, I'll have a hot wine," he said awkwardly, wondering why his banter fell flat.

"Very well, m'sieu."

He watched her while she prepared a glass of wine and a cinnamon stick, then thrust a poker into the bright red bed of coals in the stove. She was very young, younger than he, a good-looking girl with pale blond hair and a fresh complexion, Alsatian, he guessed. She wore wooden shoes and heavy stockings, each of which had a hole in the heel. As she bent over the charcoal fire, her dress was pulled tight against her back and thighs, revealing the contours of a young, strong figure. Le Poitevin is no fool, Balzac thought. There's a beautiful figure, underneath that shapeless skirt.

There was an angry sound as the hot poker was plunged into the wine. A strong, sweet smell rose instantly. A moment later the drink was ready. Yvette put the glass on the table.

84

"Thank you," he said, looking up. "Monsieur le Poitevin not here tonight?"

"As one can see without difficulty," she said, glancing at the empty tables.

"You're not busy at the moment," he said cautiously. "Won't you have something with me?" He glanced at Madame Lagatta and added, "If madame won't object, that is."

"She won't object if it's paid for," Yvette said blandly. "I'll have the same as you're having."

She fixed a second glass of hot wine and sat down at the table with him.

"You're very blond," he said. "Are you Alsatian?"

"My people were Flemish," she said. "Myself, I was born in Artois."

"Are your parents there now?"

"Both dead," she said. "I have an old uncle here in Paris, an old soldier of the Grand Army, a terrible drunkard but a good sort. Outside of him, I'm all alone."

"I saw you that day, at le Poitevin's house," he said shyly.

She shrugged and said, "You have eyes. Why shouldn't you see?"

"Are you fond of le Poitevin?" he asked, suddenly blunt as a police sergeant.

"He's all right," she said. "He talks too much."

"Then you don't like him?"

"I didn't say that." She looked at him closely and shook her head. "You're an odd one, Monsieur Balzac. Sometimes when you come in here for lunch, you look as if you wanted to kill somebody. First time I saw you, I thought you were some kind of a crook. You know, we get a few tough ones in here. They come for the beans."

"You took me for a cutthroat?" Balzac asked, quite pleased with the idea.

She nodded. "Then they told me you were a writer. You don't look like a writer."

"What does a writer look like, please?"

"Well you know," she said, nodding toward the laboring poet. "Like that one over there, with the beard."

"He looks like a writer, but I don't?" said Balzac, smiling.

"You might be a farmer, almost," she said. "Or a policeman. Or, like I said, a crook."

"What about Monsieur le Poitevin? Does he look like a writer?"

"Oh no!" She shook her head emphatically. "He looks more like one of the others. The ones who make money out of it. What do you call them? Publishers?"

Balzac roared with laughter. "You are marvelous," he said. "You must have another hot wine."

She looked doubtfully at the proprietress, who chose that instant to snore discreetly. "I don't mind," she said.

He sat with her until the bells of Saint-Sulpice rang out midnight. She rose and stood beside the table. "Thank you for the wine, m'sieu," she said. "And for the company."

"Are you finished now, for the night?" he asked.

She nodded.

"Would you like to come home with me?" he said, his voice trembling a little.

"Do you have a fire in your room?" she asked.

"A little one," he nodded.

"Then I will come," she said.

"Shall I wait for you outside?"

She shook her head and said, "I will follow you."

"I live in the rue . . ."

"I know where you live, m'sieu," she said calmly, gathering up the empty glasses.

"Yvette! Yvette!" cried Madame Lagatta, rubbing the sleep from her eyes. "Closing time!"

Balzac paid his bill and went into the street, gasping as he took his first breath of outside air. The night had turned fiercely cold during the two hours he had passed in Lagatta's. The moist air had gathered on roofs and window ledges, forming a light coating of rime, like sugar icing. Balzac shivered, then huddled into his coat and began to walk toward his lodgings.

She won't come, he told himself, half-hoping she would not, half-desperate with longing that she would. She was just playing with me, he said to the collar of his greatcoat. Making fun of me. After all, why would she bother with me when she has le Poitevin? If I've got the sense I was born with, I'll go straight upstairs when

I get to the house, instead of standing in the cold like an ass, waiting for someone who isn't coming.

He waited in the doorway, shivering in the bitter cold. In a little while he saw her approaching, bent forward against the wind, wrapped in a heavy country-girl's shawl, going quickly along the pavement in her wooden shoes.

"Is there a concierge?" she asked, keeping her voice low.

"Asleep," he said, surprised by his calmness. "I have a key."

He took her hand and guided her through the dark hallway, into the passage that led to the stairs. In his room, he touched a patent match to the fire before lighting the candles on his work table. Comparing it with le Poitevin's quarters, he was a little ashamed of the room.

"It's not much of a place," he warned her, as he touched a spill to the candle-wick. "I'm going to be moving soon, to a bigger place."

"It's all right," she said indifferently, spreading her hands to the fire, which had blazed up nicely. "You have a fire. We don't have one, where we live, my uncle and me. And the roof leaks. It's a stinking place and on a night like this, it's cold, I can promise you that."

The firelight struck her face and glinted in the lights of her pale hair. She looked young and very attractive. Balzac was nervous. He had never been to bed with a girl, or with anyone but Madame de Berny. "Will you have a glass of wine?" he asked, not knowing quite how to begin.

"I don't mind."

He had nothing but a cheap red vin ordinaire. He poured it out, remembering the good Bordeaux that le Poitevin kept on hand for his guests. They stood before the fire and drank slowly. By this time the coals had caught well and the grate was glowing. The room became warm. Yvette took off her shawl, folded it carefully and hung it over his work chair. Then she kicked off her wooden shoes and the felt slippers underneath them. She wriggled her toes in the heavy, home-made stockings. A toe winked through a hole in each foot and she looked at them, then giggled. She soaked up the warmth of the fire like a cat.

Does she go home with anyone who has a fire in his room? he wondered, remembering the nights in the rue Lesdiguières when he had gone without a fire to save money. People think of hunger when they consider poverty, he reflected. They forget the cold, which is sometimes worse.

Yvette finished her wine, drank another glass, then stretched her arms and yawned. "I am tired," she said. "You do your work sitting on your arse. Mine keeps me on my feet all day."

The vulgarism fell from her lips so naturally that it did not seem offensive. Balzac laughed and went to the bed, throwing back the covers. The top cover was a patchwork quilt he had brought with him from home, a thing he had seen since childhood. When it was new, it had been used on his mother's bed. For some reason, he was embarrassed by the quilt and the white china pot under the bed. He had a moment of panic. Everything he knew of sex, Madame de Berny had taught him. He was struck with the idea that he might be impotent with anyone else.

Yvette took off her blouse and unhooked her heavy skirt, let it fall to the floor, then folded it and put it with her shawl. She balanced on one leg, then the other, and peeled off the heavy stockings. On her legs, Balzac saw the ridgemarks the coarse yarn had made. She wore nothing but a white camisole now, wrinkled but quite clean. She took the pins from her hair, putting them into her mouth as she did so. The hair fell and she shook it out, then put the pins on his work table. She went to the bed, picked up the china chamber pot, hoisted her shift and used it. Balzac stood in the firelight, blushing fiercely at the sound she made. An instant later she was in the bed with the covers pulled up to her chin.

"Do you sleep with your clothes on, m'sieu?" she asked sleepily, speaking through a half-stifled yawn.

"In a minute," Balzac said.

He blew out the candles and undressed quickly, observing, as countless men before him had done, what a clumsy set of movements were involved in getting rid of a pair of trousers, compared with the graceful ease with which a woman drops her skirt and steps out of it. Undressed, he glanced at the bed, expecting to meet a critical eye and aware that his figure was no match for that of le Poitevin. Her eyes were closed; she was half asleep. He got into the bed beside her and she murmured something, then lifted her arms to embrace him. He was aware of delicious, womb-like warmth. Her skin had a pleasant, slightly sour smell, a

88

country smell. He kissed her in the dark. He ran his hand over her body, astonished by its youthful firmness.

"Doucement, s'il vous plait," she whispered. "Gently, M'sieu Balzac, please."

He was gentle with her. Afterward, she clung to him like a child.

After a little, she slept. She is natural as an animal, he thought. He wondered if the idea of love, complex as the emotion he felt for Madame de Berny, ever entered her mind. Does she simply sleep with a man she likes, or at least does not detest, simply for the sake of the warmth? He kissed her forehead, then got out of bed, not disturbing her, and put fresh coals on the fire. It was a thing he had never done before. He always let the fire burn itself out. He banked it down carefully. It will burn until morning, he thought, and the room will be warm when she wakes up. He slipped back into bed beside her. She stirred in her sleep and murmured something. He put his ear close to her lips and listened.

"Maman," she said softly, in her sleep. "Maman."

When Balzac woke up, he smelled fresh coffee. Yvette had found his little pot and the crockery jar of cheap coffee he kept on the shelf. She had put up her hair and pulled on her stockings, but she hadn't dressed beyond that and wore only the cotton shift that had served as her nightgown. The simple, white garment made her look innocent as a young nun.

"Good morning," he said sleepily, sitting up in bed, making the cord lacings groan.

"Good morning, m'sieu," she said gravely, pouring coffee into one of the two cracked cups he owned.

"For the love of heaven, girl, stop calling me monsieur," he said.

"I can hardly call you madame," she said placidly. "Besides, in the Brasserie you must continue to be monsieur, so it is best that you are monsieur here too."

She brought him coffee and a bit of stale roll, then sat on the edge of the bed. She poured coffee into her saucer, blew on the surface to cool it, then drank rather noisily. Someone should tell her not to do that, thought Balzac idly.

When she finished her coffee she stood up, shook the crumbs

from her petticoat and said matter-of-factly but with regret, "Eh bien! I must be going. Out into the cold."

"Why so early?" he asked, half inclined to make love to her again.

"I work for my living, m'sieu," she said, buttoning her shirt.

"But it was after midnight when you quit last night."

"I open Lagatta's and close it," she said. "The place must be swept, you realize, the chairs turned down, the braziers lit in the winter time."

"Long hours," he said.

"Worse than a farm," she said, pulling on the shapeless skirt that concealed the outline of her trim thighs and buttocks. She wriggled into her felt slippers, then into her clogs. Shall I offer her money? he asked himself. He decided against it. If it's expected, she'll ask for it. If not, she might be offended.

When she was ready to leave, the heavy black shawl on her shoulders, she looked at him curiously and smiled. "You have not had a girl here before, m'sieu," she said. "Is it not right?"

She spoke without any mockery. He answered without embarrassment. "You are right. But how did you know?"

"How does one know these things?" she shrugged. Then, thinking he might be offended, she said quickly, "It is not that you weren't very nice, you understand."

"I understand," he said. "Will you come again?"

"If you like."

She was at the door. He wanted to get up and show her out, but he was embarrassed at the idea of being naked in front of her in daylight. "Au 'voir," he said.

"Au 'voir, m'sieu."

She slipped through the door and closed it quietly behind her. Balzac lay in bed, enjoying the unaccustomed morning warmth and the luxury of being served his coffee in bed. He could not repress a certain feeling of masculine arrogance. Ho there, Balzac! He checked himself. You haven't turned into a le Poitevin, simply because you've been to sleep with a girl that le Poitevin had before you. He got out of bed and dressed himself, suddenly thinking of Madame de Berny and feeling a flush of guilt. The episode of the night before had nothing to do with Madame de Berny. That was understood. A casual encounter with a servant girl, a farm wench, a prostitute, perhaps, if one was away from Paris, or

90

alone in the summertime—that was something understood, by wives and mistresses alike. It was a mark of French sophistication, of Gallic realism, of the candid mastery of life for which the French were world-famous.

There was no reason for Madame de Berny to think anything of it at all.

Yet he realized, as he shaved himself, that this would be a part of his life kept secret from Madame de Berny, and it would be the only part, for he told her everything that happened to him, down to the smallest detail.

He washed the pot and made fresh coffee, then sat down to his morning's work. It went sluggishly for a page or two, because his mind was unsettled, invaded by sharp recollection of the night before. By an act of will he cleared his brain of everything except the marching scenes of the idiotic story Lord R'hoone was concocting for his idiot public. His pen moved swiftly across the paper. He covered a dozen pages, then two dozen, before his aching wrist and his empty stomach informed him that it was time to break off and go to Lagatta's for his lunch. By God, I'm a craftsman, he thought, giving the fresh pages an affectionate glance before he put on his hat and went through the door.

At one o'clock, when he arrived, Lagatta's was jammed with people. Yvette scarcely had time to greet him, take his order, and bring his food. He sat chewing on a weedy cutlet and watched Yvette as she moved from table to table, her arms piled high with dishes. A few hours earlier that body, now sweating through her dress at the armpits, had been joined with his. This morning, when she brought him his coffee, there had been intimacy between them, tenderness, a kind of special understanding. Now, as he saw her in daylight, hard at work, she was simply the girl at the Brasserie Lagatta and not much more. It is marvelous, he thought, what animals we are, how much of the barnyard is in us. Eating, sleeping, drinking, breathing, urinating, deficating, fornicating. To sleep with a woman, to enter her body, it was certainly the most intimate act a man could perform on this earth, yet it could be done with a stranger, or with a body bought for money, or even, as soldiers did, with a sworn and desperate enemy. It was a means of communication that had nothing to do with race or class or nationality or intelligence. What part of love is in it? he wondered. What part of hate?

91

He paid his bill, nodded to Yvette, passed into the street and walked in the cold air for an hour, then returned to his room and sat down, without any preliminaries, to finish off Lord R'hoone's next book.

Chapter 9

THE FOLLOWING
afternoon, just before tea time, he slipped into the Hôtel de Berny
by a side door, using the key he had been given shortly after the
de Bernys had returned to Paris from the country. He disliked
creeping into the house like a servant or tradesman, but there was
no help for it until he managed to get a decent establishment of
his own, where Madame de Berny could be received.

She was waiting for him in a little parlor on the third floor of
the big house, a room that adjoined her bed-chamber, and made,
with a dressing room and bath, a small private suite. In the days
of the old regime, it had been the custom for ladies of fashion to
hold court in apartments like these. Now no one came here except Balzac and Madame de Berny's personal maid, a leather-
faced old Breton woman who was the soul of discretion.

The sitting room was round, built out from the main wall of the
house like a turret or tower, and two thirds of the curving wall
contained windows that overlooked a fine garden behind the
house. It was Madame de Berny's favorite room. The walls were
covered with grey-pink damask, shot with threads of gold. Suspended from the ornate plaster ceiling was a chandelier that might
have come from the palace at Versailles, a marvelous arrangement
of crystal teardrops that caught the light and threw it back like
so many hundreds of diamonds. The carpet was a mild grey, with
a pink undertone, especially dyed to go with the damask of the
wall coverings. The furniture was covered with grey satin, the
arms of the wooden chairs picked out with gold leaf. It was a
bland, civilized room, created by a woman whose taste was precise, whose knowledge of her own strength was exact. The one
bold note was a small desk lacquered shiny black with gold ornamentation, the writing surface covered with scarlet leather. On this
bright and luxurious surface, rested Lord R'hoone's dreadful
novel. Balzac saw it at once, and his pulse quickened with nerv-
ousness.

93

Madame de Berny rose to greet him. She wore a negligée, of grey chiffon that matched the walls. There was a fresh rose at her bosom, and her hair was dressed informally. Balzac embraced her before he uttered a word of greeting. Gently, she pushed him away.

"Really, what an impetuous boy you are," she said. "It is not quite civilized to be kissed like that, in broad daylight, without warning. Sit down and behave yourself. We are going to have tea and conversation. That is what civilized people do at four o'clock in the afternoon."

"Tea!" he said, making a face. "One would think we were English, you and I, the quantities of tea we consume. They say that it rusts the vital organs, like water."

Madame de Berny laughed.

"It's used for tanning hides, you know," he said. "Certainly it must tan the stomach."

"You may have coffee if you like. Or chocolate," she said. "But you won't get wine at this hour of the day, as if you were at some cheap café."

"Tea, by all means," he said. "As a matter of fact, I rather like it. Of course, my vital organs are of brass, and naturally are impervious to rust. My father's were the same."

He was playing the fool in order to keep his mind off Lord R'hoone. Now he decided to face it. He got up, crossed the room, and picked up one of the volumes.

"Have you read this little plum I brought you?" he asked, trying to make his voice sound as if the matter were of no importance.

"Honoré, put that down at once," she said. "I want my tea and a sweet cake and a chance to look at you for a moment. Then I will tell you what I think of this book by your friend Lord R'hoone."

"Oh, he's not a friend," Balzac protested.

"Really?" She arched her eyebrows in disbelief. "I beg your pardon. I had the impression, somehow, that you knew him very well indeed."

At this moment the maid entered, carrying a silver tea service. She knew Balzac and greeted him with a nod, her old eyes opinionless as those of a good soldier on parade. The tea was placed on a a low table in front of Madame de Berny's sofa.

"That will be all, Brigitte," said Madame de Berny.

The maid withdrew. Balzac knew that nothing less than the house on fire would cause her to return until she was summoned. To everyone—the children, the casual caller, the master of the house, the King of France himself, she would be "occupée" until such time as she wished to be disturbed. Here in her private apartment she was secure from the world as a monk in his cell.

"About Lord R'hoone," she said, handing Balzac his tea. "Of course it's a dreadful book. Even worse than the paper it's printed on. But there are certain scenes, certain lines."

"Yes?"

She put down her cup and looked at him frankly, then said, "Let us stop being childish, Honoré. You did write it, didn't you?"

He nodded.

"Of course," she said. "I was certain of it. And now you have come for your punishment. You expect me to be shocked or angry, to tell you that you are squandering your talent, is that it?"

"Something like that," he admitted.

"You misjudge me," she said. "I am a snob where books are concerned, it's true, but not so much of a snob that I can't see the few good things in Lord R'hoone. You are only a boy, really. You've had no experience with women or money. You've never traveled, never been to war. And yet you can write this. It's extraordinary. Can you make any money from it?"

He explained the terms of his partnership with le Poitevin.

"I don't like the sound of him," she said. "And I'm certain that you should be getting two-thirds instead of one-half. But it doesn't matter. What's important is that you make some achievement, even if it's only pot boiling. And the money is important. You must be free of your family, of your mother, or you will suffocate."

"You make my mother sound like a monster," he said mildly. "In her own way she does what she thinks is right."

"Most people do," said Madame de Berny. "Only the Devil himself is an exception. But often their own way is wrong. I don't mean to speak ill of your mother, but she bears the world a grudge, and it is always necessary to examine the motives of people who bear grudges."

Balzac felt that it was disloyal to discuss his mother, even with Madame de Berny. He went to the bank of curved windows and drew back the curtain, looking down into the garden. The tender bushes had been wrapped in burlap to protect them from frost. The evergreens stood out blackly against the walks, which were of light grey gravel. There were small figures carved from intensely white Italian marble, voluptuous cherubs, dancing naked in the cold. It was a miniature Tuileries—the exquisite expression of a world gone by, the world to which his mistress had really belonged. Somehow the sight of this garden seemed to express the gulf between them that was caused by more than a difference in age.

He let the curtain fall back into place and returned to his chair and teacup.

"Must we talk about my mother?" he asked. "She doesn't concern us. Tell me honestly what you think about this potboiling of mine. Am I going to hurt myself? Will my talent be damaged?"

"The real you, nothing can hurt," she said without hesitation. "You will hammer out your own ideas and your own view of life. I am certain of that." She hesitated and frowned, then went on. "But language, that is another matter. I mean the words themselves. The French language is a demanding mistress. Treat her casually, neglect her for a moment, and she will never forgive you."

"You are suggesting that I may hurt my style?" he asked.

"Not style exactly," she said. "Something even more subtle than style. A woman who has had too many lovers may lose none of her beauty. But a certain inner delicacy will have been flawed. An unseen coarseness will be there. The lack of discrimination leaves a scar beneath the surface."

"I see your point," he said. "But do you know, my Cromwell taught me one thing, and the lesson was worth all the effort the cursed play cost me. I am not a pretty writer, whatever else I am. Your garden out there," he said, inclining his head toward the window. "It's like a pretty writer. Everything in that garden has some small purpose. The pattern is perfect. Each shrub, almost each leaf, plays a part and has its little meaning. It is beautiful. I admire it. But I am not like it. I am like a forest, a jungle with great thick trees, dense undergrowth, impenetrable bogs. . . . a jungle filled with dangerous beasts: lions, tigers, boa constrictors. Beasts that prey on one another."

"You've answered your own question," she said. "A malformed tree or a crooked bush would ruin my garden. In a jungle, they would mean nothing."

He picked up a volume of Lord R'hoone and slapped it with the back of his hand, as a man might slap an unruly dog.

"I do this with my left hand," he said. "It means nothing. Some day, next year, the year after, I will hear a certain note. In the night, perhaps. Or mixed with the sound of a church bell. I will recognize that note as my own. In the meantime, Lord R'hoone will buy my cassoulet and give me coals to put on my fire." He looked down his nose at the book in his hand. "What on earth has a fellow like me got to fear from a fellow like Lord R'hoone? he asked. "An Englishman, a milord, if you please. Probably wears a single eyeglass and walks like this with his nose in the air, as if the smells of France displeased him."

He got up and minced across the room, imitating an Englishman of the kind to be seen by the dozens in the garden of the Palais-Royal. It was skillfully done. Madame de Berny laughed heartily and said, "You're a marvelous mimic, you know. If you weren't a writer, you would certainly be an actor."

"A clown, more likely," he said, patting his thick, powerful chest. "I haven't got the figure for a leading man."

He sat down in a light chair, filling it with his bulk, making the frame creak under his weight. He smiled at Madame de Berny, a tender smile, filled with affection.

"We are alone in the house," she said, as if by afterthought. "De Berny is in London on some financial mission for the King. The children are in Burgundy, visiting an aunt. I can give you supper here, if you like. Would it please you?"

"Nothing more," he said.

Supper with his mistress was a rare thing. On most evenings, family obligations demanded her presence and Balzac seldom saw her except in the afternoons. It was a necessary arrangement, but one that never permitted them to forget the illicit, clandestine quality of their relationship. Both of them hated the furtiveness, but there was no help for it.

Madame de Berny ordered a table set up in front of the fireplace. The meal was served by Brigitte, her personal maid. The winter darkness came early and the circular room, lighted only by a pair of tall wax tapers on the table, seemed to become smaller. The polished silver gleamed self-confidently. The rich white napery was like virgin snow. There was a pale golden wine at first, chilled and poured into slim glasses, then a full-bodied red from the Côte d'Or.

97

The food was superb. The de Berny chef, like his mistress, was a product of the old regime, a survivor, who practised an art of the past. Balzac smiled. He had been asked to supper almost casually, but he realized that the meal had been planned at least a day before. There were a pair of delicate trout, with the skeletons removed and replaced with a layer of herbs, cooked in parchment envelopes. There was breast of chicken, simmered in pale wine. There was a cutlet to which something magic had been done, so that the meat was tender as butter, yet firm to the teeth.

"Eat more slowly, Honoré," she said. "After all, we are not in a race."

He laughed and paused for a moment, wiping his mouth. No matter how many times she reminded him, he could not seem to prevent himself from attacking his food like a hungry peasant.

"I'm not used to eating anything worth taking time over," he said. "Mostly, I stuff myself with white beans."

She made a face. Her taste in food was aristocratic. Her knowledge of gastronomy was precise and encyclopedic. She kept the menus of her great dinners pasted in a book bound in pale blue suede, stamped with the de Berny coat of arms in gilt.

"Beans have their virtues," Balzac said defensively, thinking of the Brasserie Lagatta, of the cassoulet, of Yvette, and, unaccountably, of the holes in her rough woolen stockings. "Beans are common, but they are healthy."

"Please, Honoré, we are at the table," she said, half-seriously.

They had a simple sweet, then moved to deeper, more comfortable chairs and drank coffee from cups the size of large thimbles, made from eggshell porcelain. The coffee was rich and winey, more aromatic than any he had ever tasted before. She told him that it came from Turkey and he made up his mind to put in a supply.

The candles on the table made a pool of golden light, on the edge of which sat Madame de Berny, her face touched by the soft glow, her hands delicate as white moths, when she moved them to refill the cups. Balzac sat in deep shadow, filled with splendid food and wine, enchanted by the fragrance of the rare coffee. He was happy as a well-born cat. He almost purred.

They sat this way for an hour, not talking very much, but intensely aware of each other's presence. The candles burned down slowly. One of them seemed to falter. Madame de Berny put out

98

the flames with a silver snuffer. For a few seconds the room seemed pitch black, then, as their eyes became adjusted, the moonlight showed at the windows, giving curious shapes to the objects in the room.

She stood beside his chair for a moment. He could smell her perfume. Then she touched his cheek. He kissed her hand. After a moment, she turned and went through the door that led to her bedroom. They were experienced lovers now, without need for words or awkward interchanges. He gave her time to undress and brush out her hair, then went into the darkened room.

He stayed the night.

Over the coffee cups in the morning, she regarded him with what seemed to be amusement and said, "Honoré, why didn't you tell me that you have been unfaithful to me?" she said lightly.

"What do you mean?" he said guiltily.

She laughed, a laugh filled with feminine superiority, the kind of laugh that sets men on edge.

"I assure you I'm not jealous," she said. "Merely curious."

"How did you know?" he demanded, genuinely astonished.

"How does one know these things?" she asked. "I am a woman. A woman knows." She smiled teasingly. "Is she pretty? Young? Who is she?"

"Not pretty at all," he said bluffly. "A serving girl at the Brasserie. It happened quite by accident."

"Of course. It always happens by accident."

He scratched his head and said awkwardly, "You see, it was a very cold night. I was at Lagatta's until quite late." He stopped for a moment, embarrassed. "She is quite unattractive, really. There are holes in her stockings."

Madame de Berny laughed heartily.

"Honoré, my darling, you are priceless," she said. "A serving girl with holes in her stockings."

"I promise you, it means nothing," he said earnestly.

"Of course it means nothing," she said, managing to sound as if she believed it.

Walking home along the banks of the Seine in the clear, bright winter morning, Balzac brooded, his chin buried in the collar of his greatcoat, his breath making clouds of white vapor.

99

"Women!" he said, half-aloud. "What a mystery they are!"

How did she know about Yvette? he wondered. What gesture in the midst of love had betrayed him? Or had it been nothing physical at all, but merely a subtle change in his manner, so slight as to be imperceptible to himself, yet enough for her? Or are women really clairvoyant, as his mother sometimes insisted?

He paused near the Pont-Neuf, watching the river for a few minutes. He had become a Parisian; the Seine was a living thing to him, with changes of mood and temperament. There was mist on the water and chunks of ice were floating moodily downstream. The effect was hypnotic.

Women! He was fascinated by them, fascinated by the secret world of women, intrigued by their morality, so different from the morality of men. I know nothing of women, really, he thought. My own mother is a mystery to me. So is the woman I have just left. So is my sister. Even a girl from the country, who cannot read or write, whose life consists of wiping tables, carrying beans, making fires, sleeping with anyone who will keep her warm on a winter's night—she is a mystery to me, an enigma, a being whose behavior follows laws and impulses I do not understand.

"I know nothing about women," he repeated to himself. "But I mean to know everything."

He turned away from the river, swinging his arms to take the stiffness out of them, and strode off toward Saint-Sulpice, bursting with energy, ready for work.

Chapter 10

THE FICTION FAC-
tory hummed. Thirty, forty, fifty pages a day flowed from Balzac's
pen. He wore out ten quills in three days. He wrote a novel a
month. He wrote a play, to be produced under someone else's
name. He wrote articles that were in questionable taste. He wrote
anything that anyone would pay for. Le Poitevin hawked the
company's wares, and Balzac scourged himself to keep up with
the demand.

Once a month, he passed the weekend with his parents, at
Villeparisis. His mother grudgingly admitted that he was making
a kind of living out of writing. His father was delighted.

"You are putting water in your wine, my boy," said Bernard-
François. "A good thing. Give the public what it wants, I say.
That's the way to make money. But why don't you put your name
to it, lad? If you got two thousand francs for this last one it must
have good stuff in it. Why don't you sign it? Are you ashamed of
the name Balzac?"

"It's because I am proud of my name that I didn't sign it,
father," said Balzac dryly.

Madame de Berny, who had seen no danger at first, now became alarmed. "You will ruin your health," she warned him.
"You live on coffee. You work all night. You will burn yourself
out."

"If it earns money it is worth it," he said grimly.

He was obsessed with the idea of earning a good-sized sum
of money, investing it shrewdly, and living off the proceeds while
he wrote great books.

"Nothing is worth it," his mistress said. "Honoré, I was wrong.
You are degrading yourself. You are putting your talent in peril,
as well as your health."

"I know, I know. I must stop," he agreed. "Another book or
two, then I'll clear out, I promise you."

101

But he did not stop. He went on. He became a whore serving several pimps. There was no part of the literary slum too degraded or depraved for him. He wrote a pornographic play for an old pederast, who hired actors, actresses and scenery and had the piece put on in his own home. He wrote a Royalist pamphlet for a politician. There was scarcely time to live.

Sometimes Yvette came to his room, after midnight when Lagatta's had closed. He grew rather fond of her, in the way one grows fond of a servant. One morning, when he had known her for several months, he offered her money.

"No thank you, Monsieur Balzac," she said. "If I become a whore, my clients will not be writers."

He bought her a pair of stockings, a dress, one day a box of candy. She took these things solemnly, with the gratitude of a child. She made no demands on him. If he wanted her, she came. That was all there was to it. The arrangement went on for a year and for part of a second. She no longer went to le Poitevin's rooms, but Balzac knew that she went with other men. It did not matter.

One morning she made coffee as usual, then sat on the edge of the bed, drinking from the saucer, and told him she was going away.

"Where?" he asked, thinking she might be going to the country for a visit.

"To Marseilles," she said. She hesitated, then blushed a little, and added, "I am going with Silvio, to be his woman."

"Silvio?"

"He comes to Lagatta's sometimes. You don't know him, Monsieur Balzac. He is a thief."

"Is he a good thief?"

"He is not in the galleys," she said with a shrug.

"Why are you going away with him?" asked Balzac.

"Because he has asked me, monsieur."

"That's no reason."

"Is it not? Would you ask me to come and live with you, monsieur? Would Monsieur le Poitevin ask me?"

"No," said Balzac.

"Very well then, Silvio has asked me," she said, a little note of pride in her voice.

A few days later, she disappeared from Lagatta's. Her place was taken by another young girl from the country, a Burgundian
102

with great innocent eyes, like those of a mild, slow-witted cow. She was promptly seduced by le Poitevin, who urged Balzac to share her with him.

"Of course she is stupid," le Poitevin agreed. "But in bed she is something. Give her just enough brandy to warm her up properly and I tell you, my friend, she goes off like a cannon."

"I am not an artilleryman," Balzac said.

"You will enjoy it," le Poitevin insisted.

"I would just as soon go to bed with a sheep," said Balzac.

"That is more for the country," said le Poitevin amiably. "Here in Paris, it is difficult to find a seduceable sheep. One takes Jeannette there, instead." He glanced across the room at Jeannette, who was laboring under a heavy tray. "Look at those breasts," he said. "Look at those backsides. You are an odd fellow, Balzac. When you sleep with a woman, you want a lecture in philosophy thrown in."

"Do you never think of anything else?" asked Balzac angrily.

"Only when necessary," said le Poitevin, unruffled.

"You make me sick," said Balzac.

A few weeks later, Balzac dissolved his partnership with le Poitevin. To his surprise, le Poitevin took it good naturedly.

"I don't blame you," he said. "You don't need me any more, and that's a fact. You'll be better off selling direct."

He even volunteered to introduce Balzac to the publishers and printers with whom he did business.

For a week or two, they made the rounds.

Balzac rather liked the printers. They were honest fellows in leather aprons, with ink on their hands and the ends of their noses. He liked the smell of printers' ink and wet paper. He liked the efficient sound of the presses. He liked to hold a printer's mallet in his hand, to run his thumb over the surface of a piece of type.

The printers were craftsmen. He understood them.

The publishers were another matter, at least the lower-class publishers with whom le Poitevin had connections. They were shifty-eyed men in stylish clothes that had become seedy. They operated from their lodgings or from grimy offices near the Palais-Royal. They were unctuous and flattering when it served their purpose, cruel as Moors when they were finished with a writer.

Very quickly, Balzac realized that these scavengers preyed on

103

each other as well as on the writers they exploited. They had the morality of whoremasters. They were always ready to steal the next man's author, or rob his book idea.

"They contribute nothing," Balzac complained to Madame de Berny. "And that nothing is second-rate. I am a whore. Very well, I admit it. But a whore is something. A whore gives value for the money, at least. These people, these publishers, they are worse than pimps. But they can be beaten at their own game. The thing to do is to be crafty. Play one against the other. Make them compete. Make them bid against one another. That way, you see, I'll have the whip hand."

"You are a writer, not a coachman," Madame de Berny said sharply. "What you are supposed to have in your hand is a pen, not a whip."

When he was brought to the verge of nervous collapse by overwork and the pressure of haggling with publishers, Balzac would throw some clothes into a bag and go off to Bayeux to visit his sister. The de Survilles were always glad to see him. They gave him a big square room on the top floor of the old stone house, and left him to himself. He could sleep as late as he liked, undisturbed, or get up with the chickens, as he sometimes did, and go for a long, solitary walk in the woods before breakfast.

Laure set a good table. There was plenty of rich Norman butter and delicious cream, so thick it could not be poured but had to be dished out of its stone crock with a spoon. In the pantry there was always a succulent, well-smoked ham, with a sharp knife nearby, so that between meals a man could always shave off a slice or two.

And there was Laure, one of the two women in the world to whom he could speak without fear. It was to Laure that he first admitted that he had written himself into a trap, a dead end.

"I am twenty-four, nearly twenty-five," he said. "I work like a savage, and the more I work, the more I become a slave. I had hoped to free myself by writing novels." He made a gesture of contempt. "What novels! The other day, in Paris, I picked up a book from a stall in the Palais-Royal. I read a few pages, casually, the way one does. My God what trash! I said to myself. Who wrote it? I wonder. The fellow ought to be ashamed of himself. Then I looked at the title page and read the author's name. Saint Aubin. My God! I began to turn to jelly. Saint Aubin. Myself! I com-

104

posed this garbage, which should never have been committed to print. I. Balzac! I tell you, Laure, I wanted to die, to drop dead, right there on the pavement."

"But you are young, Honoré," Laure protested. "You must give yourself time."

"I am a year older than that black fellow, Dumas," said Balzac miserably. "He is a success. Look at Victor Hugo. He is three years younger than I am, and already famous. I haven't even begun."

"Perhaps you need more time than Dumas or Victor Hugo," his sister said reasonably.

In other terms, Madame de Berny told him the same thing, when he went to her in despair, to complain that he made no progress.

"The kind of books you will write when you are ready will demand maturity," she said. "They are inside you now, those books, growing inside you, the way a child grows inside his mother. They will come out when they are ready to survive in the world, as a child comes out when he is ready."

"A child cooks in nine months," Balzac complained, tapping his stomach with a blunt finger. "These babies of mine take a bit longer, eh?"

When he did not complain about his predicament, he joked about it, but he was becoming more and more dissatisfied with himself and worried about his direction. He made money and saved some of it, but it was never enough to permit him to give up hack work and turn his attention to something serious. He did not live luxuriously, but the money he earned seemed to disappear. He loved books and as soon as he had money in his hand he began to make a collection. He could never resist the request for a loan from some fellow writer or artist down on his luck. Consequently, after four years of hack work, he seemed to be selling himself for nothing.

The crowd at the Palais-Royal was fickle.

"They are getting tired of novels," publishers reported to Balzac. "Nowadays, the rage is for non-fiction, codes, manuals, things like that."

Balzac wrote codes, manuals of style, dress, manners and sex,

105

cribbed from a hundred sources, rehashed, and served up with a sauce of cheap wit. The work was exhausting. Each night he wrote until his wrist and forearm went numb and his eyes smarted as if filled with smoke. The nervous pressure affected his digestion.

The first few books he had written after breaking with le Poitevin, he had revised in manuscript. Nowadays he was indifferent, hardly looking at a page after he had covered it with words. His prose was slovenly, sometimes downright bad. It didn't matter. He did not care.

When his mother complained of his bad grammar and suggested that he revise his books before they went to the printer, he simply shrugged and said, "What does it matter? Neither the publishers nor the readers know the difference between good French and bad. I'm beginning to doubt that I know myself."

"Bad habits are hard to break," his mother said severely. "You are betraying your education."

"And a good thing too," Balzac said rudely. "It was a bad education."

"Who is to blame if you wouldn't study?" challenged his mother. "Whose fault is it that you were thirty-first in Latin, in a class of thirty-two?"

She had never gotten over his poor record at Lepître's school. He laughed and said, "Mother, do you really imagine that my troubles as a writer come from the fact that I was thirty-first in Latin?"

"The subject is important," she said primly. "It is the mark of an educated man."

"I am a writer," he said. "A writer must get his own education, otherwise his books merely give back what the schools shovel out, or parrot what he's read in other books."

"The books you are writing are not quite original," she said tartly.

Balzac's mother was no fool. In spite of her various failings, she knew a good book from a bad. A whole indictment was contained in the phrase she had just uttered. Balzac colored slightly, and said defensively, "My mind is working. I'm reading, I'm developing."

"You should marry," she said bluntly. They were sitting in the parlor at Villeparisis. She got up and went to the window, looking out at the garden. "I don't mean to be unkind, Honoré, but that woman. She's not good for you. You need someone who can help you. Someone who can give you a home. Madame de Berny is wrong for you."

It was the first time she had used Madame de Berny's name. Always, before this, it had been "your friend" or "your companion" or "that woman" or simply "she." Hearing the name uttered openly put Balzac on his guard.

"She is my life," he said flatly. "If I survive, I owe it to her."

His mother turned. The blue-violet eyes narrowed.

"She is a grandmother, Honoré," she said. "Whatever else she is to you, tutor, friend, literary critic, mistress, teacher of etiquette—one cannot escape the simple fact that she is a grandmother, while you are twenty-four."

Balzac turned his head and focused his eyes on the edge of a table, to avoid looking at his mother. His vision blurred. Of course, what his mother had said was true. His mistress was a grandmother. Soon, very soon, she would reach the age where being his mistress would be grotesque, almost unnatural.

On the way back to Paris, he sat in the rocking stagecoach and brooded over his situation. In some way, money always seemed to be at the centre of his problems. If only he were rich, it seemed to him that the rest of his life would take care of itself. He would live in comfort, without fear. His books would be written at leisure. He would have public respect and approval. The rich always had that. Even Madame de Berny's age would somehow be more bearable, if only he were rich.

But how was he going to get rich?

Not by doing hack writing. Four years of bitter work had taught him that much. Publishers might become rich, printers, even booksellers, but not writers, except for those like Sir Walter Scott, whose books Balzac devoured. There were no writers like Scott, nowadays, in France. There were writers, yes. He had met some of them. There was Victor Hugo. There was that insufferable black fellow, Dumas, that he had met at the Arsenal Library and instantly disliked. There were men who had written a book or two, a play, published a volume of verse. There were others, like himself, who had turned out words by the thousands and signed them with invented names.

There were no Racines, no Molières, no towering figures.

107

France yearned for genius. What she got, mostly, was hack work or minor efforts from 'prentice hands.

That night, Balzac tossed in his bed for several hours, pursued by his mother's sharp observations and by his own sense of disenchantment with his life.

When he fell asleep, he began to dream, the kind of dream that contains images sharper than those in real life, the logic clean as a knife-blade, frightening in its simplicity.

He saw himself at a full-dress ball in a glittering house. The women were in décolleté, bare shoulders white with powder, jewels in their hair, at their waists, on their wrists and fingers, their feet in enchanting satin slippers that winked under their skirts as they danced. The men were in black, with lace shirt fronts, white gloves, shoes with paper-thin soles.

Balzac had never worn such a costume, but he was dressed this way in his dream and it seemed perfectly natural to him.

He stood in a great arched doorway, quite at ease, watching the dancers as they dipped and glided under crystal chandeliers, each of which bore hundreds of candles. Servants in livery moved about, offering food and wine to the guests. A footman came toward Balzac, carrying glasses on a silver tray.

"Champagne, monsieur?"

As he took a glass from the proffered tray, Balzac's eyes were drawn to the coat-of-arms embroidered on the breast of the servant's uniform coat. He recognized it at once: the halberd, the coronet, the motto of the de Berny family.

"So it's her house!"

He felt a spasm of fear.

But not the house she lives in now. The time is different. It must be before the Revolution. He lifted himself on his toes and peered at the moving sea of dancers. After a moment, he discovered Madame de Berny, dancing with her husband, not the Madame de Berny he knew, but a young woman in her twenties, her mouth carefree and reckless, her eyes flashing with excitement, her full breasts nearly exposed, after the fashion of the period. Monsieur de Berny, who, in life, Balzac had seen only once, as a living corpse in a wheel chair, was a healthy nobleman in his forties, with the straight back of a horseman, the alert, dangerous eyes of a swordsman.

108

Balzac felt a pang of desperate jealousy. He drank from the delicate glass in his hand. The bubbling wine tickled his nostrils, the taste was sharp on his tongue. He glanced at the glass and saw that the glove that covered his hand was filled with holes, as if the kid had been nibbled by mice. He saw that the cuffs of his dress coat were frayed, that his dancing pumps were cracked and wrinkled. My God, I am a pauper! he thought. I am poor, desperately poor. What am I doing in this great house?

He put down the glass and felt in his pocket. His fingers found six gold Louis, and he understood that this was all the money he had in the world.

The music came to a stop with a flourish. The dancers began to move toward the sides of the room. Balzac straightened up as Madame de Berny came toward him, on her husband's arm. De Berny wore the star of some order or other on the breast of his beautifully cut coat, an affair made of gold and silver, studded with jewels. Balzac's eyes were drawn to this decoration as the handsome couple approached him. There was a ruby in the center of the star and it held his gaze like a hypnotist's bangle.

Then Madame de Berny uttered a high, heartless, contemptuous laugh, the sound of which affected Balzac as though a dagger had been thrust into his chest. He gasped, as if from mortal pain, turned blindly and rushed from the room, out of the house.

It was a winter's night. There was chill in the air and patches of dirty snow clung to frozen ruts in the street. He turned up the collar of his shabby cape, thrust his hands into his pockets and struck off in the direction of the Palais-Royal. Through the soles of his dancing shoes, he felt the cold of the paving cobbles. He stamped his feet, making them smart with pain. His fingers closed on the six gold coins in his pocket. His hand clung to them as if they contained his life. He quickened his pace, eager to be at the gaming tables, to stake his life on the turn of the wheel and the croupier's dispassionate verdict. He was determined to recoup his fortunes, or put an end to his misery by throwing himself into the Seine.

At the Palais-Royal, he entered one of the larger gambling houses, gave up his hat and cloak, received a numbered disc in return, and went up the stairs to the tables.

The sounds of play reached his ears before he finished climbing the staircase: the whirr of the wheel, the click of the ball, the

109

sound of the croupiers' voices, calling the play. He entered the room. There were six tables, under brilliant gaslight. Men and women leaned forward intently, watching the spin of the wheel.

Balzac moved forward and took a place at a gaming table. Shall I play one gold piece at a time? he asked himself, or risk it all on a single turn of the wheel? Why prolong it? a voice whispered. You are doomed. Why try to break your doom up into little pieces? He thrust his hand into his pocket and drew forth the six Louis. The black seemed more appropriate to his situation than the red. After a moment's hesitation, he placed all his money on the black. The croupier spoke: *"Mesdames, messieurs!"* and his thin, evil hand came across the table to spin the wheel. There was a general holding of breath as the wheel spun, the colors blended, and the little ball danced madly on the rim.

The wheel slowed, the ball danced uncertainly, then fell into place.

"Red, mesdames, messieurs! Red, Twenty-five!"

Balzac turned away from the table and walked slowly from the room. He took his hat and cloak from the servant, shrugged at the man in lieu of a tip, and went into the street with a curse in his ears.

"So this is the end," he said to himself. "This is the end of Balzac."

He passed through the arcades of the Palais-Royal and entered the rue Saint-Honoré. He walked on and went into the Tuileries Gardens. The beautiful flower beds slept under blankets of manure. The long formal pathway beckoned to Balzac. He crossed through the gardens, turned and walked toward the Pont Royal. At the river, he stopped. There is no hurry, he thought, looking at the oily, implacable water. The river is not impatient, like the roulette table. The river will wait.

He walked along the Quai Voltaire, then turned into a narrow street, attracted by the light of a curio shop that for some reason had remained open after all other shops were closed. He stood in front of the narrow window, looking at the objects displayed there, which were mainly oriental, hammered brass pitchers and pots, a curved sword with arabic engraving, an odd lamp, a waterpipe, a pair of kidskin slippers with pointed toes that turned back on themselves. Drawn by some mysterious force, he opened the door and entered the shop. A tiny bell on a spring tinkled, oper-

110

ated by the door. Through a curtained opening in the rear of the shop came a man that Balzac took for a Syrian or perhaps a Turk. He was old, with the face of an emaciated oriental hawk and hands with long clawlike fingers.

"Monsieur Balzac?"

"I am Balzac."

"What you seek is here. Come with me."

The shopkeeper parted the curtain and Balzac passed through a narrow door to the rear of the building, where there was a large, windowless room, the walls covered with magnificent hangings. There were Oriental rugs underfoot. Incense smouldered in a brass burner suspended from the ceiling by thin chains. All sound was eliminated by the heavy rugs and hangings. There was a thick, uncanny silence. Perhaps I am already dead, thought Balzac. Perhaps I have crossed over, somehow, into the other world.

"Turn around," the shopkeeper said. "Look at that skin that hangs on the wall behind you."

Obediently, Balzac turned. On the wall, fixed to the richly embroidered hangings, was a crudely tanned skin, the size of a fox's pelt. A strange light seemed to come from its surface. Balzac went closer. As his eyes became adjusted to the curious light, he saw that there was writing on the skin, arabic letters that seemed to have been burnt into the surface of the leather. Though he knew not a word of Arabic, in his dream Balzac was able to read the words as easily as if they had been simple French.

> *Who possesses me*
> > *possesses everything*
> *but his life is mine*
> > *for God has willed it.*
> *Wish and the wish will be fulfilled,*
> > *but measure desire,*
> *for with each wish, I shrink,*
> > *even as the life of a man shrinks.*

"Take the skin, young man," the shopkeeper said. "But beware."

Balzac took the skin from the wall, rolled it up and put it in his pocket, then left the shop and retraced his steps through the narrow street, back to the Quai Voltaire. At the river's edge, he halted, turned and looked behind him. The light that had drawn

111

him to the shop was gone. The narrow street was dark. He turned back to the river, contemplating the black surface of the water, into which he had promised to throw himself.

An old hag, bent nearly double, her pinched face encased in a ragged shawl, approached him. She gave him a malevolent glance and said, "Poor weather for drowning yourself, monsieur. The Seine is cold and filthy."

She cackled with mirth and moved on. For an instant, Balzac had the urge to smash her thin old skull against the cold wet granite of the Quai wall, to throw her wasted body into the water that waited for his own. His anger passed and depression gripped him. I am too young to die, he thought bitterly, with most of my life unlived, tempting as the unread pages of a book. But to live as a pauper, without possessing the woman he loved, to live under the bridges of the Seine, like the old crone who had mocked him—that was a prospect intolerable to him.

He put a hand into his pocket. His fingers touched the skin he had taken down from the wall of the shop. "If only I were rich, titled and famous," he thought.

Beneath his fingers, it seemed to him that the skin moved convulsively, as an unborn child moves in his mother. He became aware of a tingling sensation that began at his toes and passed through his body, a unique, invigorating sense of life.

He straightened up and began to walk toward the Pont Royal. He came to a pool of light cast by a high window, and chanced to look down, avoiding a patch of ice on the road. His feet were covered by new, glossy pumps. He stopped and examined his clothing. His cloak was new, made of beautiful stuff. He touched his throat. The lace of his shirt front was crisp.

Out of the shadows came an old beggar.

"Charity, for the love of St. Catherine," begged the hideous voice, hollow with sickness. "A penny, a copper, please, sir."

Balzac reached into the pocket from which he had taken the six Louis he had squandered at the gambling table. The pocket should have been empty but his fingers closed on a handful of coins. He held his palm in the light and selected a five franc piece and dropped it into the beggar's hand.

"The blessings of heaven on you, sir. May your days be lengthened."

The beggar stood for a moment, then his voice seemed to be
112

stopped in his throat. He stared at Balzac, his eyes expressing mortal terror. Then he threw the coin to the ground and shrieked, raised a hand to his face as if to ward off the devil, and moved back into the shadows.

Balzac shrugged and began to walk away from the river, toward a fashionable part of the city. At a magnificent house, he halted, and turned in without thinking. The doors opened noiselessly. A servant in livery bowed.

"Monsieur le duc," he said.

Balzac gave him his coat and hat. With his cloak off, he glanced down. On the left breast of his coat was a jeweled decoration.

"Madame is waiting, Monsieur le duc," the servant said.

Balzac nodded absently. He passed through the marble entrance hall into a mirrored room, aware, without being in the least surprised, that this was his own house he had entered. He went through a door at the end of the mirrored room and came into a private sitting room. There was a table, with wine in a cooler, glasses, a tray of food. A woman waited on a satin sofa. Her face was turned away from him. He took a step toward her. He saw her hand and arm, a graceful finger. He saw the hair, glistening and lovely. It was Madame de Berny, young, as he had seen her at the ball. She turned and his blood turned to ice. The face was that of the old hag who had taunted him near the Pont Royal, the face of a Madame de Berny who had lived twice, three times, the normal span of years. It was the face of living death, the face of loathsome age, a face that was nothing but a rotting skull, under the taut and rotting skin. As he watched, the awful mouth moved and formed a hideous smile that became an obscene mixture of lewdness and death.

He screamed in terror, then screamed again, trying to run, unable to move.

He felt a hand on his shoulder, shaking him.

"Monsieur Balzac! Monsieur Balzac!"

With difficulty, he came awake. He was in bed, in his room. Beside him stood the concierge, wrapped in a heavy grey bathrobe, her face filled with concern.

"Thank God, monsieur, it was only a nightmare," she said, "When I heard you scream, I thought you were dying."

Balzac sat up in bed and rubbed his eyes with his fists.

"Only a nightmare," he said. "Thank you, madame, for your kindness."

"Of no importance, monsieur," she said.

When she had gone, he got out of bed, pulled on a pair of coarse stockings and donned a heavy dressing gown. He looked at his watch. It was four o'clock. No more sleep tonight, he thought. He felt shaken. He brewed a pot of coffee, then sat in his armchair with the cup and saucer balanced on his knee.

The awful, aged skull face of Madame de Berny was burnt into his mind. He closed his eyes, put down the coffee, and pressed his thumbs against his eyes, hard enough to cause pain. His eyes were shot with metallic, vicious color, then with a rain of stars, like those from a fireworks rocket. They disappeared. His eyes were dark. The hideous face returned. He shook his head like a tormented bull, opened his eyes and gulped some coffee, scalding his mouth. The pain helped edge his mind away from the world of the dream, toward the reality of his rather chilly room, where he sat in a dressing gown with a half-filled coffee cup on his lap.

What does the dream mean? he asked himself.

He had an intense interest in dreams, his own and those of other people. He suspected that the secrets of the soul were sometimes betrayed in dreams, while the dreamer was off his guard.

He finished his coffee, got up, stretched himself, and sat down at his writing table, taking up a fresh pen and dipping it into his inkpot. He wanted to put the dream on paper before the details grew cold in his mind.

Someday I'll make a book of it, he thought, as his pen touched the paper. As he wrote, his mind focused absolutely on his words. The dream that had caused him to awaken in terror, screaming for his life, was turned into an arrangement of words, sentences and paragraphs, no longer something to be feared, but a thing to be mastered.

Chapter 11

THE DREAM, ONCE
it was written down, ceased to be a source of fear, but it plagued
him. He could not get it out of his mind. There was some meaning in it that he did not understand, and he went about for a number of days aware of a discomforting sense of frustration.

He itched for a change in his way of life. He was twenty-five,
an age at which men are often prompted to look for a new turning. At twenty-five a man is young enough to make a beginning,
but his youth is salted with sufficient experience to give firmness
to his decisions and authority to his attack.

Hack writing was a blind alley and Balzac had known it for
some time. Paris was filled with middle-aged men who eked out a
meager living doing exactly what he had been doing. He wanted
a change, and during the weeks that followed his dream, the need
for a change became an obsession.

"I have got to break with all this," he told Madame de Berny.
"I have got to change my life."

She agreed with him. She was troubled by his failure to cut
loose from the fourth-rate publishers, and she was concerned
about his health. In his effort to acquire a reserve of cash, he drove
himself too hard, eating improperly, sleeping badly, forgetting to
change his shirt or his socks until she reminded him that they
were dirty.

She knew him well enough to realize that this crisis was basic,
not something that would pass in a few days, as had crises in the
past that had been brought on by disagreements with publishers
or dissatisfaction with a piece of writing he had just finished.
Those had been fits of depression and irritability common to
writers. What Balzac felt now was a true demand for climax and
for radical change.

"Perhaps I should have taken my brother-in-law's offer," he
said moodily.

115

A year earlier, Laure's husband had offered him the chance at an administrative job with an engineering firm, arguing that Balzac's legal training would help him make a success in business. Balzac had refused.

Madame de Berny shook her head. "It wouldn't have been right for you," she said. "It would have been even more wrong than your mother's suggestion that you go back to the legal profession."

"She only says that because she feels the money was wasted to get me my degree in law," he said. "She thinks I'm a failure. Perhaps she's right."

"Of course she's not right!" Madame de Berny said indignantly. "You haven't really begun as a writer. How can you be a failure?"

They were sitting in a café near the Place de la Bourse, a place frequented by business men and stockbrokers. At a table nearby a group of men from the stock exchange were drinking coffee and talking business amid an atmosphere of fine self confidence. They were young men, sleekly dressed, shrewdly barbered, and the expressions on their faces indicated that they believed they owned the earth. Balzac looked at them with a mixture of envy and contempt.

"Business," he said bitterly. "That's the thing I should get into. Given a touch of genius, a man should be able to make a fortune in business and do it with his left hand."

Probably in all of France there was not a man less fitted for business than Balzac, but Madame de Berny did not dispute with him. For all her kindness and lack of pretension, she was an aristocrat to the bone, with an aristocrat's contempt for the process of making money. To her, money was something one simply had. To be concerned with its acquisition was a way of life that involved another class altogether.

"There can't be so very much to business," she said. "It's simply a matter of buying and selling, is it not?"

"One buys cheap and sells dear," Balzac observed wisely. "That's the secret of the thing. A dunce can do it with some success. A man of intelligence should be a sensation."

Madame de Berny encouraged him. She wanted to see him break away from the thanklessness of hack writing. If business was the answer, then let it be business.

Balzac's mother would have set him straight. She came from the very class that Balzac regarded with contempt. She was a

116

bourgeoise to the core, with a congenital understanding of mundane affairs. She would have warned Balzac that while business might be less elegant than art and less distinguished than the professions, still it was not an affair in which fools were likely to make progress.

Balzac did not consult his mother.

He and Madame de Berny entertained one another by talking about the fortune that he would make, once embarked on a business career that would be brief but brilliant. His success was taken for granted.

To Balzac, the idea of business quickly became an obsession. He took to reading the commercial journals, and followed the fluctuations of the stocks and bonds on the Paris Bourse. Overnight he acquired the vocabulary of a man of affairs, and talked largely of discounts, short sales, notes of credit, capital investments.

"I'll know a good thing when I see it," he promised Madame de Berny. "Then it's a matter of striking while the iron is hot. In business, it is necessary to pounce upon the right thing as a cat pounces on a rat."

For some weeks, Balzac toyed with various ideas.

Then, one bright, cold morning during the last days of the winter of 1824, opportunity struck like a bolt of lightning. That morning, Balzac called on one of the publishers with whom he did business, a certain Urbain Canel, who had an office at No. 30, Place St. André des Arts. Balzac had come to offer Canel his latest novel, WANN CHLORE, an exotic romance that he planned to issue anonymously, rather than under one of his noms de plume.

Canel was delighted to have the book. There was not a third-rate publisher in France who was not happy to have a manuscript from the fiction factory that Balzac operated under a half dozen names. Canel was one of the more respectable members of the group that published cheap fiction, and he aspired to better things. He was a short, intense man in his forties, with black hair that was going thin on top, an acquiline nose that gave the impression of constantly being on scent, and a pair of gold-framed spectacles that were always highly polished. Unlike most publishers, Canel had been to school and even, for a year or two, at the University of Paris. He preferred to think that young Balzac regarded him as an educated man and an equal.

When the business transaction was finished and Balzac's novel had changed hands, Canel unlocked a cabinet that stood behind his desk, took out a decanter and glasses, and offered Balzac a drink, suggesting a toast to the success of WANN-CHLORE.

"I'll drink with you," Balzac agreed. "But not to that pile of garbage for which you have just paid fifteen hundred francs, and from which you will undoubtedly make five thousand. Let us drink to our mothers or our mistresses, to bloody war or the devil himself, to anything on earth you like except that novel. I am fed up with bad fiction."

Canel laughed and poured brandy into the rather smeary glasses.

"What can one do?" he asked. "The public taste is the public taste." He looked at Balzac speculatively, then said, "I am fed up as you are, my friend, with this nonsense." He waved a hand toward a shelf of popular three and four decker romances, issued by himself and others. "Let me show you something that will interest you." He unlocked a drawer of his desk and took out a fat volume, bound in boards. On the front cover was printed: MOLIÉRE: *Complete Works.*

Balzac took the book in his hand.

"Complete works?" he said. "A complete Molière runs to six volumes, minimum."

"Open it," Canel said. "That's only a dummy, of course, but you will get the idea."

Balzac opened the book. Most of the pages were blank, for this was merely a publisher's dummy, made for the purpose of estimating costs, weight, and bulk. The first signature had been set in type and roughly proofed. It was Molière, all right, the text set in narrow columns, in a type face several sizes smaller than that ordinarily used in books. Balzac turned a page or two, then put the book down.

"Holding it in the hand is exhausting," he said. "Reading it would encourage blindness. It is not an object of beauty. Let me ask you, Canel, what is its purpose? Is it a doorstop?"

Canel laughed. "A doorstop," he said. "That's a good one. In the long run, perhaps that's the most useful purpose they'll be put to." He leaned forward confidentially, hands on his desk, fingertips touching. "Do you know what a good set of Molière costs? Of Racine? Of Voltaire?"

"A good set?" said Balzac, shrugging. "I don't know. Two, three hundred francs, I suppose."

"More," said Canel. "Then there's the cost of binding individual volumes. That can run to whatever one pleases. Owning the classics is a luxury that only the rich can afford. In the past, it didn't matter. Ordinary people, most of them, couldn't read. Nowadays, nearly every Frenchman is literate. It is one of the things we are famous for." He picked up the dummy and gazed at it with admiration. "All of Molière in one volume. Every word he wrote, bound between two covers and sold at a price within the means of every shopkeeper. I tell you, Balzac, it will sell by the thousands. In this country, nowadays, there is a passion for self-advancement that amounts to a disease. Every dairyman expects that his son will grow up to be the first minister of France, or at least a lawyer or a judge. And what is the secret of self-advancement?" He held the book in the air. "Learning. Anyone you stop in the street knows that. And what is the basis of learning for a Frenchman? French classics. I tell you, Balzac, this is a certainty. It is a chance to do a service to French literature, and at the same time to make a small fortune. Think of it, man!" He put the book down with an emphatic thump. "Fontaine, Molière, Racine, Voltaire . . . complete works, in one volume, at ten francs a volume."

Balzac leaned forward, his eyes bright with excitement. "Can it be done?" he demanded. "Do you have the costs?"

Canel spread his hands like an Arab merchant. "I am a publisher, Balzac," he said. "With a project like this, the first thing a publisher asks himself is: 'What will the first edition cost?' "

He took a work sheet from his desk drawer and handed it to Balzac.

"There are the figures, my friend," he said. "Look them over. Look for an error in my reckoning. You won't find it. I promise you that. I've been over those figures a hundred times."

For several minutes, Balzac studied the estimates, noting the prices charged off for paper, printing, binding, engraving. Then he put the sheet on Canel's desk.

"What's holding you up?" he demanded.

Canel shrugged. "What usually holds up a project like this?" he asked. "Capital, or rather the lack of it. The idea is here." He tapped the dummy with his index finger. "All I need is money enough to get my first printing on press. Then the cash will come rolling in. The man who is lucky enough to invest now will get in on the ground floor. In six months, a year, his original investment will have been multiplied fifty times, perhaps a hundred."

Balzac sat up straight in his chair, assuming a businesslike attitude. "How much do you need?" he said briskly, as if financing publishers were a thing he did every day of his life.

"For the first edition, including the cost of distribution, about ten thousand francs," Canel said easily.

Balzac, the investor, wilted a little. He had only half of that sum. He stared at the dummy Molière and the work sheet with the estimates on it. Then he brightened up.

"I might be able to raise it," he said. "Between myself and a friend or two."

"You won't regret it," Canel promised. "Nor will your friends. It is a sure fire thing. A gold mine."

Balzac left Canel's office walking on air. It's the chance I've been waiting for, he thought. The chance to make a fortune, to get out of this swamp I've been living in, of hack-writing and misery.

As he turned into the rue de Rivoli, walking under the arcade, he was carried away by his imagination. He saw himself as a publisher, the first publisher of France, brilliant, successful, rich, showered with fame and the decorations of a grateful nation. This is it! he said to himself. This thing of Canel's is the magic skin that was in my dream.

Madame de Berny was almost as enthusiastic as Balzac himself. To publish the great French classics in editions that the common people could afford—this was an undertaking that appealed to her sense of noblesse oblige. The project had elements of benevolence in it, almost of charity. One of the faults of the old régime had been its refusal to consider the people. This was the kind of thing the old aristocracy should have done.

"The idea is marvelous!" she decided. "And there is no one in France better qualified to supervise the work than yourself."

Meanwhile, there was the question of money. Balzac supplied two thousand francs. Madame de Berny invested four thousand, and she got the rest from friends. The contract with Canel was drawn up and signed. Balzac was in business.

120

The first volume of the projected series was to be La Fontaine.

"He is the logical choice," said Balzac. "He may not be our greatest writer, but he is our most characteristic. It is difficult to imagine France without the good Fontaine."

Canel agreed.

"And now there is the matter of illustrations," Balzac said.

"Illustrations!" Canel exploded. "I had thought of little vignettes, nothing more."

"One cannot offer the French public a Fontaine without illustrations," said Balzac placidly. "Fontaine without illustrations would be like an egg without salt, like a woman without perfume, breakfast without coffee, an Englishman without a stammer."

"The idea was to keep things cheap," said Canel.

"There must be illustrations and good ones too," Balzac insisted. "In the long run, you see, it will be cheaper. The illustrations will help sell the books, and when you consider the quantities we're going to get rid of, the few sous per copy spent for engravings won't mean a thing."

Balzac saw Canel's shop piled to the rafters with Fontaine, saw the narrow street outside blocked by draymen loading orders for booksellers all over France, saw Canel's wooden till overflowing with ten franc pieces.

Canel shrugged and shook his head, regretting the day he had broached this project to the excitable Balzac. He had hoped that Balzac would see the thing as a good chance to turn a profit, and he had expected him to put up the money and then go back to his writing table, leaving the business to himself, Canel.

Not Balzac!

From the moment he signed the contract, he had haunted Canel's office, assuming the role of senior partner, testing samples of paper, inspecting different type faces, interviewing artists. Canel's original idea of doing things cheaply had been forgotten. Now the books were to be beautiful examples of the printer's art, impeccably designed, exquisitely produced. This morning, Balzac had dropped his bombshell in Canel's office. The books were to be illustrated.

For Canel, this was the last straw. He had put up no money himself, his share of the project having been covered by his contribution of the idea and the use of his premises. With the fatalism often possessed by the petty entrepreneur, he shrugged his shoulders

121

and turned his back on the scheme, allowing Balzac to have his way.

"Canel would have ruined the idea with his cheapness," Balzac told Madame de Berny. "He has no imagination, you see, no vision."

Balzac went to Alençon, to confer with the engraver he had selected, one of the best in France and one of the most expensive.

"There should be chapter headings, Monsieur Balzac," the old engraver said. "After all, this is Fontaine, not some upstart scribbler."

"Chapter headings by all means!" Balzac agreed.

"And tail pieces, monsieur?"

"Naturally, there must be tail pieces," Balzac said.

He was bending over the engraver's workbench, squinting at a burnished copper plate held in a vise. He picked up an engraver's tool, testing the needle point with his thumb. He sniffed, aware of a curious, attractive odor.

"Acid, monsieur," the engraver said. "For biting copper."

He walked to a pair of soapstone sinks suspended from the wall. Balzac followed him.

"For a deep bite, I use this acid. Strong stuff," the old man explained. "For a standard bite, this." He pointed at one bottle, then at another. "You are interested, monsieur?"

Balzac nodded.

"I am finishing a plate this afternoon," the engraver said. "If you will honor my table, I shall be pleased to have you watch the work, after we have eaten."

Balzac did justice to an honest provincial meal, then put on a black leather apron and stood beside the old man, watching the skillful hands as the plate was etched again and again, until just the right depth was achieved.

He came away from Alençon, having ordered a set of engravings that would cost almost as much as Canel had allowed for all of the preprinting costs. But he was happy. He had learned exactly how a fine engraving is made, what each tool is called, why the work of one good man is different from that of another. It was not merely that engraving was in a sense related to his own work as a writer of books; he would have been equally interested in watching an undertaker lay out a body, watching a surgeon ampu-

122

tate a leg; he would have hidden himself in a boudoir closet to watch a lady's maid do a coiffure. With intense interest he had watched a chêf put the finishing touches on a dish designed to dazzle a gourmet. He soaked up facts like a sponge. There was nothing that did not interest him, except the books he had already written.

By the time La Fontaine was being set in type, Balzac was already at work on the volume to follow, the Molière. Canel threw up his hands and announced that he was going to the south of France for a holiday. Balzac was not displeased. Canel was a small-minded fellow, too unimaginative even to appreciate the impact of his own ideas.

He had the office to himself while Canel was away. He took over Canel's desk, stepping into the part of manager and enjoying the role. He had decided to write prefaces for the Molière, as well as for the Racine and the other books in the series, because, as he explained to Madame de Berny, nothing that had been written about these great men really did them justice, or was of sufficient merit to warrant inclusion in these definitive editions.

Between periods of work on the introductions and visits to Alençon to inspect the engravings, Balzac bullied the unfortunate printer who had been engaged to produce the first volume.

"This type is vile!" he roared. "You aren't setting a handbill, man. This is Fontaine, one of the jewels in the very crown of French literature. You see how this verse sparkles? The type must sparkle too. I want something graceful, something witty, do you understand?"

The printer scratched his nose with an inky finger, concluded that he was dealing with a madman, and decided to increase his charges.

At the papermakers, the story was the same.

"What? You expect me to print my Fontaine on this sleazy stuff?" demanded Balzac. He tore the sample sheet in half and performed a vulgar pantomine. "That's what this stuff is fit for, man. To wipe your backside with. Show me something better."

The bills began to come into the Place St. André des Arts, addressed not to Urbain Canel, but to Honoré Balzac. Canel had taken care of this detail before departing on his holiday.

"I can't understand it," Balzac complained to Madame de Berny. "Look. Here are Canel's estimates." He showed her the sheet Canel had offered him when the project had first been mentioned. "You see. Typesetting, fifteen hundred. The thief has charged me a thousand more. Paper for three thousand copies, eight hundred francs. The monster wants two thousand! Printing, Canel's estimate allows for seventeen hundred francs. This brigand wants three thousand, half before he will start to print."

"What is this last bill?" Madame de Berny asked.

"This one?" Balzac said awkwardly. "Well, you see, that's for the engravings. I can't blame Canel for that. He hadn't allowed for illustrations. But these others!" He lifted the sheaf of bills and slapped the edge of the table with them. "It is preposterous. Canel is either an incompetent or a swindler."

Madame de Berny was unperturbed.

"Canel is used to doing things cheaply," she said. "That's why he is of no importance as a publisher, my dear. He is small-minded."

She took the bills from Balzac and glanced at them. As a principle investor, she felt that she had some understanding of these things.

"How much will you need, my darling, to pay these and insure delivery of the Fontaine?" she asked.

Balzac shrugged. "Another five thousand," he said hesitantly. "Then there will be the binder's bill, and the fee for the draymen. Say another seven, in all."

She folded the bills and handed them to him.

"You must not be distracted from your main purpose by the lack of a few thousand francs," she said. "I will have the money for you tomorrow."

"I will give you a promissory note," said Balzac. "In six weeks, you will have the money back, with interest, I promise you."

"You don't have to give me a note," she said. "I have faith in you."

He shook his head. "Faith is all very well," he said. "But this is a matter of business, you see. In business, that is the way things are done. One puts things on paper."

"As you wish, my dear," said Madame de Berny.

The books were delivered two weeks later. The shelves and

124

bins of Canel's shop were piled high with copies of La Fontaine, just as Balzac had imagined.

The first copy went to Madame de Berny, with a suitable inscription from the publisher. It was one of twenty copies that left Canel's shop. The others remained on the shelves or in the unopened cartons in which the binder had packed them. In order to recover the investment, it had been necessary to price the books at twenty francs a copy. This was five times the cost of an ordinary book. The dealers on the Quai Voltaire laughed in Balzac's face.

"Twenty francs a copy, eh?" said one. "At that price, young fellow, my customers would expect a tart along with every book, to keep them company when they got tired reading."

"Look at the paper," Balzac argued. "Look at the printing, the illustrations."

"Printing, paper, illustrations," the bookseller said disenchantedly. "Put them together and what have you got? A book. For a book, I tell you, any book, twenty francs is too much money."

Balzac tried his luck at the bookstalls in the Palais-Royal. The gentry who ran these establishments had no use for La Fontaine at any price.

"Fontaine?" a dealer said. "Look around you, my boy. Most of my customers have never heard of Fontaine. As for twenty francs a volume, I'm not saying they won't pay it, mind you, for a book with the right kind of pictures in it."

The bookseller unlocked a cupboard under his stand and took out a book bound in violet suede, locked with a brass clasp and key.

"For this little item, now, I'm asking fifty francs. And I'll get it."

He opened the book and leafed through it, chuckling. Over his shoulder, Balzac looked at the pictures. The book was a version of the famous work entitled TWO HUNDRED ASPECTS OF THE ART OF LOVE, a well-known piece of pornography.

The bookseller closed the volume and locked it, then put it back into the cupboard. He faced Balzac, still chuckling, and poked a finger into his ribs. "That's the kind of stuff to offer in the Palais-Royal, my friend, if you want to get high prices from the English milords and the high-class whores." He tapped Balzac's Fontaine with a grimy finger. "Your book is all right in its way, but it's got the wrong kind of pictures in it, to please the trade we get here."

He poked Balzac's stomach again, chortled merrily, and turned to wait on a young English dandy, who pointed to a stack of popular novels with his stick.

"Do you have something by Lord R'hoone, m'good man? I do like his books, you know. Never a dull moment in them, what?"

"Lord R'hoone?" the bookseller said. "Certainly, sir. Here is his latest. And best. Three francs and worth twice the price."

"Sold!" the Englishman said. "Do wrap it in a bit of paper, please, like a good fellow. I enjoy reading Lord R'hoone awfully, but he's not quite the sort of author an Oxford man ought to be seen carrying about, what?"

Balzac turned away, La Fontaine under his arm. He passed through the crowd that sauntered in the gardens of the Palais-Royal—fastidious, effeminate young men, dressed in the current Anglophilic fashion, twirling walking sticks elegant as wands, some of them fitted with concealed sword blades—women in tight bodices and flowing skirts, with elaborate hair styles, pointed slippers, mouths of a bright unnatural scarlet.

The scraps of conversation he overheard were inane. Not one of the young men around him was armed with anything but wealth, he thought. They were men whose sole occupation was pleasure, whose only education was in the field of expensive depravity. They knew how to order a suit of clothes or an expensive dinner, how to walk with a cane, how to lose money at the gaming tables, how to sit on a horse without falling off. Perhaps a few of them understood the arts of love. As for the women, most of them were, when you came down to it, whores. Not like the poor creatures who tugged at a man's arm in the dark streets in the Marais, or the painted young country girls to be found in middle-class bordellos, but whores nonetheless, women who sold themselves for a month, six months, a year, a lifetime.

Balzac passed out of the beautiful, formal garden, sickened by the worthless humanity around him, feeling contempt mixed with anger. They were *his* readers, these people, readers of Lord R'hoone. To offer them Fontaine was not only bad business. It was an insult to Fontaine and to French literature.

Meanwhile, there was the problem of what to do with the books that were piled up in Canel's shop. Balzac reduced the price to thirteen francs, which meant a loss on every volume. He sold ten copies. He went down to ten francs. The booksellers refused to order. The idea had been bad from the start; the books were not wanted at any price. Canel had been ahead of his time.

"Get Fontaine to sign them, young fellow, then maybe I'll order a few," a dealer suggested.

"Fontaine has been dead these hundred years," Balzac said angrily.

"I know," said the bookseller. "That adds something to the value of his autograph."

Canel returned from the south of France.

"When you talked about illustrations, Balzac, I tried to warn you," he said patiently. He looked around the shop, which was piled from floor to ceiling with the unwanted volumes. "We'll have to get rid of these," he said. "I need the space for stuff that will sell. I'm in the publishing business, man, not in book collecting."

"Can you find someone to take them off our hands?" asked Balzac.

"Off your hands, Balzac," Canel said firmly. "They are in my shop, but they're your property and your responsibility."

"Can you get rid of them?" Balzac demanded.

Canel shrugged. "Perhaps," he said. "But mind you, the price will be shocking. You may not get much more than what it would cost to cart them away."

"Get what you can," said Balzac desperately.

Canel knew the tricks of the trade. A few days later, a rat-faced individual in a badly fitting coat, came to the shop and inspected the books.

"Give you fifty centimes apiece, and take the lot," he decided.

"Fifty centimes! It's less than the cost of the paper," Balzac objected.

"Take it or leave it," the scavenger said.

Appealingly, Balzac turned to Canel for advice. With what seemed to be genuine regret, the publisher spread his hands in a gesture of helplessness and said, "You won't do better, I'm afraid, Balzac."

"All right," said Balzac. "Take them for fifty centimes."

When the remaining man had gone, Balzac sat down heavily in Canel's second chair, the one reserved for authors. Canel got out the brandy bottle and poured a drink for each of them.

"No hard feelings?" he said. "Remember, I tried to warn you."

Balzac shook his head. "No hard feelings."

He drank his brandy, shook hands with Canel, and went out of the shop into the street. Across from Canel's shop was a place that sold secondhand furniture of the best quality, things that had come from great houses. In the window was an armchair covered with expensive red fabric. Balzac stood on the pavement, looking at the chair. He had been planning to buy it. Though he had never sat down in it, he knew instinctively that it would just suit the curves of his body.

"Ah well, it's not the chair everyone will want," he thought. "Perhaps it will still be for sale when I've recouped my losses."

He turned out of the Place St. André des Arts, going slowly along a busy street, on the way to his rendezvous with Madame de Berny.

Chapter 12

HALF AN HOUR after he left Canel's office, Balzac's depression had worn off. By the time he reached the little restaurant where he sometimes lunched with Madame de Berny, he was in downright good spirits and no one would have suspected that he had just been overtaken by disaster. He turned into the cul-de-sac where the restaurant was located, whistling a popular tune, eager to see his mistress.

The restaurant was not what one expected to find in an alley. It was one of the best restaurants in the world, and one of the most expensive, a place known only to the few. The windows were covered by heavy curtains of handmade lace. There was a room with half a dozen tables and beyond that, behind velvet draperies, several private cubicles.

The patron had known Madame de Berny since the days of the old régime, when his most distinguished client had been Marie Antoinette. He bowed to Balzac and led him to one of the private dining rooms. "Madame is waiting, monsieur," he said, lifting the curtain deferentially.

The little room was furnished with a dining table, a pair of gilded chairs, a miniature sideboard, and a long, low divan covered with wine-colored velvet. There was a small crystal chandelier. By some note of magic in the decor, the room escaped the clandestine odor usual in such places. A thousand adulteries had been achieved on these divans, yet no hint of the sordid or shabby remained in the pleasantly scented air.

Madame de Berny sat on the divan. Balzac kissed her hand, then embraced her.

"I am famished," he said. "I could eat a wolf!"

"I'm sure you could get a wolf here, at a price, if you gave them notice," she said. "But I've ordered volaille de Bresse. Before that, quenelles. To follow, asparagus. For a sweet, the little gateau you always eat too much of."

129

"Good! Good!" he said heartily, rubbing his hands together, then touching the bellpull to summon the waiter.

The meal was served. Balzac speared a quenelle on his fork, tasted it, and sighed like a man who has just been reprieved from the gallows.

"Delicious!" he said. "Exquisite. Who but a Frenchman could make poetry of fish, and fresh water fish at that, I ask you?"

Madame de Berny laughed. She enjoyed seeing Balzac eat, because he took such pleasure in it.

The chicken that came from Bresse was acknowledged to be the best in the world. The meat was white, firm and tender, bathed in a light, aromatic sauce. The asparagus that followed—three spears only—had been blanched with the rich black earth of Berry to a uniform waxy whiteness and it was tender its whole length. The rich little cake, soaked in brandy and honey, was covered with a purée of chestnuts and topped with bland, rich cream.

By the time they had moved to the divan with little cups of strong rich coffee, Balzac had eaten enough food for three men. He undid two buttons of his waistcoat, sipped his coffee, and sighed with contentment.

"Now you must tell me what has happened," Madame de Berny said.

Balzac put his coffee cup on the table.

"The fact is, instead of making a profit, I wind up eight thousand francs in debt," he said.

"It wasn't your fault," she said. "The printer swindled you. You told me that."

"You are right about that," agreed Balzac. "He is a thief, that fellow. A regular bandit! He took advantage of me. And the papermaker! He should be in prison, you know. He is nothing but a highwayman."

Balzac became positively enthusiastic over the causes of the debacle. All of his difficulties, it seemed, rose from the fact that he had been obliged to deal with a pack of thieving incompetents. As he talked, delivering the indictments, his own blunders and extravagances became inconsequential. Everything was to be blamed on someone else, the printer, the binder, the papermaker, the man who had supplied the binding glue, even the drayman who had carted the books from the bindery to Canel's shop.

130

Everyone was at fault except La Fontaine, Balzac himself, and the old craftsman at Alençon who had made the engravings.

"You see, it's no good simply being a publisher," he concluded. "The cream is skimmed by the printer. They are the fellows who make the money, because they get theirs first, do you see? A printer is a regular little king. He stands in front of his presses and not a wheel will he turn until he sees the cash on the barrelhead. I tell you, they are rolling in money, these printers. A publisher is out of luck, when it comes to dealing with them. He takes what's left when the printers and others have had theirs—the crumbs from the table, do you see?"

"But why not become a printer then!" Madame de Berny exclaimed.

"By God! If I knew of a shop!" Balzac said, striking his palm with his fist. Then his face clouded over. "But of course it is out of the question. For one thing, there's the question of money—capital, you understand. A publisher does his business from a hole-in-the-wall. He has a desk, a couple of chairs, an inkpot, a dictionary, a bottle of third-rate brandy with which to befuddle authors. A printer is different. He must have machinery—presses, type, ink. He must hire workmen, skilled people." He shook his head. "No. It is out of the question." He sat staring at his coffee cup, the fiasco of La Fontaine forgotten. "But I could make a go of a printing shop. By everything holy, I'm sure of it. I have a feeling for printing, you see. An instinct for it."

"Surely there must be a printing shop for sale, somewhere in Paris," she said. "After all, people retire, or die."

"But the money?" he said. "And the permits? One doesn't simply buy a printing shop. One must first have a Royal Warrant, permission from the Crown, and that's not something you get from the notary on the corner. Don't forget, I was trained as a lawyer. I understand the regulations that govern such things."

"I am sure the money can be raised," she said. "After all, it will be a sound investment. Even your parents will see that. As for the King's permission, I may be able to help there. Even at this upstart court, there are a few people of importance who have not altogether forgotten me."

"Do you think it could be managed?" he asked.

"Of course it can be managed," said Madame de Berny, in the voice of a woman who was not used to encountering things that

131

could not be managed. "You find the printing shop. Somehow, together, we will find the money."

"I know an excellent compositor," Balzac said thoughtfully. "Barbier, his name is. He's employed as chief typesetter by the thief who printed my Fontaine, and he's unhappy with the job. He's a craftsman, you understand, this Barbier, not a moneybags. He will know what's going on. But the Royal Warrant comes first. Without that, one can hardly examine the premises of a printing house. With it, every door is open."

"Leave that to me," said Madame de Berny confidently.

When Honoré Balzac's application for a license to operate a printing press was presented to the King of France, one of the recommendations attached to it read as follows:

"This young man has been known to me for a long time. The correctness of his convictions and his understanding of literature are, in my opinion, a guarantee that he is fully aware of the responsibilities and obligations that will be imposed upon him in this important profession.

(Signed) Gabriel de Berny
Former Counselor to the Crown

There were a dozen influential men who would have signed such a chit for Madame de Berny, but it appealed to her feeling for the sentimental to have the de Berny name on Balzac's application.

Monsieur de Berny's signature and a word whispered to the proper person at the palace did the trick. A few weeks later, Balzac possessed a piece of parchment that gave him the right to carry on the trade of printing with the permission and blessing of the King of France. In the ordinary course of events, an applicant without special connections might wait a year or two from the date of his application until he was granted his printer's license, if, indeed, he ever received it. France, having passed through a series of bloody revolutions, understood that in dissident hands a printing press was more dangerous than a battery of artillery, and care was taken that the means to print did not fall into the hands of people disloyal to the Crown.

Once in possession of his license, Balzac had no difficulty in finding a print shop for sale. It was the establishment of Laurence Baine, in the rue des Marais Saint-Germain, a dark, romantic alley

132

on the left bank of the Seine. The house was next door to the one in which Racine had died a hundred odd years ago and Balzac took this as a good omen.

He and his newly employed foreman, André Barbier, inspected the premises on a fine spring morning in 1826. Watching Barbier's skilled fingers run through a font of type, Balzac felt a fine flush of excitement. The little shop might be grimy and tucked away in an airless corner of Paris. Most of the type in stock might be old and battered. The big press might groan and creak as if to complain that it had served its time and deserved to be retired. The splintery floor boards might bend under the weight of stored up paper. It didn't matter. This was no dirty middleman's hovel, like that of Canel, with no real excuse for being. This was a printing shop, by God! where real work was done, where a writer's words were turned from manuscript into metal and then into printed pages.

"What do you think, Barbier?" he asked.

Barbier was a Norman, a big man with straight black hair, a lock of which usually fell across his forehead. He was ten years older than Balzac, and had learned his trade in Rouen, under a stern master. As a compositor, he was superb. The type seemed to be transported from box to compositor's stick by magic, so nimble were Barbier's fingers, so expert his eye.

Before answering Balzac's question, he looked around the shop again. Then he shrugged.

"With a little work, the presses will do," he said. "They've seen their best days, mind you, but they'll do. Most of the type is worn out."

He took a letter from a case—an E—and held it between his thumb and forefinger, squinting critically at the printing surface.

"You see, the serifs are nicked off here," He pointed to the hairlines. "And the letter is worn down. All right for smashing out handbills, which is what this dump has been doing, mostly." He tossed the letter back into its box. "No good for books, at least, not for books that would be worth printing."

"We can buy new type," said Balzac.

Barbier grinned sardonically. "If a man had the money, I suppose he could buy the Palais de Louvre. A good font of type doesn't come cheap, you know. That's why our friend here uses this worn out crap."

Balzac took a deep breath. The smell of the shop excited him,

133

the heady mixture of ink and oil and metal and paper that has touched the nerve strings of certain individuals since the day printing was invented.

"I like the place," he said. "There is something about it I like. Does it appeal to you, Barbier?"

Barbier grinned, a healthy, honest grin.

"I am a printer, Monsieur Balzac. This is a print shop," he said. "To me, it is a place to work. But yes, when you put it that way, I kind of like the place at that. It's a friendly old dump." He crossed the room and touched the driving wheel of the number one press, the big one. "I'd like to put this old cow to work, after I've tightened everything up."

"Do you think we can make a go of it here?" Balzac asked.

Barbier shrugged. "Who knows a thing like that?" he said. "But we can print here, and good work. I promise you that."

Balzac was determined to buy the shop. He asked Barbier to estimate the cost of replacements that were absolutely necessary, if they were to be able to turn out first class work. He was convinced that the way to make money was to concentrate on quality printing, and he trusted his own taste and judgement.

When Barbier's figuring was done, Balzac sat down at his desk and totaled up the initial costs of his prospective venture. The shop and equipment would cost thirty thousand francs. Barbier wanted a guarantee of twelve thousand, which was no more than fair, since he was quitting a good job. There would be ten thousand needed for new type and miscellaneous supplies. Barbier would need four or five journeymen printers and two boys—printer's devils. Something must be allowed for their wages and for the boys' keep. Then there would be his own expenses, while he was putting the business on its feet.

He leaned back in his chair, looking at the sheet he had covered with figures. "I'll want at least sixty thousand francs," he told himself.

For a man already in debt to the tune of fifteen thousand francs, whose one venture into business had been a failure, it should have been a staggering sum, indeed, a prohibitive sum. Failure would mean that he would face half a lifetime of debt, if not actually the debtors' prison.

Balzac, however, was not the man to permit failure to enter into his considerations. The debacle with Fontaine was forgotten. He

134

was filled with faith in his own talents and alive with excitement at the prospect of turning the little shop in the rue des Marais Saint-Germain into the greatest printing house in France.

In his mind's eye, he saw the grimy little shop replaced by a towering building with a marble front, housing dozens of bright new presses, sheltering hundreds of contented workmen, the store-rooms piled high with first quality paper, the shipping room floor groaning under the weight of books and pamphlets waiting to be carried away to scores of satisfied customers. He saw a gilded sign on the building: IMPRIMÉRIE BALZAC.

All over Paris, all over France, people would nod knowingly and say, "If you want the best printing in France, you must go to Balzac. Of course his prices are high, but if one wants quality, one must be prepared to pay. For fine work, there is no one else in the field; the fellow has destroyed all competition."

Once Balzac started to dream, he dreamed all the way to the top. He saw himself appointed printer to the King! He opened a branch in Marseilles, another in Lyons, a third in Rouen. His London shop, of course, was small, operated more for prestige than profit, limited to work on the finest, handmade Oriental papers, of a quality beyond the competence of the unimaginative British. America? A possibility. But does anyone read in America? I must ask Barbier to find out. Meanwhile, there is this nonsense to be printed for the King of Prussia.

With prospects such as these, sixty thousand francs seemed a trifling sum, yet there was the awkward problem of getting the money together, before he and Barbier could take possession of the rundown shop in the rue des Marais, from which all this spendor was to rise like a Phoenix. Balzac did not want Madame de Berny to raise the entire sum, though she offered to do so. He was already embarrassed by the fact that she held his promissory notes, and he sensed that it would somehow be inappropriate to permit his mistress to buy him a print shop, no matter how eagerly she wanted to do it.

No, he decided. Madame de Berny could put up a few thousand francs for good luck. Besides, it wouldn't be fair to exclude her. This was like investing in a gold mine and she must have her share of the loot, but the bulk of the working capital ought to come from another source.

He had said nothing to his family about his unfortunate venture

135

into publishing. In the beginning, when his hopes had been high, he had planned to wait until the one volume classics had made him rich, then to present the whole enterprise to his mother as a fait accompli. When the scheme went sour, a natural prudence dissuaded him from mentioning it at Villeparisis. As far as his father and mother knew, he was still making his living by hacking out cheap, pseudonymous romances.

This project, however, was altogether another matter from the fly-by-night affair with Canel. There was property involved. A shop, machinery, type, paper, things one could feel, that would not evaporate the way an idea goes up in smoke. This was the kind of venture that would appeal to his mother, and Balzac knew it. She would see it as something solid, far more substantial, and therefore far more respectable than the scribbling of unsigned books.

He rode to Villeparisis in the stagecoach, taking his Royal Warrant with him, along with a set of work sheets he had drawn up by an accountant, signed and stamped with a seal.

"You see, mother, I'm twenty-seven," he announced self-confidently, showing Anne-Charlotte the papers. "It's time for me to settle down. I want to make money, and I think this is the way to do it."

There was a family council of war. Balzac's mother went over the figures carefully, nodding her head in satisfaction.

"It would seem that what one has here is a sound business, whose owner has let it go off a bit, during the years before he retired," she concluded.

"Precisely, mother," Balzac said. "With a young man in charge and a foreman like Barbier in the shop—there's not a better craftsman in Paris—the shop will be humming in a few weeks time."

"I think you've got a good thing there, boy," Bernard-François said heartily. "Printing. It's a solid trade. No matter what kind of government we have, there will always be things to be printed, you see."

"Be quiet, monsieur," said Balzac's mother.

Bernard-François wagged his head and wandered off to the garden. Balzac's mother pursed her lips, her eyes on the Royal Warrant.

"If you are acting on the advice of your mistress, perhaps for

136

once she has done you a service," she said. "I approve of this, Honoré. After all, as you say, you are twenty-seven. It is time you gave up wasting your energies writing cheap novels and settled down to honest work. And it is time you stopped living in quarters a crossing-sweeper would be ashamed of."

Balzac laughed. The squalidness of his various rooms and flats, from the rue Lesdiguières on, had always been a sore point with his mother, whose sense of caste was offended.

"I agree with you, mother," he said. "The time has come to put all that behind me and get on with the business of making my fortune." He tapped the papers with his finger. "This is my big chance. I can feel it. I know that I will succeed as a master printer, just as sure as my name is Balzac."

His faith in himself was so complete that even his mother was convinced that he had finally seen the light of day. A family syndicate was formed, including a few close friends and relatives. Within three weeks, Anne-Charlotte placed a draft for forty-five thousand francs in a Paris bank at Balzac's disposal. The rest of the capital, she thought, was to come from Balzac's savings. Actually, of course, it came from Madame de Berny.

Chapter 13

Aʙᴏᴠᴇ ᴛʜᴇ sʜᴏᴘ
in the rue des Marais were living quarters that had been occupied
by the former owner, an apartment of three rooms, with an alcove
in the rear intended for a servant. Balzac decided to use this flat
as his residence. For years he had yearned for a place in which
he could entertain Madame de Berny properly. Now at last he
was to have it.

Taking his mother's criticism of his former lodgings as authorization, he decided to spend a portion of the new firm's capital on
furnishings, repairs and decorations. A free lance hack could live
anywhere; a master printer was a business man, a substantial
citizen. He had to live in accordance with his station.

Balzac's first purchase was the red armchair he had seen in the
Place St. André des Arts, across from Canel's publishing house.
By a miracle, it had not been sold, and Balzac took this as an
omen. He was filled with small superstitions.

He ordered the rooms cleared of the odds and ends of furniture
left behind by the former owner, sagging chairs and couches, rickety
tables, a soggy and threadbare rug.

The house had never been a grand one, like some of its neighbors in the district, now fallen into disrepair, but it was a sound
old structure and the rooms above the print shop had a certain
grace. Balzac put thought and care into the furnishing of them.
He also spent a good bit of money out of his working capital.

Instead of having the bedroom walls repapered, he ordered
them hung with blue percale, giving the room an effect of luxury
and intimacy. By this time, he owned a library of several thousand
books, most of them handsomely bound in leather. He had a carpenter build shelves and the books became the chief decoration of
his new study, into which went the red armchair. He combed the
antique shops in the district and picked up a number of good
pieces.

138

The total effect was successful. It was his first real home, and Balzac was delighted with it.

So was Madame de Berny.

She came every day to the rooms above the shop, sometimes only for a few minutes, long enough to make him a cup of tea and listen to his news, sometimes for long, rapturous hours, when they would be alone, secret and secure. She kept oddments of clothing in the place, a peignoir, slippers, a warm robe when the weather turned cold, but she would not stay the night with him. No matter how fervently he pleaded or how late the hour or inclement the weather, she never failed to return to the Hôtel de Berny before dawn.

"What difference will it make?" he would argue. "No one will know."

"I will know," she would answer.

It was an idiosyncrasy, a thing that baffled him. After a time he accepted it and no longer urged her to stay. Not until much later did he understand her purpose, which was to simplify for him the inevitable parting, when the time for it came.

Balzac quickly became at home in the district that centers on the spire of Saint-Germain-des-Prés. The quarter had been favored by the rich of the seventeenth century, who had left their mark on the district in the shape of a number of great houses with arched gateways and paved courts, once the height of style and elegance, now broken up into flats or business premises. The narrow, romantic rue du Bac was nearby and it was only a few steps to the Quai Malaquais and the river bank.

There were dozens of small shops in the area, occupied by curio dealers, antiquarians, rare book merchants and the like, and, as in most sections of old Paris, there were any number of interesting cafés and restaurants, places with history attached to them. It was a district made to order for a man who liked to prowl the streets on foot. Given the time, Balzac would have searched every dark corner, investigated every narrow alley, learned the history of every one of the run down mansions.

Unfortunately, his time was limited.

As soon as Barbier had rounded up a staff and put the presses in working order, Balzac discovered that the life of a managing proprietor did not contain much leisure. Barbier and his crew did the actual typesetting and printing. Balzac did everything else. Except when Madame de Berny came, all of his waking hours were passed in the press room or in the little front office that one entered from the street. He estimated costs, bought paper and ink, read proofs and corrected them, wrote invoices, solicited business, haggled with clients over prices. When the workmen were rushed, he put on a printer's apron and performed the apprentice's task of distributing type to the cases, after a form had been broken up.

Though he hoped eventually to do nothing but fine printing, for the time being he put his ambitions aside and printed whatever came his way—books, brochures, broadsheets, handbills, catalogues, manuals. His clients were a shabby lot. In many cases, their credit was doubtful.

Barbier wrinkled his nose and complained. "All small jobs, boss. And what jobs!"

"It doesn't matter," Balzac told him. "The great thing is to keep those presses busy, no matter what we're printing. Plenty of time later to pick and choose, when we're well established."

"You are the boss," his foreman said cheerfully.

It was true. Though Barbier had been promised a percentage of the profits, and so in effect was a partner, all of the responsibility was Balzac's. Barbier was a technical man. Outside the press room, he knew nothing of business.

For a time, things seemed to be going well. There was plenty of work, of a sort, and the shop was always humming with activity. After a bit, Balzac's lack of business experience began to make itself felt. Getting the work and turning it out was one thing. Collecting the bills was another.

For a ferret-faced old midwife, the Imprimérie Balzac printed five thousand each of two circulars. One advertised a preparation guaranteed to cure barrenness in women. The other sung the virtues of a formula guaranteed to prevent conception.

"Hee, hee, hee!" the old witch giggled gleefully, when she came to the shop to order the circulars. "Both out of the same barrel, see?"

Balzac helped her write the throwaways and laughed at the joke, thinking that anyone gullible enough to pay good money for her worthless brews deserved to be swindled.

Six or eight weeks later, he went 'round to the midwife's lodgings to collect his bill and found that she had disappeared from the district.

"Been gone for a week, and good riddance," a slatternly concierge told him. "Lots of people came to see her, though, when she was here. All women though. You're the first man ever asked for her. What's the matter? You got a girl in trouble? I can tell you the name of a better butcher than that old bitch you been asking for."

In spite of himself, Balzac laughed. He was out the cost of the circulars, but at least there had been a joke in it. Others who took advantage of him offered not even that. The most ironic bit of printing he did was a booklet entitled: THE ART OF PAYING DEBTS AND SATISFYING CREDITORS . . . A MANUAL OF COMMERCIAL LAW FOR THE USE OF BANKRUPTS.

Toward the end of his first year in business, his affairs were in poor estate. His "clients" owed him thousands of francs, and his credit with the paper dealers was over-extended. His workmen demanded their wages in cash. The inkmakers hounded him for their money. Night after night, he sat up until after midnight in his little office, a green eyeshade on his forehead, going over and over the accounts.

In spite of his efforts to conceal it from her, Madame de Berny realized that he was in trouble. She drew the truth from him, or at least a version of the truth, for Balzac stubbornly refused to concede that the greater part of what was owing him would never be paid. He saw himself in a credit squeeze, not as ruinously in debt.

"You see, I can't pay what I owe, until people pay me what they owe me," he explained to his mistress. "It is a kind of circle, with Balzac in the middle."

"It would seem that all you need is the use of a few thousand, until things even out," she said sagely.

"In effect, that is so," he agreed.

To the best of Balzac's knowledge and belief, it was an honest answer. He had never in his life cheated anyone, nor had the idea occurred to him. He was honest by nature, honest as the sky. It was impossible for him to persuade himself that in business, cheating was not the exception, but the rule, positively the order of the day. Among the small tradesmen, promoters, petty entrepreneurs, schemers, and so on, with whom he had been doing business, it was taken for granted that the craftsman who did work on credit was simply asking to be swindled. Experienced printers, dealing with this kind of clientele, asked for their money in advance, as the man who had printed his Fontaine had demanded cash from him.

Balzac's mother would have straightened things out quickly and taught him the facts of business life, but he was afraid to go to his mother. He was dealing with Madame de Berny, who was ingenuous as himself. She provided him with cash to meet his payroll and with enough more to quiet the most impatient of his creditors.

The first crisis was passed.

Balzac began his second year as a printer, determined to depend no longer on odd jobs, circulars, brochures, handbills and so on—but to go after a big contract, where the profit would be worthwhile.

"Something that will keep the presses going for a month or two, six months, perhaps," he told Madame de Berny.

"You might try Badouin," Barbier suggested, when he asked the foreman for advice. "He usually has a big job going. Of course, he'll beat down your price if he can. They all do that. But at least he should be good for the money."

Badouin was a respectable publisher, dressed in a black frock coat, in the buttonhole of which was the scarlet rosette of an officer of the Legion of Honor. He wore a beard with a sharp point, and his moustache ends were waxed. There was a crease in his striped trousers. He was altogether different from the publishers to whom Balzac had sold fiction, during his days as a hack, and so was his office. It was furnished with a good desk and chairs. Underfoot was a fine rich rug, like a cushion to the feet. In a fruitwood case, behind glass doors, were copies of the books he had published. They were not the kind of books that were sold in the booths at the Palais-Royal.

Badouin looked with some approval at the sample sheets Balzac had brought him. They had been designed by Balzac and set by Barbier in a new type face. The spacing was perfect, the impression sharp and clear, the type block grey and pleasing to the eye. Barbier had a sense of elegance rare in even the best printers and it showed in these samples.

142

Balzac saw that the publisher was impressed.

"Frankly, monsieur, my firm is a new one," he said. "But we are prepared to turn out work as fine as any shop in Paris. We have the equipment and the craftsmen for it. My foreman is an artist. All we want is a chance to show what we can do."

"It is a chance you deserve," said Badouin. "I am going to give it to you." From a drawer of his elegant desk, the publisher took a manuscript and a printer's sample sheet. "Here is a sample sheet and estimate from Tablence et Fils," he said. "They've done a lot of printing for me, and they're a good firm, but if you can better their price and give me the same workmanship, this jobs is yours."

"You will have my estimate tomorrow," Balzac promised, trying to conceal his elation. "I think I can show you something that will interest you."

That night he was up until four in the morning, burning the lamp in his little office, figuring and refiguring the costs on Badouin's job. He cast off the copy, counting the number of words in a line, the number of lines to a page, then worked out the cost of composition, first one way, then another. He figured his paper costs and the press time for the edition of five thousand copies that Badouin wanted. By cutting corners here and there, he bettered his competitor's bid by nearly a thousand francs, still leaving a decent profit.

It was his first big job, and when he got the contract, the next day, he was exhilarated.

"The ice is broken," he told Barbier. "If we make good on this one, there will be more work from Badouin, depend upon it. And from others too."

"We will see," commented Barbier.

He was an old hand; his enthusiasms were behind him, except for his enthusiasm for his craft. His passion for printing was the central fact of his life. The journeymen, to whom typesetting was simply a good trade, a way to make a living, like another, joked about Barbier's love for type.

"That one," they said. "He'd rather set type than sleep with a woman. I'll bet he's got a compositor's stick inside his pants instead of a you-know-what."

Nevertheless, they respected Barbier and were even a little afraid of him. When he broke up the Badouin manuscript into

143

takes and doled them out to the compositors, he gave each man a warning.

"Mind you, watch your spacing on this one. No sloppy work. The boss wants a first class job, and he's going to get it, if I have to tan your backsides for you. A lot depends on it."

The men took Barbier's words to heart. When proofs of the first galleys were pulled, the composition was perfect. Reading proof in the front office, Balzac was pleased.

"If this doesn't satisfy Badouin, then tell him to have the book hand-lettered by a bunch of monks," said Barbier, pleased with himself and his men.

"He will be satisfied," Balzac promised confidently.

He was enjoying the sense of well-being that comes to a man when he works hard without worry. The only break in his day was when Madame de Berny paid him a visit. Then he put Badouin's job from his mind, and relaxed for an hour or two in his rooms above the shop. They talked, drank tea, even made love, with the presses rumbling on the ground floor, making the old house tremble slightly.

Balzac loved the sound of the machines, moving rhythmically back and forth, like a great heart beating.

"Someday, presses will be run by power," he said.

"If you say so, Honoré," said Madame de Berny lazily.

She was resting on the bed in his blue room, wearing the filmy peignoir that she kept in Balzac's flat. It was late afternoon and the light that came into the room was poetic, the peculiarly heartbreaking grey light one meets only in Paris, a haunting light that at certain hours bathes the city like perfume. As it fell on Balzac's mistress, it softened her features and the outline of her body, giving her the Grecian stillness of a painting by David. He looked at her, filled with love.

During these months, when he was working hard in the shop and seeing his mistress every day, Balzac was happy in a way that was new to him. He had a sense of purpose, expressed by his work, and a kind of domestic contentment involved with the rooms upstairs that he had furnished himself and grown fond of. All his life he had been driven, by the priests, by his mother, by publishers, by the need for money; for the first time in his life, he experienced

144

contentment that lasted not for an hour or two, but for days and weeks at a time.

When, after three months' work, he called on Badouin, bearing a mint copy of the book, the publisher was delighted.

"You've done a fine job, Balzac," he said. "There's not a printer in Paris who wouldn't be proud to have produced this. When can I have delivery of the full edition?"

Balzac gave him a date.

"Good!" said Badouin. He put the book on his desk and folded his hands. "Now, Balzac, I'm going to make you a business proposition," he said. "As a business man, it may appeal to you. For this job, I owe you twenty-two thousand francs, correct?"

"Twenty-two thousand, five hundred," Balzac answered.

"Twenty-two five," Badouin agreed. "Well then. I can give you the cash, in the customary thirty days. Or I can give you these ninety day notes, which, taken together, come to twenty-eight thousand, as you will see when you examine them."

Balzac looked at the promissory notes Badouin handed to him. They were from provincial booksellers and had passed through a bank in Lyons. Each merchant had guaranteed his note by pledging his stock, which, in both cases, Balzac noted, considerably exceeded the face value of the documents.

"But this is six thousand francs more than you owe me," he said, handing back the notes.

"Exactly," said Badouin with a smile. "I told you my proposition might appeal to your business instincts. You see, this is the situation. I have your cash ready for you, and of course if you want it, it's yours. But I have a chance to buy a book that every publisher in Paris is after, and I can use twenty-two thousand francs right now, as heavy artillery. If you can afford to wait for ninety days, you will get a bonus of six thousand francs and the chances are that with the extra cash, I will be able to outbid everyone else in the city." He paused, tapping the promissory notes with a very clean fingernail. "This new book, the one I'm after," he said confidentially. "It will be an interesting printing proposition, if I get it. I can't see the first printing running much less than ten thousand copies."

Badouin's hook had been baited twice—a bonus of six thousand francs in return for two months' delay in collection, and the promise of an order that would make any printer's mouth water. Balzac sat, thinking for a minute. The notes were as good as gold. He was sure of that. After all, they had passed through a powerful bank. They were backed up by the stock-in-trade of two prominent merchants. He looked across the desk at Badouin. It was impossible to imagine that there could be anything off color in a business arrangement proposed by a man of Badouin's character. One had only to look at his office, at the list of authors he published, at the red rosette in his buttonhole. Badouin was solid as the Bank of France.

"Of course, monsieur, I will be happy to take the notes," he said.

"Good!" said Badouin. "I don't like giving money away, ordinarily, but this will work out to our mutual benefit."

Balzac went back to the rue des Marais, impressed with his own perception of affairs. He was getting on, no doubt about it.

"Badouin is more than satisfied," he told Barbier, rubbing his hands together. "There is another big job in the offing. I won't be surprised if we get all of his business, in the long run."

The long-legged foreman leaned against a press. There was a smear of ink on the tip of his nose that gave his saturnine features a rather comic look.

"See here, boss, I like you," he said. "You're a good chap. Take a piece of advice from an old hand. In this business, never count on a job until it's been printed, bound, delivered and paid for. That way, you see, you won't be disappointed."

"But Badouin as good as said that the next job is ours," said Balzac. "And Badouin is no Canel, old boy. In publishing, he's one of the biggest men in Paris."

"The bigger a publisher is, the louder the splash he makes going into the Seine," said Barbier cynically. "Mind you, I'm not saying we won't get the job. I hope we do. All I'm telling you is, don't reserve the presses for it, if something else comes along in the meantime."

"Ah, Barbier, you look on the dark side of things," said Balzac, laughing and clapping his foreman on the shoulder.

"That's because I was born on the dark side of things," said Barbier, softening his bitterness with a grin. He glanced at the big clock on the wall. "Time to eat," he said. "I'm going to the corner for a plate of choucroute." He hesitated, then said, "It's not much

146

of a place, but it's clean and the cabbage is good. I don't suppose you'd want to join me?"

Balzac usually had lunch in his rooms, but Barbier's invitation appealed to him.

"You're wrong," he said, an arm around the foreman's shoulder. "I'd like it very much."

The place on the corner was dark and the ceiling was low, but as Barbier had promised, it was clean and the smell that filled it was magnificent. A waitress brought them steaming plates of sauerkraut and sausage and a basket of tough black bread. The food was delicious.

"Tell me, boss," said Barbier, speaking with his mouth full of sauerkraut. "Do you really expect to make money in the printing business?"

"Why not?" said Balzac. "Others have done it."

Barbier shook his head. "Not printers." He stabbed the air with his fork. "You know who makes the real money? Papermakers. Type-founders. Ink mixers. They're the ones who take the cream. The poor bastard of a printer takes what's left."

Balzac laughed.

"You think it's funny?" Barbier said. "Wait 'til you've been in the trade for twenty years, the way I have. Then you won't think it's so funny, I promise you that."

"I wasn't laughing at you, Barbier," said Balzac. "When I took my flyer in the publishing business, everyone told me that the printers took the cream. Or was it the gravy? I was just wondering who it is who skims the cream from the share of the papermakers and the type-founders and the ink mixers."

Barbier shrugged and said, "Who knows? The King, maybe."

"If you had said the author, I would have thrown this choucroute in your eye," said Balzac, laughing.

"Authors get fame," said Barbier. "What do they want with money?"

They finished their sauerkraut and drank a cup of bitter coffee. Barbier insisted on paying the bill.

"Save your money, boss," he said. "You'll need it. You've got wages to pay, and the papermaker. . . ."

"And the type-founder and the ink mixer and the tax collector," Balzac said.

They came out of the café together, laughing, arms around each other's shoulders.

A month passed, six weeks. Balzac did a few small jobs and kept his presses busy. In a slack period, he even printed a book of his own, the only one to be issued by the Imprimérie Balzac. It was a thin volume called A LITTLE DICTIONARY OF THE STREET SIGNS OF PARIS, by An Habitué of the Sidewalks.

When two months had gone by without word from Badouin, Balzac put on his black coat and his best cravat and went to call on the publisher. Badouin received him courteously, but not with enthusiasm. He regretted that the big book was not yet under contract. No. He was sorry. At the moment, he had nothing ready for the press. There was a little slump in the book trade. Nothing serious, mind you. A seasonal matter. Nevertheless, he would find that most publishers were pulling in their horns just a bit. Monsieur Balzac was fortunate to be a printer. There was a trade where business was always good. If one didn't print books, he turned out pamphlets, if not pamphlets, then handbills. At any rate, there was always something to be printed, whereas in publishing a man was ground between two millstones: the unreliability of authors and the fickleness of the public taste.

"Writers are a perverse lot, you know," he said. "They get onto a good thing, something the public will buy by the bale. Then, just when interest is at its height, they turn their backs on it. They are bored, they say. They want to do something new. They are in a rut. They must change. And the new thing, unfortunately, is almost always something one cannot sell or even give away.

"As for the reading public! My dear Balzac, until you have published twenty books, you have no conception of what savage treason lurks in their breasts and bosoms. They will take up a writer, idolize him, lionize him, write him letters, send him gifts of money, devour his books as if they were sweetmeats. One cannot print copies fast enough to keep up with the demand. It would seem that no one in France reads any other writer.

"Then one day, without warning, the literary weather changes. One issues the man's latest romance—neither better nor worse than his last, or his first—and the public turns up its collective nose. The books languish in the stalls. They gather dust. The pages curl. The paper yellows in the sun. The booksellers weep and

148

tear their hair and want to return the books for credit. The author sulks, then rages, and sometimes challenges one to a duel. He takes to drink, or takes a new mistress, or casts himself into the Seine, carefully selecting a point where he is certain to be fished out by a conveniently present barge captain."

Badouin fingered the red rosette in his lapel. "I tell you, my good young friend, stick to the honest trade of printing. Publishing is not a profession any longer. It is a curse, a malady, an affliction, a disease, and one that is always fatal."

He stood up, shook hands briskly, and promised Balzac he would not be forgotten when the next job of printing came along.

Balzac went back to his shop. He was disappointed, but not worried. His reserves of cash were very low. When he had paid his workmen on the first of the month, the till would be nearly empty. But there were twenty-eight thousand francs coming due in less than thirty days, when the notes he held reached maturity. That would more than tide him over a slack period, while he waited for Badouin's job to come through, or found another just as good.

Three days before the notes were due, Balzac took them to his bank and asked that they be put through for collection. The bank manager was happy to oblige. A man with nearly thirty thousand francs to his credit was entitled to a little deference in an establishment where money was the normal commodity.

A week later, the same manager summoned Balzac to his office. This time he was not smiling. Balzac's notes were on his desk.

"Monsieur Balzac," he said gravely. "I regret to tell you that this paper appears to be worthless."

"Worthless?" cried Balzac. "Surely you're wrong! How can these notes be worthless? They are signed, sealed, and guaranteed by the maker's stock-in-trade. How can they be repudiated?"

"Last week, both booksellers entered petitions in bankruptcy," the manager said grimly.

"Both of them?" said Balzac. "It's incredible. I don't believe it!"

"I admit that it's unusual," the manager said. "But I'm afraid it's true. Here are the reports from our branch in Lyons."

"But the stock?" said Balzac helplessly. "Surely I have rights in that. I took these notes in good faith, in lieu of cash."

The banker smiled knowingly. "And no doubt the face value

149

of the notes was for somewhat more than the sum you had coming to you?"

"That's true," Balzac admitted. "But what has that got to do with it?"

The bank manager spread his hands. "Nothing," he said. "It's a normal business procedure, a normal risk one takes, in the expectation of making a profit. In the book business, however, it is not always an intelligent, or, shall we say, a recommended risk. You have been unfortunate. As to the stock, of course you have the right to claim your share, along with the other creditors. Speaking from experience, however, I think I should warn you to expect nothing. The stock of a bankrupt bookseller usually doesn't amount to much. Books don't keep, you see, except in the physical sense. Now if it was hardware, or lumber, or even flour or sugar, something tangible, you see, you might get fifty centimes in the franc. You might even get the full amount, in the end. But books? Books, you see, are another matter."

Going out of the bank, Balzac shook his head. Books, it seemed, were always "another matter"—whether one wrote them, printed them, published them or sold them.

Though he knew it would do no good, he went to call on Badouin. The publisher was full of apologies.

"I assure you, Balzac, when I offered you those notes, I thought I was doing you a good turn. If I had the cash on hand, I would make good your loss, or part of it, at least. Unfortunately. . . ."

He left the sentence unfinished, conveying his meaning with a shrug and a helpless spreading of the hands.

"Unfortunately, at the moment, your cash is tied up elsewhere," said Balzac curtly. "I understand, monsieur. I have been a publisher myself in a small way."

There is no point in wasting my energy being angry with Badouin, he told himself, keeping his temper under control, going out of Badouin's office. The bank manager had assured him that Badouin had done nothing illegal. At the time the notes were given in payment, they were good paper, worth face value. That both makers had chosen to go bankrupt at the same time was coincidence, nothing more, an unfortunate accident.

Chapter 14

IT WAS AN ACCI-
dent that placed Balzac himself very close to bankruptcy. The terms
of the notes permitted him to wait until the booksellers' estates were
liquidated, at which time his notes would be redeemed at so many
centimes in the franc. Or, if he wished, he had the right to take
over the stock of the defaulting merchants.

He could not afford to wait, which was the more sensible procedure, so he hired a bailiff and ordered the man to impound the
stock and see that it was brought to Paris, hoping to realize some
immediate cash by offering the books at bargain rates. Until a
few weeks earlier, both shops had been going concerns. The stock
must be worth something, he reasoned.

The final act of the tragicomedy occurred when the books arrived at Balzac's shop in the rue des Marais. Balzac stood by
while the workmen pried the covers from the crates.

"I hope there are plenty of good standard sets," he said to
Barbier, who stood beside him. "And dictionaries. They always
find a market, if the price is right."

Barbier nodded absently.

When the first half dozen crates had been opened, he and Balzac knelt on the floor and began to go through the books. There
were no sets of standard authors, no dictionaries, no prayer books,
no confirmation Bibles, no cook books, no guides—none of the
staples one should have found in the stock of a decent provincial
bookseller. There were several thousand copies of ten year old
novels, books that had once been good sellers but were now a drug
on the market. There were even a few dusty copies of books by
Lord R'hoone and Saint Aubin.

Balzac and his foreman stood up.

"One thing," Barbier said. "At least we know why they went
bankrupt."

Balzac nodded, staring at the towers of worthless books being

151

erected by his workmen. He had been swindled. He understood that. Obviously, both booksellers had secretly sold off the cream of their stock before they filed their petitions, and this, of course, was illegal.

"You could bring a criminal charge and put both of the bastards in jail," said Barbier. "It's what I'd do myself."

"What would be the point?" Balzac asked. "My money's gone, in any case. I'm not interested in revenge, especially against a couple of people I've never set eyes on in my life."

The worthless novels were put back in their boxes and sold as second hand paper. Balzac put on his black coat and went into the streets again, trying to drum up trade. There was not much work to be had. For days at a time, his presses were idle and his journeymen lounged about the shop, drank wine, played dominoes.

Regretfully, after a few weeks, Balzac told Barbier to lay off half the staff.

"Tell them I'll take them back as soon as things pick up," he said. "Right now, the fact is, I simply can't pay their wages."

A few weeks later, the rest of the men were let go. The entire staff of the Imprimérie Balzac now consisted of Balzac himself, a printer's devil, aged eleven, and Barbier, whose wages had been paid in advance.

The bad news traveled with proverbial speed. As the discharged printers sought work elsewhere, or passed their days in the various cafés favored by the printing fraternity, word rapidly got around that the Balzac firm was in trouble. Prospective clients refused to see Balzac when he called to solicit business. The firms that supplied his paper demanded cash and declined to accept his promissory notes, even when these were secured by the pledge of his presses and equipment. Some of his suppliers demanded immediate settlement of their accounts. When their demands were not met, they began to hound Balzac, besieging the little glass-partitioned office in the front of the shop, clamoring for their money.

In desperation, Balzac took to getting up before dawn, brewing himself a pot of coffee, then going out of the shop at daybreak, wandering about the city, avoiding his creditors. He realized that he could not go on this way for very long, and as he walked through strange parts of Paris, he cudgeled his brain in search of an answer.

152

The prospect of appealing to his family depressed him. He could imagine his mother's contempt. He did not have the heart to reveal the truth to Madame de Berny. He was determined to get out of his difficulties by means of his own initiative. He went on, fighting for a few small jobs that he and Barbier turned out together. He set type, turned the presses, melted metal, collated, tied up bundles, even trundled the handcart over the cobblestones himself, one day when the apprentice boy was ill.

It was no use.

By the end of September, 1827, a little less than eighteen months after he had received his Royal Warrant, he had reached the end of his rope. There was not a sou in the till. Even the boy had to be discharged. Barbier, whose guarantee had run out, was obliged to take day's work as a journeyman, in order to feed himself without dipping into his savings.

More than once, during the closing weeks of summer, Barbier would stop by the rue des Marais in the evening, carrying an oil-cloth bag that contained a loaf of black bread, some dried herring or a length of sausage, a bottle of cheap red wine.

"Eh bien, boss!" he would say, taking a swig from the bottle and passing it to Balzac. "Don't give up yet, eh? Something will turn up, don't worry."

Balzac would take a drink of the tart, metallic tasting wine and look back into the dark, silent press room.

"Something is certain to turn up, even if it's only the sheriff, come to take the presses out of their beds," he said.

"Over my dead body," said Barbier. "I leveled up those bastards myself. Nobody touches them but me."

One evening when Barbier came to the rue des Marais, he had something on his mind. While he and Balzac were eating, he seemed to be turning it over. Finally, he said, "You know, boss, the last few days I've been working for Gaston Laurent?"

Balzac nodded. Laurent was proprietor of a fairly successful type foundry.

"Well, Laurent has just acquired the rights to a new process that was invented by a bloke named Déréchail. Pierre Déréchail, his name is. An engraver by trade, and a good one, I'll bet my arse. You know what a pain in the backside stereotyping is, the way we do it?"

Balzac nodded. Stereotyping was the process by means of which

153

type or engravings were copied in metal, from which printing could be done.

"Well, Déréchail has a system that makes it simple. No casting. No need to reverse. Fonterrotype, he calls it. I tell you, boss, it's going to revolutionize printing, this thing."

A new idea always made Balzac brighten up.

"You say Laurent has the rights?" he asked.

Barbier nodded, his mouth full of fish.

"Is he trying to put the system on the market?"

"He'd like to," Barbier said, wiping his mouth on the sleeve of his printer's black smock. "The thing is, you see, he's got his own business to worry about. It would be a lot of work, selling the thing. And then there's the matter of money. Laurent is doing all right, but I don't suppose he feels like risking it all. I tell you though, there's a fortune in this thing of Déréchail's, if it's handled right. I'm a mechanic, mind you, not a business man. I don't know anything about financing, but I know when a thing is good in the shop, and this is good." He rattled the bit of newspaper that held the food. "You're not eating anything. Have a piece of fish."

Balzac munched on a piece of herring and chewed on a heel of black bread. After Barbier had gone, he sat in the swivel chair in his front office, not bothering to light the lamp when darkness fell. His business was in bad shape, but he didn't feel that he had failed as a printer. He had failed as an entrepreneur, a business man, and he promised himself that he had learned his lesson. It will be a long, long time, he thought, before I take another promissory note instead of the cash that's coming to me. I've had my business baptism, and it will be a smarter man than Badouin who swindles me the next time.

If he could only get another stake, he knew in his heart that he could build up his printing business. This thing Laurent had his hands on sounded good. If he could raise a little money on his presses and type, perhaps he and Laurent could get together. Barbier had some money put by. Maybe he would come in. After all, it won't be long now before everyone in France can read and write. The printing business is bound to get bigger and bigger. That is only common sense.

The next day, after a brief talk with Barbier, he went to see Laurent at his shop in the rue Garoncière. Laurent was a small man with an overbearing manner. Balzac didn't care for him, but after all, this was a matter of business, and Laurent owned the rights to the new process.

Balzac managed to borrow a few thousand francs, with his presses as security. Madame de Berny advanced him another ten thousand. Barbier took five thousand from his savings. A few days later, a new company was formed, with Laurent as general manager, Barbier as technical director, Balzac in charge of sales, publicity and general exploitation.

Embarked on a new project, Balzac's spirits soared. He leaped into the business with enthusiasm, supervising the preparation of a magnificent album of type faces, ornaments, rules and stock engravings that the newly reorganized foundry was to offer its clients, together with an illustrated prospectus of the Déréchail process, soon to be put on the market.

He passed his mornings calling on printers, drumming up trade for the foundry, his afternoons in the office, writing letters, conferring with Laurent, learning the details of stereotyping.

During the first few weeks, the new firm had no difficulty getting credit. Stocks of type metal, wood for forms, paper for the sample books, all were received at the foundry, as well as two new casting machines and a proof press of the latest model. Balzac signed notes for these consignments and Barbier supervised the installation of the new equipment.

Balzac quickly realized that Barbier was the key man in the venture. When he called on printers to sell them type, he found that Barbier's name had an almost magical effect. Every master printer in Paris knew and respected the big Norman as one of the most accomplished mechanics in the trade.

Ironically, Laurent also realized Barbier's importance, and resented it. From the first there was bad blood between the junior partner and the managing director. More and more often, when he returned to the foundry at noontime, after a morning of canvassing printers, Balzac would find the two of them at each other's throats.

The first row had started over the installation of the proof press. While Barbier was sinking the metal bed into the floor beams, Laurent stood over him, keeping up a running fire of commentary, advice and criticism. Finally, when Barbier bruised his thumb with a hammer, Laurent made the mistake of laughing. Barbier stepped out of the press pit.

"Look here, my friend," he said, in a voice that was dangerously level, his r's rolling a little. "Get back to the front office and keep your arse out of the press room."

Trembling with rage, Laurent drew himself up like a peacock.

"I am the managing director," he insisted. "I have the right to be where I please and to supervise all operations."

"Go and do your managing directing from behind a desk," Barbier said contemptuously. "I am putting in this press and I don't want to be interfered with."

"Barbier, you forget yourself!"

"Get out!" Barbier had shouted, striking the floor at Laurent's feet with a heavy hammer, making the little man jump with fear. "Go on, get out, you little bastard, before I brain you with this hammer."

Laurent retreated to the front office, smouldering with rage and fear. Barbier had meant nothing. It was only his way. But the little man was outraged. His dignity had been injured.

"Barbier is impossible," he complained, when Balzac returned to the shop. "He is only a mechanic, a crude fellow, but he seems to think that the fact that he has invested five thousand francs makes him king of the press room."

"Barbier's all right," Balzac said, putting his sample case on the desk. "Once you learn how to handle him, he's one of the best fellows in the world."

"You defend him?" Laurent cried. "I tell you he threatened me with a hammer, drove me out of the press room. Me! The managing director."

Balzac sat down, laughing. "I remember once, when he was my foreman in the rue des Marais, he was moving a form and I was in the way, rubber-necking, I suppose. 'Come on, junior, haul your arse, if you don't want to lose a piece of it!' Barbier yelled at me. I remember going back to my front office and sulking for the rest of the day. My arse wasn't hurt, but my dignity was, or maybe my sense of self importance."

Laurent was not amused. A pompous little man and a snob, he was blind to all of Barbier's virtues and alive to every one of his faults. Although he was a member of the firm, not an employee, Barbier, by preference continued to wear his black smock, the

156

badge of the hired workman. For Laurent, this alone was enough to place Barbier in a lower class.

"It was a mistake to make Barbier a partner," he said to Balzac. "You and I are really the principals, after all. We are educated men, men of affairs. Barbier is really only an employee by nature. That smock! My God. Has it ever been washed?"

"It is bad luck to wash a printer's smock," Balzac said. "Barbier washes himself on occasion, and that's enough for me. Look here, my friend," he said to Laurent quite seriously. "What you think of Barbier personally is one thing. It's your own affair. I'm not suggesting that you take him home to dinner or offer him one of your daughters in marriage, though you might do worse. The fact is, in this business of ours, believe me, we need him."

"Nonsense!" objected Laurent. "My dear Balzac, you exaggerate the importance of this fellow Barbier. He is a printer, nothing more. Better than some, inferior to others, a printer in a black smock, with ink on his nose and in his fingernails."

At this point, there was a sound at the office door leading into the press room. Balzac and Laurent turned. Barbier stood in the doorway, his hands on his hips.

"Yes, monsieur, you are quite right about Barbier," he said. "Ink on his nose. Ink on his fingers. Ink on the tip of his pecker that gets there when he takes a pee. I am a printer, for the love of Christ! A printer without ink on his hands is like a tart without paint on her face. It means he's out of business at the moment." He held out his hands, palms down, looked at them, then turned them over slowly. "For the sake of the three of us, who've got our money in this joint, the inkier these babies get the better."

He turned without waiting for comment and went back to the press room. A moment later they heard the sound of his hammer, as he went back to his work again, finishing the job of setting the press.

"You see what an impudent pig he is," said Laurent. "I did not exaggerate his insolence. He is insufferable. His conduct is insupportable."

"He is Barbier," said Balzac with a shrug, remembering the meals of bread and sausage he had shared with Barbier. "His conduct? Well, it's a mixture. One third Norman peasant. One third printer. One third Barbier, who is unique. Get used to it, my friend, I urge you. We need him in the shop. With him, we may

157

make a fortune. Without him? Well, I'll tell you. Without Barbier we are just a couple of ambitious fellows with intelligence and clean hands, no different from a thousand others in Paris."

During the hours he was in the shop, Balzac did what he could to keep the peace, but most of the day he was not in the shop but on the street. Things grew worse. Laurent became obsessed with the idea that Barbier was systematically trying to terrorize him. Barbier became convinced that Laurent was an incompetent leech who fattened on the labor of others.

"I work my guts out here in the shop," he shrieked at the little manager. "Balzac wears out his shoe leather walking all over Paris trying to drum up trade. And what do you do, you little toad? You sit there on your little chair that turns like a lady's piano stool and you manage things. What in hell do you manage then? Not me, I'm sure. Not Balzac, I can tell you that. For all the good you're doing here you might as well be in the whore house. Or have you ever been in one?"

"Pig! Animal! Sow!" Laurent would mutter, swinging himself in his swivel chair.

In his anger and prejudice against the little man, Barbier was being unfair, as Balzac tried to point out.

"At this stage of the game there's nothing much for him to do," he explained to Barbier. "Right now, you and I are doing all the work, it's true. But later on, when we begin to fill orders and ship them, Laurent will have plenty of work, I promise you that."

"You know me, boss," Barbier said sheepishly. "I don't mean anything, but I always fight with those fellows. I'm just a rebel in my heart, I guess, the way my old father was."

Barbier's father had been a rebel and lost his head for his ideas. Only when he was half drunk did Barbier talk about it, and then his conversation was apt to take a politically dangerous turn. Balzac, though he was monarchist to the core, a king's man, nevertheless understood the centuries of injustice and oppression that were at the roots of Barbier's bitter class feeling. The truth of the matter was that both he and Barbier were out of step with the times. Balzac was infatuated with the glories of the old régime. Barbier was the Frenchman of the future, whose ideas would find voice half a century later, on the barricades of the Commune. The man of the present was Laurent, the self-respecting bourgeois, who looked with fear and suspicion alike on the working man and the aristocrat. Paradoxically, as often happens, the extremes got on with each other better than they did with the center.

"I agree with you," Balzac told Barbier. "He's a miserable little creature. But we're in business with him, you big cow. Let's try to get along with him until we get things started. Then maybe we can buy him out, you and I."

"I'll try, boss," Barbier promised. "Let him stick to his office and out of my press room and maybe things will work out."

Barbier kept his promise. He tried. For a week, Laurent had no complaint against him.

"I think it's going to be all right," Balzac told Madame de Berny. "As long as they keep away from each other, we will have peace."

"Your man Laurent sounds abominable," said Madame de Berny. "Must he stay on?"

"He must," said Balzac grimly. "He holds the right to Déréchail's process. Perhaps he stole it from Déréchail, as Barbier insists. The fact remains, it's his, and without it we are simply another type foundry. Believe me, my darling, I know. I am in printing shops every day. We need the Déréchail process, which means we need Laurent, for better or worse. And we need Barbier. Ah, how we need Barbier!"

"Why is Barbier so important?" she asked.

"The working printers trust his judgment," he explained. "They don't know me, and they think Laurent is a pompous ass, but Barbier they trust."

Chapter 15

FOR SEVERAL
weeks, Balzac kept the peace, or at least preserved an armed
truce. Barbier sulked and cursed Laurent, but he kept to the press
room, out of sight. Laurent was peevish and jealous of his status
as managing director, but he confined himself to the front office.

Things seemed to be going well, until, one afternoon, Balzac
returned to the shop to find Laurent absent from his chair in the
office. He made his way through the passage that led to the press
room. There was Laurent, wearing an eyeshade and black cham-
bray sleeve guards, directing a group of printers who were getting
a job on the press. Balzac guessed the truth before he spoke.

"Where is Barbier?" he demanded. "What are you doing back
here? Why aren't you out front, where you belong?"

"I belong back here just as much as I belong out front," Laurent
said smugly. "As for Barbier, he is gone, thank God."

"Gone?" said Balzac. "What do you mean? Has he gone to the
café? Is he on a bender?"

Sometimes, Balzac knew, Barbier succumbed to bouts of com-
pulsive drinking, passing three or four days in combat with the
Calvados of his native province.

"He is gone for good," said Laurent, wiping his hands on a rag,
then stripping off the sleeve guards and folding them carefully,
with irritating precision. "He is no longer either a member of the
firm or an employee. I have bought him out."

"You've bought him out!" Balzac cried. "You have no right.
The agreement was signed by the three of us, with twelve years
to run."

"There is nothing in the agreement that prevents one partner
from buying out another," said Laurent. "Read it, my friend. Have
your lawyer read it, as I have done."

"I am a lawyer myself," Balzac said impatiently. "I don't question your legal right. What I question is your good sense. And
your good faith."

160

He turned and strode out of the shop. In the street, he hesitated for a moment, then plunged into a wet, stinking alley, heading for the nearest cheap café. As he expected, he found Barbier sitting at a lop-sided table, his long legs stretched out in front of him, a bottle of applejack at his elbow. The bottle was half empty and Barbier was quite drunk. Balzac pulled up a chair and sat down.

"Barbier, can't you say hello?" he said. "Can't you offer me a drink?"

Without answering, Barbier lifted the heavy bottle and put it in front of Balzac, bringing it down with a thump that made the table move. Balzac called for a glass and poured himself a measure of Calvados. He disliked the powerful, fiery drink, but he didn't want to offend Barbier by ordering the dry white wine he would have preferred.

"Barbier, what happened?" he said.

"Didn't Laurent tell you?" Barbier said, waving a drunken hand. "He bought me out. I'm through."

"But why?" Balzac demanded. "What happened?"

Barbier poured a glass of Calvados with infuriating deliberateness. He drank, throwing his head back so that his neck seemed to snap. With maddening slowness, he refilled his glass, using the careful movements of an apothecary. When the glass was full he smiled at it, pleased with his own skill.

"You want to know what happened?" he said. "I'll tell you what happened." He trailed a finger through a puddle of wet on the table. "You know Méras? Little Méras? Little fellow with one leg? Compositor? Good one? Grandfather?"

"I know him," Balzac said.

"Laurent fired him," Barbier said moodily. Then he snapped his fingers. "Fired him just like that. But before he fired him, you know what he did? He kicked him, that's what he did. Kicked him right in the arse and knocked him into the press pit. Little fellow. Old fellow. Fellow with only one leg, understan'? Lost the other leg in Russia, he did. Froze off in the snow, you see. And Laurent kicked him right in the tail, little fellow like that." Barbier drank slowly, then filled his glass again. Balzac marveled at his capacity. "I am a printer. A workman," he said. "I don't want to be partners with a man like Laurent." He shook his head, then ran a hand across his forehead, as if he were baffled. "I helped old Méras out of the pit, see? Then I stood there, looking at

161

Laurent. I was going to go for him, but something held me back. I couldn't move. I felt something on the back of my neck. Right here, see?"

He bent his head and touched the nape of his neck.

"You know what it was?" he asked. "It was the knife. The Old Lady. The guillotine. I could feel it plain as that." He touched his neck again. "If I'd put a hand on Laurent, I'd have killed him, just as sure as I'm sitting here. And then they'd have taken my head off, just the way they did my daddy's. So I didn't move. I just stood there. Then I said finally, 'Laurent, you are a pig. You are the backside of a pig.' And then he offered to buy me out, free and clear, cash on the line. Anything to be rid of me, see? I tell you, I didn't give him a chance to change his mind."

Barbier dug into his shirt and took out a packet of banknotes, flinging them into the puddle on the table.

"There you are. My investment," he said. "Glad to have it back again." He raised his head, looking Balzac in the eye. "You'll never get yours back, boss. I can promise you that."

"I'm afraid you're right," said Balzac grimly.

"Let me tell you something, boss," said Barbier. "You're a good fellow. Too good. You'll never make out in business. You think you just had bad luck, when you were in with Canel, when Badouin took you over? That was ordinary luck. You just don't have the right kind of heart for business. Go back to writing books, boss. Leave business to people like Badouin and Laurent and the other pigs."

As soon as the news of Barbier's departure circulated through the printing trade, Balzac found that his orders fell away to a trickle, then stopped altogether. Cancellations began to come in for orders already booked.

"You are the salesman," Laurent complained. "It's up to you to make them understand that Barbier's going makes no difference."

"That would be a lot simpler, if I believed it myself," Balzac said coldly.

He detested Laurent, and only the fact that he was so heavily involved persuaded him to make the effort he did. There was, of course, no question of Laurent's buying him out. Five thousand francs was one thing. Fifty thousand was another.

162

Wearily, Balzac went from one printing house to another, meeting rebuffs. His heart was no longer in the work. He began to give up, after making a call or two in the morning. He would sit in a café, or, if the day was fine, go to the Luxembourg and feed the birds, killing time until noon, when he would return to the shop.

Soon the fiasco that had been enacted in the rue des Marais was repeated in the rue Garoncière. One by one, the journeymen were laid off, then the stereotypers. The casting pots were cold. The presses were still. A smell of death pervaded the shop, the aroma of defeat that Balzac recognized, having encountered it before.

Both partners realized that there was no point in going on.

"We must try to sell out," Laurent said. "With luck, we may get back something of what we put in."

Balzac agreed. This time, he realized, there could be no question of concealing the debacle from his family. The blow was fatal, as far as his business career was concerned. Whatever role the future offered him, it would not be that of entrepreneur. As a business man, he was finished.

With his pride in his pocket, he made the journey to Villeparisis. He talked with his mother first, in private. She surprised him by accepting the disaster with an almost icy calm. Her concern was for the family name.

"The name Balzac must not appear in the bankruptcy lists," she said flatly. "Whatever it costs, that must be prevented."

Balzac marveled at his mother. Had she been a man, he realized, she would have made a brilliant career in business or law or politics. When she approached a business problem, her thinking was unencumbered by sentiment or personal considerations. She went straight to the point.

Her object here was to save her son from the humiliation of declaring himself a bankrupt.

"There is your father to be considered," she said. "His heart is weak. The shock might kill him. There is your brother, who still has his career to make. There is your sister and her husband. It is a family matter."

She questioned him closely about his affairs, making notes, writing with a fresh quill in a sharp, precise hand. Balzac felt like a schoolboy, called to account for his misdeeds.

When she had gone over the facts, she called a family confer-

163

ence. Fortunately, Bernard-François was off on one of his mysterious expeditions to the country. Neither his age nor the condition of his heart had been permitted to interfere with his pursuit of a pretty farm girl.

Feeling the need of an impartial arbiter, Balzac's mother had called on one of her cousins, a certain Monsieur Sédillot, a notary and business man of about her own age. Sédillot was a well-groomed and dispassionate man, who approached Balzac's problems with clinical precision. At the family conference, he sat at the head of the table. Balzac's mother sat at the foot. Balzac was on his mother's left, next to his brother Henri, whom he scarcely knew. Across the table sat Laure and Eugène de Surville.

Sédillot conducted the family conference as if he were presiding at a business meeting in Paris. He outlined Balzac's predicament, then began a detailed analysis of his indebtedness, speaking in a dry, astringent voice that seemed used to the sound of figures. He was a man thoroughly at home in the world of assets, liabilities, credits, debits, interest rates and loan terms.

Listening, Balzac squirmed in his chair and turned red. He thought that he had always been scrupulous in his business affairs. He always gave promissory notes for whatever he borrowed, and put copies of them into a brassbound writing paper box that he had brought to Villeparisis and turned over to his mother, along with copies of the balance sheets of the foundry and his printing plant in the rue des Marais. He had been scrupulous in his mind; he was honest as rain. But it had never occurred to him to add up what he had borrowed—from Madame de Berny, from his mother, from banks, from family friends, like Dr. Nacquart, or what he owed to various papermakers, type founders and so on.

Asked to make a rough guess of what he owed, Balzac would have put it in the neighborhood of sixty thousand francs. He could not believe that he heard properly when Sédillot announced a grand total, on the debit side, of more than two hundred thousand.

"But it can't be that much!" Balzac cried. "Surely you've made a mistake."

Sédillot shook his head and leafed through the papers.

"I'm afraid not," he said easily. "I've been over the figures carefully, several times. Of course there may be additional liabilities that don't show here."

Balzac was stunned. His brother Henri, foppishly dressed in a lemon colored coat and a white silk stock, nudged him and said in a stage whisper, "You must have been living high in Paris, to go through that much, old boy, even though your coat doesn't fit. Would you like the name of my tailor, old chap? A man who goes bankrupt for two hundred thou' at least ought to look the part."

"Silence, Henri!" Anne-Charlotte said. "For a young man who has yet to earn a sou, you talk far too much."

Henri blushed and apologized. He was the favorite, but he was under her thumb, dependent on her for pocket money.

"Bankruptcy is not a subject that lends itself to joking," Anne-Charlotte went on. "Besides, your brother is not yet a bankrupt, and we are here to prevent him from becoming one. Not for his sake, mind you, but for the good of the family name." She turned to Sédillot and said, "Please go on, my dear cousin, and forgive the interruption."

"The situation is difficult but not hopeless," Sédillot observed. "Neither the printing business nor the type foundry is fundamentally unsound, do you see? In themselves, they are good undertakings. It is a case." He smiled at Balzac and said parenthetically, "Please forgive me, my boy. I don't mean to be offensive, but in matters of this kind it is safest to be frank."

Balzac nodded. Sédillot coughed and went on.

"As I was saying, the enterprises themselves are not unsound. It has been a case of mismanagement, you see. Mismanagement growing out of overambition and complicated by lack of experience, combined with extreme gullibility. The episode of the promissory notes accepted from Monsieur Badouin. Well. . . !"

"We are prepared to concede that my son has a gift for being cheated," Anne-Charlotte said briskly. "The question is, what is to be done?"

"There will be losses," Sédillot told her. "It is regrettable but they cannot be avoided."

"We are prepared to accept losses," said Anne-Charlotte. "Provided they are no larger than necessary to protect the family name."

"The first thing to be done, of course, is to separate Honoré from the situation at once," Sédillot said. "It must be made clear to his creditors that his affairs are now in the hands of responsible and competent people and that he has nothing more to do with them." He glanced at Balzac and asked, "Are you still living in the quarters above the shop in the rue des Marais?"

"Naturally," said Balzac. "It is my home."

"You must move at once," Sédillot told him.

"I can be out by the end of the month," said Balzac.

Sédillot shook his head. "Not good enough," he said. "You must move tomorrow."

"Tomorrow!" Balzac exploded.

"Tonight would be better," the notary said grimly. "A month ago would have been better still."

For a moment the fire of rebellion flared in Balzac's breast. It was intolerable to be put out of his home, the first real home he had ever had, on twenty-four hours notice. It was inhuman. Unnecessary.

"But surely I will be needed in liquidating these affairs," he said. "After all, I am more familiar with the details than anyone else. Why can't I stay on in the rue des Marais while I am working with you, monsieur?"

Sédillot smiled patiently.

"Again, my boy, I must ask you not to be offended by what I have to say, or to take it personally," he said.

"Very well," said Balzac.

"You have managed to complicate your affairs in such a way, my poor fellow, that with the best luck in the world, and a good deal of solid work, mind you, it will take at least a year to put things in order," Sédillot said. "The best contribution you can make to the task is to refrain from complicating things still further. Get out of the situation. Clear out of the rue des Marias at once, so that no one can serve you with a writ or a summons, while we are doing the preliminary work. If possible, for the time being, leave Paris altogether."

"Leave Paris!" Balzac exploded. "I can't simply run away like a thief. I've done nothing wrong. Nothing dishonest. Why must I leave Paris?"

"You will do as Monsieur Sédillot suggests," his mother said bluntly. "We are trying to help you, since you seem incapable of helping yourself. Please show your gratitude by not raising objection to what my cousin suggests. He has experience in these matters. Obviously, you have not."

Balzac subsided. His brother nudged him again and said, "Come out to the colonies with me, old man. We can go to Martinique and become romantic exiles. What do you say to that? A pair of ne'er-do-well brothers together. Appropriate, what?

And surely, at that distance, there will be no danger that either of us will disgrace the name of Balzac."

"Henri, stop it!" Laure cried. "Leave him alone. Can't you see that he's miserably sorry for all the trouble he's caused?"

She burst into tears. De Surville put an arm around her. Henri opened his mouth, to speak again. His mother's voice stopped the words on his lips. "Henri, hold your tongue! If you keep on as you have been, there will be nothing for you to do but go to the colonies."

She raised her head and addressed the Deity, who seemed to reside in the ceiling above her.

"Beloved God, why am I cursed with such sons?" she demanded. "One makes a botch of whatever he attempts. The other is content to attempt nothing."

She stood up, shaking out the folds of her velvet skirt.

"We are finished here," she said. "It is getting late, and Monsier Sédillot and I have a great deal to do before this night is over with." She turned to Balzac and said, "You are to go back to Paris. Tonight. And you are to be out of the rooms in the rue des Marais before noon tomorrow."

"Very well, mother," said Balzac heavily.

He went upstairs and packed the carpet bag he had brought with him, then walked down the road to the station to wait for the stagecoach to Paris.

Chapter 16

BALZAC ACCEPTED
Sédillot's injunction against remaining in the rue des Marais, but
he refused to leave Paris.

"Keep away from the family and from close friends," Sédillot
cautioned him. "Above all, don't see Madame de Berny."

Sédillot insisted that Balzac be provided with enough money
to keep him while he remained in hiding.

"The important thing is to make sure that no papers are served
on him, if he is to avoid bankruptcy," Sédillot insisted to Balzac's
mother. "He cannot be expected to starve, my dear cousin, and
without money he will certainly be forced to seek assistance from
the family, or even worse, from Madame de Berny."

Grudgingly, Anne-Charlotte had given him a thousand francs,
so that when he left the rue des Marais he was not altogether helpless. For a few weeks he found refuge with an acquaintance named
Henri de Latouche, a somewhat effeminate and prosperous young
man, who urged him to stay as long as he liked.

"There is plenty of room for both of us," Latouche said generously. "You can scribble away to your heart's content in that
little room on the top floor, and those bailiffs will certainly never
find you here."

Since he had board and room for nothing, and a place to work,
it would have been sensible to have stayed on in Latouche's house.
He was safe there and comfortable and Latouche maintained his
distance. Nevertheless, Balzac was not satisfied. For one thing,
Latouche loved to talk, and while he never invaded Balzac's
room, the moment Balzac came downstairs he was assaulted by
his host's birdlike chatter. De Latouche would talk about anything—the weather, clothes, politics, literature, sex, religion, food,
travel, society. For half an hour he was entertaining, but after
that, Balzac had the sensation of being locked in the closet with
a highly intelligent talking parrot. Balzac was determined to get

down to serious work. He needed peace, quiet and privacy—long hours of being alone, simply staring at the wall, if staring at the wall was what suited his need.

One morning, in the garret room Latouche had put at his disposal, Balzac was seated at the small gilt table he was using as a writing desk. It was eleven o'clock, and for all he knew Latouche might not be in the house at all. He might be driving in the park, as he often did on a fine morning. He might be visiting his hairdresser, his tailor, his bootmaker. He might be satisfying his need for love, in some secret part of Paris. Balzac heard no sound. The big house, underneath him, was absolutely silent. Yet he was aware of Latouche's presence. He could feel it. He got up and went to the window, throwing open the casement, leaning out and peering into the street, five stories below. He tossed his head impatiently, taking a deep breath of the sharp autumn air.

"My God, I've got to get a place of my own," he thought. "When I want to work, I've got to turn myself into a monk. I need seclusion, a cell in which I can lock myself up."

But the moment he rented so much as a hovel like the one he'd had in the rue Lesdiguières, a swarm of bailiffs would swoop down on him with writs, summonses, attachments, notices—God only knew what. There might be a criminal charge against him, as well as a score of civil actions. He did not know.

Simply to assume an alias would be to lay himself open to prosecution for fraud. That much he remembered from his days as a law student. What he needed was a name to borrow, a respectable name, in which he could rent lodgings. Then, if he was apprehended, he could insist that he was merely a guest in the house, with the true owner's knowledge and permission.

Laure's husband, de Surville, he thought.

He was perfect for the purpose. A minor nobleman, a government official, the member of a respectable profession. The very person! He wrote a letter to Laure, explaining what he wanted.

By return post, he had a letter from de Surville, authorizing him to rent a house in de Surville's name. Enclosed, though he had not asked for money, was a draft for a thousand francs. During these weeks he had been living with Latouche, he had spent nothing, so that he now had a capital of nearly twenty-five hundred francs —enough to live on for a year, if he was modest.

169

A few days later, he found a place in the rue Cassini, a little house in a quiet street, perfectly suited to his needs. The district was near the Observatory, miles away from his old haunts in Saint-Germain-des-Prés. It was the last place on earth one would expect to meet a printer, a writer, a papermaker, a publisher, a bailiff or an agent of the police—the kind of people he was obliged to avoid. His neighbors were the astronomers at the Observatory, the Carmelite nuns in a convent nearby, deaf and dumb children in an orphanage, and good solid bourgeois citizens with kitchen gardens behind their trim little houses. True, there was a note of the macabre. In the Place Saint-Jacques, behind the astronomers' garden, was a square where criminals were guillotined, and from time to time, in this peaceful setting, a head would fall into the sawdust.

"The district is perfect for me," Balzac wrote to his sister. "It has a little of everything, you see. It is in the provinces, yet still in Paris. It is a garden. It is a desert."

In the dead of night, with the help of Latouche and a street urchin, Balzac removed most of his possessions from the rooms in the rue des Marais.

"I don't regard this as dishonest," he insisted to Latouche. "After all, my books are the tools of my trade. Even a bankrupt artisan is sometimes allowed to keep his tools, if only so that he can earn enough to pay off his debts. The other things, my poor red armchair that I'm so fond of, things like that, well, I suppose technically they should be considered part of the assets of the business, along with the presses and type and so on, but you know what such things bring when you come to sell them. A few francs, nothing more. To my creditors, they are secondhand junk. To me, they represent the difference between misery and comparative comfort, so I don't think I'm wrong in carting them off, even though I have to do it like a thief, at night."

Latouche laughed. "Balzac, you should have been a Jesuit," he said. "You can rationalize anything to suit your own actions."

The street boy knew Balzac well. "How can a man steal what already belongs to him?" he asked simply, piling Balzac's books into the cart.

Balzac shared the house in the rue Cassini with Auguste Borget, the painter, a quiet, simple man of limited talent. Borget occupied the lower floor of the house, Balzac the upper, and the two men became friends.

For four hundred francs a year, Balzac had a sitting room, study and bedroom, together with a small marble-lined bathroom. A useful feature of the establishment was a back staircase that led from the service yard up to Balzac's apartment, making it possible for him to receive visitors in secret, or to make an escape if necessary.

In spite of the fact that he had no assets beyond the two thousand odd francs, and, for the time being at least, no prospect of earning more, Balzac could not resist the impulse to decorate his new ménage. Using the things that had been salvaged from the flat in Saint-Germain-des-Prés as a basis, he spent more than he could afford on oddments, ornaments and bric-a-brac—a porcelain clock for his mantelpiece, a crystal chandelier for his sitting room, for his study, a Persian rug, frayed at the corners but still lovely, for his writing table, an inkstand carved from a block of onyx.

Latouche made fun of him.

"Balzac, there is something perverse in your nature," he said. "You complain that you are penniless, yet you waste money on a porcelain clock. You insist that you need austerity, that you intend to live like a monk, and so on, then you proceed to furnish your quarters as if you intend to receive a steady parade of female visitors."

Balzac laughed good-naturedly.

"You are right, Latouche, I am perverse. I am the most immoral creature, a spendthrift bankrupt. In buying a clock when I have no need to know the time, I am swindling my creditors, and betraying the trust of my family."

Balzac caressed the porcelain clock and looked fondly at the Persian rug.

"It is shameful," he went on. "I am improvident, disloyal, possibly even criminal. But do you know something, old boy?"

He poked Latouche in the ribs with a finger. He was radiant with vitality; it leaped from him like electricity, expressed in his voice, his gestures, the toss of his head.

"I don't give a damn! I can taste success in my mouth, I tell you. No more potboiling for Balzac! Leave potboiling to the hacks who can do no better. No more business ventures for Balzac. Leave that to the men-of-affairs, who understand nothing else." He struck his hands together with glee, as if to applaud his own declaration. "My friend, I am going to be rich and famous. And I am going to do it by writing books, good books, that I will be proud to sign with my own name."

"But you've written nothing for months," Latouche protested. "You know, 'Noré, I believe in your talent, but unless you put something down on paper, how are you going to make your fortune as an author?"

"You are right, my good friend, I have written nothing for months," Balzac said seriously. "Actually, I have written nothing for years. I am nearly thirty, and in all my life, I have written only two things that were worth writing."

"What are they?" asked Latouche.

"Neither of them is worth a damn," said Balzac. "It is only that they were worth writing. One I wrote when I was a schoolboy at Vendôme, not quite twelve years old, a schoolboy with chilblains and a runny nose, and yet I was the author of a treatise on the human will that sprang from as honest a fist as ever held a pen, regardless of its content. I tell you, when I was eleven, I *believed* in what I put down on paper. And I took risks as a writer in those days, I can tell you. I risked having by backside beaten until it was bloody."

"What happened to your treatise?" asked Latouche.

"Oh, it was confiscated by a priest," Balzac said indifferently. "The other thing I wrote with my own blood, as you might say, that was a play, my boy. And such a play! What a horror! Written in what are quite possibly the worst Alexandrines ever composed in the French language."

He laughed so hard he brought tears to his eyes, remembering the baffled faces of his relatives and friends, gathered in the garden at Villeparisis to hear the disastrous reading. Then he became serious, recalling Laure's pathetic faith and her eagerness to believe in his genius in spite of the badness of his verse, and recalling Madame de Berny's awareness of the true talent that was somewhere buried in the morass of feeble, derivative poetry.

"It is a truly dreadful play," he said soberly. "But I believed in it when I wrote it and there are good things in it. I will never again write anything I do not believe in, my friend. Whatever I write, good or bad, will be written because I believe in it, and because I believe it is worth writing."

Latouche shrugged. "Noble sentiments, my friend Balzac. But

you will starve if you keep to them for seven days out of the week."

"Watch me, my friend. I am nearly thirty, and I am going all the way back to my beginnings as a writer, ten, maybe twenty years ago. And I will succeed."

Balzac found a little plaster bust of Napoleon and put it on the mantlepiece beside his porcelain clock. One day in a mood of grandeur, he pasted to the bust a piece of paper upon which he had printed: WHAT HE BEGAN WITH THE SWORD, I SHALL FINISH WITH THE PEN. His spirit was buoyant as it had been during the weeks before he began his Cromwell. He felt the greatness in himself again, the way he had felt it when he was a child.

One afternoon Madame de Berny, who now used his secret back staircase, found him so immersed in a book that he did not realize she had entered his study. She watched him for several minutes; he seemed to be devouring the pages, reading with incredible speed, his head thrust forward, the muscles of his great neck tense, his eyes narrowed like those of a hunter. She made a sound and he looked up. He shook his head, as if dazed, then rubbed his eyes.

"What on earth are you reading, that makes you so fierce?" she asked.

He held up the book. "Cooper," he said. "An American. James Fenimore Cooper."

"An American?" she said incredulously. "Are there American writers?"

"In some ways, I think that this American is the greatest writer I have ever read," said Balzac, with some passion.

"What! Greater than your favorite Sir Walter Scott?"

"I said in some ways," Balzac repeated. "It is a new kind of novel, this." He tapped the book with his forefinger. "These Hurons of Coopers. They are no pasteboard cutouts. They are real savages. And these forests, they are not merely painted trees. It is a real wilderness."

"You are a Frenchman," she said. "Your business is not with savages."

"We have our own savages in France," he said, with a nod of the head. "This Cooper has given me an idea, or rather, revived an old one."

173

For a long time now, Balzac had been fascinated by the Chouan War, when Breton peasants and salt smugglers had fought for the King against the Republic. It had been a wild little war in a backwater, bloody and savage. The Breton rebels had called themselves Chouans, because their secret signal was an owl's hoot.

During his potboiling days, Balzac had roughed out a story using the background, intending to blend it with a plot lifted from one of Ann Radcliffe's gothic tales. Some instinct had warned him not to waste the material and he had found the outline among his papers, the skeleton of a story he had called LE GARS, the nickname of the rebel leader. Under the spell of Cooper's novel, THE LAST OF THE MOHICANS, he had begun to breathe life into the old outline.

"Why, there is the basis of a masterpiece here!" he had exclaimed to himself one night.

From that moment on, he had been committed to the story. Though he added not a word to his outline, he began to eat, sleep, wake, breathe, only in reference to the Chouan War. He was back at work as a novelist. Every sound he heard, every smell that reached his nostrils, every form and flash of color, the texture of every surface, the taste of wine and water, was passed through the processing system of his imagination, to be tested, then accepted or rejected as food for the story. He was filled with healthy egotism.

"Until now, there have been no great novelists in France," he confided to Madame de Berny. "Why should all the glory be reserved for the English and Americans?"

"What about GIL BLAS?" she asked. "Isn't LeSage a great novelist?"

Balzac shook his head. "LeSage is great, yes. But more as a satirist than as a novelist." He frowned, not altogether sure of himself, then went on. "In a real novel, you see, the characters are not stuffed toys, to be moved about as the author pleases. Once created, they have lives of their own, wills of their own, if they've been honestly created. They decide what the story will be, the characters, not the author. Believe me, my darling, I know. I have created enough stuffed dolls in my day."

For three months, Balzac read everything he could find that had been written about the Chouan War . . . memoirs, collections

174

of letters, military documents. He persuaded Latouche to ransack the secondhand bookshops of Paris, in search of material on the period. He did not dare show himself at the bookstalls or at the Arsenal Library, where Nodier would have helped him, so he used Latouche as a kind of assistant.

Among other things, Latouche unearthed a packet of military maps that had actually been used in the field by an officer during the campaign. They were marked with artillery positions, suspected ambushes and so on, and looked extraordinarily professional. Balzac tacked them to the wall of his study and procured a packet of colored pins such as commanding generals use. He would consult his books and documents, then pinpoint various engagements on his wall maps. He even ordered Latouche to buy up a number of old weapons and other items of equipment used by rebel and Republican troops—a pair of muskets, an officer's sword, a sabre, a helmet with a bullethole in it, a battered cuirass, a dispatch case, a frayed and tattered battle standard. All of these objects were hung like trophies in Balzac's study.

"Good heavens, my child!" said Madame de Berny. "This is more like a field headquarters than a writer's study." She peered at one of the wall maps, ornamented with red, blue and yellow pins. "Is all this really necessary? After all, you are writing a story, not sitting for the final examinations at Saint-Cyr."

Balzac laughed. "I am interested in reality," he said. "These things are real. They were used in the war, by real men, who bled real blood and died real deaths."

A few days later, Balzac began to put his story on paper. He sat at his writing table for eight, ten, twelve, and finally fourteen hours at a session, composing at a steady rate of speed, getting up from his chair occasionally to stretch himself, flex the sinews of his writing hand, and frown at the diagrams of old campaigns set out on his maps with pins.

The work went well.

The words seemed to produce themselves. They dripped from his brow, sometimes like sweat, sometimes like blood from a wound. He worked like a tiger, leaving the house only for an hour or two in the early morning, to take a walk along the cool and leafy roads at three or four o'clock, consulting the stars and moon. Sometimes Borget came upstairs with a bottle of wine and a long loaf of bread, persuading Balzac to gnaw on a crust and

175

wash out his mouth with the good tart pinard. Madame de Berny came when she could, bringing a little bouquet of flowers, and they made love for an hour in his quiet bedroom. Latouche ran errands and offered advice.

This was the monkish life he had wanted, if one accepted a monk with a mistress.

In a month, he had passed the halfway mark. In two months, he was nearly finished. The manuscript was fat and healthy, the pages evenly blackened with ink. The masterpiece should have been at his elbow. Still, he was not satisfied.

"It should be good, but it isn't," he complained to Madame de Berny. "There is something lacking. Something I left out of the pot when I put the ragout on the fire."

"Perhaps you should go to Brittany," she suggested. "Actually walk over the ground."

He sat up in bed, curtained sunlight on his face.

"Of course you are right!" he exclaimed, embracing her and kissing her cheek. "You are right. I must get the smell in my nose. Here in Paris, I'm in prison. In Brittany, I will actually breathe the air of my story."

The next morning, when he sat down to work, he was struck by an idea. Old General de Pommereul, his father's friend, had fought on the Republican side against the Rebels. Of course! he thought, remembering how, as a boy in Tours, he had listened to the old soldier's stories. The general was still alive, he knew, and living at Fougères, in Brittany, a town that had seen much of the fighting. He was always fond of me, Balzac thought. I'm sure he will take me in.

He put his manuscript aside and wrote a letter to the general, telling him of his interest in the Chouan War and his need to go over the ground. "I ask you to grant me asylum for a matter of twenty days or so, and to place your distinguished memory at my humble disposal, if such an imposition is not too great. I promise that my muse and myself will not be greatly in your way."

He dropped a blob of wax on the paper and sealed the letter with his ring. Latouche carried it to the post. A few days later, he had the Baron de Pommereul's reply: "MY DEAR BOY, COME AT ONCE! YOUR ROOM IS WAITING FOR YOU."

Balzac had spent the two thousand francs that were supposed to have lasted him a year. He borrowed something from Latouche,

176

a little more from Madame de Berny, and got himself ready for the journey to Brittany. He took nothing with him but a carpetbag, containing his manuscript, a ream of blank paper, a supply of pens, a change of stockings and linen. He wore a pair of army shoes that Latouche had bought. His hair had not been trimmed for weeks, his coat was stained and wrinkled, his trousers were shapeless bags.

"You look like a tramp," said Latouche, who went with him to the stagecoach post.

"What does it matter?" Balzac said. "The Bardon de Pommereul is an aristocrat. To an aristocrat, mere appearance counts for nothing. It's what's inside that matters."

"You are hopeless," decided Latouche, helping him aboard the coach and handing up his bag. "Enjoy yourself and bon voyage."

Balzac grinned down and waved. He was vivid, bursting with energy. People looked at him and smiled.

Chapter 17

To SAVE MONEY,
Balzac had decided to cover half the distance on foot. He arrived
at Fougères looking more like a Corsican bandit than a literary
man from Paris. It was early evening and had turned cool, after
having been a hot day. The sweat had dried on Balzac's cheeks.
He was tired but filled with health and with the sense of virtuous-
ness that sometimes follows exercise. A peasant regarded him
suspiciously, then directed him to the de Pommereul château. He
reached the front door, his carpetbag in his hand, and knocked.
A manservant in livery opened the door and looked down his nose
at him.

"Go around to the back, my good fellow, if you have any
business at the château," the servant said haughtily. "Have you
lost your wits?"

Before Balzac could reply, the door had been slammed in his
face. He looked down at his clothes, realizing for the first time
that he was covered with dust from the road. He laughed and made
his way around the château, following a neat gravel path that led
to the service court, where the stables, storehouses, and kennels
were situated. The château was a great greystone pile, with a
number of towers finished off with conical, mosque-like roofs.
In Touraine, it would have been modest; here it was impressive.
Balzac glanced up at the towers, then went to the kitchen door
and knocked. A Breton cook with a splendid bosom and good-
natured eyes opened the door.

"Another tramp," she said, looking at his army boots. "I suppose you've fought in every war fought by France in the last
thirty years, including Bonaparte's campaign in Russia, at which
time you must have been at least five years old."

Balzac took off his battered hat, made a bow and smiled.

"You flatter me, Madame," he said. "I was not five, but ten, a
poor drummer boy, you see."

178

The cook sniffed, but she opened the door to let him in.

"Well, I suppose you must eat if you're hungry," she said. "The general don't like to turn anyone away. Neither do I. Come in, but mind you scrape your feet and don't track up my clean floor with your mud."

Balzac used the iron scraper that was bolted to the stone stoop, then entered the kitchen and put down his portmanteau. Deciding that the joke had gone far enough, he smiled at the cook and said, "I am hungry, certainly. And very dirty. But I'm not a tramp, really."

"What are you then?" said the cook. "The King of France in disguise, I suppose, going about the countryside, to see how his modest subjects are faring? Sit down, my good fellow. You'll get a meal here without telling lies."

"My name is Honoré Balzac," Balzac said earnestly. "I've come to spend a visit with the general. He expects me."

The cook put her hands on her hips and laughed.

"Look what he tries on for size," she said. "That's a good one! He's come to pay a visit to the general, has he? Him that hasn't had a bath since the Battle of Waterloo!"

"It's true," said Balzac. "Tell the general I am here."

Something in his tone startled the cook. She came closer to him and peered at his face.

"By all the saints, there is a young gentleman from Paris expected," she said doubtfully. "But you wouldn't be that one, for sure? A writer fellow? Surely now, writing can't be a trade that would get a man dirty as you are."

Balzac laughed and said, "I am the fellow, on my word. Will you tell the general, like a good woman, so that I can get something to eat and a bath?"

The cook looked at him again and shrugged her shoulders.

"I'll see that the general's told then," she said. "But if you're trying to make a fool of me, I'll take that meat cleaver to you, I promise. What did you say the name was?"

"Balzac."

"Balzac," she repeated, wagging her head and going off, leaving him alone in the kitchen.

It was a huge, clean room with an immaculate red tile floor. On a table sat a loaf of country bread, with a knife beside it. Balzac cut off a chunk and nibbled on it while he waited. It was delicious, the honest, hearty kind of bread one never sees in Paris. The taste of it made Balzac realize that he was as famished as any tramp who had ever knocked at a back door. He was reaching for a second slice when Baron de Pommereul burst into the kitchen.

"My dear boy, this is unpardonable," he said, embracing Balzac like a son. "Why in the name of the devil didn't you come to the front door?"

"I lost my way," Balzac said, deciding not to cause trouble for the poor footman at the front door who, after all, wasn't used to shabby writers and was only doing his duty.

The general picked up Balzac's bag and handed it to the cook. "See that this is taken to monsieur's room at once," he said. "The one that's been gotten ready."

"At once, Monsieur le Baron," she said. The poor thing looked at Balzac and said, "A thousand pardons, monsieur. A thousand pardons."

"It is nothing, madame," said Balzac. "In the circumstances, a natural error. Please do me the honor to forget it."

She smiled at him gratefully; he had made a friend. The general put an arm around his shoulder.

"You'll want a good wash, my boy," he said. "And you must be hungry. I'll have them send tea to your room at once."

They walked through a narrow passage that led to the front of the house. Baron de Pommereul was a big man, slender, with a craggy, soldier's face and well kept grey hair. He was wearing a shooting jacket with leather patches and smelt of gun-oil and the open air. He was absolutely natural and charming.

Balzac walked beside his host up a magnificent stone stairway, then up a narrower, spiral staircase, to one of the turret rooms.

"We've put you up here, my boy, thinking you'd want privacy for your work," the Baron explained. "It's quiet up here, you see. Never know anyone else was in the house."

"It is magnificent," Balzac said. He went to one of the narrow windows cut into the thick stone walls, looking down at the country. "That must be the field where the battle of Fougères was fought," he said, pointing at the plain and low hills.

"That's it," said the Baron. "But we can talk about all that later. You'll want your bath and a cup of tea."

Balzac turned away from the window. "Thank you for letting me come," he said, his voice husky with emotion.

180

When the Baron had gone, Balzac looked out of the window again. It was dusk, and a mellow, mysterious light blurred the outlines of the Breton hills. His heart leaped with excitement. Here on the ground, breathing the air my characters breathed, I shall find the missing ingredient, and I shall produce a masterpiece.

There was a polite knock at the door.

"Come!" Balzac called.

A pretty little maid who wore a Breton coif carried a tea tray into the room.

"B'jour, m'sieu. I've brought your tea."

She spoke with a strong Breton accent, odd to an ear that was used to the speech of Paris. Balzac was suddenly aware of the Celtic strain in these people, again struck by the fact that he had been right to come.

The little maid put the tray on a table, poured tea from a silver pot, made a curtsy and departed. Balzac sat down to his meal. There was a plate of Breton ham, sliced thin as paper, nearly transparent, delicately salted. There was chicken and a plate of bread cut from the loaf he had tasted in the kitchen, each slice spread with fresh country butter. The food was delicious, oddly foreign. If this is a sample, Balzac thought, I am going to put on weight while I'm here.

As he was drinking his third cup of tea, there was another knock at his door. It was the manservant who had sent him around to the kitchen. He carried a copper bathtub and a cannister of steaming water. Over his arm was a clean, rough towel. He looked at Balzac and the skin of his face turned scarlet. He put down the bath things, then lowered his head.

"Sir, as you realize, I am at your mercy," he said. "Cook has told me of your kindness. I am grateful to you." He raised his head, looking at the heavy beams of the ceiling as if he expected them to fall. "Oh, sir!" he said. "If the general ever finds out what I've done!"

"He won't find out from me, I promise you that," said Balzac.

The servant was so relieved and grateful that he clasped Balzac's hand and seemed about to kiss it.

"If there is any service I can do you, sir, you have simply to command me," he said.

"What is your name?" asked Balzac.

"Gérard, monsieur."

"Well, Gérard, do you come from this district?"

"I was born less than a mile from the château," replied Gérard. "So were my parents and grandparents."

"Your father was a Chouan then?" said Balzac.

"That is a certainty, monsieur," Gérard answered, with some pride. "He was a commander, under the banner of the Chevalier de Nougarede. A minor commander. Still, sir, you understand, it was something, for a simple peasant who could neither read nor write."

"It has been my experience that men of intelligence who neither read nor write sometimes have sharper and lengthier memories than those who do both," said Balzac. "I am interested in the Chouan War, Gérard. Do you think your father could be persuaded to talk with me about it?"

"If he can be persuaded, monsieur, I am the man to do it," Gérard said promptly. He turned and poured water into the tub. "And now, sir, your bath, before the water is cold."

Soaking himself in the warm water, Balzac blessed his luck. I'll have the general to tell me about the Republican side of the war and Gérard's father to do the same for the Rebels, he thought. The battlefield is outside my window. What writer could ask for more?

The household of General de Pommereul had not lost the atmosphere of an earlier, more graceful era. There was none of the showiness one was apt to find in Paris, now that the commercial middle class was inching its way to the top. Wellborn people in Brittany clung to the older ways, just as the Breton peasants and fishermen held to the customs and habits of their Celtic forebears, so that the wild, rocky province, its chin jutting into the dangerous sea, gave the impression of being at least a century removed in time from other parts of France.

The Baron de Pommereul was not rich—indeed, he had seen difficulties—but the cost of living in Brittany was inconsequential, compared to that in Paris. The de Pommereul table was superb, the food, except for a few cheeses, being produced on the estate. The favorite wine was a delicate Graves, served with meals and always to be had in the drawing room, along with pleasant conversation and plenty of little buttered biscuits, of which Balzac

182

quickly became too fond. Balzac had breakfast in his tower room. The midday and evening meals were formal, but not to the point of being oppressive. The food was served by Gérard and the little maid. Sometimes, at dinner, there would be only the three of them, Balzac, the general, and Madame de Pommereul, a woman fragile as a lilac flower, with a temperament as delicately scented. She adored Balzac, who treated her as if she were the Queen of France.

On evenings when there were no guests, Madame de Pommereul always withdrew soon after the meal was over, leaving the general and Balzac to their strong coffee and brandy, giving the general a chance to reminisce about the Chouan War. Balzac, lulled by delicious food and wine, soaked up the old man's memories, interrupting almost not at all, and then only with a word or two, that he hoped would evoke another spurt of recollection. For Balzac it was a first lesson in the advantages of being a good listener. The general, cut off as he was from world affairs after a lifetime of action and excitement, found the one-way conversations refreshing as a journey abroad.

Promptly at half-past nine, the general would finish the last of his brandy, put out his Havana, and say, using always the same phrase, "I believe, my boy, that it is time for us to join madame."

They would go into the drawing room, the stone walls of which were covered by tapestries faded to a delicate rose-pink, and discover Madame de Pommereul, always in the same fruitwood chair, with a needlepoint back and seat. Three nights of the week, her fingers were busy with fancy work. The other four, alternating, she devoted to the lives of the Saints, which she read in a series of volumes bound in limp black sealskin, each book with a place marker of purple moire silk ribbon.

When the two men entered the room, Madame de Pommereul would put aside her book or her needle work, and the three of them would enjoy forty minutes of conversation, or of music, played on the harp by madame, or, after the first few weeks, a session of backgammon, a game that Balzac taught his hostess to play, when he had convinced her that it was not a gambling game, in spite of the fact that dice were used.

"I assure you, madame, the gay blades at the Palais-Royal haven't the patience to play this innocent Oriental game of skill. They are much too eager to see their money disappear. They like the simple, brutal games, a whirl of the wheel, a turn of the card, not a pleasantry like this, that wants wit, good humor and patience."

"The Palais-Royal!" she exclaimed. "Surely a young writer has little occasion to visit such a place, my dear boy."

After a glance at the general, returned with something that was almost, but not quite a wink, Balzac said innocently, "Only to visit the bookstalls, madame. Most of what they offer is worthless, but sometimes one comes across an item of interest."

He shook the dice cup and threw, then bent over the backgammon board, explaining the intricacies of the game, while the Baron de Pommereul looked on. Balzac was happy. He felt a sense of peace here, a conviction that he was somehow at home.

Shortly after ten, the de Pommereuls retired and Balzac climbed the spiral staircase to his tower room, where he sat at his writing table until long after midnight, making notes of what the general had told him over the coffee cups and brandy, keeping the fine old face in his mind, as it had looked at the dinner table, the planes softened by candlelight. Sometimes the old man's words were thrilling. Sometimes they were technical and dry. Balzac put them all down, while they were bright in his own mind.

At least once a week, the de Pommereuls entertained, and Balzac had a chance to observe rural Breton society. It was his guess that there had been little change during the generation that had elapsed since the Chouan War. It seemed inevitable, for example, that Monsieur Merlier, the advocate, Monsieur Courier, the District Magistrate, Monsieur Herbélot, the District Engineer, Major Morlot, the District Military Commander, together with their various ladies, were very much like their respective predecessors of a generation ago, something that would certainly not be true in Paris or even in Tours.

At first, when the de Pommereuls had guests, Balzac found himself doing a great deal of the talking, both at dinner and afterward, in the drawing room. After all, he was a writer, one realized. He had come from Paris, the Center of the Universe. It was not surprising that the leading citizens of Fougères were eager to hear what he had to say about politics, financial affairs, women's clothes, the doings at court, the scandalous behavior of the English milords.

184

With his gift for anecdote and mimicry Balzac both awed and captivated the de Pommereuls' dinner guests.

"What a lawyer the man would make!" exclaimed the Judge, Monsieur Courier. "I can see him in court, don't you know. What intelligence! What spirit!"

Major Marlot pulled at his cavalryman's moustache and offered the opinion that Balzac would have made a first class soldier. "By the Lord, that young man knows more about military history and tactics than most of the instructors at Saint-Cyr. You should have heard him the other night, when the Battle of Marengo was mentioned! By the Lord! He had the thing at his fingertips. Enemy order of battle, disposition of our troops . . . everything! And what clarity!"

At first, the ladies marveled at his grasp of style, his understanding of the subtleties of the mode. Then, of course, he was subjected to a torrent of questions, asked to describe in precise detail the most recent costume of this or that famous beauty of the Faubourg Saint-Germain.

He was a success. He found the light, pleasant Graves a stimulant to conversation. One evening, he raised his glass to the light, cocked an eye at the delicate color, and observed with a sigh of pleasure, "Ah, monsieur, what a lovely wine. It is a graceful wine, but important. It is a wine that is full of ideas!"

Both the general and his guests were pleased. For a long time afterward, in Fougères, this compliment of Balzac's was apt to be quoted whenever a bottle of Graves was served.

Though he liked to be the center of the stage, Balzac realized that he would learn more by listening. One evening, a few weeks after his arrival, he announced that he had had his say.

"I am like a music box with a spring that is permanently wound," he said. "If I am not shut off, I will simply go on, on, and on. Tinkle, tinkle, tinkle, tee!" He imitated an extremely tinny music box and made the ladies giggle. "From now on, I am going to listen, instead of chattering like a parrot."

Everyone protested, but they were not really displeased. Like most people, the leading citizens of Fougères enjoyed talking about themselves, especially when they had a stranger to listen, so that there was an excuse to tell old stories that everyone knew. The affairs of the town and the district—the history, politics, scandal,

185

crime, economics and social rivalries of the twenty square miles that surrounded Fougères—these were the things they understood and the things that really compelled their interest. It was only necessary for Balzac to maintain innocent silence to cause the conversation to return to its normal concerns. He learned everything there was to learn about the District of Fougères, as observed from the points of view of the town's leading citizens. He became familiar with the overcrowdedness of the court calendar, with the poor quality of army recruits, with the penchant of the Breton peasant for litigation, with the shocking insolence of the present generation of servant girls, with the declining standard of efficiency of local artisans, the existence of favoritism in the provincial civil service. Seated in turn beside the various ladies, he learned something about the fires that smoulder beneath the decorous exteriors of many provincial matrons. He learned, in short, the first lesson in what was to become one of the greatest of his themes—the fact that provincial life reflects in microcosm all of human society, all of its jealousies, loyalties, faults and virtues.

Chapter 18

BALZAC FORGOT
Paris. He even forgot Madame de Berny. With a pang of guilt, he
remembered that he had promised to write every day, in the form
of a running diary, so that she could share the experience of Brittany with him. I'll write tomorrow, he promised himself, a good
long letter, filled with amusing anecdote, loaded with gossip.

He did not write.

He was too infatuated with the scene around him, and too
firmly committed to his novel, to write to Madame de Berny or
to anyone else. He steeped himself in Brittany and in the Chouan
War. His appetite for information was insatiable. When he had
digested every detail of a minor skirmish in the hills, drawn a
map of the terrain from memory, learnt by heart the names of the
men who had faced each other, had them described down to the
last placement of a tunic button—still, he must cover the ground
on foot, tracing out old breastworks, green with the grass of
thirty years, kicking in the dirt and stones with his toe, hoping to
turn over a bone or a button or a broken bayonet, perhaps the
skull of some Breton who fell trying to force his way up some now
peaceful hillock.

The townspeople of Fougères got used to the sight of Balzac,
off on his morning expeditions, on foot, or in Baron de Pommereul's wicker gocart, behind a short-legged, strong little horse.

The Chouan campaign had been different from most wars
fought in Europe. There had been few set battles of the kind
recommended to young gentlemen at Saint-Cyr, Potsdam or Sand-
hurst. The Royalist troops had been Irregulars: salt smugglers by
trade, jailbirds and cutthroats, many of them. They did not regard
war as a sport related to fox hunting. Like Fenimore Cooper's
redskins, they had taken cover behind boulders, trees and hillocks,
pot-shotting at the government troops. There was no proper battlefield, of the kind one might look for at Waterloo or Agincourt,
Pressburg or Marengo. Fougères and all of the country around it
had been the battlefield. There had been no front, no rear, no

187

flanks, no middle, no proper war at all, but only endless bitter encounters on every hill and in every ravine in the district, at every minor crossroads, under the weathered wooden Christ figures that must have looked down with horror.

As he explored the countryside, Balzac talked with dozens of peasants, picking up the dialect quickly and even learning a few words of the ancient Breton mother tongue, which had nothing whatever to do with French. It was the language the cottagers spoke by preference; indeed, some of them would refuse to speak French at all, stubbornly pretending not to understand it.

At first, the country folk were suspicious of Balzac, sometimes refusing to return his greeting when he passed a cottage door or met a farmer crossing a field. Monsieur Courrier, the judge, had promised Balzac that he would get a cold reception. "They don't care for strangers," said the judge. "They wouldn't mind robbing you, or even putting a knife in your back. They are savages really, you know, pagans, for all their Pardons and praying and Calvaries and so on."

Pagan they were, Balzac agreed. Like Cooper's savages, they seemed to possess means of communication that was secret and wordless. The land itself was poetic and melancholy, conscious of the harsh, seaborne weather, sometimes radiant under a curious, salt-filtered sun. The people, like the stunted, pious cows, seemed to have grown out of the landscape. They were proud, obstinate, fiercely jealous, courageous and incredibly hardy.

They were a difficult people to know, and Balzac put off his meeting with the old Chouan captain, father of the servant, Gérard, until he had some understanding of Breton customs and dialect. Several weeks passed before he asked young Gérard whether or not the old man would see him.

"He will see you, monsieur," he told Balzac. "But he prays me to remind you that he is no longer young, and that his memory is that of a poor and uneducated man. He warns monsieur to expect nothing of value from such a humble source."

Balzac laughed. He understood that the old man was excusing himself in advance, in the event that he disliked Balzac, or distrusted him, or for any other reason preferred not to talk.

The next morning, Balzac dressed himself in the costume he usually wore on his expeditions into the country—a white felt coat with a hood that the Bretons call a *kabik,* his infantryman's heavy boots, a pair of stiff grey trousers, and an extraordinary hat he had bought in a shop in Fougères, the only thing in stock that would fit him, a broadbrimmed object of green felt, with a high, dented crown. He carried a mountaineer's stick, and under his arm were two bottles of Baron de Pommereul's excellent Graves.

In the swaying wicker gocart, he and Gérard drove over four miles of country road that led to Gérard's birthplace. It was a pleasant morning and the little horse stepped out smartly, covering the distance in good time.

The house was a whitewashed cottage of stone, with inset granite corners and window frames, left unpainted. The roof was tile, in good condition, and the yard in front of the doorstep seemed just to have been swept. Fronting the house was a field of rye, defended by a windbreak of closely planted, stunted firs. Above the field were triple pastures, marked out with low stone fences. In one of the pastures grazed a herd of moody, undersized cows. Behind the house was a duck pond and a water wheel that served a primitive mill.

The scene was idyllic. Even the honest farmyard dog who stepped out to greet them had the air of being part of a stage-setting. It was impossible to believe that any form of violence, let alone relentless war, had ever occurred in the sight of this background.

The cottage was dark. An old woman was at the hearthside, cooking pancakes on a griddle, producing a delicious smell that mixed with the apply smell of cider. In a chair made of wood and cowhide, near the fire, sat Gérard's father, an old man with an eagle's head, his skin weathered to the color of leather. He was seventy, Gérard had said; that meant he had been in his forties when he fought with the Chouan formations.

As he shook hands with the old man, Balzac realized it had been a mistake to bring the general's wine. He put it on the floor and decided not to offer it.

"You are welcome to a humble house, monsieur," the old man said. "Before we talk, we will take refreshment."

The old woman, wearing a starched white coif, served them lacy pancakes and tart, alcoholic cider. When they were settled in chairs, the old man said innocently, "Well, monsieur, what brings a young gentleman like yourself to a peasant's cottage?"

189

Balzac smiled. The old man wanted to size him up, before he committed himself to talk. Balzac explained that he was a writer preparing a book on the Chouan War.

"From the Baron de Pommereul and others, I've heard the Republican side of the story," he said. "In this house I hope to have the honor of hearing the other side."

The old man listened courteously and, when Balzac finished, he took a pull from his mug of cider and nodded.

"A writer," he said, shaking his head. "Do you know, monsieur, if I had been able to read and write back in '99, I might have fought on the Republican side? I don't say so for certain, mind you, but it's possible."

He stared at the fire for several seconds, as if the glow of the coals carried his mind back in time, then finished his cider. Silently, his wife refilled the mug. The old fellow frowned, his eyes still on the fire. Then he raised his head and looked intently at Balzac, judging him, man to man. Balzac had the sensation that the eyes were those of a rifleman, deciding whether or not to shoot. The old man let out his breath.

"I will tell you what I can, monsieur," he said. "What would you like to ask me?"

"What was your Chouan name?" Balzac said innocently.

The old man laughed softly.

"So you know about those things, do you?" he said. "Well, my boy, there was a time when it was worth a man's neck to be caught using his Chouan name. Thunder of God! Those fellows from Paris thought we Bretons were devils straight from the pits of hell. But that's all in the past now. I don't mind telling you my Chouan name, though I don't think it's passed my lips these thirty years." The old head came up proudly. "I was March-à-Terre, monsieur."

The old woman uttered a gasp of fear. Her hands flew up to her face in terror, then she crossed herself. She was trembling. Young Gérard patted her hand.

"It's all right, my mother. Nothing to fear. Those things are done with now."

She settled back into timeless silence, watching her griddle and the fire. The old man spoke again, talking about the campaign in the neighborhood of Fougères. As he listened, Balzac realized that here was the one character so far missing from his novel. When Marche-à-Terre had been added, the cast would be complete, ready to act out his story for him. Had he not talked to another soul, the visit to Brittany would have been worth the effort. Marche-à-Terre, who sat before him, could not have been invented. He must be encountered in the flesh, on his own heath.

Once started, encouraged a bit by the hard cider, the old man warmed up to his subject.

"Ah, we had sly tricks, monsieur," he said. "I can promise you that. You see, we were outnumbered, and the other side had artillery. We had to use our wits as much as we used our guns and knives. And the women helped. More than once, one of their officers would take up with a village girl on a nice summer evening. He'd buy her a glass of wine or two, or a pancake with jam on it, and think he was doing fine, you see, counting his chickens. Then, just before dark, she would lead him off to the woods, where our fellows were waiting. Tonnere de Dieu! I tell you, the poor chap wouldn't get his pants unbuttoned before his throat was cut—so!"

The old man drew a finger across his throat, making a noise like a strangling chicken. Then he smiled benevolently and said, "One perceives that the poor fellow died, if not in a state of grace, at least in a happy attitude."

When it was time to go, the old man came out into the door yard with Balzac. It was late afternoon and the mellow light had turned the field of rye to gold. Behind the house, water spilled easily over the dam, making a gentle, homely sound. The lazy cattle, stuffed with grass, moved slowly in outline against the low horizon, ancient as cave paintings.

"Sometimes it's hard for me to remember that I killed more than a hundred men," old Gérard said quietly. He shook hands with Balzac, then put a hand on his shoulder. "God be with you, my boy," he said. "Good luck with your book. I wish I could read it when it's been printed, but I think it's too late for me to learn now, even for the purpose of reading a book about the old war."

He looked at Balzac shrewdly, with his old marksman's eyes. Then he patted Balzac's shoulder gently and said, "It will be a good book that you will write. I understand that, even if I shall never read it."

That evening, before dinner, Balzac sat in his tower room, sorting his notes. I am ready to write, he told himself. There is no

191

more studying to be done, no one else who must be talked to. Now comes the personal battle, my own Chouan War, with pen, ink and paper for weapons. Can I bring it off? Have I got the talent? A little thrill of fear went through him, making his blood tingle. His doubts vanished. He knew that he was ready. He felt brave as a lion and strong as an ox, and he whistled a tune as he got ready for dinner.

Balzac wrote the first three chapters, aware of a superb sense of power. Then he stopped. He was overtaken by the longing to return to Paris, and filled with the need to be back in his own familiar rooms.

His sister Laure had written him from Bayeux, to let him know that Sédillot had managed to bring some order into his tangled financial affairs. His debts had been consolidated and long term payments had been arranged, so that he was free to move about Paris, and no longer required to hide in the shadows like a hunted criminal.

Still, he thought, I cannot leave Fougères without some money. There are servants to be tipped, a few minor bills to be paid. And I can't arrive in Paris without a sou in my pockets.

The only thing on earth he owned, aside from his chattels in the rue Cassini, was the manuscript on the table in front of him. Perhaps de Latouche will be able to raise something on what I've written, he thought.

He made a fair copy of the five chapters he had written and sent them off to de Latouche, asking his friend to find a publisher willing to pay an advance on the strength of what was already written. Before he packed the manuscript, he took a clean sheet of paper and on it wrote his new title:

THE LAST CHOUAN

Beneath the title, centered under it, he wrote the word "by." He sat staring at the paper, terrified, his hand trembling, his mouth dry, his heart pounding. Then he drew in his breath and held it, steadied his hand by holding his wrist, and printed his name:

HONORE BALZAC

He let out his breath slowly, and stared at the title page, fascinated. After a moment, he laughed like a child. The laughter passed and he put his head on the table and wept for joy. He was thirty. For ten years, he had been a writer. For the first time he had put his name under the title of a book.

A week later, Balzac had an answer from de Latouche, who offered him a thousand francs in cash for the rights to THE LAST CHOUAN. A draft for the money was enclosed. If he accepted the offer, all Balzac need do was present the draft to the bank in Fougères for payment.

Balzac hesitated. A thousand francs was a good deal less than he had been paid for pseudonymous books in the old days, but it might be that things had changed. In any case, he had to have the cash. After all, de Latouche was his friend. He wouldn't try to take advantage of him. He signed his name to the draft and went to the bank and cashed it. THE LAST CHOUAN, one fourth written, became the property of de Latouche.

Chapter 19

Iт WAS EARLY afternoon when Balzac reached his house in the rue Cassini. The Carmelite bells were tolling gently. He had hated to leave the peace of Brittany, but now he was happy to be in Paris again, at the center of things. He let himself in by the back door and climbed the staircase to his rooms. He expected to find the place dusty, airless, and forlorn. Instead, when he opened the door, he was met by the perfume of fresh flowers.

He knew at once whose flowers they were. He dropped his bag and hurried into the sitting room. She was not there, but the room was filled with the flowers she had brought—roses, carnations, massed in his vases, arranged by a skilled and artful hand. There was a note propped up against his inkstand, simply a line, dated today, telling him that she would return at five. How did she know I was coming today? he asked himself. He had written to no one giving the date. Then he realized that she must have been coming every day, these last weeks, on the chance that he might arrive, bringing the fresh flowers with her. He was touched, but at the same time vaguely annoyed. It gave him the sense of being watched and somehow held accountable.

He heated water and stripped to the waist, scrubbing away the grime of the journey. When he opened a drawer of his chest to look for a change of linen, he found a dozen new shirts, and beside them a pair of old ones, laundered and carefully pressed. Again he was both touched and annoyed. In the expression of love, he felt invasion of his privacy. For an instant, he wished he had stayed on in his tower room at Fougères until he had finished THE LAST CHOUAN.

He sat down in his red armchair, somewhat baffled by what he felt. He was ashamed of resenting a generous gesture, but keenly aware of the reality of his resentment. The months of work in Brittany, the isolation, the sense of commitment to the novel, all had combined to change him. The day he wrote his own name on the title page of his book had been a punctuation mark in his life. His temperament was marked by a new autonomy, a sharpening of the ego that had bravery in it, but that also involved disloyalty, and the rejection of dependence.

Madame de Berny came at a few minutes past five. When he saw her, the shock was desperate. She seemed to have aged ten years, during the weeks he had been gone. For an instant, he thought she might be ill. Then he understood, with terrible precision, that his absence had simply forced him to see her clearly for the first time in years. The effect was cruel. When he went to Brittany, he had left a lovely woman of no age, with whom he was romantically and intensely involved. The woman who faced him at this moment was his mother's age. His heart fought against the truth, but the truth refused to be denied. It was the moment she had predicted, almost from the day they had met, the moment he had sworn would never come.

He embraced her, sickened by waves of guilt. I must pretend, he insisted to himself. I must not let her see.

He could not help himself. The fact of her age was in the room with them. It was like discovery of a fatal illness. They moved into his sitting room. He embraced her again and they kissed. Then she went to a chair, sat down, and began to cry silently. He knelt beside her chair, taking her hand.

"I meant to write," he said awkwardly, thinking of nothing else to say. "It is just that I got so involved with my book. I ate, drank and slept nothing but the Chouan War."

She stopped crying and touched her eyes with a handkerchief. "Don't apologize, please!" she said, almost sharply.

He stood up.

"My book is marvelous!" he said, with false enthusiasm. "Let me tell you about it."

She shook her head. "No, Honoré," she said. "I want to read this book as if it were written by an author I had never heard of before."

He got up, feeling foolish and awkward, and offered to make some tea.

"I'll make it," she said, glad of something to do.

She got up, smoothing her skirt carefully, and went into the kitchen. Balzac went to the window and drew back the heavy

195

curtain, staring into the twilit street. What he felt most strongly was neither guilt nor sadness, but scalding, juvenile embarrassment. He knew that he must somehow manage to make love to his mistress. It was expected. It was natural. Yet he almost blushed at the thought.

"Here is the tea!" she called to him.

He turned back into the room and sat down, taking the cup she offered him, burning his mouth because he drank too quickly, without thinking.

"Merde alors!" he blurted out. Then he blushed and apologized.

"Calm yourself," she said. "You are nervous as a cat."

She had regained her self-possession, lost for an instant when she had cried. She was all poise now, her usual self. Balzac shrugged.

"I am nervous," he admitted. "Overwork. Long journey. And I've just given birth to a book. There are the pangs of maternity, you know."

He tried to be nonchalant and witty. It could not be done. He stumbled over his words, even when he thanked her for the flowers and the new shirts. When they finished tea, she gathered the tea things on a tray and carried them back to the kitchen. Balzac went to the window again. It was dark now. He stared at the black bulk of a tree. He had the impulse to run, to fly down the stairs like a thief. When she came back into the room, she moved toward the candelabrum on his work table and reached for the patent lighter beside it.

"Don't make a light!" he cried.

He sprang toward her in the darkness, took her in his arms, and kissed her passionately on the mouth. For a moment, she clung to him. Then, gently, she disengaged herself. "You've come back at an awkward moment," she whispered.

Relief leapt in his breast. He took her hand and kissed it, then said, "I'm sorry." They stood in the dark for a few seconds, hand in hand, then she drew away and lit the candles.

"Honoré, I must go," she said. "They expect me at home."

He did not attempt to persuade her to stay. At the door, she kissed his cheek, and told him she was happy about his novel. He was embarrassed, unwilling to let her go, now that she was almost gone.

196

"I should have written," he said clumsily. "It was wrong, I know. . . ."

She put a finger on his lips.

"Nothing is wrong," she said. "Believe me, my darling, nothing in the world is wrong."

She turned and hurried down the stairway. He stood on the landing, listening to the sound of her heels on the wooden treads, then to the sound of the horse's hoofs as her carriage moved away from the house. He went into his sitting room and sat in his red chair, touching the overstuffed arms as if he caressed a person. "I cannot quarrel with time," he thought. "Yet I cannot lose her. I cannot."

The idea of life without Madame de Berny was intolerable. She was too much more than mistress to him. Yet she *was* his mistress, had been his mistress. She must feel degraded, humiliated, by what had just happened. He had hurt her, and he was sorry, bitterly sorry, and he was helpless.

The next day, she sent him a note to tell him that she had suddenly been called away to the country where one of her children had been taken ill, while visiting an aunt. He folded the letter and put it away in a box that held other souvenirs—a rose she had given him once, that he had pressed in a book and saved, a ribbon she had worn in her hair, a lock of the hair itself. Then his eyes blurred with tears.

"I will be back in a month or two," the note had said.

She was giving the wound time to heal. When she returned, the embarrassment would be gone. They would be friends, more than friends. He felt enormous relief, and then a burst of energy. He got out his manuscript and notes and sat down at his writing table to work.

Late in the afternoon, de Latouche knocked at the door. He wore a plum-colored coat, tightly fitted at the waist, and carried a thin ebony stick. He was in the chattering mood that Balzac always found annoying.

"My dear fellow!" he exclaimed, giving Balzac an attenuated hand. "Our wanderer has returned at last." He touched Balzac's stomach with the gold knob of his cane. "And more of him than went away. Let me look at you." He stepped back and cast a critical eye. "Ten pounds at least, I should guess. What on earth did they give you to eat? Were they getting you fat for slaughter?

197

I must say, it's not unbecoming, this new embonpoint of yours, along with the fresh country color. You are in positively rude health. Bursting at the seams. But my dear chap, you mustn't permit it to go any further. You will be positively fat! Your clothes won't fit. Not that it matters. You need new things. Those trousers! Positively. . . ."

"Shut up!" Balzac shouted. "Shut up! Shut up! Shut up!"

"Really!!!!"

"De Latouche, be quiet," Balzac said. "Come in and close the door, before you gather a crowd with your chatter."

De Latouche was impressed by the flowers in Balzac's sitting room.

"They must have cost a small fortune," he said. "Brittany has changed you. I've never known you to spend a sou for flowers."

"Madame de Berny brought the flowers," Balzac said impatiently.

De Latouche glanced at the bedroom door. "Have I come at an awkward time?" he whispered.

"I am alone," said Balzac. "And I am working."

"Working?"

"I am writing a book, idiot!"

"Another? So quickly? What energy! What vitality! What is it about?"

"I am working on THE LAST CHOUAN," said Balzac.

"THE LAST CHOUAN? That's my book. But surely it's finished, my dear Balzac?"

De Latouche became concerned.

"It is not finished," said Balzac bluntly.

De Latouche was baffled.

"But you've never taken more than a few weeks to write a book," he said.

"Look here, de Latouche, I am going to sign this book with my own name," Balzac said dangerously, taking a step forward. "Before it leaves my hands, it is going to be as nearly perfect as I can make it. You've paid for the book. Well and good! You'll get it when it is finished, and not before, do you understand what I say?"

"But I'd counted on having it," de Latouche said. "I can't get my money back until you give me the book. You must understand that, surely."

198

He went to Balzac's work table and reached for the sheaf of manuscript.

"Don't touch that, Latouche!" Balzac barked at him.

De Latouche hesitated, his hand touching the pages. Balzac took a menacing step forward. De Latouche retreated. At a safer distance, some of his courage returned.

"Surely I have a right to read what I've paid for," he said haughtily.

"You can read it when it's finished," Balzac said. "Now be a good fellow and get out of here, so that I can go back to work. I haven't time to stand here prattling, as if we were a couple of schoolgirls."

"Well!"

De Latouche shook himself like a highbred poodle whose dignity has been challenged, then straightened his coat and went to the door. Balzac gave a short, bitter laugh, then shook his head. They are all alike, these people, he thought. Let them give you a few francs and they will treat you like an employee, or a servant. It had been a mistake to sell the book to de Latouche, no doubt about it, but the thing was done and that was that. The important thing now is to see that Latouche keeps out of the way until the book is ready for the printer.

Chapter 20

BALZAC WORKED for eight weeks, living on black coffee and bread, with an occasional bowl of soup swallowed at five in the morning in one of the cafés near Les Halles, the central market of Paris, places that were open all night and catered to the marketmen. He kept to his rooms most of the time, going out only at three in the morning for a long walk through the sleeping city. He loved to stand on one of the bridges that cross the Seine, at four o'clock in the morning, resting his arms on the guardrail, staring at the water, feeling the slow heartbeat of Paris. He soaked up knowledge through his pores at night, gathered understanding of the great city, simply by standing alone in the silence, under a thin moon, aware of the classic nocturnal outline of Notre-Dame de Paris, the Tour Saint-Jacques, the Clock Tower, the great bulk of the Palace of the Louvre.

With Madame de Berny gone to the country and de Latouche successfully banished, there was no one to complain about the scandalous state of Balzac's rooms. Borget came sometimes, but he didn't care. Balzac's apartment took on the look of a looted dwelling and the smell of an animal's lair. He was not concerned. He went unwashed and in a dirty shirt. There was ink on his fingers and soup on his vest. He forgot to comb his hair. It did not matter. Cut off from the world, celibate, unwashed, released from confinement only at night, while the proper citizens of Paris slept, he was happy. He was involved with the universe of privacy, upon which the artist imposes the right of eminent domain. It is the country of the thinker, the ruler, the saint, the madman, the infant, the grand criminal, the sleeping dead—a country that demands pride, fortitude and ability to bear the cold.

To live by the clock of his own heartbeat, a man wants an oddness of temperament that touches the perverse and suggests the enjoyment of pain. Yet there are rewards. Balzac felt in his blood

200

a precise awareness of purpose, the sense that what he did now was what he had been born to do. His book was becoming a thing unique and struggling to divorce itself from identity with its creator, to stand alone. And Balzac opposed and supported it almost as if it had been a person, with a soul of its own. The struggle was invigorating, and good for the health of the spirit. It also encouraged an arrogance that others might find distasteful.

As if by prearrangement, Madame de Berny returned to Paris on the day that Balzac finished his novel. She came in the afternoon, as he was drafting a title page. When he heard the knock, Balzac thought that de Latouche had come to badger him.

"Go away, Latouche!" he bellowed. "I am busy."

Madame de Berny let herself in with her latchkey and came through the bedroom quietly. Balzac looked up to find her standing in the doorway of his study and got to his feet so awkwardly that he knocked over his chair. This completed the room's disorder.

Madame de Berny laughed. "If I didn't know you, my darling, I'd think you had taken to strong drink," she said.

Balzac hurried from behind his desk, caught her in his arms and kissed her.

"What does it matter?" he demanded. "My book is finished. It is magnificent. You must read it at once. Now."

"In this pigsty?" she said, looking around her. "No. I will put things to rights and we will have some supper. Then, if you like, I will read your book."

She sent him to the market to buy some chops, a loaf of bread, a bottle of wine, some mushrooms. It was a bright winter day. The sunlight blinded Balzac. He had not been out in daylight for weeks and his sensations were those of a prisoner, just released from the punishment cells. For a moment he was terrified by the brilliant light, the sounds of the street, the swarming crowds in the market square where he went to make his purchases. His appearance suggested that he was a lunatic who had wandered out of a madhouse. People stared at him. A woman leading a child by the hand drew back and bent to whisper, "Poor man. He is ill, my child. It wouldn't be kind to distract him."

Balzac did not care. His book was finished. In a few hours, she would read it. He was glad that she would be the first to read it, barring the few chapters sent to Latouche from Brittany. More than anyone else in the world, she had the right to read it.

When he got back to the rue Cassini, she had already started to put his house in order.

"Put those things in the kitchen," she told him. "Then sit down and keep out of the way 'til I've finished making this place habitable."

The spectacle of Madame de Berny, wearing a stylish hat with a feather and a long elegant skirt, wielding a broom like any charwoman, made him burst into laughter.

"Be quiet, my child!" she said briskly. "You should be ashamed of yourself for making fun of your elders."

The words were uttered lightly, but their meaning was profound. She was making actual announcement of the new direction that had been taken by the strong strand of love between them.

When the rooms had been swept and dusted, she made a bundle of his dirty linen, one of those neat, efficient bundles women make of dirty wash, always contriving to find a clean piece to go on the outside. Then she went into the kitchen and cooked a simple meal. He stood, looking innocent as a setter dog, astonished by her efficiency.

The food was delicious. It was Balzac's first real meal in weeks and he went at the food like a coal miner.

"Honoré," she said sharply. "Sit up properly, eat more slowly, and chew your food."

He smiled at her and slowed down.

During the meal he managed to put his book out of his mind, but as soon as they began their coffee he was nervous as a child with a surprise. He got up and crossed the room, glancing at the manuscript on his table. For a few minutes, teasing him, she pretended to have forgotten about the novel, then, taking pity on him, she said, "Bring me your manuscript, my darling."

He gave her the book and adjusted the light that stood behind her.

"Would you like more coffee? A drop of wine?"

"Honoré, put on your hat and coat and go out the front door. Go where you like, to the café, to a brothel, to see Latouche—anywhere—but give me three hours, four perhaps, alone with this." She touched the manuscript on her lap. "I am not going to try to read it while you pace the floor like an expectant father,

202

watching me while I turn the pages, leaning over my shoulder to see how far I've gotten."

He grinned sheepishly and scratched his head.

"You are right," he said.

He put on a knitted wool scarf and the white felt coat he had brought from Fougères and went out into the night, which was clear, bright and cold. He stepped off smartly in the direction of central Paris, his ironclad army boots making an efficient sound on the cobbles. He wasn't in the mood for a café and brothels had never appealed to him. De Latouche he would see in good time.

He simply walked.

One place in Paris always held his interest, day or night. That was Les Halles—situated in the heart of the city, a maze of narrow, medieval streets. He went there now and for three hours wandered through the complex of crowded streets and alleys, passing pork butchers and veal butchers and butchers selling the meat of horses.

The red-cheeked market people, men and women, swung their arms against the cold when they broke off work for a moment, and sometimes paused to warm their hands at the charcoal braziers that burnt red hot in front of most of the stalls.

Balzac loved the market.

He was delighted to watch a competent butcher addressing a carcass of beef, knife flashing in his hand, like a pagan priest performing a blood sacrifice. He would smile at the splendid arrogance of the man in the cheese stall, splitting an enormous wheel of cheese into equal segments without seeming to pause to measure.

He lost track of time, wandering through the market, his hands shoved into the slant pockets of his Breton coat, not minding the cold, which, after midnight, became intense, so that the air had the taste of steel. He bought a fistful of roasted chestnuts and accepted the blessing of God from the old crone who sold them to him. He munched his chestnuts happily, at ease with the world, in love with Paris, sublimely aware of his talent.

He turned into the rue Montorgueil and encountered a party of six people at the door of the restaurant L'Escargot d'Or, rich people, in evening dress, waiting for their coachman and annoyed that he was late. Moved by a curious impulse, Balzac made an exaggerated bow and wished them all good night. The gentlemen's fingers stiffened on the knobs of their sticks. One of the ladies said quite loudly, "Do give the poor chap something. He must be hungry and terribly cold." One of the men tossed Balzac a franc. He caught it and danced like a bear for a moment, then roared with laughter and passed on, putting the coin in his pocket.

He rounded a corner and found himself at the door of Saint-Eustache, the church of the market men and women, where the odor of garlic spices the incense used at mass. The splendid church rose in the night, looking down with benevolence on the high piled crates of vegetables and the corpses of hogs strung on spikes like hanged men on a parade of gibbets.

Balzac went into the church. Candles flashed at the altar and at the Stations of the Cross. There was a strong sour smell, mixed with the odor of simmering wax. Balzac genuflected, swallowed the last of his chestnuts, and sank to his knees in the rear of the church. Except for the knot of shawled old women who always seem to be in churches, Saint-Eustache was empty. Balzac stared at the altar lights, feeling the cold in his bones, now that he was indoors. He wondered why he was in a church, and at this hour. He went to Mass when he could not avoid it, as he had done at Fougères, but he thought of himself as a bad Catholic, and he had not confessed his sins or taken communion since the beginning of his liaison with Madame de Berny. Yet he was a Catholic, bad or not, and he believed in God.

He lowered his head and closed his eyes. The pattern of the altar lights danced against his eyelids, the after image clear, then dissolved into heatless fireworks stars. His own sins should have been in his heart, but what rose against his darkened mind was an image of his mother, with her self-righteousness, her Swedenborgian passion, her Puritanism, that made a thin skin for the hot, lewd soul beneath it.

"Mother, mother," he whispered.

He said a prayer for his mother's soul, but no prayer for his own. He stood up, crossed himself, and walked out of the church.

At the door was a wooden box with a slit for coins, the lid secured with a brass hasp. There was a sign: POUR LES PAUVRES. Into the box Balzac dropped the franc the man in the street had tossed him. The coin made a hollow sound as it struck the bottom of the box. Balzac grinned wryly. The poor do badly tonight, he thought, passing through the doorway into the bitter cold. He stood on the steps for a moment. Just beneath him, an old man was making water against the ancient stones of the church. Balzac laughed. Somehow, the sight shook off the sombre mood he had met inside. "Piss away, old boy," he said, going down the steps and into the night.

There was a flurry of snow and half a dozen flakes struck him in the face. He pulled the draw string of his hood tight and lowered his head, striding along, close to the wall. The bells of Saint-Eustache struck the hour. He listened, then raised his head, catching the snow in his face. It was three o'clock! He had been gone five hours, nearly six. He crashed off toward the Observatory District, his steel shod heels slipping on the slick stone.

He found Madame de Berny sitting as he had left her. She was crying softly. As he moved toward her, she raised her head, unashamed of the tears.

"I've only just finished," she said. "How did you know I needed more time than I asked for?"

"I didn't," he said. "Or perhaps I did."

He took the manuscript from her lap, riffled the pages, and put it on his writing table.

"Well?"

"Surely you had no doubt of what my opinion would be?" she said. "The man who wrote this book was as sure of himself as ever a writer can be."

"I had no doubt," he said candidly. "But I am glad to hear the words. Your words."

That was all that was said between them about THE LAST CHOUAN. There was no need to say more. He went into the kitchen and made coffee, good, strong, black coffee. They drank it slowly, not speaking. Then she bent over his chair and kissed his forehead, smoothing back his hair with a cool dry hand.

"It is late," she said.

"There is a storm," he said. "A bad one. You must stay the night."

They went into the bedroom together and undressed themselves.

"I can sleep on the sofa in the sitting room, if you prefer it," he said.

"Why should you pass an uncomfortable night?" she asked, hairpins between her teeth. She nodded at the bed, which she had

205

made up with clean sheets, this afternoon. "There is room here for both of us, I think. And it will be warmer, you know."

She undid the lacings of her stays, under her chemise, then let them fall to the floor and stepped out of them.

"There," she said, shaking out her hair. "I'm ready for bed."

She threw back the covers and got into bed. After a moment he blew out the lamp and joined her. For a few minutes, they lay together in the darkness, their bodies not touching. Then she found his head and drew him to her, so that his cheek was against her breast. Her flesh was cool and sweet smelling. He breathed deeply, a long sigh, and stirred a little.

"Go to sleep," she whispered. "Go to sleep, my child."

They slept this way, like mother and child, undisturbed by passion. When Balzac woke up, he was alone in the bed. He looked for her clothes on the chair where she had placed them last night. They were gone. He got out of bed and drew on his shabby flannel robe, then padded barefoot into the kitchen, calling to her. She was not there. He went into the sitting room and found a note propped against the manuscript.

"I waited until two, then I had to go. I hadn't the heart to wake you. You were sleeping like a baby, though snoring like a trooper. Your book is wonderful."

The china clock on his mantle had run down and he had no watch. As he stood with the note in his hand, still not quite awake, he heard the chimes at the Carmelite Chapel and waited until the bells struck the hour. It was four in the afternoon. He had slept through the day.

He scrubbed his face and shaved with cold water, being too lazy to start the kitchen fire. The razor scraped and pulled at his beard and he knicked himself on the chin, but the process brought him full awake. He dressed himself, putting on one of the new shirts. The linen was soft, of better quality than he had ever bought for himself, and the shirts had been made by one of the best chemisiers in Paris. He stroked the sleeve, feeling full of self-confidence.

He stacked the books of his manuscript, then went through his rooms, looking for something to wrap it in. He could find no paper. It had stopped snowing, but the sky was threatening and he did not want to risk getting the pages wet. He picked up the shirt he had worn through the previous week, one of his old ones. It was sweat-stained at the armpits and the cuffs were filthy, but

206

the linen was good coarse stuff that would keep the weather off. He wrapped it around his book, put on his *kabik,* tucked the package under his arm and went down the front stairs.

There was a café on the corner, a little place that smelt like a public urinal, made warm as an oven by a fierce little stove. Balzac asked for chicory. The patroness, a dark, emaciated widow, drew a cup of the bitter brew and put it on the dented zinc.

"Alors, Monsieur Balzac," she said. "You have the goule de bois, no? A throat of wood from last night?"

Balzac laughed. The woman had seen him a score of times, but she still took him for one of the workmen who lived in the narrow alleys behind the Convent. You couldn't imagine Victor Hugo being taken for a laborer, he thought. Or Musset, or any of the others, except, perhaps, Dumas. He hugged the manuscript under his arm. That's the reason my Breton peasants and tough Republican rankers talk the way they should talk, he said to himself.

He finished his chicory, paid for it, and went out into the bitter cold, shifting the heavy manuscript from one arm to the other. The sky was low and filled with snow. People hugged the building line and walked with their heads buried in their collars. It was turning into the kind of night when a hundred paupers would freeze to death, under the bridges of the Seine.

De Latouche was at home, getting ready to go out, dressed in an evening suit that had been cut by a London tailor. A decoration of some kind was pinned to the left breast of his coat.

"What the devil is that?" Balzac demanded, pointing at the star with a finger which wasn't quite clean.

De Latouche glanced down at the jeweled star, set with a ruby too large to be real and a pair of doubtful diamonds.

"You like my star?" he said. "I do think it's handsome."

"What kind of a decoration is it?" Balzac asked.

"My dear fellow, I haven't the faintest notion," de Latouche said with a shrug. "Russian, perhaps. Or Swedish. I bought it in a little shop in the Quai des Augustins." He played with the star for a moment, making the light strike the fake diamonds, so they gave off a dazzling brilliance. "When people ask, I simply look mysterious and make some casual mention of my friend the Tzarevich."

For the first time, de Latouche noticed the bundle under Balzac's arm.

207

"What on earth is that?" he demanded. "Surely you haven't brought your dirty wash for my servant to do? Really, Balzac, I am your friend, but this is going too far."

Balzac uttered an unprintable word. He unwrapped the manuscript and put it on a table with slender gilded legs. The manuscript, in its sturdy bindings, looked out of place on this table as Balzac himself looked out of place in this scented and overdressed room, with its corrupt furniture and decorations. Balzac was uncomfortable, irritable, and he detested the obligation to turn over THE LAST CHOUAN to an ass like de Latouche.

At the sight of the book, de Latouche clapped his hands. "At last!" he exclaimed. "I am delighted. And you, Balzac, must be relieved."

He took the dirty shirt from Balzac's hand.

"Let me have that object."

He handled the shirt gingerly, between thumb and forefinger, mincing across the rug to the fireplace and tossing it into the flames. He wiped his fingers on a handkerchief, and made a face.

"You are well rid of that rag," he said. "It was beyond the powers of any laundress."

"I didn't bring you the shirt," said Balzac. "I brought you my book."

De Latouche picked up a volume of THE LAST CHOUAN and leafed through it quickly.

"I'll read it tonight, when I come back from Madame Récamier's reception," he said. "As soon as I've finished, off it goes to Canel, and then to the printer."

"Canel!" said Balzac. "Do you mean Urbain Canel, the one with an office in the Place St. André des Artes?"

"Canel the publisher," said de Latouche. "Is there another?"

"Do you call Canel a publisher?" asked Balzac.

"Is he not?"

"He is more in the way of being a pimp," said Balzac. "Look here, de Latouche. When you wrote me in Brittany, you told me you intended to place the book with one of the best houses in Paris. Now you tell me it's going to Urbain Canel, a fourth-rate fellow who is never more than three jumps ahead of his creditors. Why even in the old days I took my stuff to Canel as third or fourth choice."

"My dear Balzac, publishing has changed since the days when you were in the business as Lord R'hoone. Canel has moved with the times. He's bringing out good things now. In any event, I'm afraid it's too late to humor your prejudice against him. All the arrangements have been made."

"I've a good mind to cancel my agreement with you," Balzac said angrily.

"That might be done," de Latouche said smoothly. "It would involve paying me a thousand francs at once, plus a factor's fee, and a penalty. Roughly two thousand in all. I've no intention of releasing the book because of your whim about Canel. And if you'll excuse my presumption, I don't think you are in the position to begin action in the courts."

Balzac clenched his fists. Of course, De Latouche was right. While he was no longer on the run like a criminal, he could not risk appearing in court. He checked his anger. The important thing, after all, is the book, he thought. Once it is published, my reputation is made.

"What does it matter? Canel or another?" he said. He frowned, staring at the manuscript, reluctant to let it pass from his hands, fearful for its safety and jealous of the treatment it might get from others, ambivalent as a father who gives away the bride.

"I shall want to correct galley proofs of course," he said.

"Of course," de Latouche agreed.

"Page proofs as well," said Balzac.

"If you insist," de Latouche nodded.

"I do insist," said Balzac. "You mustn't forget, I was once a printer. I know all the odd things that can happen between the galley trays and the composing stone."

De Latouche wore a watch on a heavy chain. Portentously, he took it out, opened the case and frowned.

"I'm very sorry, Balzac," he said importantly. "I must be off to Madame Récamier's. One isn't late at the Abbaye-aux-Bois."

"You mentioned your destination earlier," Balzac said rudely.

He was amused by Latouche's effort to impress him, but he was annoyed as well. He and not de Latouche should be the one who was going to visit the most beautiful woman in France.

De Latouche pulled on a pair of white kid gloves that fitted his hands like a second skin.

"I've a carriage waiting. Can I take you somewhere?" he said. "The streets are in abominable condition, after that quite unnecessary snow."

"I prefer to walk," said Balzac bluntly.

"Well then. . . ?" said de Latouche.

Balzac looked at him. They had once been friends, or at least, on friendly terms. Now they were enemies.

"Well then, Latouche, I bid you good night," he said bluntly, not offering to shake hands, simply turning his back and marching firmly out of the house into the street, where it was snowing again and bitter cold.

Chapter 21

As BALZAC HAD expected, Urbain Canel employed a printer of the second class and the galley proofs were peppered with errors . . . misspelt words, lines left out, letters from the wrong font, bad spacing. Each galley was a catalogue of the sins that are shunned by good printers. To complicate matters, when Balzac saw the text in print, he had a squadron of his own corrections, things to insert, a phrase that wanted changing here, a whole paragraph there. He labored over the galley proofs in the same way he had labored over the manuscript in various drafts, trying to make the book perfect.

When de Latouche saw the proofs, he shrieked as if Balzac had stabbed him.

"My God man, what are you doing?" he cried when he recovered his speech. "Are you trying to rewrite your book after it is in metal?"

Balzac laughed and said, "There are a few changes."

"A few changes!" De Latouche waved a galley in the air. It looked as if a beetle had been dipped in ink and permitted to walk over the page. "Balzac, this is incredible. There are changes on every sheet. And what changes! On some of these galleys there is more to reset than was set in the first place."

"Perhaps," said Balzac indifferently. "I didn't count words. On the page proofs, I promise you that the changes will be made to fit. After all, at that stage it does become more awkward to insert new matter."

"Are you trying to ruin me, Balzac?" de Latouche said helplessly. "Have you any idea what these changes will cost?"

"A very good idea," said Balzac amiably. "Again, you are forgetting that I was trained as a printer."

"Be reasonable," de Latouche pleaded. "You are costing me a small fortune and you are holding up publication. Canel is eager to get the book out. He thinks it will sell."

"Canel was your choice," said Balzac. "He is your problem. My problem is the text."

Balzac knew his rights. Under French law, the publisher could not issue a book without the author's bon à tirer, or final okay of the proofs. No amount of urging by de Latouche or Canel could persuade Balzac to give up a chapter until he was satisfied with it. He was happy with the general plan of the novel. What worried him were certain defects of style, clichés, graceless phrases, vulgarisms, extravagances of expression—the legacy of his potboiling years, when he had written too much and too fast. Reading from the proofs to Madame de Berny, sometimes he would come on a phrase that was straight out of Mrs. Radcliffe, through the pen of Lord R'hoone. He would groan, black out the phrase and rewrite it.

"God in heaven, will I never recover?" he complained.

"You were warned," said Madame de Berny. "But of course you will recover."

Finally, Balzac initialed the last batch of page proofs, gave his permission to print, and the book was sent to the press. Balzac immediately moved into a swamp of depression, profound melancholia of the kind women are said to experience after giving birth to a child.

Madame de Berny, who had had some experience with giving birth, tried to reassure him.

"It will pass. Put your mind on the next book," she told him. "And I suggest a good cathartic. A certain sluggishness always attends this kind of episode."

He took her advice on both counts.

It was good advice. In a few weeks, his mood was better. He became restless and impatient, eager to be at work again.

The problem of what to write next was solved for him by accident. Some years earlier, during the days when he had been writing handbooks and codes, he had collected an advance payment from the publisher Alphonse Levavasseur for a short book he had intended to call A MANUEL FOR MEN ABOUT TOWN.

Now that Canel had announced THE LAST CHOUAN, every publisher in Paris was sniffing the air, as publishers do when they hear the rumor that something good is on the presses. Somehow, Levavasseur ran Balzac to earth in the rue Cassini. A mild-man-

212

nered man with myopic eyes that blinked behind thick lenses, he
called on Balzac to remind him of the old obligation.

Balzac, as always, was short of cash and he was shrewd enough
to realize that Levavasseur might be just the man to refill his
purse.

"I can't deny that I owe you a book," he said expansively. "To
tell you the truth, in the press of affairs, I've simply forgotten
about it, but you know I'm a man of honor. Put your mind at
rest. Your investment is safe."

Balzac had found that book publishers often respond to the
pompous manner. He spoke to Levavasseur in accents larded with
self-importance and the shortsighted publisher blinked back importantly. He was impressed.

"The book we agreed on, the manual, I'm not so sure of that,"
Balzac went on. "It was a good idea when you thought of it first,
some years ago."

"It was your idea, monsieur," said Levavasseur. "I merely paid
the advance."

"So?" said Balzac. "At any rate, the point is, those short books
are out of vogue these days. What gets attention in the present
market is the longer book, the definitive work, do you not agree?"

Behind his appalling lenses, the publisher's eyes blinked nervously.

"Ah, yes. The fuller treatment," he said. "I won't quarrel with
you there."

"In the book trade, monsieur, you have a reputation for imagination, courage and honesty," Balzac said smoothly. "Rare
qualities anywhere. In our profession, almost unheard of, taken
together."

Levavasseur's head bowed politely, but his publisher's guard
came up. Years of dealing with authors had taught him that they
always wanted something, and he had learnt that on principle it is
best to say no in advance.

"I owe you a few hundred francs," Balzac said carelessly. He
had forgotten the actual amount, but he assumed it was small.
"Naturally, for that amount, I can't give you much of a book. A
few pages, that's all. More of a pamphlet than a book, really, and
as we have just agreed, pamphlets are out of fashion these days."

Levavasseur was silent; even his eyes were silent. The light fell
on his polished glasses, making two diamond points that gave him

the look of a child's stuffed toy with brilliant buttons in place of eyes.

"Now if you were willing to add to the old advance, let's say, two thousand francs, for the sake of round numbers, I would be willing to give you the book I'm working on now," said Balzac. "It is a full length work—oversize, in fact—and it is certain to take Paris by storm."

Levavasseur sat up straight as if someone had stuck him with a pin.

"What is the title?" he asked, his eyes blinking like moths again.

Balzac smiled knowingly, as if uncertain of whether or not to reveal the title of his masterpiece. His mind turned like a water wheel. In thirty seconds he had plucked a title from the air between himself and the publisher.

"THE PHYSIOLOGY OF MARRIAGE," he said triumphantly, congratulating himself.

Levavasseur was a publisher but he was no fool. He knew a good thing, even when he had been hit on the head with it. The title was a gold mine. If the text was any good at all, it was a gold mine studded with diamonds.

"Two thousand francs, you say?" he asked.

"Make it twenty-five hundred," said Balzac, realizing that his fish was hooked. "On a royalty basis, of course."

"A thousand now," said Levavasseur. "A thousand more when you deliver."

"Agreed!" said Balzac. "I was never the man to quibble over five hundred francs."

They shook hands and Levavasseur promised that Balzac would have his money in the morning.

"Cash, mind you," said Balzac. "Not a note of account."

"Cash," the publisher agreed.

When he had gone, Balzac rubbed his hands in glee. A thousand francs! He was solvent again. He snapped his fingers, then sat down and wrote out the title he had given Levavasseur, wanting to put it on paper before it slipped out of his mind. He read it over after it was written. THE PHYSIOLOGY OF MARRIAGE. Not a bad title, he thought. He wasn't sure what it meant, but it had a good catchy sound.

214

Chapter 22

O N THE DAY HIS
advance copies of THE LAST CHOUAN were delivered, Balzac went
to Villeparisis to visit his father and mother.

His mother gave him the room that had once been Laure's, a
pretty room in the back of the house with a window that faced the
garden where he had met Madame de Berny. He looked across
the fields at the low hills, behind which was hidden the de Berny
château. He felt a pang of nostalgia and a sense of lost years.

He lifted his portmanteau to the bed and unpacked his things.
Then he carried the copy of THE LAST CHOUAN he had brought
with him across the room to Laure's little writing table. There
were four slim volumes, not badly bound at all, and very well
printed, thanks to his campaign of harassment that had driven de
Latouche to the wall.

He opened volume one to the page before the title and dipped
the pen into the ink. As the nib of the pen touched the paper he
hesitated. He had intended to inscribe the book to his father and
mother, but for some reason he did not. He held the tip of the
pen to the page for several seconds, then wrote as if his hand was
automatically guided: *"To the author's mother, with love and
thanks."* He paused, dipped the pen again, and wrote: *"Honoré,
Villeparisis, March, 1829."*

Why on earth did I do that? he asked himself, when he had
blotted the page. The old man will be hurt. He thinks of himself
as a gentleman author, a gifted amateur. He sat for a while, brooding over the emotional quirk that had prompted him to inscribe the
book to his mother. She had been merciless, even contemptuous,
in her criticism of the trash he had written under half a dozen pen
names. She had recognized trash and pronounced it trash, without
the slightest regard for his feelings. He had no doubt that in THE
LAST CHOUAN she would recognize a good book and pronounce it
a good book.

When he was called for dinner, he took the books downstairs with him and gave them to his mother. She looked at the outside cover, raised her eyebrows, and said, "Thank you. I hope you have not made a mistake in putting your own name to it."

"I think not," he said.

"I shall read it tonight, after dinner," she said, putting the books on the sideboard, stacking them neatly as laundered napkins.

When they gathered for dinner, Balzac asked for his brother Henri. Bernard-François coughed nervously. There was a moment of silence.

"He has been sent to the colonies," Anne-Charlotte said.

"The poor chap had compromised himself to a point where there was no other solution," said Bernard-François defensively. "It was for his own protection, you understand?"

"It was for the family's protection," said Balzac's mother. "As far as Henri himself was concerned, he might have gone to prison, for all me."

"Prison?" said Balzac. "Surely there wasn't a serious question of Henri's going to prison."

"Ha, ha! A lot you know about it," his mother said. "I tell you, we got him on the boat in the nick of time."

"Why didn't you let me know?" asked Balzac. "I might have helped."

He meant this quite sincerely, though he had always detested his brother.

"How could you have helped?" his mother asked sarcastically. "This was not a question of philosophical advice, Honoré, but of money. Would you have paid his debts? Would you have made good what he 'appropriated' to use Sédillot's euphemism? Would you have married *both* the girls he had promised to marry, before he got them big with child? Would you have fought a duel for him, with one of the best shots in France?" She shook her head. "No, Honoré. You couldn't have helped. He is better off where he is. Let us say no more about him."

Balzac was shocked by his mother's cold-blooded attitude. Henri had always been her favorite. Had it been himself or Laure, no amount of harshness would have surprised him, but Henri had always been spoilt, treated like a little princeling when a child, with indulgence as a young man, allowed to exist on the strength of his good looks and superficial charm. It was odd that Bernard-

216

François, who had never particularly cared for Henri, seemed to regard the catastrophe with genuine regret.

Anne-Charlotte served an excellent bourgeois dinner—a good grainy pâté maison, soup flavored with fennel, a leg of lamb, pink in the center, a bowl of green beans, hot and buttered. There was a modest Burgundy, served in the second best glasses.

When the first course was brought to the table, Balzac looked up automatically at the servant who put the plate before him. He gulped. The girl was young, not more than sixteen, and exceedingly pretty, with a slim waist, fine dark hair and the high coloring of the countrybred. Balzac looked at his father. For as long as he could remember, his mother had always employed unattractive servant-girls, because she had learnt that her husband could not keep his hands off the pretty ones. There had been a girl with a club foot, another with a strawberry mark that covered half her face, a third with a growth of hair that was repulsive, a hunchback, once, and a number of fat girls. If his mother had a girl like this in the house, the old man must at last have outgrown the demands of the flesh. Yet he looked the same as ever. The thin white hair was neatly brushed. The ruddy cheeks were perfectly shaved. His linen was immaculate. Balzac, as much as ever, envied his appearance.

Now that the first course had taken the edge off his appetite, Bernard-François began to talk of the stock market, the government, the perfidy of the British.

"There are British agents everywhere in France, trying to stir up revolution," he said.

Balzac nodded politely.

"A nation of shopkeepers," said his father, forcefully as if the phrase had just been formed in his mind. "Counterjumpers. Yet they will insist on running the world."

"Those who can assume power, do so," Anne-Charlotte said dryly. "Finish your lamb before it is cold."

When they had finished dinner, coffee was served in the front parlor. Balzac's mother never took coffee. As soon as she had poured out, she excused herself and retired, leaving the two men alone. The old man waited until he heard her close the door to her bedroom, then winked at Balzac and went to a side-cabinet, taking out a bottle of brandy and two glasses. He poured carefully, admiring the fine color of the liquor, and handed a glass to his son.

"Your mother insists that brandy offends the heart," he said. "Is that one of Swedenborg's theories? At any rate, I try to humor her, though Nacquart tells me it is nonsense and perhaps the reverse of the truth."

Nacquart, the doctor who had delivered Balzac, had moved from Tours to Paris and was becoming one of the most famous physicians in France, writing medical monographs that even the Germans admitted were brilliant.

"Nacquart should know," said Balzac idly.

He was nervous. He knew that his mother had gone upstairs to read his book, for he had heard her go into the dining room to get it. He had the old schoolboy feeling of facing an examination.

"What are you writing these days, my boy?" his father asked. "Something that will sell, I hope."

While his mother read the book upstairs, Balzac had no desire to talk about THE LAST CHOUAN. "I'm doing a kind of manual," he said casually. "A thing I call THE PHYSIOLOGY OF MARRIAGE."

"Splendid!" his father said. "Something with meat in it. Much better than wasting your time with novels. After all, any scribbler can make up a silly story and spin it out to three or four volumes."

"Even women can do it," Balzac agreed. "And do, worse luck."

"But to write something with meat on the bones, facts, you know, like my study of unmarried mothers, for example. Now that wants a man with brains."

His father beamed at him; Balzac did not dispute the point.

The old man refilled the glasses, holding his own up to the light, then conferring upon the room a long, aristocratic sigh.

"After all, my boy, there is no reason why you shouldn't become one of the first thinkers in France. There is noble blood in our veins, as good as any in Europe."

"Truly?" said Balzac politely.

"Of course, my lad," his father said confidently. "We are descended from François de Balzac, the Segneur d'Entragues. An important man, I tell you. Councillor of State, Governor of Orléans, Lieutenant-General of Orléanais."

"Are you sure of this?" demanded Balzac.

"Absolutely," his father said. "I've had it all looked up, you see."

218

"Then we are entitled to the particle," said Balzac.

"As much as anyone in France," said his father benignly, "I've thought of using it myself."

Balzac frowned. In his heart, he knew that his father's pretentions to the aristocracy were nonsense, yet he preferred to believe them, he yearned to believe them. De Balzac, he said to himself. Honoré de Balzac. It would sound impressive. And look impressive, on the title page of a book. He leaned forward, intending to press his father further, then changed his mind. He would have the thing looked up himself, when he returned to Paris.

"Is it true that Henri got two girls into trouble at the same time?" he asked.

"Eh, what's that?" his father asked, disconcerted, having been lost in his genealogical reminiscence.

Balzac repeated his question.

"Oh, yes. Quite true," his father said. He shook his head. "I can't understand it," he said, apparently without guile or the intention of irony. "That boy had a good background. I always set a good example, if I do say so myself. He had only to follow in my footsteps, and he would have been a success. I simply cannot understand how the boy could have gone wrong. You see, in view of all his advantages, it is so unintelligent."

Balzac had been listening with a growing sense of impatience. Now his resentment flared up, resentment that reached back into childhood.

"Tell me, Father, do you feel that there is nothing in your life to be regretted?" he asked.

There was an edge to his voice and a harshness that made his father look up and blink. Suddenly, Bernard-François looked pathetically old. He was a man preparing to die. Instantly, Balzac was sorry for the question and the tone of voice. He need not have bothered. The significance of his question simply failed to penetrate his father's skin of self-centeredness.

"Regret, my boy? Oh yes, many things," his father said. "For one thing, I regret that I didn't have more time for my writing. It wasn't lack of talent that stopped me. It was the want of time. These things are difficult, when a man has a family to look after, a position in the community, and so on. You'll find out for yourself, one of these days, when you're married, my boy."

Balzac looked at the old man and marveled. You could not

219

describe him as a hypocrite. A hypocrite is conscious that he is a fraud. My father is conscious of no such thing. He believes it all. His self-deception is sublime. He is invulnerable to the grave, defended by an ego without a crack. It is ridiculous to resent him; he would not understand what was being resented. He feeds on a diet of his own excellence, and for him it is nourishing.

They talked for another half hour about trivial matters, then the old man nodded. After a little he was fast asleep in his chair, snoring beatifically, chin resting on his chest, hands folded limply on his lap—the old bishop, resting after a life of good works. In repose, his age was no longer hidden by his clothes or his little tricks. He was somehow shrunken. There was no suggestion of strength. A child could have kicked him to death.

Balzac touched his shoulder and said gently, "I think it's your bedtime, sir."

The old man groaned in his sleep, then came awake against his will, shaking himself, rubbing his eyes, looking at Balzac blankly, surprised to find him there.

"Honoré?"

"You had fallen asleep," said Balzac, smiling.

The old man sat up belligerently, straightening his shoulders, lifting his numismatic head.

"Nonsense, my boy!" he insisted. "I closed my eyes for a bit, that's all. Rest them from the light, you see."

He stretched his arms, yawned, got stiffly to his feet, taking a fine watch from his pocket, looking at it with a frown. He rubbed the gold affectionately, then put the watch away.

"It is getting late," he admitted. "And I must be up early tomorrow."

Balzac bowed and said good night. The old man went to the staircase, walking carefully, using the handrail on the way up, a thing Balzac had never seen him do before. He is old, old as God, Balzac thought dispassionately.

Balzac had the feeling that he was alone in the house, though he knew that his mother was awake upstairs, that the old cook and the new maid were asleep in their garret room, that his father was directly overhead, probably at this moment pulling off his boots. He listened, standing quite still. In a moment, he heard the first boot drop, then, after a long pause, the second. The homely sound made him smile.

Left to himself on the lower floor, Balzac had the sense of adventure mixed with fear that a child feels in an empty house, when he has been left alone and has promised to be good, good, good ... a glorious sense of freedom to prowl among forbidden things, to become temporarily a proprietor.

He wandered into the dining room, which was dark, the table and sideboard given bulk by the half-light from the parlor lamps. The glass-doored cabinet that held his mother's best china stood opposite the sideboard, just as it had stood in the dining room at Tours, though neither sideboard nor cabinet were the same, Anne-Charlotte's preference for Louis XIV furniture having passed.

The cups and saucers behind glass were the same.

It was the fragile porcelain which he had been beaten for looking at because his nose had smeared the glass. He stared at the arrangement of china, ghostly white in the hoarded light. He tried the door of the cabinet and was reassured to find it locked. Had it been open, he would have been profoundly shocked and resentful. He had no doubt that the key, the only key, was where it had always been, on a ring, locked in his mother's jewel case.

He stood in the silent dark, carried back into childhood by the familiar smells of the house, by his parents' presence above him, by some trick of the light. He knelt, leaned forward, and touched the glass of the case with his nose. Then he squinted at the place he had touched.

"She is right," he said, profoundly impressed. "It does leave a mark."

He had never believed it. He wiped the glass with his handkerchief, then stood erect, aware of danger, delightful danger. He had never in his life handled the cups. He wondered if anyone had touched them since they left the ovens in Limoges, thirty years ago, except for his mother, who dusted them once a week with her own hands. In her mind, they were not really cups at all, but symbols of elegance and taste, not useful household objects but almost works of art, and they gained in value and importance by virtue of never being used.

Balzac felt in his pockets for his penknife and extracted the smaller blade. He slipped the blade between the doors and sprung the lock as expertly as any veteran cat-burglar. The doors swung open, the hinges uttering a little sigh. Balzac picked up a cup and carried it into the parlor, holding it to the light. It was weightless in his hand. The porcelain was almost transparent. He turned

221

the cup upside down. There was a maker's mark and the word: Limoges, 1802.

He tapped the cup with his fingernail. It rang as true as a silver bell.

Balzac went to the china cabinet and took out the saucer that belonged to the cup. He passed through the service hall and pantry, into the sleeping kitchen, navigating carefully in the dark, a hand on the wall to guide his path. He felt for the work table, found it, and put down the cup, sighing with relief.

He lighted the kitchen lamp, causing a thousand points of reflection to dance on the polished copper and brass that covered the wall behind the great black stove—saucepans, kettles, molds, skillets of every size and shape, huge pots for boiling stock, tiny pans hardly larger than a thimble, used for heating drawn butter. It was an immaculate kitchen, smelling of cleanliness and spice.

Balzac stirred the slumbering fire, being careful not to make a noise. He added half a scoop of coal and put the teakettle on to boil. He made tea in the kitchen pot, an honest, fat-bellied object made of brown crockery. When it had steeped long enough—he liked it atrociously strong—he carefully filled the porcelain cup, holding his breath as he poured, as if afraid that the cup would break—from the unaccustomed heat, or simply in aristocratic protest against being used in the kitchen.

The porcelain did not break.

Balzac sat at the kitchen table and drank three cups of rank, iodinic tea. He enjoyed them. He had always laughed at Madame de Berny when she insisted that tea had a different taste when held by an elegant cup.

"Tea is tea," he had insisted. "How it tastes depends on how you brew it and where it came from in the first place."

One afternoon she had made him drink tea from half a dozen different cups, starting with a servant's heavy mug, ending with eggshell porcelain not unlike the cup in his hand. Stubbornly, he had refused to admit that there was any difference. Yet there was a difference. Of course there was a difference. All the difference in the world.

He felt rather sorry for his mother, who denied herself the pleasure of tasting the difference. In effect, she did not consider that she was good enough to drink from these cups, but only good enough to own them.

222

A sad thing. Very like his mother.

He rinsed the cup and dried it carefully, then took it back to the cabinet. Using the tip of his knife-blade, he managed to lock the doors without marring the brass escutcheon that decorated the keyhole. When the door was fastened, the raped cup safe inside, Balzac laughed softly, delighted with himself.

The unfamiliar country sounds roused Balzac early in the morning. For a moment, half-awake, he thought he was back in Fougères, in the tower room of the Pommereul château. He heard the morning cry of a rooster, then the cajoling voice of a peasant, urging his beasts along the road that passed in front of the house.

Early sunlight slanted through the imperfectly fitted slats of the shutters. A fine day. Balzac disciplined himself, resisting the urge to remain in bed, resolutely turning back the covers. He felt marvelously alive, and hummed a tune as he shaved himself.

He found his mother in the dining room, drinking her morning chocolate. It was the only nourishment she took before midday. She greeted Balzac and touched the bell, summoning the maid.

"Coffee for my son. He likes it strong," she said. "And two rolls?"

"Two," he agreed. "With butter, if you please. And if there should be an egg, I promise it won't be left uneaten."

"An egg in the morning?" his mother said, as if he had asked for brandy.

"A barbarous habit, I grant you," said Balzac. "One I acquired in Brittany, from those outlandish Celts."

"Very well," said his mother. She looked at the maid. "Two eggs for my son, if you please."

He glanced at his mother, trying to guess how far she had progressed with THE LAST CHOUAN. She always read slowly, making notes, and she made it a rule never to read for more than an hour after she retired, believing that reading by artificial light caused the flesh around the eyes to become wrinkled.

There's no point in asking her anything now, he thought. She can't have read more than a chapter or two.

The maid put his breakfast in front of him, fresh rolls with butter, a little dish of honey, coffee that smelt delicious, and the barbarous eggs he had asked for. When he had poured his coffee, his mother cleared her throat.

223

"Well, Honoré, you have found yourself as a writer," she said. "That much is clear. There is quality on every page." She paused, frowned, then went on. "I once believed you to have been mistaken in your choice of a career. I was wrong."

There was an intense silence. Balzac heard his own heart beat. Unaccountably, he felt dizzy, as though he might faint.

"Believe me, Honoré, I am not displeased to have been mistaken," his mother said candidly.

"How much did you read?" Balzac asked, fighting the tremor in his voice.

"I finished the book not quite an hour ago," she replied, dispassionately as if reporting on the weather. "It is one of the few books I have ever been obliged to read at a sitting. Not merely because you wrote it. The subject is fascinating, and you have treated it with imagination and power. Great power."

It was the moment for Balzac to take his mother in his arms, for them to cry together for happiness, the tears washing the scars of the past. He could not do it. He sat with his fists clenched on his lap while his eggs cooled in their plate.

"Thank you," he said stiffly. "You are kind to say these things."

From the bodice of her morning costume, she drew a sheet of note paper, folded twice.

"There are a few errors, and a few things that seem to me in questionable taste," she said. "If there is another edition, you may want to make changes. I have made notes."

She handed him the bit of paper. Without looking at it, he tucked it away.

"Would you like more coffee?" she asked.

She gave the words no special significance, but they had meaning. She had always frowned disapprovingly in the past, when he had asked for a second cup.

"Thank you, I would like it," he said slowly, watching her slim, graceful hand move toward the silver bell with which she summoned the servant.

Neither he nor his mother mentioned THE LAST CHOUAN again, nor did she have occasion to comment on the way in which the book had been inscribed.

Balzac did not suggest that his father read the novel. Indeed, as far as he knew the old man was unaware of the book's existence, let alone of the fact that there was a copy in the house.

Balzac could not account for his motives; he simply realized, and with a sense of loss, that his father's opinion, his father's approval, were no longer of real significance to him. He had made his peace with his father's ego, recognizing that it was his father's prison, and when this had been done, what his father thought or omitted to think no longer mattered.

Balzac returned to Paris, expecting to find that THE LAST CHOUAN had taken the literary world by storm. He was disappointed. The reviewers were kind enough. A few even predicted that he might have a future. Everyone praised his sense of history.

The public failed to respond. Less than a thousand copies were sold. Canel and de Latouche, who lost money, were furious. After the first bitter flush of disappointment, Balzac shrugged it off. He had made a beginning and he knew it. The future would take care of itself. When he had finished the book he owed Levavasseur— THE PHYSIOLOGY OF MARRIAGE—he would at once begin another novel. Whether critics or public knew it or not, Honoré Balzac had begun his career in earnest and nothing on earth could prevent him from becoming a success.

Chapter 23

THREE MONTHS after THE LAST CHOUAN was published, Bernard-François Balzac was dead, sixteen years short of the century mark toward which he had pointed for most of his life. He had been suffering from a diseased liver and Nacquart, called from Paris, had given him something to ease the pain, warning him against venturing out if the medicine made him drowsy. Bernard-François ignored the physician's advice, and overdosed with the opiate. One fine morning in June, riding out across country on one of his mysterious adventures, his horse had stepped in a pothole and thrown him from the saddle.

They carried him home, alive but unconscious, with both legs broken. He regained his senses only long enough to express regret that he would not collect the lion's share of the tontine Lafarge, the annuity of which he had hoped to be the last survivor.

Balzac heard the news as he was working on a chapter of THE PHYSIOLOGY OF MARRIAGE, and by one of those odd chances, he had just been thinking of his father and some of the borrowed aphorisms he had heard from the old man as a boy.

Though he should have been prepared for the death, he wasn't. He read the note his mother had written in her careful, petulant hand and caught the doorframe to steady himself. There had not been much affection between them, but Bernard-François was a symbol.

"Does monsieur wish to send a reply?"

The voice broke in on Balzac's thoughts. It was the baggage boy from Villeparisis, a lad of fourteen or so who carried messages as a side line.

"No. No reply."

He gave the boy some money, then trudged through his sitting room and sat down in his red chair, reading his mother's message again:

"Your father died this morning, after an accident involving his horse. He had no pain. It was necessary to destroy the horse."

226

A marvelous note, Balzac thought. It must be used, sometime, in a novel. He folded the paper and tucked it away in his waistcoat pocket. He sat for an hour without moving, permitting himself to absorb the news. A man who has taught himself to deal with human emotion in his daily work does not respond to standard crises precisely as do other men. A writer, doctor, actor, priest —any of these uses death, real or imagined, as one of his ingredients. Personal death, close to him, is at once less real and more significant.

Balzac was a novelist.

He regretted the death of his father, but he could not prevent himself from trying to assign it a place in the narrative of his own life, asking how did it fit the plot of the novel he was actually acting out.

He got up after the hour and went back to his writing table, where he had been sitting when the messenger knocked. He shook himself like a wet puppy, shaking off the outside world, then took up his pen and addressed the page on which he had been working. When his chapter was finished he dusted the page, stacked the sheets and put them away, after they had been counted. Twenty-three pages. A good day. He nodded self-approval, touched his stomach with affection, and went into his bedroom to pack a bag for the journey to Villeparisis.

To Balzac, the number of people who mourned his father was astonishing. There were people of all ages and from every class. An archbishop could not have hoped for a more various turnout.

It was a hot day and the discomfort was increased by the airlessness of the crowded church. Wearing a dark, heavy coat, Balzac felt as though he sat in a steam bath. He swabbed his forehead, then glanced at his mother and sister beside him, cool and sad in new stiff black, apparently unaffected by the heat or the stifling atmosphere. He had been told that women sweated differently from men. Half listening to the intonations of the priest, he wondered if this were true, or if it wasn't more likely that they simply refused to sweat out of sheer, obstinate vanity and concern for their clothes.

Balzac had no conviction of death. Sitting here in the church, a few yards from where his father's body lay on decorated trestles, amid delicate, living flowers, he did not feel maggoty death,

227

bloody death, cruel death, of the kind he had made real on the pages of THE LAST CHOUAN. What he felt was nothing more real than the sanctimonious atmosphere of mass in a village church on Sunday, everyone concerned with making an impression, and the young girls after the young men, flirting over their prayer books.

Even beside the damp grave, next to the healthy smell of the earth, he had no sense of finality, of worms and rotting and putrefaction. It seemed monstrous to have been more moved by the death of a character in a book, an invented soldier, falling on an invented field, than by the death of the father from between whose legs his own precious spark of life had come.

He had looked on the face of his dead father and felt nothing. He felt nothing now. He held the clod of earth in his fingers, crumbled it gently, dropped it into the grave and felt nothing. It is wrong, he protested, feeling cheated. I should feel something. I have the right. I should feel grief or triumph or pain or at least the awareness of loss. I feel nothing, nothing at all, nothing but the heat and the sweat between my legs.

He looked at Laure. She was weeping with the propriety of the mourner in a picture. His mother stood in command as always, straight as a dragoon, magnificently smart in a well-cut dress, her mouth firm, eyes clear and dry, untouched by grief, heat or fatigue.

The priest made the sign of the cross in the air, the grave was sprinkled, the army of mourners crossed themselves, the grave-diggers came forward, looking like ancient men-at-arms, long spades held like pikes, earth-burnished steel flashing in the sun.

In the back of the crowd, some idiot loudly cried: "Amen!"

Laure sobbed and swayed. Balzac caught her arm. He looked at the grave and all at once felt a stab of fear, a quick sense of his own death. His mouth hardened. He refused the implication. He was determined not to die.

Slowly, the funeral party dispersed, straggling out of the cemetery. There were hired carriages at the gate, waiting to take the family and close friends back to the house. Balzac rode in the first carriage with his mother and sister, grateful for the slight breeze stirred up by the movement of the vehicle, offering token relief from the heat. Across the low-lying fields, thunderclouds were beginning to form. Suddenly there was a barrage of thunder, then, quite without warning, a vicious, dispassionate streak of lightning shocked all three of them out of whatever private areas they had entered.

228

"Summer storm," Balzac said pointlessly, in the tone of false sagacity people reserve for comment on the weather.

"Father always liked storms," Laure observed timidly.

"He did not like storms," contradicted the widow. "He merely found them useful. The slightest cloud always served as an excuse for not coming home."

"Mother, he is barely in the ground," said Balzac wearily. "You'll have many years in which to catalogue his faults. Why not give him the rest of the day in peace?"

Anne-Charlotte sniffed and subsided, looking defiantly out of the window, ignoring her children. The carriage rolled to a creaking stop and Balzac helped his mother and sister climb down. They went indoors while he tipped the driver, a husky man with a wine-drinker's rich complexion, who leaned down from the box and said, "I knew your father well, monsieur. A good man he was. Always had a kind word for the common people, and a bit of silver for the man who needed it. There's many a family 'round about here that would have gone hungry or ragged 'cept for him. He'll be missed, I can tell you, in Villeparisis."

The driver looked down at Balzac speculatively, sighed, as if in regret that he was not the man his father had been, touched his cap and started his horses with a slap of the reins that raised dust from their rumps.

Watching the carriage move away, Balzac frowned and kicked at the dry earth of the roadway. No doubt most of the citizens of Villeparisis would agree that Bernard-François Balzac had been an admirable citizen of France and a lovable man to boot. Yet this paragon, this friend of the entire countryside, had been for years powerless in his own house, without effect on his wife and children.

Balzac went into the house. His mother hovered over a long table, rented, and already laid for the funeral banquet. Balzac was tired and aware of a heaviness in the chest. He was not hungry; indeed, the idea of food was repellent, but the meal was something to be gotten through, the way the rest of it had been managed. If, in the end, he mourned his father, his grief would have no relationship to all this public acknowledgment of death.

Whatever she may have denied him in life, Anne-Charlotte could not be accused of skimping her husband's memory. The funeral dinner was superb, impeccably served by extra servants hired for the day. Balzac sat beside his father's empty chair. Down the table was Dr. Nacquart, turning grey at the temples now, razor-thin, intelligent looking as a steel engraving of Voltaire. There were General de Pommereul and his lady, the Margonnes, from Saché, in Touraine, various officers of the army, a whole company of people unknown to Balzac. Everyone handled his knife and fork with the daintiness appropriate to death. Once he had started to eat, Balzac began to enjoy the food but he thought it would be bad taste to show it, so he ate like the others, very slowly, with special attention to his manners.

Outside, the storm broke. There was thunder and bright, apocalyptic lightning, then the intemperate rain, lashing at the windows, drumming against the side of the house.

"It will bring relief from the heat," someone said sagely.

"Perhaps," commented someone else. "Often it merely makes it hotter."

Knife and fork in his hands, Balzac sat in his place, trembling at the inanity, wanting to pound on the table with his fists. Across the table, Laure sat, her eyes moving nervously. At the head of the table, implacably, Anne-Charlotte ate her dinner.

The next day, when Dr. Nacquart and the others had gone, Balzac and his mother went through the old man's personal possessions. Handling his father's clothes, his walking sticks, his gold watch, Balzac for the first time had an awareness of loss, not of grief, but of finality.

Expertly, his mother went through the clothes in his father's closets. Shaking out a blue frock coat that had been one of his favorites, she scrutinized the cuffs for wear.

"It will be best to have these recut by Lurade, here in Villeparisis," she said. "He is cheaper than anyone you will find in Paris and his work is quite satisfactory."

"I beg your pardon?" Balzac said.

His mother repeated her advice.

"The things you don't want, and those that are too worn to be worth recutting, can be turned over to Father de Raz. He will see that they are distributed among the deserving poor of the parish," she said.

"Let the deserving poor have them all," said Balzac bluntly. "I have no intention of dressing myself in my father's made-over clothes."

"Are your books making you so rich then?" asked his mother tartly.

"In the end, I intend to be rich," said Balzac. "If not from my books, then from something else."

The makings of a row were in the air between them. After a moment, his mother decided to let it pass. She folded the blue coat and put it on the bed.

"Very well. Please yourself," she said. "It is pleasant to know that you are so prosperous you can afford to refuse valuable clothing."

Balzac picked up one of his father's walking sticks, the slim, gold-headed one with which his mother had once whipped him up the stairs. It was a nicely balanced stick, too long for him, but it could be shortened.

"I'll take this as a keepsake," he said.

"Please yourself," answered his mother.

Three days later, Balzac drove to Versailles with Laure and her husband. Some months earlier, de Surville had been transferred to Versailles and they had a pleasant house there, in the shadow of the great palace. Balzac went with them out of a sense of obligation, expecting to be bored. He adored his sister and he was fond of her husband and her children. When he was in the right mood for them, he could be happy and relaxed in their household, but he was not in the right mood now. His father's death had broken in on one of his bouts of work, just as his mind was coming to focus on the new book.

The second night he was at Versailles, there were guests for dinner, a Major Carraud and his wife, regular army people from the nearby military academy at Saint-Cyr L'École. The major was a large, gaunt man with haunted eyes, gentle-voiced for a soldier. His movements were languid, almost those of a chronic invalid, or the victim of one of those mysterious, debilitating tropical diseases.

Madame Carraud was twenty years younger than her husband, a dark, ardent, intelligent woman who had been at boarding school with Laure.

The moment he saw Zulma Carraud, Balzac felt the challenge of fate. There was affinity between them, not the affinity of sex, but something deeper, more mysterious. Looking into her eyes, he had the strange conviction that he looked into the depths of his

231

own soul. Somewhere he had encountered the idea that each human soul had its complement, the other side of the medal, and that these things were arranged in heaven. Looking at Zulma, he was struck by the sense of destiny that sometimes intervenes between us, an extra-logical perception of significance, a matter of recognition. He kissed her hand and held it a moment longer than decorum permitted. It was a warm, dry hand with calm fingers. She withdrew it gently and smiled at him. He blushed, feeling the roots of his hair tingle.

At dinner he was seated beside her. Directly across from them sat the major, apparently unaware of whatever unspoken communication had passed between his wife and Balzac, though Balzac, in the instant he had held her hand, had been certain that everyone in the room must have felt the electrical charge produced by the contact between them.

Balzac was not surprised when Madame Carraud began to speak of THE LAST CHOUAN, familiarly, almost as if they had discussed the book before. Nor was he surprised to discover that she understood his purpose more completely than any of the professional critics, including those who had praised the book most extravagantly.

"You like it then?" he said, unnecessarily.

"It is not a question of liking it," she said. "It is an accomplished fact, something one must relate to, simply because it exists, in its own right."

It was the highest praise Balzac had ever received as a writer, and the most direct. He was embarrassed.

"I don't deserve such praise," he said awkwardly, sounding falsely humble, though it wasn't what he intended.

She made an impatient gesture and said, "It is not necessary for us to be trivial. You know it is not a matter of praise. Praise is for children and obedient animals."

He laughed, the embarrassment gone. He was impressed by her intelligence and the refreshing, forthright, almost masculine quality of her mind. Yet she was not unfeminine. There was nothing of the British bluestocking literary lady about her.

They had coffee in the front parlor, a pleasant, rose-colored room, innocent as Laure herself. Sitting beside Madame Carraud, a cup balanced on his knee, Balzac became aware that his sister watched them apprehensively, shooting quick glances across the room, while she talked with the major. Madame Carraud smiled.

232

"I am fond of your sister," she said. "I suppose she is my best friend. But there are parts of her mind that are not subtle. At the moment, she is beside herself because she thinks I'm flirting with you."

"Would that she were right," said Balzac, with fine, false gallantry.

Zulma Carraud looked at him keenly. "Did Laure tell you that I asked to meet you?" she said.

He shook his head.

"It was weeks ago," said Zulma. "The day after I read THE LAST CHOUAN. I'm sure she thinks I was fearfully bold and unconventional."

"What does it matter?" Balzac asked with a shrug. "It was certain that we would meet in any case. That much is clear. But now that we have met, what happens?"

"What is happening now?" she asked.

He thought for a few seconds, frowning, then said, "Believe me, madame, I don't know. The experience is a new one for me."

"And for me," said Zulma.

Whatever it was, there was something between them, instantly recognized by both. It was neither love nor simple friendship, but it was related to both. Balzac was both attracted and frightened. He was not sure that he trusted himself in a relationship with this woman, who was his sister's friend and the wife of a man who commanded respect. Yet he was drawn to her as the tides are drawn by the moon.

At the end of the evening, he found himself standing beside her.

"You must come to dinner at Saint-Cyr," she said.

"By all means," echoed the major.

"On Thursday week?" said Zulma.

Balzac bowed and accepted. But when he got back to Paris, he found the prospect of dining with her too disconcerting to contemplate. He sent his regrets, a short note, and thought he had ended the matter.

He was wrong.

Madame Carraud answered, giving him carte blanche invitation to come and stay at Saint-Cyr whenever the pressures of life in Paris became too great for his temperament.

"We are informal here, despite our military surroundings," she wrote. "There will always be a bedroom for you and a place where you can work in peace."

233

Chapter 24

FOR THE TIME
being, Balzac did not go to Saint-Cyr l'École, but the meeting with
Zulma disturbed him. He needed a woman, not simply a woman
for the night, of the kind he could have for the asking, but a
woman of some complexity, with whom he could have an affair.

He found her.

Not long after he returned to Paris, he was invited to a party
given by one of the financial backers of his new publisher, Levavasseur—a certain Monsieur Duclos, stockbroker and social
climber, whose wife was attempting to create a salon. Levavasseur
had been ordered to produce a quota of writers for Madame
Duclos's soirée, and he had persuaded Balzac to put himself on
exhibition as one of the minor celebrities. The sales of THE LAST
CHOUAN had been disappointing, but the reviews had been good
enough to give Balzac's name a certain currency.

"You'll get a free meal, and a good one," Levavasseur had
promised. "All you want to drink, of course. Champagne. And the
chance to run into something interesting in the female line, if that
sort of thing appeals to you. Besides, it's not a bad idea to show
your face in public. People are always inclined to buy a book when
they've met the author, at least those of them who don't assume
that having met the author entitles them to a free copy, at the
publisher's expense."

Balzac accepted because he was bored. Madame de Berny was
in the country and since his break with de Latouche, he had
avoided most of the literary cafés.

The rather contemptible little monarchy that had followed
Napoleon's downfall had spawned a whole generation of nouveau
riche, people who had been little bourgeois, who were now big
bourgeois, and who were trying to step into the shoes of the aristocracy of the old régime.

Levavasseur's backer, Duclos, was one of these people, a sleek, cruel-mouthed man who had profiteered in army stores during the years of the Empire, and used the profits on the stock market with such skill that he now was one of the new millionaires.

Neither Duclos nor his wife was impressed with Balzac. They had never heard his name, his clothes were shabby, his manners were not impressive. They suspected that he wasn't a writer at all, but a café hanger-on who was masquerading for the sake of the free food and wine.

Balzac was just as well pleased, for they left him to himself. Levavasseur was occupied with the literary critic of a third rate magazine, and Balzac had been abandoned.

The Duclos house had once been the home of a powerful family, wiped out under the Terror. The ballroom was enormous, a quarter of an acre of parquet under triple chandeliers, with great windows through which one might have driven a horse and carriage. Two or three hundred people milled about under the glittering lights, most of them drawn from the class of their hosts, the women very much overdressed, showing off their jewels. The men looked ill at ease in their finery. They were the kind of men who should have been comfortably seated in businessmen's cafés, their waistcoats opened a button or two, playing cards or dominoes or talking importantly of affairs. There were a few hungry aristocrats, the genuine impoverished article, and half a dozen writers of small reputation.

Making his way through the crowd, Balzac regretted having come. He felt out of place, and his old dress suit no longer fitted him comfortably. It chafed at the armpits and the trousers were too tight at the crotch.

He found himself at the buffet table. Levavasseur had not lied to him. There was an elaborate spread—cold meats of all kinds, halves of small roasted birds, pâtés of goose liver from Strasbourg, sturgeon eggs brought from Russia, in silver pots. There was champagne. On a separate table, sweets were displayed.

The sight of the food made Balzac hungry. He moved up to the buffet and a servant wearing dubious livery filled a plate for him. He went through an arched doorway into an adjoining room that was dimly lighted and looked empty. There was a good deal of expensive furniture, badly arranged on a gorgeous rug. Balzac sat on a gilt chair and addressed his plate of cold food, so preoccupied that he did not realize he was not alone until he was startled by a peal of laughter. He looked up. In a corner of the room sat a handsome woman wearing the jeweled headdress of a duchess. Clumsily, Balzac made as if to rise.

"Please don't get up," the duchess said. "You are much too hungry to run the risk of losing your dinner. Besides, think of the rug."

Balzac sank back to his chair. After a moment, he looked across the room at his companion. She was a few years older than he, a good-looking woman with a certain swagger and a mobile, voluptuous mouth, a mouth that was just a trifle too large for her face, utterly sexual, disturbing. The lower lip was full and moist, the upper, thin and expressive. If the lips were painted, it had been done with extraordinary skill. It was the mouth of a woman born to devour her lovers, a mouth that inspired the most obscene imaginings.

"Well, monsieur, I won't say I'm not used to being stared at, but I think you've set some kind of record," the woman said candidly, without anger.

The voice was low and reckless, with a throaty undertone that Balzac found attractive. He answered with equal candor, meeting her eyes, not flinching.

"For the sake of convention, I will say I am sorry to have stared at madame," he said. "It is not the truth. I enjoyed it."

"If my dignity was easily injured, I shouldn't be here," she said coolly. "By the way, in the event that you are unfamiliar with the more decadent echelons of the French aristocracy, monsieur, I am the Duchesse d'Abrantès. If you are afraid of being corrupted, make your apologies and go join that well-dressed rabble in the other room."

Balzac got up and bowed. "I am honored, madame," he said. "I am Balzac. Honoré de Balzac."

He slipped the particle into his name almost without thinking. It was an action he had considered ever since the night his father told him the lies about the family's connection with the house of d'Entragues. The duchess offered him a hand. He moved forward, bowed to kiss it, and held it for several seconds. He got a whiff of heavy scent, one of the new African perfumes that the more daring Parisiennes were taking up, an odor that was dangerous and heavy, suggestive of harems and promising oriental corruptions.

236

"Be seated before you fall into my lap," the duchess said, spearing a morsel of lobster and popping it into her mouth while Balzac moved back to his chair. She looked at him, chewing the lobster, regarding him with what Balzac took to be amusement, combined with frank sexual curiosity.

"Why are you here, Monsieur de Balzac?" she asked. "By the cut of your clothes you don't belong to the Duclos set. Besides, you're much too intelligent looking."

"Until we met, I had been asking myself the same question," Balzac answered. "Why are you here?"

"There's a simple answer to that, monsieur," she said. "I came for the food. Duclos is a horror and his wife is a charwoman in diamonds, but the chef is first-class. I know. He used to be mine."

For a few minutes both of them busied themselves with the food. Then the Duchesse d'Abrantès said, "I want more champagne, monsieur. Please touch the bell-pull."

Balzac tugged at the velvet rope. A footman who looked like an ex-convict came into the room.

"Bring a bottle of iced champagne and a plate of pastry," the duchess said.

The footman hesitated, rubbing his forehead.

"At once, my good man! Don't keep us waiting!" she spoke with all the authority of an old sergeant-major.

The servant was sure of one thing, and that was the voice of authority. He came to attention, disappeared, and in a few minutes returned with the wine and pâtisserie. Balzac laughed. What magnificent arrogance, he thought. The duchess eyed him over the rim of her champagne glass.

"You are impressed with me," she said. "You have good judgment."

They finished a bottle of champagne. The duchess's eyes became brighter. The great, moist, hungry mouth challenged Balzac, a few feet away.

"You have a marvelous undercurrent of vitality," she said, not taking her eyes off him. "And you are arrogant. Arrogant as a great bull one sees in the rings in Spain. I would like to sleep with you, monsieur. It would be good for my health."

Balzac roared with laughter.

"It is a therapy I would enjoy administering," he said.

At this moment, the door was flung open so abruptly that it

237

crashed into the wall. Duclos appeared. He was flaming with anger. Ignoring Balzac, he strode to the duchess and stood above her.

"Why are you hiding in here?" he demanded. "I paid you a thousand francs to attend a party, not to sit here guzzling with Monsieur whatever-his-name-is."

Balzac came to his feet.

"Monsieur is offensive!" he said sharply.

Insolently, the Duchesse d'Abrantès rose from her chair. She crossed the room, touched Balzac's cheek, and said, "Calm yourself, monsieur. Our host was born to be offensive. It is his métier. However, he has employed me for the evening. I must give him his pound of flesh." She turned to Duclos imperiously. "Your arm, monsieur! Let us join the canaille."

Balzac was left alone in the room. He was amused and excited. He went into the ballroom. Half of the guests were drunk by now. A woman swayed, hiccupped, then giggled and said in the accents of the Paris gutter, "What are you doing alone, you? Come with me."

She clawed at his arm. He brushed her away and moved on, looking for Levavasseur. He found him near the doorway, blinking through his lenses at the drunken crowd.

"Well, Balzac, have you had enough?" he asked with a grimace. "A man wants a strong stomach for more than an hour of this."

"I am ready to go," said Balzac.

In the carriage with Levavasseur, Balzac asked about the duchess.

"The Duchesse d'Abrantès? Of course I know her," the little publisher said. "A fascinating woman, but dangerous, Balzac. Dangerous. She lives by her wits."

"She should live well," said Balzac.

"A man-eater, Balzac. She cares for nothing. Her conduct is so scandalous that she is not received at court, in spite of her title."

"Does she sleep with Duclos?" Balzac demanded.

"Duclos? Of course not!" Levavasseur assured him. "Impossible to imagine. Impossible."

Balzac was relieved. He had the feeling that Duclos would contaminate anything he touched.

"Do you have her address?" he asked.

"I will send it round to your place in the morning," the pub-

238

lisher promised. "But I warn you, my friend, you are running a risk. That woman would castrate a man with her teeth if the idea appealed to her at the moment."

"My teeth are just as sharp as hers," Balzac said confidently.

The next day he sent the duchess a copy of THE LAST CHOUAN. He got back a note of thanks and with it a dozen roses. A few days later, she came to his rooms for supper and champagne. He gave her breast of chicken and succulent, cold asparagus spears. The champagne was of a grade much better than he could afford. The situation was straightforward and Balzac was rather surprised by the ease with which he carried it off. His ego did not permit him to give most of the credit to the duchess, who behaved with the adroitness of a royal mistress.

It was Balzac's first encounter with a truly wanton woman, and the experience was intense enough to be shocking. She was what Levavasseur had called her, a man-eater, a sexual savage, totally without restraint or shame.

He was like a virgin boy in her hands.

It was a night of erotic delirium, the act of love performed with technique so skilled that it became a form of perversion.

Nothing that burns so intensely can burn for very long. The encounter had the character of a fierce, violent duel, but in spite of its brevity, it had importance for Balzac.

The Duchesse d'Abrantès became his friend. She was shameless, she loved scandal, there was a vicious streak in her, she was exhausting, but he liked her. When she had taken too much wine, she swore like an old noncommissioned officer. She was the widow of General Junot, one of Napoleon's great commanders, and she had followed the army in its great campaigns.

She was shrewd and she knew everyone in France. She was an anatomist of gossip, and she knew as much about the boudoirs of Paris as any woman in the kingdom. Soon, she began to help Balzac with his PHYSIOLOGY OF MARRIAGE. He read sections to her and she made suggestions which were almost always good. Balzac became infatuated with the book. It grew. What had been planned as a pamphlet, then as a short, potboiling book, became, in the course of a few weeks, a fat volume of four hundred pages, the wit of Rabelais brought up to date. It was a spoof on marriage, sex, adultery, social practice, the whole thing done with grand flair.

Meanwhile, the Duchesse d'Abrantès undertook to improve Balzac's appearance. She succeeded, where Madame de Berny and others had failed.

"You simply cannot go about Paris dressed like a day laborer or a provincial schoolmaster," she informed him. "You are going to be a success, and it is necessary that you look the part. Believe me, Balzac, appearance is important. Many a colonel became a general simply because he had sense enough to go to the right tailor for his tunic."

"I can't afford to buy clothes," Balzac objected. "You know what my situation is. Until I deliver this book to Levavasseur, I've got three hundred francs to my name."

"Only the wretched bourgeoisie concerns itself with money," she said scornfully. "A really first-class tailor doesn't respect you unless you run a bill for at least a year, and a good-sized bill at that."

"First it is necessary to know the tailor," said Balzac.

"I may not be received at court, Balzac, but I know Paris," said the duchess. "I assure you, the King's priggishness has not impressed the shirtmakers, bootmakers and tailors of this complicated town. I have credit, little one. And if I have credit, so have you."

She took him to Buisson, a shrewd little tailor with a shop in an alley off the rue Saint-Honoré, where the cutting room was hung with the patterns of princes, dukes, marquises, German barons, Spanish counts, a Russian archduke. She marched into Buisson's shop like a conquering officer commandeering billets, brushing aside the assistant who came forward to greet her.

"Where is that little eater-of-pickled-cabbage who has the effrontery to call himself a gentleman's tailor?" she demanded, in her first sergeant's bellow.

"Monsieur Buisson is engaged, madame," the clerk said meekly. "If madame cares to wait. . . ."

"Nonsense, my good fellow. Madame never waits."

She went through a curtained door into the rear of the shop, commanding Balzac to follow. The shop assistant was wringing his hands and insisting plaintively that ladies were positively interdicted from entering the fitting room.

The rear of Buisson's shop was a windowless hole piled high with bolts of fabric. One wall was hung with garments in various stages of work, some nearly completed, others merely basted together. There were coats of every description—evening dress faced with satin, riding coats of scarlet cloth after the English style, frock coats for cabinet members, gorgeous military uniforms, with encrustations of gold braid. There was a suffocating odor of damp cloth, damp canvas, thread, tobacco smoke, and male bodies. Balzac doubted that the place had been aired in twenty years.

On a wooden platform that raised him a few feet from the floor, stood a gentleman clad in his drawers, wearing a glittering monocle. At his feet knelt the tailor, a rabbit wearing a pince-nez, his mouth full of pins, tape measure round his neck, trouser stick in his hand. The tableau was like a cartoon from one of the comic magazines.

The Duchesse d'Abrantès stood in the doorway, hands on her hips, and bellowed, "By the love of the Sainted Virgin, Harry, you are a sight in your English drawers. You've been on a horse so much of your life, your legs are shaped like a horse's backside."

"By the love of God!" the Englishman cried.

He and the Duchesse d'Abrantès spoke in English. Balzac stood by, not understanding a word. Buisson got to his feet, groaned, took the pins out of his mouth, and kissed the Duchesse d'Abrantès's hand. Then they embraced like old friends.

The Englishman got down from the platform and drew on a pair of skin-tight mauve colored trousers, then put on his shirt and tucked it in. The monocle seemed to be glued to his eye. It fascinated Balzac.

The Duchesse d'Abrantès took Balzac's arm.

"Balzac, I want you to meet a good tailor and a worthless soldier," she said, drawing him forward. "Monsieur de Balzac, this is Buisson, who cuts cloth like an artist and sews it like an angel. This object, whose shortcomings were on display, is the Colonel, his Grace, the Duke of Hartington. If Wellington had had more men like him, I assure you we'd have won at Waterloo."

Balzac shook hands with the tailor and the duke.

"Harry, my darling, why is an Englishman having his trousers cut in Paris, even by the good Buisson," demanded the duchess. "Has there been a fire in Jermyn Street?"

"A matter of money, old girl," the duke answered blandly. "After ten years, my credit in London has at last been exhausted. God only knows what I'll look like in consequence, but I'm reduced to swindling Buisson here until my Uncle Ferdie has the good sense to die and leave me his money."

Bemoaning his uncle's longevity, the duke finished dressing, adjusting his cravat at a cloudy mirror that hung crookedly from the wall. Fully dressed, he was the caricature of the impeccable English milord—slender, nipped in at the waist, suavely trousered, holding a smartlooking stick in one hand, an excellent pearl grey hat in the other.

"If I could afford it, my fascinating witch, I'd ask you to dinner at Fouquets, but I can't, and I know you won't ask me," he said to the duchess, kissing her hand again, nodding to Balzac and the tailor, making an exit that an actor might have envied.

The duchess and the tailor exchanged glances, then burst into laughter. Balzac found that he had joined them, though he didn't quite know why he was laughing. After the scene he had just witnessed, Balzac was prepared for anything. He would have been only mildly amazed had the duchess and Buisson ignored his presence and made love on the fitting platform from which the duke had just climbed down. In three weeks with the duchess, he had become prepared for anything, and ready to meet anyone, from a scullery maid to a Prussian prince, to dine on anything, from squab under glass to beans and rough sausage, to see anything, from a funeral Mass at Notre-Dame to a pornographic pantomime staged in a high class brothel. The Duchesse d'Abrantès, he had learnt, knew not only everyone in Paris, but everyone's mistress and everyone's servant as well. Thanks to her indefatigable good nature, she was on excellent terms with all the world, a situation that permitted her to live without an income and without a crushing load of debt.

"Buisson, this gentleman is de Balzac, the distinguished authority on tropical birds, of whom you most certainly have heard," she was saying to the tailor.

Buisson bowed and acknowledged that everyone certainly had heard of the distinguished ornithologist.

"He has just returned from the South American jungle, as you

242

can deduce from his attire," the duchess went on. "He has no clothes. He needs everything. I have brought you a bonanza, my dear Buisson."

"Buisson is honored," the tailor bowed.

The duchess ticked off on her fingers the items of apparel that Balzac required.

"At least three ensembles for the street," she said. "One of them cut from that marvelous plum-colored stuff over there." She pointed to a bolt of rich melton. "Evening dress in the English style, of course. A riding coat and doeskin pantaloons. And one of those hairy tweed affairs of the kind that Englishmen wear in the forest when they are attempting to shoot things other than Frenchmen. An evening cape, naturally, and something for him to wear on the street when the weather is bad."

Buisson nodded solemnly and made notes in a little book.

"Uniforms, Madame la Duchesse?" he asked, peering over his pince-nez at Balzac. "The gentleman is military as well as scientific?"

"No uniforms, for the present," the duchess decided.

I have wandered into a madhouse, Balzac decided. He opened his mouth to protest, but the duchess cut him off.

"I assure you, my dear Balzac, I've ordered the absolute minimum," she said. "You've been away from civilization for so long you've forgotten what must be included in a gentleman's wardrobe. Leave everything to me. All you must do is stand quietly while this magician takes your measure."

Balzac got on the fitting stand. He had learned not to argue with the duchess when she was in this state of exhilaration. Buisson called his assistant, who took down Balzac's measurements as the master tailor called them off.

While the measuring was going on, the duchess rummaged among bolts of cloth. By the time Buisson was finished, she had selected the fabrics for Balzac's clothes.

"Now then, sir," said Buisson. "Since you have nothing but what you are wearing, one supposes you'd like these new things as soon as possible?"

"Of course he's in a hurry," the duchess said. "When can you give him a fitting?"

"Week today," said Buisson promptly.

243

When they were in the street, the duchess laughed brightly, clinging to Balzac's arm.

"How do you like the game we play, Buisson and I?" she asked.

"Very amusing," said Balzac. "But I'm sure he wasn't taken in by your nonsense about South America."

"Buisson? Not for a moment," she said.

"Then what is the point of all this?" he asked. "You know I can't pay for a pair of trousers, let alone for the other things you ordered."

"Balzac, you astonish me," she said. "What is this nonsense about not being able to pay for a pair of trousers? At the end of the year, you will get some kind of bill from Buisson, which, of course, you will ignore. Twelve months later, you'll get another. If it's convenient, you will send him something on account, say ten percent. Really, my dear boy, you are a genius, but you have a great deal to learn about simple matters."

Balzac stopped in the street, turned and faced her.

"I understand that Buisson is an old friend, who made your husband's uniforms," he said. "But I'm certain he doesn't give credit on that basis."

"Do you insist on knowing all my little secrets?" she asked. "The fact is, Buisson and I have a business arrangement. Do you remember Duclos, the shopkeeper with a château?"

"One could not forget him," said Balzac.

"Last year Duclos spent thirty thousand francs with Buisson," she said. "Do you suppose that a good tailor could live these days if he had to depend on people like Harry Hartington or his French counterparts? This is the nineteenth century, my darling, the age of the pork butcher, the banker and the hosiery vendor. In a very discreet fashion, I am Buisson's best agent, and that is why he is never disinclined to oblige me with a favor. Now come along. We have a great deal to do before teatime."

"Where are we going?" Balzac demanded.

"The shirtmaker. Then the bootmaker." She glanced at the object on his head. "And then, *mon Dieu!* to the hatter!"

She was so volatile, so good natured and so utterly without morals that Balzac could not resist her. She towed him along, from one shop to the next, ordering a dozen of this and two dozen of that.

He enjoyed himself. He enjoyed being with her, and she taught him a good deal more than the art of dressing like a dandy. From

Madame de Berny he had learned something about the faults and glories of the old régime, the pre-revolutionary court at Versailles. The Duchesse d'Abrantès belonged to another school. She was part of the lusty aristocracy spawned by the French Empire, and there was something Napoleonic in her temperament, a kind of spendid, hopeless defiance. The desperate, compressed, Napoleonic world in which she had moved like a bright star had made her inveterately cynical, convinced that there wasn't a man alive who would not sell his honor or his sister for money if only the sum were large enough, or a woman whose legs could not be parted if the advantage were great enough.

"People are not good and bad," she insisted to Balzac. "There are those who are witty and those who are dull, those who manage and those who do not."

She was brittle, shallow, callous, hard. The Empire had embalmed her in its cynicism. Yet sometimes the mask slipped and the woman beneath it was revealed.

One night they made love in Balzac's narrow bed. In the heat of passion she was her usual self, taking an almost masculine role, uttering in the darkness the words of the gutter and the barrack-room. But afterward he realized that she was crying, sobbing quietly, like a girl.

He was baffled. There was not much tenderness between them, for her temperament made it impossible. Balzac hesitated to offer simple human comfort. After a little, she turned and clung to him, still weeping. He held her in his arms, saying nothing, asking nothing.

When she had cried herself out, she drew away from him gently and got out of bed, moving across the room in the darkness to the washstand against the wall. Balzac heard the clink of pottery as she poured water into the bowl, then a gentle splashing as she bathed her eyes. Her white body moved like a ghost in the pitch black room. She found a candle and lit it. The flame flickered, then rose and cast wavering shadows on the walls. She pulled on a light silk robe that she kept in Balzac's room and sat in a straight chair a good distance from the bed.

"I'm sorry," she said. "I detest people who cry, especially in front of others. It's just that today is the anniversary of Junot's death and for some reason it seems to depress me more than usual this year."

She fell silent.

Balzac lay in the bed, looking at her as the candle light fell uncertainly on her face and shoulders. He saw a woman he did not know at all, a woman who was deeply in love, irrevocably in love, and with a man who was smashed and dead.

Balzac knew the story of General Junot, the Duc d'Abrantès. Who did not, in France? Junot had been the most fearless officer to serve on Napoleon's staff, famous for his coolness under fire, inspiring soldiers to incredible performance by the example he set for them. On the battlefield at the siege of Toulon, during a fierce bombardment, he sat at his field table, writing a report for the Emperor. An enemy shell fell near him, killing three of his officers, covering Junot's table with dirt. Junot shook the dirt from his papers, winked at his orderly and said, "Bien! We had no sand to dry the ink. Now, as you see, we have some."

He had been a legend in the army, a beau sabreur, brave, truculent, dissipated, rapacious. Everyone took it for granted that he was invulnerable. Then, one grey morning, a shell came out of the enemy emplacements at Lorato, burst near him, and sent a fragment of metal into his skull. He joked with the surgeon who dressed his wound, making the usual comment about how lucky he was to have been hit in the one part of his body that was useless.

"The wound is serious, my general," he had been told. "You should go to the rear for treatment."

Junot laughed, called the doctor a sawbones, and went back into the battle.

Less than a year later, Junot began to lose his reason. At last, in a fit of gross depression, unwilling to pass most of the time in the agonizing climate of insanity, he had thrown himself from the window of his room, dying on the cobbles of a service courtyard instead of on the field of battle. When he leaped, he smashed more than himself. He had killed his wife's soul, for from that moment she had lost her faith in God, cursed Him and the day she was born.

Such is my mistress, Balzac thought, watching the duchess in the candlelight. She has slept with kings, probably with the Emperor himself, yet she cries as simply as a servant girl because the man she loves is dead. He got up, went to her, drew her back into the bed and held her as one would hold a child, stroking her cheek until she slept. He yearned for love of the kind she felt, and wondered whether he would ever obtain it.

246

When Balzac's new clothes were ready, the Duchesse d'Abrantès began to introduce him to the brilliant salons of Paris. She took him everywhere, excepting only the salons of the Faubourg Saint-Germain, stronghold of the old régime, where neither novelists nor Napoleonic duchesses had much currency.

In a few brilliant weeks, Balzac entered most of the important drawing rooms of Paris, and kissed the hands of women whose wit, beauty, wealth or daring had made them figures of legendary power. The salons were the seminaries of art, politics, finance, society. In the gilded drawing rooms, reputations were made and lost, newspapers were launched or murdered, nonentities were turned into cabinet ministers, cabinet ministers into nonentities. It was a world where French women used power they did not possess to gain ends with which they were presumed to have no concern.

For a literary man, the most important of all the salons was not a salon at all, but the simple home of Madame Récamier, now living quietly in rooms at the Abbaye-aux-Bois, in the rue de Sèvres.

Juliette Récamier was a legend. She had been married at fifteen to a man rumored to have been her father. Dozens of men had loved her. She had been the intimate of Madame de Staël. She lived unperturbed in a sea of gossip, secure in the incontestable fact that she had been since childhood the most beautiful woman in Europe. She was enigmatic. The great David had painted her, full length on an Empire sofa, a masterpiece that summed up an age in the delicate features of a young woman. Gérard had painted her as a Greek goddess, a classic beauty, but in spite of the trick, she remained French. During her exile in Rome, Canova had done her into flawless marble, and lost his peace of mind in the process.

No one was invited to the Abbaye-aux-Bois. He was taken there by a member of Madame Récamier's circle, or he learnt in some roundabout fashion that his presence would not be unwelcome. In one way or another, the greatest men and women in France found themselves sooner or later in the calm rooms at the Abbaye.

When the Duchesse d'Abrantès proposed the expedition, Balzac concealed his excitement. A long time ago, in the rue Lesdiguières, he had permitted himself to dream of the day when, as Balzac, the famous writer, he would kiss the hand of the famous beauty. Now that he was to meet her at last, he was excited, but he regretted the fact that most of his fame was still in the future.

He was not yet a lion, not even a cub; still, THE LAST CHOUAN was something. There were those who recognized his name.

It was a beautiful spring evening, of the kind that encourages Paris to be seen at her best, the grey stone touched with pink, the building contours softened by the pale and feminine light, so that the effect is that of a pencil drawing, monochromatic, but faintly tinted with pink chalk, as if by afterthought. It is the best of the city's moods and one that inspires pride of possession.

Balzac had dressed himself in one of the coats Buisson had made of the plum-colored cloth the duchess liked. The coat was successful; it flattered his figure and the color was good for his complexion. The duchess had tied his cravat and given a last brush to his hair. She was satisfied with him.

"Balzac, you are coming on," she said. "You will never be a beauty, but you have got power, and a good tailor makes a great deal of difference."

In the carriage, driving toward the rue de Sèvres, Balzac was nervous as a schoolboy being led to his first dancing class.

"Calm yourself. There is not a kinder woman in France than Juliette Récamier," his mistress told him, patting his knee. "You must never be afraid of encountering rudeness in really important people you know. It's the merely rich, the pompous frauds, the Duclos of this world, who find it necessary to be unkind in order to assure themselves of their importance."

The Abbaye-aux-Bois was one of the few convents in central Paris that had escaped damage during the revolution. It was a little way back from the rue de Sèvres, guarded by a small garden. There was a lofty iron gate and balconies decorated with flowering shrubs in pots.

Balzac and his mistress climbed down from the carriage and passed through the gate into a courtyard.

"Third floor," the duchess said. "Take a deep breath, my friend."

The staircase was steep and narrow. By the time he reached the top landing, Balzac was winded and beginning to sweat. He touched his forehead with a handkerchief and paused to catch his breath. The duchess laughed at him. She was untroubled by the stiff climb.

Balzac followed her into a vestibule. A dark corridor separated the two rooms of the apartment and as Balzac passed through this

248

he caught a glimpse of Madame Récamier's bedroom. There was a handsome bed with a silk canopy, a harp, and a spinet decorated with gilding. The windowsills held geraniums in pots. Over the chimney piece was a portrait of Madame de Staël. From the open door came the innocent, intensely personal odor of sandalwood.

The sitting room was much larger. It was lighted by the rays of the dying sun, pouring through a bank of eight windows that overlooked the gardens of the Abbaye. There were the high branches of an acacia tree and beyond that a series of rooftops and steeples pointed against the sky, blue slate roofs touched with pink and gold. On the horizon stood the hills of Sèvres, moody and violet, quite unreal.

At the moment Balzac entered the room, the Angelus was ringing. Madame Récamier sat at her piano, and the sound of the bells mixed with the closing notes of Steibilt's "Invocation to the Night."

Balzac stood in the doorway, entranced by the beauty of sound and light, the perfection of the tableau before him. He had stepped into another world. The people in the room were motionless as figures in a painting. There was the sense that time had paused.

Then music and bell stopped, almost at the same instant. An impressive silence replaced the sound. No one moved until the spell was broken by the sound of a cart in the street below, rolling over the rough stones.

Juliette Récamier turned away from the keyboard of her piano. Balzac caught his breath. It was the beauty we associate with Greece, the face that launched a thousand ships. All of the Récamier legend had not prepared him for the experience. His reason abandoned him. He followed his impulse and rushed forward, dropping to his knees, seizing her hand and kissing it.

"Madame . . ." he faltered, his voice lost. "Madame. . . ."

There was a moment of shocked silence. Balzac remained on his knees. Someone tittered. Balzac blushed to the roots of his hair and got awkwardly to his feet, brushing the knees of his trousers. Just behind him, the Duchesse d'Abrantès uttered a peal of nervous laughter.

"My dear Juliette, please forgive my impetuous friend," she said. "He's quite sane, I assure you, in spite of what one might think."

Balzac stammered an apology. Madame Récamier raised a beautiful hand.

"Don't spoil a gallant action with an apology," she said. She reached out and touched Balzac's cheek, then said to the duchess, "But he is extraordinary, your friend. He looks as one imagines Rabelais to have looked, bursting with vitality, alive with the will to create."

Balzac had recovered most of his poise.

"I was born in Touraine, madame," he said. "Rabelais and I are countrymen."

Madame Récamier nodded. Behind Balzac a little queue of people stood waiting to greet her. Balzac moved away, the duchess at his side.

"Rabelais indeed!" she whispered into his ear. "I think you overdid it, my child. Falling on your knees! Still, she was impressed. Perhaps I'm wrong."

There was music and conversation. Balzac was introduced to dozens of people, some of them famous editors, others well-known politicians. The composer, Rossini, was there, leaning on the piano. So was the great draftsman and painter, Ingres. On the other side of the room stood Prosper Merimée, staring at Balzac curiously, as if trying to place him. The critic, Sainte-Beuve, little and ugly, regarded Balzac with open distaste. Balzac looked for de Latouche and was relieved when he couldn't find him.

All at once, the room fell silent. A tall, commanding figure with unruly hair and a bearing of splendid arrogance had entered the room. He was a man in his sixties, straight as a soldier, dressed in old-fashioned clothes, wearing immaculate white gaiters.

"Chateaubriand!" the duchess whispered.

It was the great Chateaubriand, writer and politician, a man who had risked life and fortune for the sake of his beliefs. He crossed the room in a straight line, ignoring everyone except the hostess. He bowed stiffly, kissed her hand, and sat beside her on a little stool someone had moved into place.

"He sends her a note every morning and comes every afternoon at three," said the duchess to Balzac. "They say that people set their clocks by his coming and going."

Balzac stared at the great man. He was impressed. Chateaubriand looked exactly as one expected a famous writer to look, handsome, austere, above the herd.

"A morbid man, really," the duchess observed. "Brilliant, I grant you, but morbid. He detests life. And arrogant! How he

250

ignores everyone! He behaves as if there were no one in this room but himself and Juliette."

"You are wrong," said Balzac, staring at Chateaubriand's face, seeing what the duchess missed. "He acts as if there were no one else on the face of the earth but she."

After Chateaubriand's arrival, the gathering began to break up. Balzac was one of the few who managed to have a word with Madame Récamier before taking his leave.

"You must promise to send me your books, monsieur," she said. "A man who reminds one of Rabelais ought to be worth reading."

"I shall be honored," said Balzac, bowing.

"Rabelais!" snorted Chateaubriand. "What's this about Rabelais? Nobody reads Rabelais these days."

"On the contrary, he is one of my favorites," Juliette Récamier said. She touched Balzac's cheek, as she had done when he fell to his knees. A little thrill passed through him. There was more than beauty to this woman; she gave off a kind of aura that had the effect of elevating the spirit of those around her.

"Do you think I dare send her my book?" Balzac asked, in the carriage.

"You're a fool if you don't," the duchess told him. "You've impressed her, you know. Not every minor novelist is asked to send a copy of his book to the Abbaye-aux-Bois."

"I am not a minor novelist!" said Balzac furiously.

"Excuse me. I am always forgetting," the duchess said smoothly. "Nevertheless, I should send the book. If Juliette hints that a book has amused her, everyone begins to read it."

"THE LAST CHOUAN wouldn't be right," said Balzac. "She won't be in sympathy with the point of view. I'll send her my PHYSIOLOGY OF MARRIAGE. Levavasseur tells me the first copies will be off press next week."

"If she likes it your worries are over," said the duchess firmly. "She could push the sale of a state report on the fauna of Corsica, if it amused her to do so."

Chapter 25

Bᴀʟᴢᴀᴄ ᴡᴇɴᴛ ᴛᴏ bed one night in the late winter of 1830, penniless, almost unknown, a former hack with a minor success to his credit.

He woke up famous.

Tʜᴇ ᴘʜʏsɪᴏʟᴏɢʏ ᴏғ ᴍᴀʀʀɪᴀɢᴇ had taken Paris by storm.

It is one of the characteristic ironies of the literary profession that Balzac came to the public notice on the strength of a book he cared little about, rather than ᴛʜᴇ ʟᴀsᴛ ᴄʜᴏᴜᴀɴ, into which he had transfused a portion of his life's blood.

The novel was received with temperate praise.

The sales were modest.

A few months later, on the stalls of Paris, appeared the first copies of ᴛʜᴇ ᴘʜʏsɪᴏʟᴏɢʏ ᴏғ ᴍᴀʀʀɪᴀɢᴇ. With unpredictable impudence, the book caught on at once. Through the rich streets of Paris, in the gilt salons and drawing rooms, in the best restaurants and the best brothels, one question was uttered before all others: "Have you read it yet?"

It was not necessary to mention the title. Within a week, the book was "it." For several weeks after its appearance, there was no other title worth mentioning. No one was reading anything else.

Soon a second question began to follow the first.

"Who is Balzac?"

Immediately, to this query, Paris offered a hundred answers. Suddenly, dozens of fashionable people professed to be on intimate terms with the unknown author.

"My dear, of course it's a woman," one duchess would say to the next. "No mere man could know that much about us." Then she would lean forward and whisper, "As a matter of fact, my dear, she's someone I know quite well. Of course, I've promised not to tell. Her husband is furious, of course. Livid, my pet. Livid!"

Variously, the book was attributed to Delphine Gay, to the Duchesse d'Abrantès, to Madame Récamier herself. A dozen hack journalists hinted that it was not impossible that they had a hand in the matter.

Naturally, all these rumors promoted the sale of the book. Quickly, Levavasseur went back to press with a second edition and ordered paper for a third. He was not much of an editor and his taste was faulty, but he knew how to sniff the wind, and the wind of Paris told him he had a great best seller.

From the first, with their baffling ability sometimes to sense that a book will sell before they have read it, the book-sellers in the Palais-Royal and along the rue Saint-Jacques, pushed the PHYSIOLOGY as they had not pushed a book in years, making capital of every rumor, even inventing a few of their own.

"You'd better get your copy now, Madame la Duchesse," they would advise a hesitant client. "It is said that the Archbishop of Paris intends to have the book suppressed."

"It is going on the Index, for a certainty, madame. Meanwhile, of course, a Catholic may read it with a clear conscience."

"The next edition is to be revised. The best passages will come out. If you want the original, as the author wrote it, get your copy today, monsieur."

During the intervals between editions, copies were sold at outrageous prices, dealers asking whatever they thought the traffic would bear. Copies were passed from hand to hand, worn out in a few days time. If a man chuckled or a woman laughed anywhere in Paris, it was taken for granted that the source of amusement was a line from Balzac's book.

Three weeks after publication, Levavasseur's office was swamped with mail, letters on every kind of paper, sealed with every crest and device. They poured into the publisher's office and overwhelmed the small staff.

"You need a secretary," Levavasseur complained. "You will have to hire someone to open all these letters."

"Send them around to my flat in bundles," Balzac said happily. "I'll see that they're opened."

The Duchesse d'Abrantès went through the letters first, as each batch arrived. Sometimes she identified the writer merely by glancing at the heraldry pressed into a fat blob of red, blue or yellow wax.

"That old crow!" she would exclaim scornfully, tossing the letter into a basket reserved for mail that was to be ignored. "She probably wants you to tell her why she can no longer hire lovers even by the hour, let alone for the night. I could tell her quickly enough. In addition to being a great-grandmother, she stinks like an abattoir. An African savage wouldn't have her."

Quickly, she would go through the stacks of mail, tossing most of the letters aside, from time to time pausing to slit one open with her paper-cutter, glancing at the contents, placing the letter in a special pile, saying, as the case might be, "You must accept this invitation, Balzac. The woman is a pig, I grant you, but dangerous. Too dangerous to ignore." Or: "Ah, the Comtesse Dranouel. Rich as hogfat. Reeking with money." Or: "I think this one should get a personal letter. They listen to her at court."

Balzac did as she told him. He was enjoying himself, drunk with his new notoriety.

The duchess laughed, reading a letter.

"Here is a man who insists that you meet him with pistols in the Bois de Bologne. He wants to defend the fair name of French womanhood, which he believes you have blackguarded."

There were offers of marriage, threats of murder, indecent proposals from all three sexes, requests for money, requests for advice, pleading letters, wheedling letters, threatening letters, flattering letters, contentious letters, obscene letters, illiterate letters.

There were letters, by the bushel and bale, and from every part of France, even from Germany and Belgium and Holland.

And there were invitations.

A few weeks earlier, Balzac could have starved in the street, died of loneliness in his rooms, gone to the colonies in a fit of depression, and no one would have taken the slightest notice. Now he was inundated with invitations to tea, to dinner, to supper, to the theater, even to breakfast. There were bids to receptions, soirées, salons, weddings, séances, christenings, duels, gatherings of spiritualists, political clubs.

The madame of the best brothel in Paris offered Balzac five thousand francs to select the most accomplished whore in the house, after sampling each resident in turn. The fortunate girl would then be proclaimed the Choice of Balzac, an accolade that would double her fees and encourage clients to form a queue while they waited to enjoy her favors.

Balzac declined.

"I love all women," he announced. "To select one above the others would be to betray my principles."

There were letters that contained a single line.

254

"You are a pig, monsieur!"

"Balzac! You should have your private parts cut off, in the unlikely event that you have any."

"Go back to England, pig-of-a-pig!"

"Only a German could write such nonsense in such bad French!"

One class of communication Balzac put aside, to read at leisure when the duchess had gone. These were the letters from publishers and from the editors of periodicals of every description, many of them men who had snubbed him a few weeks earlier, men who had been too busy to see him when he had called at their offices. For years he had peddled his wares like a literary huckster. Now it seemed that every editor in Paris wanted work from his pen at the highest prices.

At the end of a month, there were demands for work that would have kept the ordinary writer busy for a good twelve months.

Balzac was not the ordinary writer.

He took everything that was offered and asked for cash in advance. In a week his writing table was piled high with checks, bank draughts, cash and notes-of-credit. One enterprising editor sent the fee for an article in gold coin. Another promised to double the price if Balzac agreed to deliver copy in ten days time.

"Balzac, you have gone mad," the Duchesse d'Abrantès told him. "To meet these commitments you would have to employ a stable of writers, the way Dumas is said to do."

"Nonsense. I will write every word myself."

"You are simply inviting people to sue you by taking money you cannot earn," she said.

"I will meet every one of these commitments, and rewrite your mémoires, just as I've promised," he said. "You have never seen me work. I was trained in a tough school."

He was good as his word. Writing sometimes for as much as thirty-six hours at a stretch, stopping only to gulp a pot of the strong black coffee he loved, he turned out page after page, articles on almost every subject, short stories, pieces on politics, love, gastronomy, the art of the French toilette, philosophy, religion, "the morality of a bottle of champagne," "the physiology of a cigar."

The publishing world was startled, then shocked, then staggered

255

by Balzac's output. It was not unusual for a French writer to be a jack-of-all-trades. The best men of the period did it. What was astonishing and perhaps without parallel in the history of literature was the fantastic speed with which Balzac turned out his work, and his extraordinary change of pace, the ease with which he would finish an article on the Society of Jesus and, without so much as changing pens, take up the question of modern manners as revealed in the way a fashionable Parisienne handled her gloves.

In a single week, Balzac's name appeared in the columns of *Le Voleur, La Silhouette, La Caricature, La Mode,* and *La Revue de Paris.* For a time, it must have seemed to the readers of French magazines that there was no writer alive and working other than the ubiquitous Honoré de Balzac.

The "de" was firmly attached to his name by now. He used it as a writer and in society. After a time, he began to believe that it was his by absolute right. His mother sniffed at his presumption. His sister was shocked. Madame de Berny thought it vulgar. Balzac did not care. He was de Balzac from now on. If the particle wasn't his by right of heredity, he intended to earn it with his pen.

During the year that followed publication of THE PHYSIOLOGY OF MARRIAGE, Balzac wrote an average of sixteen printed pages a day—the equivalent of a good-sized book every two weeks. There was dross of course, but there was also gold. Among the short things he published were a number of minor masterpieces. . . . A PASSION IN THE DESERT, AN EPISODE UNDER THE TERROR. . . . brilliant examples of the short form.

While he was working at white heat, drugging himself with work and coffee, he was sometimes unable to distinguish the good from the bad in the stream that flowed from his pen like water from an inexhaustible spring. Even the cynical Duchesse d'Abrantès complained that he wasted his talent and risked his health.

"Also, you saturate the market," she told him. "Hold back a little. People can get too much, even of a good thing. It is the same with a writer as with a woman. No matter how beautiful, how desirable, how artful, if she sleeps with everyone, whenever everyone wants her, she soon finds that everyone has turned into no one."

"Very pretty," said Balzac. "You would be more persuasive, if it were not for the fact that you are a living refutation of your own theory."

256

She slapped his face. He laughed, caught her in his arms and kissed her, wrestled her into the bedroom and pulled her skirts up to her waist, taking her with her clothes on, laughing all the while. She lay on the bed in dishevelment when he had finished with her.

"Son of an illegitimate pig," she said, actually quite invigorated. "You have the manners of a stud bull."

He laughed at her, closing his trousers.

"I was proving a point," he said. "I am by no means no one, and as you perceive I cannot get enough of a good thing."

She got up from the bed and washed herself, not bothering to take off her skirt. The spectacle was obscene, suggestive of something seen in a brothel. As she squatted over the basin, Balzac slapped her rump.

"Change into something spectacular," he said. "We are going out to dine like kings."

They went to Véry's Restaurant, where Balzac ordered a tremendous meal, with a separate wine for each course, always the most expensive bottle in the cellar. People stared at him and whispered.

"Balzac!"

"It's Balzac, the writer."

"De Balzac, the fellow who wrote that hilarious book."

"Balzac!"

"Balzac!"

"Balzac!"

He adored it. He basked in it. He wallowed in notoriety and took it for fame, overlooking the real fame that his best work was creating for him, all over the world.

He was earning money, large sums of it, and spending it faster than it could be earned. He dined out lavishly, left enormous tips, bought clothes and jewels for his mistress. He owed a large sum to his mother, and various debts to the creditors of his printing and publishing days. He should have paid these accounts but he put them off, reminding himself that this was only the beginning of success.

"You are like a pirate from the Caribbean, drunk and squandering what he has stolen," his mistress complained.

"Call me what you like," Balzac said. "You will be right. I am a mass of contradictions, but contradiction suits me."

He seemed to do without sleep, during this first year of success. He met every social demand as well as those of the editors. He

257

went to the Abbaye-aux-Bois and had the pleasure of hearing Madame Récamier praise his wit as well as his daring. On his first visit to the rue de Sèvres he had been a nonentity whose only distinction was falling on his knees at the Récamier feet. Now he was the most notorious figure in the literary world of Paris. Young writers asked his advice. Older writers stared at him with envy. Women crowded around him, prodding him with outrageous questions, flirting without shame. Had it pleased him, he might have set up a harem to equal that of an Oriental prince.

He found it ironic that he had made his reputation as an authority on women, when actually his experience with them had been sharply limited. Until now, he had regarded the generality of women as beyond his reach. Now it seemed that the whole nation of women was there for the taking.

The stumbling block was the Duchesse d'Abrantès.

He was getting tired of her. Her stock of anecdotes was exhausted. Her wit was becoming repetitive and altogether predictable. The sexual fire was burning out.

The fact is, the affair is finished, he told himself. But how does a man go about getting rid of a woman like the Duchesse d'Abrantès?

He did not know.

The liaison dragged on for months after Balzac had ceased to find it rewarding.

It was Madame de Berny who came to his emotional rescue. Early in March, she returned from the south of France, where she passed the winter with her children. Balzac gave her dinner at the little secret restaurant, which for a number of years had been their favorite dining place.

She had changed.

She was a grandmother, and looked it. She had permitted her hair to go grey, almost white at the sides, and the effect was becoming. She wore black silk, trimmed at the neck and shoulders with velvet in a delicate shade of mauve.

She put him at ease at once. By the time they had finished an apéritif, sitting in one of the private rooms, he was on excellent terms with her again.

"So you have your wish at last," she said. "You are certainly well-known, if not yet famous. Even in Provence, people talked about nothing but the brilliant young writer who has revealed to the world the secrets of French womanhood."

258

Balzac laughed wryly.

"Tell me honestly what you think of it," he said. "I can't judge, you know. Sometimes I think it's trash and sometimes I think it's the cleverest book ever written."

"Of course I think it's neither one," said Madame de Berny carefully. "It's clever, yes. Very amusing. And it's not unsound. But there is a great deal of Rabelais in it. And, if you will forgive me, a certain amount of the wicked and witty Madame Junot, or, as you probably prefer to call her, the Duchesse d'Abrantès."

Balzac shrugged awkwardly and said, "She helped me. I don't deny it."

"Do you still see her?"

"I still see her, yes," he said. "You see, it's awkward."

"Naturally," said Madame de Berny. "You are tired of her, just at the moment when you are most valuable to her ego and her social prestige. You have a kind heart. You don't want to hurt her feelings and so on."

"What shall I do?" Balzac asked.

She smiled and patted his hand.

"It's the simplest thing in the world, my child," she said. "You simply go away, and you go to a place where she cannot possibly think of going with you."

"Go away?" Balzac said. "Now? Just when things are coming in my direction?"

They were interrupted by the waiter, bringing a platter of grilled sole. When the fish had been served, Madame de Berny picked up her fork, looking speculatively at Balzac.

"After all, you are a writer, not merely a celebrity," she said. "You are not one of those people whose only function is to decorate the fashionable salons. You probably enjoy being fussed over, but your real business is to sit down and write."

"If you knew how I've worked this last year!" he protested. "Articles, stories, essays. There's nothing I haven't written."

"Have you written a novel?" she demanded bluntly.

"Not exactly. But I have plans," he said defensively.

"Precisely. You have plans," she said earnestly. "They will come to very little if you go on as you are, with your journalism and dandyism, and self-exhibition. You are a novelist, Honoré. A good one. I have read THE LAST CHOUAN three times. You are a writer who knows how to use a large canvas. Stop playing with success. Sit down and write another novel."

259

He gave a long, weary sigh.

"You are right, as usual," he said. "On the other hand, look at the figures. I sweated blood over THE LAST CHOUAN. Months of labor, months of writing. Rewriting. Endless correction. What did it bring me? A thousand francs."

"Well?"

"I did THE PHYSIOLOGY OF MARRIAGE almost as a joke. It was written in a few weeks. It's brought me fifty thousand, and it's still very much alive."

"You know what the public is like," she said. "Too clever for their own good. If it takes a dirty joke to draw their attention, what does it matter? You have their attention now. They will read whatever you put your name to, good, bad or indifferent. For the time being, at least, you are in control, my child, not the public or the publishers."

"I know I should write a novel," he said. "Somehow, I haven't been able to get started."

"Then go away!" she said. "Sleep in a cool bed for a change. Get some rest and good food and a taste of country air."

"You sound like my doctor, Nacquart," he grumbled. "Rest, food, country air! I like Paris, I tell you."

"Then stay in Paris and be led about like a monkey on a stick by your slightly shopworn mistress," she said angrily. "Really, you are something of an ass, you know."

There were tears in her eyes. She was hurt. Balzac took her hand.

"Of course, of course. You are right," he said. "I will go away, I promise you. And I will write a novel. A novel that will make THE LAST CHOUAN look like the work of an amateur."

When he got back to his rooms in the rue Cassini, Balzac sat in his red armchair and stared intently at a point on the wall, staring like a man being put into a trance by a hypnotist. To sit this way was a habit with him, when he faced a problem that wanted thinking out.

Of course Madame de Berny was right.

He was fed up with the Duchesse d'Abrantès. He was fed up with fancy restaurants, fed up with salons, soirées, and success. For the time being, he was fed up with Paris. He felt the need to refresh himself for the plunge into a long book.

But where to go?

The prospect of going off by himself did not appeal to him. If he simply went to some fashionable resort outside of Paris, the Duchesse d'Abrantès would certainly follow him. He owed his mother a visit, but the idea of being alone with his mother did not suit his needs. He thought of Laure. The de Survilles would make him welcome, of course, but Laure was busy with her own affairs, and there was always the chance that his mother might decide to pay a visit.

Thinking of Laure made him think of Zulma Carraud. During the year that had passed since he met her, Balzac had put her out of his mind. Now she returned.

"If ever you feel the need of a rest among simple people, come to us," she had told him. "There will always be room for you at Saint-Cyr."

He scowled at the wall, asking himself whether an honorable friendship was possible between a man like himself and a woman like Zulma Carraud. What had attracted him at Versailles had not been Madame Carraud's beauty. It had been an unstated sense of alliance, a feeling of mutuality. What had warned him off was fear that what might begin as Platonic friendship would drift into something else.

Yet it might be possible, he thought.

Other writers, in the past, had enjoyed such friendships with women. He was tired and confused, battered by the success he had sought. He felt the need of someone who believed in him, someone who offered him peace as well as companionship, someone like Madame de Berny, but without the past to loom in the present.

He struck the arms of his chair with his hands. His mind was made up. He was going to Saint-Cyr l'École.

He sent a note to the Duchesse d'Abrantès, telling her that family affairs had called him away from Paris. He packed a bag that night, and the next morning he climbed aboard the stagecoach that went toward Versailles.

The moment he was settled in a first-class seat, he felt an enormous sense of relief, an awareness of having been saved from himself. He stared through the window of the stagecoach, watching the orderly trees pass by, feeling more intensely alive than he had felt in months.

Chapter 26

Oɴᴇ ᴍɪɢʜᴛ ʜᴀᴠᴇ
thought that a military school, alive with cadets and bugle calls,
was the last place on earth where a tired author in search of peace
would find what he was looking for. Balzac's contradictory temperament made it exactly the right place. He had always been fascinated by the military, and during the writing of ᴛʜᴇ ʟᴀsᴛ
ᴄʜᴏᴜᴀɴ his interest had been quickened by the task of going over
old campaigns and by General de Pommereul's reminiscences.
Saint-Cyr appealed to him as if it were a second home.

Major Carraud, as Director of Studies, had a modest but comfortable house, somewhat removed from the academy buildings,
the most important of which were the dreary stones of what had
once been a convent.

Zulma had a gift for decoration and gardening. She could have
made something attractive out of a prison courtyard. Though the
major had little beyond his pay, his wife had turned the drab,
cramped army house into a home that had character and charm.

Balzac was welcomed as a friend and as a man of letters. This
is the only term that reveals what Zulma felt about him. She had
a passionate, almost devotional respect for literature. She judged
a novel not by how many copies it had sold, or what the critics
had said about it, but as a work of art, entitled as such to full
respect, but also liable to total indictment.

Madame de Berny had seen the talent in Balzac and the energy.
The Duchesse d'Abrantès had recognized the potential literary
man of affairs, capable of stirring up a storm, achieving notoriety
and making money. Zulma saw the artist in him, the deep, under-
ground stream of his soul that fed the best of his work, of whose
existence Balzac himself was not always precisely aware.

Balzac was an artist—a man condemned to create for the sake
of the thing created. No matter how desperately he tried to become a journalist, entertainer, professional cynic, the artist in him

262

always rose in the end, to defeat the other forces. It may be that Zulma Carraud was more alive to the will to integrity in Balzac than was Balzac himself. There was a proud, fierce vein in her that gave force to her ideas, and her central idea was a throbbing belief in the dignity of man. She was French to the core, and serious-minded.

She detested THE PHYSIOLOGY OF MARRIAGE.

Balzac had sent her a copy, after some hesitation, and guessed at her disapproval when he heard nothing from her after the first polite acknowledgment. When he had been at Saint-Cyr for a few days, he decided to take the risk of mentioning the book.

They were in the front sitting room of the little government house, a square, low ceilinged box that Zulma had rescued by covering the walls with brocade salvaged from a set of curtains picked up for a few francs in a secondhand shop in Paris.

Major Carraud dozed by the fire, a cold pipe in his hand, a military textbook on his lap, place marked with his thumb. Balzac sat in a low leather chair that fitted the contours of his body almost as well as his red armchair at home. Opposite him sat Madame Carraud, dressed in brown serge, wearing no jewelry except for her wedding band and a plain gold locket on a thin chain. Between them, on a small marquetry table, was the backgammon board. Balzac shook the dice in the cup, but hesitated and did not complete the throw.

"You know, madame, I am very grateful for your good opinion of THE LAST CHOUAN," he said.

"It is a work of genius," she said firmly. "Imperfect, sometimes out of proportion because you tried to do too much, but without question a work of genius, a permanent part of French literature."

"And my PHYSIOLOGY OF MARRIAGE?"

"I hoped you would not force me to say what I think," she told him.

"You found it vulgar?"

"Vulgarity does not frighten me," she said. "It has its place in literature."

"Well then?"

"I don't want to offend you," she said.

"I am indestructible," he assured her. "Fire away."

She took the dice box from his hand, shook it and looked inside to see how the dice had fallen.

"I don't like to see you turned into a performing seal for the diversion of people in Paris who care nothing for ideas or for art. If I sound sentMC? I mean, sorry. It is what I really feel."

"Did you finish the book?" he asked.

She shrugged and said, "I read perhaps a third of it."

His vanity was hurt by the idea that anyone could begin one of his books and put it aside unfinished.

"I can understand your feeling," he said. "The early chapters are cynical, perhaps even cheap. But had you gone on, I think you would have found a firm defense of morality."

"Please do not go out of your way to misunderstand me," she said. "I do not object to the material—moral, immoral, amoral, obscene. That part doesn't matter. I object to the borrowed tone of voice."

"I beg your pardon?"

"It is Honoré Balzac speaking in an accent that God never gave him. It is Balzac in masquerade, taking off Rabelais, Boccaccio, certain offensive popular authors, Rousseau at his worst, occasionally, Laurence Sterne, who cannot be successfully imitated."

Balzac winced and said, "You use a sharp knife, madame."

"The honest reader is being cheated, you know," she said. "He pays for a book by Balzac and what he gets is a pastiche, a patchwork quilt put together with snippets filched from the cloth of other writers."

Balzac did not defend himself. The fact was, and he realized it, she had hit the mark more closely than most of the professional critics. All his life he had possessed the gift of mimicry, the ability to catch tone and gesture in automatic parody. People had told him that he would have made a gifted actor. It is a common talent in good writers, and useful, for it offers a test of dialogue and helps a man recognize the subtle rhythms of speech. In the course of his hack work, however, Balzac had become a literary mimic, imitating not from nature, but from the pages of other writers.

He did this with great skill. Often the literary false whiskers were altogether convincing. With the PHYSIOLOGY, he had fooled most of Paris, but that didn't matter. The thing was a curse that he was aware of, that he hated and fought. When he made his assault on the galley proofs of THE LAST CHOUAN, he had literally scrubbed the prose, rooting out wherever he found them the marks and patterns of other men, sometimes stubbornly insisting on a graceless phrase of his own instead of a smoother exposition derived from the style of someone else.

"You are a critic, madame," he said, looking Zulma Carraud in the eye. "Your mind goes straight to the heart of the matter, and you have taste."

"I am not a critic. I am a mother and a wife of an officer of the army," she said. "But I promise you one thing. Whatever you hear from me about your work will be what I really think, and never something said to please you. I am willing to praise a hideous waistcoat, or concede the beauty of your latest mistress, no matter what I think about them. Books are another matter."

He leaned forward and caught her hand.

"Zulma!"

She recovered her hand and put the backgammon board back into position.

"Shall we play?"

"Of course. Of course."

They played until half-past nine, when Major Carraud woke up. He rubbed his eyes then looked around him, as if startled to discover that he had fallen asleep. The heavy book fell to the floor. Zulma picked it up.

"Ah, Balzac!" the major said. "My dear chap, please forgive me. I must have dozed off."

Balzac bowed and made his good nights, then went upstairs to the whitewashed bedroom that Zulma had given him, saying, "It is yours for as long as you like."

It was a room that suited him. The walls were rough-plastered. The wide floorboards had been painted. There was a narrow wooden bed, the cover pulled tight as the skin of a drum. There was a table near the window, covered with new green baize. "How in the devil did she know I like to work on a green baize surface?" Balzac had asked himself. He shrugged, letting it pass. She had adopted him. That was enough.

He undressed, put on a flannel bathrobe, and sat down to work for an hour or two. The night was black and soundless. If he listened intently at the window, he could hear the sound of a sentry, pacing on a graveled walk. Every hour on the hour, from a distance came the sentry's voice: "*Post Number Four. All is well!*"

In the morning, he heard a bugle, then a flourish of drums as

265

the young gentlemen were turned out into the dawn, scrubbed, polished and eager. By the time they were marched off to breakfast, Balzac had gone back to sleep.

Balzac had been wary of Major Carraud, but to his surprise he and the major very quickly became friends. Carraud was a gentleman, a brave soldier, a good man, but tired now and ill, pursued by gout and bad luck. He was a graduate of the Royal Technical College, an engineer and scientist as well as a gunner. He had been one of the finest artillerists in the army and had fought with distinction in Italy, until the British had captured him. For eight years he was in the British prison hulks. The army had passed him by in his absence. When he was repatriated, in 1815, he had been given the Legion of Honor and tucked away at Saint-Cyr.

Balzac respected the major and soon grew fond of him. When his gout permitted, the major enjoyed rough shooting, and Balzac fell into the habit of going along with him. The major gave him a pair of moleskin trousers and some stout army boots, and he had his pick of the well-kept guns that were locked in a rack in the main hall.

The young bachelor officers made Balzac welcome in their mess. Here his literary status counted for nothing at all. The instructors at Saint-Cyr were hunting and riding types, who read no books but army manuals. They welcomed Balzac as a good fellow, with a sharp wit and a splendid arsenal of off color stories. They cheerfully defeated him at billiards, lost to him at backgammon, loaned him a horse when he wanted to ride, taught him to load, point and fire a cannon, drank him under the table on the rare occasions when he was rash enough to make a military evening of it.

For a time at Saint-Cyr, Balzac enjoyed the advantages of a gentleman's club as well as those of a home. He was happy there. Zulma's son called him Uncle. The young officers called him 'Noré. Carraud called him Balzac and came to regard him with grave affection. Zulma treated him with a mixture of candor and fierce respect.

On his first visit to Saint-Cyr, Balzac stayed for eight weeks. Sometimes he went to Versailles, to see his sister Laure, and twice he had been to Paris to call on an editor or two. Most of the time he had simply enjoyed the luxury of being permitted to do as he

266

pleased, writing in the night if it suited him, sleeping through the mornings, riding or shooting in the afternoons, in the evenings getting to know the rare quality of Zulma's mind.

When he left Saint-Cyr, he was on an even keel again, cured for the time being of the need to inflate his ego by accepting every invitation that came to him in the morning's mail. He had promised himself that he was going to stop playing the fool in order to impress fourth-rate people, stop spending money like an English milord, stop writing trash.

He entered his rooms in the rue Cassini, whistling a catchy tune of Béranger's, then singing a few lines:

> J'avais vingt ans, une folle maîtresse
> de francs amis, et l'amour des chansons
> Bravant le monde, et les sots, et les sages,
> sans avenir, riche mon printemps
> Leste et joyeaux, je monteais six étages
> Dans un grenier, qu'on est bien à vingt ans!

The words were gay and reckless and the tune appealed to his mood. But he was not twenty, nor did he sleep with a fine mad mistress. He was ten years late with his career and in his fourth decade. The need for time was like a bomb with a fuse that burned away inside him. He must hurry, he must rush, he must make up for the ten years during which he had been obscure. Everyone seemed to have passed him—Victor Hugo, Dumas, Lamartine, Eugène Sue—they were his age, most of them, but they had all established for years. He must catch up and overtake them. He could not accept his place in the race, or persuade himself that there was no race.

One by one, his good resolutions dissolved into mist. Borget, the painter, was going abroad and giving up the lower floor of Number 1, rue Cassini. Balzac decided to rent from the artist, and thus he came into possession of the entire house.

With a house on his hands, it was obvious that he needed a servant. Left to himself, he might have hired a footman and put him into livery, or an exotic Oriental manservant of the kind being kept nowadays by fashionable young men. Zulma Carraud, with the help of Laure, persuaded him that what he needed was a good French maid of all work, a bonne à tout faire. Zulma was delegated to find a suitable person.

What she found was Rose, a good-natured, slow-witted girl

267

from the Vendée. Certainly she will be no distraction when I am at work, thought Balzac, when he met the girl. Even his father would have found it possible to have resisted her charms.

She was in fact a distraction, but only because of his inability to teach her to brew coffee the way he liked it.

"Look here, Rose," he said one day, after she had presented him with a cup of lukewarm stuff that was faintly colored with coffee. "Do you know the soup they make in your part of the country? The soup in which a spoon will stand alone?"

The servant girl's eyes brightened.

"Oh yes, monsieur," she said confidently. "Everyone from the Vendée knows how to make the soup of the standing spoon."

"Well then," said Balzac patiently. "That is the way I like my coffee, do you understand? Thick and strong, like the soup in which one can stand a spoon."

"One comprehends, monsieur," she said.

That evening, at his writing table, he bellowed like a trooper, "Rose! Coffee!"

A few minutes later, Rose appeared, bearing a tray that held, instead of the familiar battered pot, a bowl of some steaming concoction that gave off a gastronomic perfume dominated by the thematic odor of cabbage.

"For the love of the God who died for us all, what have you got there, girl?" Balzac demanded.

Rose beamed happily and placed the tray on his writing table.

"Voilà, monsieur," she said proudly. "The soup in which one stands a spoon. Very nourishing. Very delicious. It has been cooking all day."

"Oh my God," groaned Balzac, striking his forehead with the palm of his hand.

When he was working, the thought of food, or of anything other than strong coffee, was distasteful to him. He intended to tell Rose to take the soup away, but when he looked up and saw her face he hadn't the heart to hurt her feelings.

"Good girl," he said. "Now run along to bed. I shan't need you again tonight."

Rose went happily off to bed. Balzac took a mouthful of soup, swallowed it, and made a face. Ordinarily, he would have finished the bowl, pronounced it magnificent, and called for another, for he had a taste for peasant food and Rose's soup was delicious. But

268

at this hour his hunger was for work, not food. Nothing would do but coffee. He carried the soup into the kitchen, emptied the bowl into the slop pan, poked up the fire and made coffee.

Back at his writing table, he held the cup to his nostrils and inhaled the precious odor. He took a swig of the bitter brew, sighed happily, and went back to work.

After that, he made his own coffee, as he had done before he had a servant. He was happy when Rose complained that there was too much work for one person. He made her a cook and confined her duties to the kitchen, and hired a man as his valet, a thin-faced, loyal chap named Auguste, who seemed at once to understand his needs.

Chapter 27

DURING THIS
year, Balzac developed the pattern of work that was to serve him
for the rest of his life, and become the subject of gossip, legend,
ridicule and awe.

He discovered that he worked best by turning the timetable
upside down. He went to bed at six P.M., leaving strict orders that
he was not to be wakened. At eight in the evening, when most of
his friends and acquaintances were getting ready for an evening
of relaxation, Balzac was in his bed, alone, asleep.

He slept through the fashionable dinner hour of Paris.

Nine o'clock, ten o'clock, when theaters, music halls and restaurants were crowded with people at play, Balzac was asleep. At
eleven, when the theaters were turning their crowds into the streets
and the boulevards were thronged with Parisians on their way
home, Balzac was still asleep.

At a few minutes before midnight, when Paris was beginning to
yawn and nod, Balzac began to stir. At midnight, he was awake.

Now that the city had gone to bed, he was assured eight or ten
hours of blessed solitude and quiet, a span of time when there
would be no visitors, no letters, no creditors, no printer's devils
bearing proofs to be corrected, nothing to interrupt the labor of
composition, nothing to cause the furnace to cool, once the fire
and been stoked and lighted.

"My thoughts drip from my forehead like water from a spring,"
he told Zulma Carraud. "With me, at any rate, the process of
creation is altogether unconscious. I sit at my table in the dead of
night, alone, silent, undisturbed. From somewhere, I'm not altogether sure where, there come to me sentences and paragraphs,
characters, incidents, ideas, falling into place, one after the other.
I cannot work the way Dumas does, whenever there is an hour to
spare, sandwiched between one girl and the next. Oh no! With me,
two or three hours are useless, when it comes to real writing. And
if I am forced to break off, it is hopeless."

Once awake, Balzac stretched himself and put on the special

270

garment he had finally decided was the ideal thing for writing—the white, hooded robe of a Carmelite monk, open at the throat, comfortable, permitting freedom of movement, providing the warmth required at night, without being oppressively heavy. Around his waist, over the robe, he wore a thin gold chain, from which dangled, instead of a Carmelite's crucifix, a paper knife and a pair of scissors.

Balzac had persuaded himself that the monk's robe had been chosen merely for its comfort and suitability. He laughed at his friends when they suggested that he fancied himself a kind of monk, once he had put on the habit and addressed himself to the night's work. Of course his friends were right. It was no accident that he dressed himself in the costume of a religious order, instead of wearing a dressing gown that would have been equally comfortable.

He had several changes of habit, warm cashmere for the winter months, robes made of first quality linen for warmer weather. They were always immaculate. He became superstitious about spilling so much as a drop of ink on the sleeve.

His work nights were invariable.

At a few minutes past midnight, wearing his Carmelite's robe, he drank a cup or two of coffee, standing alone in the silent kitchen. Then he flexed the muscles of his arms and legs, like an athlete testing himself, getting rid of the last kinks of sleep.

Wide awake, he marched into his study. His writing table, the same that had served him in the rue Lesdiguières, was covered with green baize of the variety used on billiard tables, for he found that the color was kind to his eyes and that the surface, under a piece of paper, was just right for the pressure of his pen.

At his left hand was a silver candelabrum, fitted each night with six fresh candles, casting a steady light on the green surface of his work table. The rest of the room was in darkness. Brocaded curtains lined with black felt closed out such sights and sounds as remained after Paris had gone to bed. Even the light of the moon and the stars were unwelcome while Balzac was at work.

The dawn was barred; he rejected even the natural clock of the sun.

At his right hand was the night's supply of pens, prepared from ravens' quills. They were both rare and expensive, but he would use nothing else. His inkpot had been filled and a spare bottle stood beside it. Once started, he wanted no interruption.

Near the candelabrum, on his left, was a green-covered common book of the kind in which schoolboys write out their exercises. It contained a miscellany of thoughts, ideas, words, phrases, images, that might be useful somewhere in the book he was engaged in writing.

There was no other equipment—no outline, no books of reference, no source material, nothing that might break the free flow of composition, once the process had been set in motion.

Balzac sat down at his table, pushed back the right sleeve of his robe, rubbed his arm, took up a pen, tested the nib on his thumb, dipped it into the ink, and touched the point to the paper. He spoke gently to himself as a skilful rider speaks to a highbred, nervous horse.

"Come along, now, Balzac. Enough of this nonsense. It is time to work."

He coaxed himself into motion, urging himself on, until, after a few minutes, the raven's quill was gliding over the costly blue-tinted paper on which he wrote. Once started, the powerful, resourceful engine of his imagination continued to operate, almost without halt, for eight, ten, twelve, sixteen, sometimes as much as twenty-four hours.

His thoughts tumbled over one another, sometimes producing themselves with such speed that the flying quill could not keep pace. Balzac abbreviated recklessly, and after a time began to use a kind of shorthand that became the despair of every printer in Paris. His handwriting became almost indecipherable, the letters frantic and ill-formed.

At the end of five or six hours, his mind would still be going strong, but the complaints of his body would intervene. In spite of the blue-tinted paper, his eyes began to smart with pain. His head throbbed. The muscles of his neck and back ached. His buttocks were sore. His writing hand grew numb. His nerves were so tightly drawn that he would start like a frightened animal when one of his candles spluttered without warning or some sudden sound managed to penetrate the felt guard at the windows.

Against his will, Balzac at last put aside his pen and rose from his chair, stretching the aching muscles of his back, flexing the fingers of his right hand, rubbing his temples. Then he would shake his head, like a dog coming out of the water.

"Ahhhh, Balzac! It is time for coffee!" he would say aloud to the darkened room.

272

He hated tobacco—one of the few things on which he and Alexandre Dumas were in agreement—and with wine he was temperate. But coffee! That was another matter. He was addicted to coffee; it was his vice.

"Too much coffee is bad for the stomach. It may even injure the brain," Zulma protested.

Balzac laughed at her, insisting that coffee was a gift of the gods. "Nothing so delicious could possibly be harmful," he argued. "Coffee glides into the stomach and sets everything in motion. Ideas advance like battalions. Memory comes to the front at the double. Without coffee I could not work. Without coffee, I could not live."

His coffee machine took on the character of a fetish, along with his Carmelite's robe, his ravens' quills, the gold dust with which he dried his pages, the table covered with green baize. These were his magician's props as well as the tools of his trade.

He brewed his own coffee, because he had learned that he could depend on no one else to make it the way he liked it—a thick, black, oily brew made from a mixture of Bourbon, Mocha, and Martinique, blended in equal proportions. Each kind came from a different shop—the Bourbon from a dealer in the rue Montblanc; the Martinique from a shop in the rue des Vielles; the Mocha from an enigmatic Turk, who had a hole-in-the-wall in an alley in the Faubourg Saint-Germain.

Balzac insisted on inspecting the green bean first, testing it between forefinger and thumb, sniffing critically, chewing a bit and spitting it out, then waiting until the beans had been roasted according to his directions. The purchase of a month's supply of coffee involved a journey half way across Paris and a good deal of time passed in waiting while the beans were in the oven, but it was one demand on his time that Balzac did not object to meeting.

Usually, at about eight in the morning, Balzac pushed back his chair, tossed his blunted quill aside, and rang for Auguste, his valet.

In a few minutes, the servant brought him breakfast on a silver tray. Trained to his master's habits, Auguste uttered not a word, not even a good morning. There might be a final word or phrase in Balzac's mind, not yet put down. Silently, Auguste put the tray on the table, then drew the heavy curtains, permitting daylight to enter the prison. With some ceremony, Auguste then put out the candles, by now burned down to stubs.

At this point, ordinarily, Balzac conceded the battle and said good morning to his servant. Slowly, he returned to the world he had abandoned at midnight, when he had picked up the first pen.

He ate his breakfast, a light meal, becoming aware of the sounds that came from the street—children calling to each other, on the way to school, the shouts of carters berating their horses, the clopping of hoofs on cobblestones, the high morning laughter of a young girl. All of these sounds of life were less real to Balzac than the imagined sounds of the other world from which he had just emerged.

While Balzac was eating breakfast, Auguste prepared a warm bath in an enormous tin tub that Balzac had ordered made in London when he failed to find what he wanted in Paris. Having read that Napoleon refreshed himself with an hour's soak in the morning, Balzac did the same. The tepid water relaxed his nerves, which had been abraded by the night's work, and he was able to meditate in privacy as he came all the way back into the world of the living.

By the time he had finished with his bath and rubbed himself down with a rough towel, there was usually a queue of people waiting to see him—printers' boys with wet proofs, other boys from other printers, sent to demand manuscript, publishers wanting books, editors wanting articles, young men in search of advice, young women in search of romance, and creditors.

Always, there were creditors, or their agents, armed with papers, reminding, wheedling, coaxing, blustering, shouting, threatening. Sometimes it seemed to Balzac that there was not a living soul in Paris to whom he was not in debt. He was making money, lots of it, but it never seemed to be enough. His household was expensive and when there were a few thousand francs to spare, there was always "the debt"—the hideous, seemingly permanent lien that went back to his days as a printer in the rue des Marais. To avoid having Balzac declared a bankrupt, Sédillot had been forced to agree to outrageous rates of interest on the outstanding indebtedness; consequently, reducing the load was like pushing the rock of Sisyphus uphill, a self-defeating occupation that would have ruined the disposition of most men.

Balzac's disposition remained astonishingly good. For a man in a notoriously dyspeptic trade, his good humor was phenomenal. Only where his work was concerned was he harsh or demanding. Here he was demanding to the point of being bizarre.

Most writers composed with the pen, glanced through the manu-

274

script, making minor changes, and sent it off to the printer. They read their galleys quickly, catching an error here and there, making an occasional change for the sake of style.

Not Balzac.

From THE LAST CHOUAN on, he began to regard the manuscript as nothing more than an outline, or tentative statement. He could not really feel a sentence or taste the flavor of a phrase, until he had it before him in type. If he could have had his own way, he would have set his books in type himself, and made his revisions in metal.

He did the next best thing.

Because his corrections were so extensive, he found that ordinary galley proofs, printed on cheap, yellowish paper, would not do. He insisted that his proofs be pulled on oversize sheets of white stock of the best quality. When these came to him from the printer, he set to work, tearing to pieces what he had written in the silence of the night, adding whole pages of material, altering nearly every sentence, changing names of characters, sometimes changing the grand plan of the story itself, supplying a new ending or a fresh beginning.

When a proof page was so covered with symbols, crisscrossed lines and deletions that nothing more could be added, Balzac patched out the galley with scissors and paste. When he had finished with the first set of proofs, they were scarcely decipherable.

Back they went to the unfortunate printer.

Even the most experienced compositors were baffled and only men who had been specially trained could master the hieroglyphics which Balzac presented to them. Most typesetters refused to work on Balzac's copy for more than an hour a day, and all of them demanded a premium rate for setting and revising his material.

"I tell you, Monsieur Balzac, it's a good thing you weren't writing books in the days when they were chiseled on blocks of stone," a grizzled old compositor told him. "Somebody would have brained you with a hammer."

Balzac laughed, slapped the man on the back, and gave him five francs.

He didn't care that people laughed at him, or that editors and publishers raged. He didn't care about the cost, which often came to him. When he was working he cared about one thing only, and that was the quality of the finished product. It was a preposterous way to write a novel, but it was his way. It suited his temperament. He went on revising a book until he thought he was finished with it, sometimes insisting on as many as sixteen sets of galley proofs before he would permit the printer to put the book into pages. Sometimes he forfeited half his fee, on a few occasions the whole of it, in order to work as he pleased. Publishers threatened to sue. A whole contingent of printers served notice that they would not work on his manuscripts, no matter what wages were offered.

He would not change. It was his way.

He worked on his proofs through the morning, then, at twelve-thirty or one, put them aside and ate a light lunch—an egg, a little sausage, a slice of ham, never anything more, for he believed that overloading the stomach caused the mind to become sluggish, and his work day was not yet completed.

When he had eaten the last of his lunch, back to the green baize table he went, to read his mail, answer letters, jot down notes in his copybook, outline a magazine article or two.

At five o'clock he was finished.

Auguste brought him his supper on a tray, unless he was entertaining a guest, which happened rarely when he was working. Madame de Berny came sometimes. Zulma Carraud would look in when she chanced to be in Paris on a shopping expedition.

That was all.

Though he was making a reputation as the one writer in France who really understood the secret lives of women, while he was working he was celibate as if he had actually been a member of the order whose habit he wore. Someone had told him that it would be hygienic to go to a brothel. He had tried it, and disliked it.

At six o'clock in the evening, when most men were beginning an evening of relaxation or pleasure, Balzac went to bed, falling immediately into a heavy, dreamless sleep, almost as if he had been drugged. Around him, Paris danced and laughed and played. He slept on. At midnight, with a gentle knock at the door, Auguste woke him up, then went to his study to light the candles. Balzac groaned, yawned, shook his head like a bull, then got up and put on his habit.

"Coffee," he muttered to himself, padding away toward the kitchen. "Good strong black coffee."

Another night of work had begun.

276

Balzac worked in this way for weeks, sometimes for months, without breaking his stride. Sundays, holidays, were swallowed up in the creative rhythm.

"Even infantry in battle are relieved from time to time," Zulma suggested mildly. "Certainly a few days in the country will not destroy the flow of your thought."

"It is my way," Balzac insisted stubbornly, refusing the invitation.

In Paris he became a legend. Every kind of rumor was circulated concerning his personal habits. It was said that he took drugs, hashish for preference. He was reported to keep a wild black mistress in a grass skirt, a savage with a ring in her nose. The fashionable pederasts boasted that he was a member of the confraternity and dozens of rouged young men blushed shyly and confessed that it was Balzac who had seduced them. Women he had never met insisted they had slept with him and described the adventure with relish. There were those who insisted he was a woman, or at least that he dressed in women's clothes, a story started by a printer's boy, who had seen him in his monk's robe.

Most of the gossip came back to Balzac.

He laughed at it all.

"Let them talk," he said happily. "The more they talk, the more the name Balzac gains currency, no matter what they say."

Balzac's way of life when he broke off work helped keep his legend bright. His extravagance became famous and his appearance invited notice and comment.

Buisson made him a blue frock coat with solid gold buttons of larger than usual size. With this he wore a pair of lemon-yellow trousers. He had a passion for gorgeous waistcoats and there were several dozen in his closet. He had hats of the best velours,

277

blocked to designs he evolved himself. He had shoes that were kept in walnut trees, various gloves, lace cuffs, silk stockings, ruffled shirts, three dozen walking sticks.

When he was composing the description of a room, Balzac's eye was flawless and his mind pounced on the slightest detail that might be revelatory. In all of Europe there was no writer as sensitive to detail or as passionate in the pursuit of accuracy. He could describe the costume of a duchess and prompt women of fashion to command their dressmakers to copy it. Yet he was blind to his own bad taste and stubborn in his refusal to take advice from others.

One evening when Madame de Berny came to his rooms for dinner, he put on the coat with the gold buttons. She threatened to leave unless he changed into something less flamboyant. His feelings were hurt, but he put on a plain grey coat of which she approved.

At dinner she reasoned gently with him.

"To be always at the height of fashion is an occupation in itself," she said. "Almost a minor art, like being a chronic, well-behaved drunkard. Unfortunately, people always at the height of fashion never have time for anything else."

"Why shouldn't I wear the latest styles?" he asked.

"It is simply not your métier," she said. "Leave the dandyism to de Musset."

De Musset was an acquaintance of Balzac, a writer, ten years younger, and forty pounds lighter. He was the most elegant literary man in Paris.

"A man doesn't have to be a bean pole like Musset in order to be well-dressed," Balzac argued.

"But it does help," said Madame de Berny, not meaning to be unkind. "Wear what you like when you play the clown in public, but when we are together like this, please select something from the more modest end of your closet."

He laughed and promised to dress like a schoolmaster when she came to dinner. He could not be angry with Madame de Berny. But when he ventured out—to the theater, the cafés, the fashionable restaurants he liked, or to Delphine de Girardin's salon, he dressed himself in the most extraordinary garments he could persuade Buisson to cut.

His bills were enormous.

He complained of his debts to Zulma Carraud, who looked at him sagely and said, "The fact is, you are unhappy unless you are in debt. Being in debt seems to stimulate you, even more than the yearning for fame. It is a perversion."

Balzac did not argue with her. He went on running up bills and working like a convict in the penal galleys. Always, ahead of him, were the shadows of Hugo and Dumas, his own age, but ten years on.

When he was exhausted both by work and the social life of Paris, he disappeared, going to Saint-Cyr to visit Zulma, or to Saché, in his own Touraine, where Monsieur de Margonne, his father's old friend, always had a room for him. To his friends in Paris, Balzac never announced his departure. One day he simply disappeared, gone off no one knew where. In a week, two weeks, a month, he would be back in the rue Cassini, refusing to admit that he had been away.

He was at Saché in the summer of 1830, when a short, bitter revolution in the streets of Paris forced Charles X from the throne of France.

On a hot morning in July, Balzac and Monsieur de Margonne drove into the village from Saché and found the tricolor flying from the staff on the City Hall. A crowd of workmen and farm laborers gathered in the dusty village square, chanting, from time to time, "A bas les Bourbons!" When the chanting stopped, the square was silent. Bees droned in the weary trees. Horses hung their heads and panted.

Balzac looked up at the Republican flag that hung limply in the still air, then surveyed the crowd in the square.

"Revolutionists!" he said with contempt. "Not one of them has the intelligence or spirit to rebel against his wife. Still, from the flag, it would seem that the king has been too stubborn to listen to reason."

"He is a foolish old man," de Margonne agreed. "He confuses himself with the great kings who ruled France in the past."

"He is finished," said Balzac. "Now God only knows what kind of government we will get." He glanced up at the flag again. "I suppose Dumas is in the streets, dressed up in a uniform. How he loves to display himself!"

They waited for the stagecoach from Paris, joining the crowd

279

that surrounded the driver when the vehicle came to stop, shouting excitedly, demanding news. The driver was a big, dark fellow with a red cockade pinned to his coat. There was a bottle on the box beside him, nearly empty.

"There is shooting in Paris!" he announced, standing up in the box. "The National Guard has fired on the people, a thing they'll regret, I can promise you."

"What about the king?" someone demanded.

"What about Charley Boy?"

"Has the fool had the good sense to quit?"

"Not yet," said the driver. "But soon enough, lads. Soon enough. Or else. . . ."

He drew his finger across his throat as if it were a knife. The crowd laughed. Balzac shook his head.

"This fellow doesn't know anything," he said. "It will be days before we find out what's really happened."

"In the meantime there's not much point in standing here in the sun," de Margonne said sensibly. "Let us go back to Saché, where we can enjoy the revolution in comfort."

Saché was a comfortable estate some eighteen miles from Tours, a modest château, with beautiful gardens and vineyards that went straight to the banks of the well-groomed River Indre. In front of the house was a broad, flat lawn and there were shade trees that provided haven from the midsummer sun.

Balzac and his host sat in iron chaise longues in the shade of an ancient oak and refreshed themselves wtih a bottle of slightly chilled Saché, the excellent minor wine produced by the Margonne grapes.

"I am thirty-one," said Balzac. "Not a great age. But in my lifetime, France has changed her form of government on five occasions."

"That will not be the final score in the game," de Margonne ventured, sipping his wine. "We French are a volatile people. We enjoy change for the sake of itself."

Balzac shook his head, staring at a cast iron dog which stood guard near the Margonne gates.

"I don't care much for the British," he said. "But when it comes to writing novels and to government, France could take lessons from them. France ought to be a Constitutional Monarchy, like England. We should have a hereditary Royal Family, a chamber

280

of peers, to represent the aristocracy, and a second chamber, elected, to speak for the middle classes."

"Aren't you forgetting the people?" asked Margonne.

"Not at all," said Balzac. "There should be universal education, eventually free, so that talented members of the peasantry and the working classes can pass easily into the class above. In that way the middle class will be refreshed and sustained, protected from dryrot."

By instinct, upbringing and association, Balzac was a Royalist. He believed in the monarchy, the Bourbon monarchy for preference, because he believed in stability. Yet he also believed in the rights of the people.

De Margonne was older and politically less naïf. He filled a handsome meerschaum pipe and lit it with a patent match that flared up like a torch, giving off the poisonous odor of sulphur.

"You are young," he said. "You expect too much of your poor tired country. We shall have a republic, not the British monarchy. And if we do not have a republic, we will have a shopkeeper king and a government of shopkeepers."

"God forbid it!" said Balzac with passion. "Better go back to the senilocracy we had under Louis XVIII."

De Margonne chuckled softly and puffed at his pipe.

"There is an advantage to living in Touraine instead of in Paris, 'Noré," he said. "My vines grow peacefully, you see, no matter what kind of king sits on the throne in the capital."

There had been shooting in Paris, it was true, and the Royal Guards had fired on the people, but as a revolution it was a fiasco, a three-day travesty of the Great Revolution of a generation earlier, that had put an end forever to absolutism, old style.

It was also true that Alexandre Dumas had put on a uniform and sword and led a contingent of rebellious Parisians in the direction of the Tuileries. He had been stopped at one of the bridges by a good-natured regular officer who had read and admired his books.

Victor Hugo had written an ode to the heroic revolutionists, singing of men, women and children, running to the fight against the well-drilled Guards, "while the panting tocsin, sounding from the belfries, summoned the workers from their quarters with its fearsome death rattle."

281

Alphonse Lamartine had joined the rebels in earnest, and committed himself to politics from this point on.

The revolution simmered, boiled and stopped. At the end of three days, the creaking Bourbon, Charles X, stepped down from his throne and went into exile. The Duke of Orléans was chosen by the middle class to be Louis-Phillipe, the first bourgeois King of the French, a king who wore a grey hat and carried an umbrella.

When the government fell, Balzac's first thoughts were for the Carrauds. He knew that the military school at Saint-Cyr was suspected of being in sympathy with the Bourbons, and he was sure that the new régime would cast a cold eye at the regular army. He wrote to Zulma, urging her to persuade the major to take steps to protect himself in the military upheaval that was certain to follow the installation of the new king.

"Perhaps there will be a place for him in the Technical School," he wrote. "At any rate, he must be prepared to jump, and he should decide on a place to land."

Balzac did not have much hope that Major Carraud would heed the warning. The years in the British prison hulks, followed by periods of duty in various military backwaters, had caused Carraud to be chronically resigned about his career and given him the habit of expecting the worst.

Balzac had no answer from Saint-Cyr.

When he returned to Paris, he tried to trace the Carrauds through the army office, but the confusion there was so great that no one knew where anyone else had been sent.

"For all we know, monsieur, the king may abolish the army tomorrow and hire Germans to take our places," a tired adjutant told him.

Finally, Balzac learned that Zulma and her family had gone to Frapesle, her childhood home, to wait until things quieted down and a post could be found for the major.

Politics were as confused as the army. There were four major parties and scores of factions. Everyone seemed to be involved in intrigue—for the government, against it, in favor of the new king or the old. There were even a few imperialists, who yearned for the glories that were gone with Bonaparte.

In the literary cafés, the followers of Saint-Simon were agitating quietly for the establishment of heaven on earth. Bearded refugees from Russia whispered that bombs were the only answer. The

282

governing chamber was filled with old men, who debated endlessly and did nothing.

The great, ancient bureacracy went on without interruption, stamping papers, filling out forms, granting permission to open sewers, refusing permission to build new streets.

In short, France was normal.

Listening to the nonsense he heard in cafés and theater lobbies, Balzac was struck with the idea of going into politics himself. If he could get elected to a deputy's seat, it would be only a step to the cabinet. For a man of his ability, the step would surely be a short one. He discussed it with Madame de Berny.

Being a woman of sense who had known a great many politicians, she attempted to discourage him.

"You don't think I can get elected?" he said.

"On the contrary," she said. "If I were certain you'd lose, I'd have no objection to your standing for office. It might be amusing. But with France in her present state of confusion, you might very well be elected to something or other and that, my child, would be fatal."

"You make fun of me," he protested.

"Never," she said. "But I know these people in the Faubourg Saint-Germain, whose drawing rooms, bedrooms and boudoirs you assume would be open to an eager deputy of the Right. They would use you to the limit, meanwhile laughing behind your back. In the end they would destroy you as a writer and as a human being."

"You forget, I am Balzac," he said. "I am indestructible."

"As a writer yes, you are very nearly indestructible," she said. "As a politician, you would be a very perishable article indeed. They would eat you alive."

He was stubborn enough to ignore her advice. He persuaded General de Pommereul to enter his name in the elections for the seat representing Fougères. He had no money to make a campaign and no supporters, but he was a candidate, nevertheless, and all of his friends in Paris knew it. When the votes were counted, Balzac had fourteen, most of them, one presumed, cast by friends of the general.

For the time being, he put his political aspirations in his pocket, though from the sidelines he continued to observe the antics of government with keen interest and a growing sense of amazed incredulity.

"The last government was like a first-class whore," he said. "It was corrupt and corrupting, but there was a thread of humor in it. One could laugh, sometimes, even at the corruption. This government of Louis-Philippe—well, it's got all the airs of a virtuous woman who will sell her favors dearly but sell them all the same."

Drinking coffee at the café one day with a young socialist writer who suggested that innovations were in order, Balzac laughed and said, "Oh, yes, you Saint-Simonians are innovators, no doubt about that. You have invented in 1830 the philosophy that Voltaire professed in 1790."

The truth was that like most writers, he agreed really with none of the parties, each of which had a plan that was guaranteed to save France—from the future, from the past, from the looming Germans, from herself.

There was not much logic in his politics.

He wanted a strong, proud king and a court with all the pageantry of Versailles, an intrenched class of nobles, complete with estates, servants, lace at the cuff, jewels, horses, courtly intrigue. Politically, his mind was in the past. He romanticized the old régime and saw it as a time when art and beauty had flourished happily under wise and well-kept monarchs. And he was fascinated by the old aristocracy, now encamped in the Faubourg Saint-Germain.

He also wanted a contented, efficient and well-dressed middle class, a squirearchy, comme les anglais, and a happy, aspiring proletariat, for whom free education was to be provided, so that the best could rise to the class above.

"But who then will sleep under the bridges?" asked Madame de Berny, laughing at him.

"Writers!" Balzac answered.

In the autumn, Balzac began to contribute articles on politics to Le Voleur, a weekly journal owned by Emil de Girardin, publisher of La Presse, which was the most powerful organ in France. It is a commentary on the state of French politics that Balzac's articles were not only published, but read and taken seriously—discussed in salons and cafés.

Perhaps his sense of humor saved them. What he lacked in logic he made up in wit, and his "Paris Letters," as the series in Le Voleur was called, often made lively reading.

He had always been an admirer of the Marquis de Lafayette. Now that he found himself in disagreement with the distinguished old man, Balzac simply observed that "even the greatest of men ought to know how to go to heaven at the right time."

Meanwhile, he was spending money—on clothes, food, jewelry, furniture, books, bibelots, perfume, walking sticks—anything that could be purchased, he bought, paying for it if he had cash in his pocket, more often than not simply going a bit further into debt with each new acquisition.

He fell behind in his payments to his mother. When she wrote to him in complaint, he replied lightly, "Sooner or later, politics, journalism, a rich marriage, a stroke of luck in finance or the business world—one of these will make me rich as Croesus. So why worry? We must simply suffer a little longer."

To Balzac's mother, flippancy of any kind was in bad taste. To be flippant about money was intolerable, an outright sin, perhaps a sign of insanity. She wrote angry letters that Balzac destroyed, pretending to be indifferent.

He was not indifferent.

The old war with his mother that had started before he was born, went on as always, a deep river of discontent, not understood or always admitted, but always there.

As a result of his "Paris Letters," Balzac became a favorite at the salon of Madame de Girardin—the powerful and incomparable Delphine.

The de Girardin salon was not the society to which Balzac aspired—the haughty, aristocratic, inbred society of the Faubourg Saint-Germain—but it was all the same a glamorous theater, a place where he met rich men and beautiful women, where he exhibited his new clothes, where he found a chance to display his flair for wit and conversation.

He liked Delphine and admired her shrewdness almost as much as her beauty. She was a successful adventuress, daughter of the English beauty, Sophie Gay, who had been as famous for her many lovers as for her sardonic novels.

To Delphine, being Emil de Girardin's wife was a profession like any other. She had been in love with Alfred de Vigny, danced with him, slept with him, wanted very much to marry him. Unfortunately, de Vigny was an aristocrat, in spite of the fact that he was a writer. To fall in love beneath his station was one thing, to marry beneath it, quite another, so Delphine had formed her alliance with the illegitimate son of General le Comte Alexandre de Girardin.

The marriage was an arrangement that gave each party for value received. De Girardin, who was ambitious, got the most effective hostess in Paris. Delphine got the luxury she wanted. Love had nothing to do with the matter, and it was no secret that Delphine sometimes formed discreet attachments.

Balzac would have found it charming to have joined this select society. Delphine was exciting and he was certain that sleeping with her would be delightful.

He was not invited into her bed.

Her old lover, Alfred de Vigny, told him that he was wasting his time.

"You are in your thirties, Balzac," he said, in his aristocratic drawl. "That's much too old for Delphine. She likes young men, very young men. It's only a matter of time before she begins to experiment with virgin boys of fourteen or so."

Everyone of literary importance came to Delphine's soirées. Dumas was often there, boasting of his latest conquest in literature or love. Alfred de Musset, slim and elegant, was an habitué. So was young Théophile Gautier. Victor Hugo sometimes came, always chiding Balzac for his old-fashioned political views.

Balzac disliked Dumas, though he admired the man's energy and his ability to be utterly indiscriminate where women were concerned. Dumas could roll into bed with a kitchen maid or a duchess, or with anything in between, and roll out again in the morning with never a look behind him.

"Dumas could sleep with a cat and enjoy it," said Balzac to his friend de Musset. "I envy him that. With me, in order to enjoy sleeping with a woman, I must be in love with her a little, or at least be presuaded that she loves me."

"Very un-French," de Musset told him. "That's what comes of having gorged yourself on English novels when you were young."

Women continued to complicate Balzac's life.

He had brief ineffectual affairs that were stale almost before

286

they were started. He was bored with the women he met. His sexual appetite was keen and he longed for a woman, but his nature demanded more than the simple use of her body.

What he truly wanted he could not have, for he yearned to be loved alone, to be both possessed and possessor, in a total arrangement that persists, if anywhere, only in heaven.

In his books, he was often writing from the depths of his soul to an ideal creature who existed only in his mind. In this way, he created powerful effects and the women who read his books responded to him in extraordinary fashion, writing love letters to him, sometimes even waiting on his doorstep, ready to offer their favors.

Single handed, Balzac created the woman of forty.

Until he appeared on the scene, the heroines of fiction had been virginal girls, usually under twenty, dewey-eyed with the innocence of youth, utterly unstained.

Balzac changed all that.

He gave his heroines faults as well as virtues, vital organs as well as pearly complexions. His heroines were not girls, but women. Madame de Berny had taught him that a woman of forty can love and be loved with an intensity of which youth is incapable.

Fully grown men had realized this for a long time, of course, but the thing simply wasn't mentioned in books. In books, women of forty were mothers, with passion all behind them.

Balzac broke the convention.

Women all over the world read his books and applauded.

There were men who complained, among them the critic, Jules Janin, who was old enough to have known better.

"Balzac's books are an insult to the young, marriageable women of France," wrote the petulant Janin.

Janin somehow involved the Honor of France with his distaste for Balzac's heroines. He denounced Balzac as a dangerous man whose books encouraged adultery, contempt for marriage, and a decline in the birth rate that would decimate the ranks of the glorious army that had given France her greatness.

Balzac was amused by Janin's attack. Not so his friends. Delphine de Girardin was furious and came to Balzac's defense with an article in *La Presse*. The argument raged. Woman continued to read Balzac, to write to the author, to call on him, to send him gifts.

Balzac would have been less than human had he not been flattered by all this feminine attention. He read the letters that came to him, and answered those he found amusing or that piqued his curiosity. When he was not working, he sometimes entertained the ladies who waited on his doorstep.

By reputation, he was becoming a cynical libertine; at heart, he remained an incurable romantic.

Always and everywhere, he was seeking the woman who had been created for him and for him alone. He looked for her, this unknown, in the letters that came to him from strangers. He sought her in the salons, at the theater, in the streets of Paris. In the dead of night, by candlelight, dressed in the habit of a cloistered monk, he pursued this woman God must have created for the arms of Honoré de Balzac.

He had, of course, a conception of her.

She was beautiful, possibly blonde, certainly of noble birth, in all probability rich. She was the princesse lointaine who existed neither in this world nor the next, a fairy princess who would turn into a puff of smoke if he found her.

To be a famous writer was to capture the public imagination as a personality. Sometimes, Balzac literally found women waiting for him on his doorstep.

One of these was Maria du Fresnay. She was twenty, a pretty creature with soft southern skin and a shower of glossy black hair. She had read his novel, THE MAGIC SKIN and become infatuated with the author, sight unseen.

THE MAGIC SKIN, partly based on Balzac's old dream, was the first of his novels to reveal his uncanny insight into the secret thoughts of women. It was a sensational success; all over France women read it and marveled at Balzac's almost diabolical ability to plumb the depths of the feminine soul. The book had a strange effect on most of the women who read it, seeming to stir them with the desire for fulfillment, to make them aware of their own passions.

One woman so affected was Maria du Fresnay.

She wrote to Balzac, asking for permission to call. Some note of freshness in her letter prompted him to answer and say that he would be glad to see her.

He had instantly forgotten both her letter and his own reply, but a few weeks later, when he was returning from Delphine de Girardin's salon at two o'clock in the morning, she was waiting for him in front of his house in the rue Cassini. She stood up as he got down from his carriage and walked toward the door. He saw her in the shadows and drew back, startled.

"Who's there?" he called. "Who is it?"

"I am Maria," the girl replied. "I wrote to you, from Toulouse."

Balzac remembered nothing about it. Then he saw that the girl was shivering. The night had turned cool, and she wore only a light cloak.

"Poor child, you are freezing," he said, taking her arm. "Come into the house. I'll give you something to warm you up."

He raised the knocker and rapped smartly. Auguste opened the door, dressed in his nightcap and a flannel gown.

"Good evening, monsieur," he said sleepily. Then he saw the girl and raised an angry finger. "I told you to go away," he said. "You should be ashamed of yourself, at your age, sitting on people's doorsteps." He turned to Balzac. "She has been here since four o'clock, monsieur. I told her to go, but she doesn't seem to understand simple French."

"Calm yourself, Auguste," said Balzac. "The young lady is cold. Get her some brandy, the Armagnac. And bring my coffee machine. Come along, my child," he said to the girl. "We'll soon have you warmed up."

He intended to give her some brandy and coffee, then send her off and settle down to his night's work. He took her upstairs to his study, lit the candles on his worktable, and gave her a chair. The light fell on her face. She looked very beautiful, very young, very frightened and very cold.

"Auguste!" Balzac shouted. "Hurry along with that brandy."

Muttering his disapproval, the servant appeared, carrying a fat bottle and a pair of the best glasses.

"Give me those," Balzac demanded.

He poured out a double brandy and handed it to the girl. She held it in both hands, like a child with a bowl of porridge.

"Drink!" Balzac commanded. "That will take the chill out of your bones."

Obediently, she took a sip of the powerful stuff and coughed. Balzac laughed and sat down in his red armchair. He looked at her, across the room, really seeing her for the first time.

"You are beautiful. And only a child," he said.

She smiled at him placidly and took another sip of brandy. In that light, her face had the enigmatic quality of a fifteenth century madonna carved out of wood and painted. She was innocent as a young nun, yet there was a curious candor in her eyes.

It was disconcerting.

"You are from the south, by your accent?" he said.

"From Toulouse," she said.

"That was my father's part of the world," he said. "But what brings you to Paris? Are your parents with you?"

She shook her head, tasting the strong, bitter coffee.

"They are in Toulouse. They have never been elsewhere," she said. "My father keeps a shop, linens, draperies, things by the yard. We live above it. It is dull, monsieur. Toulouse is dull, and my father's shop is perhaps the dullest place in Toulouse."

She smiled, stretching herself like a kitten, a voluptuous movement that was at the same time innocent.

"Sometimes, monsieur, it is so dull that one can imagine he has died and is waiting in a limbo that smells like cloth," she said.

Balzac laughed. The girl had an odd, poetic turn of phrase and her accent was charming.

"So you have left the limbo that smells like cloth," he said. "You are visiting relatives in Paris?"

She shook her head.

"Friends?" he asked.

"I am visiting you, Monsieur de Balzac," she said, her voice filled with an odd self-assurance.

"You are insane!" Balzac said impatiently. "To come all the way to Paris to see a writer, simply because you have enjoyed his book. It is preposterous."

"Until I read your book, I was no one," she said, matter-of-factly. "When I had read it, I understood that I was a human being."

"Do you have any money?" Balzac asked, feeling a flash of responsibility.

"Oh yes. A hundred francs," she said confidently.

"And when that's gone?"

She shrugged.

"I shall work," she said indifferently. "I can cook and sew and serve, you see. I shan't go hungry."

Balzac leaned back in his chair. It is time to go to work, he thought. I must send this idiot child away and get into my writing clothes.

But he did not get up.

He drank three glasses of brandy, for him a very large amount. Then he closed his eyes and let his head rest on the back of the chair. He was tired. More than tired. He was on the edge of nervous exhaustion. He half slept in the chair, his arms limps, legs outstretched, one hand trailing the floor. The alcohol worked on him slowly, calming his nerves a little.

He felt a cool hand on his forehead. The girl was stroking his forehead gently, with a slow, calming rhythm. He felt the tension ease. She knelt in front of his chair and loosened his shoes.

"You are tired," she said.

"Yes, tired," he said, moving a hand, his eyes closed, touching the girl's cheek.

She remained on the floor beside his chair, her head pillowed on his thigh. For an hour neither of them moved. The candles on Balzac's worktable flickered occasionally in the slight draft that managed to come through the heavy curtains. The room was still. The only sound was the ticking of Balzac's porcelain clock.

Gradually, the nervous fatigue left Balzac's body. It was as though a series of knots were being loosened in his arms and legs, the back of his neck. He was calm, but intensely aware of the young body that touched his own, as if he drew life from it. Finally, not altogether conscious of his actions, responding automatically, he put his hands on her shoulders and drew her close to him. She sat curled up on his lap, her cheek against his. He moved his head and their lips met. Her mouth was fresh and sweet, the lips cool.

When he touched her she moaned and he felt her body shudder. He had a sense of unreality, as if he handled a statue rather than a living creature.

Then at last she stirred.

"I belong to you," she said. "Do what you like with me. Love me. Beat me with whips. Burn me in the fire. Kill me if you like when you are finished with me. But need me, love me, I beg you. Make use of me."

He lifted her in his arms and carried her into his bedroom. A hint of light came through the doorway from the candles in the study. He stood beside the bed with Maria in his arms. She weighed no more than a child. He lowered his head and kissed her gently.

"Maria," he whispered. "Maria."

She lay on the bed, bright and naked, motionless as a statue, her eyes filled with wonder and astonishment, but without fear, her lips moist and slightly parted, her hair loose and like a black pool that framed her face. He realized that she was a virgin. He went rigid.

"It does not matter," she said. "Do what you like with me."

When it was over he felt the perverted exhilaration a murderer must feel at the moment he plunges the knife into the breast of his victim. Then, because there was no real cruelty in him, he felt profound, bitter shame.

"I am sorry," he said.

"It doesn't matter," she said.

He got out of bed and went to the washstand, filling the basin with water. He sloshed his face, then his body, and rubbed himself with a rough dry towel. Then he put on his Carmelite's robe. Maria watched him, wonderingly.

"My working clothes," he explained.

There was a china bidet in a curtained alcove. He drew the curtain so the girl could see it, then kissed her and went into his study. He felt refreshed as though he had taken some kind of drug that was tonic to the nerves.

The candles had burned down one-third of the way. Without looking at the clock, Balzac knew that the time was between half past three and four. He rubbed his hands together to stimulate the circulation, then pushed back the right sleeve of his gown and picked up a fresh quill.

"My God, I feel marvelous!" he said.

He dipped the pen into the ink and went to work. In three minutes, his pen was flying. At the end of an hour, when he paused for a moment to flex his wrist, he realized that he was working better than he had worked for months.

At dawn, Auguste brought his coffee, strong, hot and fragrant. Balzac finished a cup, poured himself another, and sighed. Halfway through the second cup, he remembered the girl.

"Good Lord!" he exclaimed, spilling coffee on his wrist, scalding himself.

292

He got up and hurried into the bedroom, the skirts of his robe trailing behind him.

The bed was empty.

Sometime during the night, while he had been immersed in his work, she had dressed herself and crept past him, leaving a note to tell him that she could be found at the inn of the Golden Lion in the village of Montmartre.

He sat on the edge of the maculated bed, trying to remember Maria's face. He could not produce an image in his mind. He could only remember the warmth of her body, the fresh, sweet taste of her mouth, her young voice saying, "I belong to you. Do what you like with me."

Was it a form of madness, hysteria?

He did not know.

He only knew that for him the experience had been therapeutic, miraculous as a glass of water offered to a man who is dying of thirst.

Chapter 29

To MADAME DE Berny, Balzac's political aspirations were preposterous. To Zulma Carraud they were reactionary and dangerous. To one group of people in France, they were of great speculative importance, though Balzac did not know this.

The Legitimist Party, partisans of the Duchesse de Berry and the Bourbon cause, represented the extreme right wing of the royalist movement. They were almost without general support. The important writers of France, except for Balzac, had attached themselves to more liberal causes. Hugo, Dumas, Eugène Sue, Jules Sandeau . . . all looked on the Legitimists with scorn.

The Legitimists had funds and shrewd leaders. They needed a popular figure with a voice, and they set a trap for Balzac, who was made to order for their purposes.

The leader of the Legitimist cause in Paris was the Duc de Fitz-James, a shrewd, suave and ambitious adornment of the aristocracy of the Faubourg Saint-Germain, the very aristocracy that Balzac was eager to enter.

"We need Balzac and we need him badly," the Duc de Fitz-James confided to his colleague, the Duc de Rauzun. "But how to get him?"

De Rauzun shrugged, playing with a gold lorgnette.

"I have met him, you know," he said. "He is a revolting creature, dressed in the most incredible clothes. He would not be an asset sartorially."

"If he can be persuaded to write for our cause, he can dress in his underwear," said Fitz-James bluntly. "We need him, my dear chap. In politics, one must hold one's nose and associate with odd companions."

"He is supposed to be extremely susceptible to women," said de Rauzun. "You know his reputation. It is said that a pretty face can destroy his reason."

294

The Duc de Fitz-James frowned.

"You have given me an idea, de Rauzun," he said. "We will offer this Balzac some tasty bait. Bait he will never be permitted to swallow, mind you, but bait so attractive he will be unable to resist."

"What have you in mind?" asked de Rauzun.

"I am thinking of my niece, the Duchesse de Castries," Fitz-James told him.

"But will she do it?" de Rauzun asked, frowning. "After all, she is a sensitive woman. I tell you, this Balzac is a gross creature."

"She will do what I ask her to do," said Fitz-James. "It is not so much that will be asked. I told you, Balzac will not be permitted to swallow the bait."

"May God forbid it," said de Rauzun.

In setting the royalist trap for Balzac, Fitz-James had selected a lure that Balzac could not have been expected to resist. The woman who was to draw him into the Legitimist orbit answered every one of Balzac's demands. She was Henriette Marie, Duchesse de Castries, daughter of the Duc de Maille, who had been a distinguished Marshal of France. The quarterings on his coat of arms went back to the eleventh century. The duchess's mother had been a Royal Stuart, the beautiful Duchesse de Fitz-James. Her husband, the Marquis de Castries, was a grandson of the famous soldier.

The romance that surrounded Marie de Castries might have served as the plot of one of Balzac's novels.

At twenty-two, she had been one of the most glamorous women in France, daughter of a great house, married into a great family. Then she had fallen blindly in love with Victor Metternich, son of the Austrian chancellor. She had moved out of her husband's house, openly, without pretense. Young Metternich had turned his back on a brilliant career. The lovers had gone into exile in the Austrian Tyrol.

The idyll was a short one.

The Duchesse de Castries was thrown from her horse; her spine was injured, so that she was obliged to pass most of the day on a sofa or chaise longue. Victor Metternich, never robust, caught tuberculosis and died. The duchess returned to Paris, to her father's mansion, the Castellane Palace, where she lived in solitude and sorrow, seeking consolation in books.

By chance, she was reading Balzac's THE MAGIC SKIN when her uncle, the Duc de Fitz-James, approached her and appealed for her cooperation. She was bored with life and the prospect of playing spider and fly with Balzac was one that amused her.

"But how shall I meet him?" she asked.

"Write to him," Fitz-James advised. "Be tentative at first. Lead him on. The whole thing must be handled with tact, do you see?"

So the Duchesse de Castries became one of the several thousand women who addressed themselves to Balzac in admiring letters. Once he learned her identity, Balzac was wild with the desire to meet her. All his life he had been fascinated by the romance of the old régime. What was left of the old régime now had its existence behind the ornamented façades of the great mansions in the Faubourg Saint-Germain, and to Balzac one of the great ambitions was to be accepted in the drawing rooms of these fine houses.

Of all the great mansions of the Faubourg, the Castellane Palace, where Marie de Castries lived and held court, was one of the most splendid. Balzac begged her for permission to call. He was refused. He wrote again, and again.

At last the cloistered duchess relented. Balzac had his wish. He was asked to present himself at the Castellane Palace, in the Faubourg.

He was out of his mind with delight, and saw a new sun on his social horizon.

Chapter 30

W HEN THE GREAT
day came, Balzac dressed with extreme care, wearing his lemon-
yellow trousers, his blue coat with gold buttons, a cravat made of
heavy Persian silk.

"Auguste! My cane!" he demanded.

"Which cane, monsieur?" the servant asked dryly. "There are
nineteen."

Balzac laughed. He had a weakness for walking sticks and could
not resist buying one that appealed to him.

"The new one. The ebony," he told Auguste.

Auguste brought him a fine ebony stick with a gold band and an
ivory ball on top. With the stick in his hand, Balzac addressed his
image in the gilt-framed pier glass that had recently been fitted
to the west wall of his dressing room.

He approved of his appearance.

In this coat, with its high, semi-military collar, he believed he
resembled his father, and Bernard-François to the day of his death
had carried his clothes with more grace than any man Balzac had
ever known.

He went downstairs and passed through the garden, winter-
barren and forbidding, the flower beds and bushes sheltering under
heavy blankets of manure. It was a cold raw day. The sky was low
and lead colored and there were light snow flurries, borne by the
thin, knifing wind.

Balzac shivered and turned up the collar of his cape. He had
ordered a carriage and it was late. There were patches of ice in
the street and the mud was frozen solid. Perhaps the liveryman's
horse has slipped, he thought. My God! I can never make it on
foot from here to the Faubourg Saint-Germain.

He began to pace up and down, his heels making a hollow
sound on the ground, which was frozen hard as mortar. At last the
livery carriage appeared, twenty-five minutes late. Balzac swung
himself aboard.

"Palais de Castellane, in the rue du Bac!" he called to the driver. "And hurry, man. You are late!"

"Can't hurry when the streets are frozen," the driver said indifferently.

Balzac looked at his gold watch. "I do not dare be late," he thought. He felt in the pocket of his waistcoat for his purse. As usual, he had forgotten it. He almost never remembered to carry money on his person.

"Driver!" he called.

"Monsieur?"

The driver slowed the horse and looked through the hatch.

"You see this watch?" Balzac asked. "It is solid gold. Worth a hundred francs. It's yours if we reach the rue du Bac before I hear three o'clock by the bells of Saint-Germain-des-Prés."

"Monsieur is joking with an old man," said the driver. "It is not polite."

"You have the word of de Balzac," Balzac said firmly.

The driver glanced at the roadway and shrugged.

"It could just be done," he said. "And God knows I risked my life at Waterloo for a lot less than a hundred francs. Hold on to the strap, monsieur. We will find out how much the good Lord cares about us, you and me."

Balzac caught the strap. He heard the sound of the long whip as the driver galloped the horses. The carriage swayed madly as a caisson in battle, skidded on the frozen mud and nearly turned over, then righted itself and they were off.

It was a mad ride.

Hanging on to the stout leather strap, Balzac felt as though he he had been lashed to a gun carriage and galloped across the open country, a punishment he understood to be favored by officers of the Prussian army.

The driver knew this part of Paris as well as he knew his own kitchen. He took short cuts through back streets and narrow alleys where the carriage scarcely had clearance way, shouting madly at pedestrians, who cursed back at him as they leaped to safety. The carriage rocked, bumped and skidded. Balzac clung to the strap and prayed. The driver seemed to be enjoying himself.

They turned into the rue du Bac and came to a skidding stop in front of the imposing façade of the Castellane Palace. Balzac sat back on the hard seat. The carriage was still swaying a little. Then the bright clear bells of Saint-Germain-des-Prés began to ring the hour. The driver climbed down from his box and opened the carriage door. Balzac got out, detached his watch from its chain, and handed it to the driver.

"Thank you, my friend," he said. "It is quite possible that you have saved my life."

The driver moved off, walking his winded horse. Balzac stood in the street, looking up at the face of the building that sheltered his romantic correspondent. It was a mansion built of cool grey stone, more than two hundred feet wide, with tall windows facing the street hung with puckered curtains of glimmering beige satin. Into the stone above the doorway had been carved the elaborate arms of the family of the Duc de Maille.

Balzac took a deep breath, held it for a moment, then let it out. He climbed the stairs to the great double doors and tugged at the bellpull. While he waited, his heart pounded. He was at last about to enter the secret world of the Faubourg Saint-Germain, one of the three or four most aristocratic quarters in the world, and he was terrified as a schoolboy waiting to be seen by the headmaster.

Noiselessly, the doors were opened. Balzac was confronted by a footman in green livery, white knee breeches and a powdered wig.

"Monsieur de Balzac," he said.

The servant bowed gravely and ushered him into the house, taking his hat, cape and stick, then showing him into a small room that led off the marble entrance hall.

"Be seated, monsieur."

The footman bowed and departed. Balzac sat down on the edge of a fragile satin-covered chair. The house was quiet as a vast Egyptian tomb. A delicate, soundless fire burned on a small iron grate, set into a chimney piece carved from a block of alabaster.

The room was soft grey and beige, with gold-framed portraits on the walls. It was also warm. In a few minutes, Balzac felt beads of sweat break out on his forehead. Soon they trickled down his cheeks. He mopped his face with his handkerchief, then cursed as he began to sweat under the arms.

He waited.

To him, the elegant little room was like a condemned cell. She has changed her mind, he thought. It is senseless to wait. I may as well go now and avoid the embarrassment of being shown out by the footman. She was playing with me. She never intended to see me.

From outside, muffled by the thick stone walls and the heavy curtains, came the mocking sound of the church bells, marking the half hour.

Balzac waited.

His handkerchief was a limp rag. His shirt was soaked with sweat. His clothes felt tight. He waited.

The church bells struck four o'clock.

He got up and went to the window, parting the curtains so that he could look into the street. It was snowing steadily now, thin driving snow that was beginning to stick to the frozen ruts. The sky was low and malicious. I'll wait five minutes more, then go, Balzac assured himself.

"Monsieur de Balzac?"

He turned. It was another servant, this one wearing livery more gorgeous than that worn by the man who had opened the door.

"If you will follow me, monsieur. Madame la Duchesse is waiting."

They passed through the marble hall and went up a curving grand staircase, then down a richly carpeted hall, lined on either side by doors ornamented with gilt. They were approaching an open door. Balzac heard voices, a man's, then that of a woman. His heart fell; he had hoped to find her alone.

The servant halted at the open door and bowed.

"Monsieur de Balzac!" he announced.

Balzac entered the room smartly. It was a high-ceilinged chamber at the back of the palace, with lofty windows that looked down on a garden the size of a small park, the duchess's private sitting room, a miracle of taste and distinction. The walls were covered with apricot colored satin. The carpeting was a rich, edible brown. There were a number of chairs covered with brown velvet. A gilt clock stood on the mantlepiece, the porcelain face decorated by a follower of Watteau.

On a chaise longue reclined the Duchesse de Castries herself, wearing a peignoir of brown cashmere with voluminous skirts that trailed gracefully to the floor. Beside the duchess stood a tall man dressed in a black frock coat.

Balzac moved forward, then stopped in his tracks as if he had suddenly been frozen. His eyes were on the duchess.

My God, she is beautiful! he thought.

The Duchesse de Castries was indeed at the absolute peak of her beauty. Her face was small, the features delicate, almost doll-

300

like, and the impression of fragility was heightened by a slight, becoming paleness. She had a great deal of hair, Venetian red, fine as silk, shaped into an elaborately detailed coiffure. The eyes were like intense blue stones, agile and intelligent.

Balzac gathered his forces, moved forward, bowed and kissed a hand that might have been made of Sèvres porcelain.

"Poor Monsieur Balzac, we have kept him waiting," the duchess murmured. "It is a pity, monsieur, but one must make allowances for an invalid. It is one of my bad days, alas."

Balzac said that he was sorry.

"My good friend, Doctor Blanchard, has been trying to persuade me to go to a warmer climate."

"Since he has failed, he will take his leave," the doctor said, bowing. He nodded to Balzac, said "Monsieur!" curtly and went out of the room with swift little steps. Balzac at last was alone with his duchess. She smiled at him and raised a languid hand.

"Come and sit near me, where I can see you," she said. "You are the first author I've met, monsieur. Perhaps I should be frightened. People say that authors are dangerous men who regard themselves as above morality."

"I am the one to be frightened, madame," said Balzac. "As for being dangerous, I assure you that outside my books I am mild as a lamb."

He took a straight chair that was near the chaise longue. As he sat down, he became aware of her perfume, a subtle but authoritative scent with which he was unfamiliar. He had the odd sense of being out of his own element, in another world. Is she mocking me? he wondered. The small pale mouth was guileless, the ice blue eyes were innocent. On a small table was a copy of THE MAGIC SKIN. It had been expensively bound in morocco of a rich crimson color, stamped in gold.

The duchess picked up the book and leafed through it, then let it fall to her lap.

"A brilliant book, but terrifying," she said. "It shatters the armor of the soul."

"There is life in it," Balzac admitted.

"Life, yes," she said. "A frightening amount of life, monsieur." She looked at him curiously. "Your heroine, Fédora. Is she drawn from life, from a real person?"

Balzac shrugged. Actually, Fédora had been roughly based on

301

the character of Madame Récamier. Balzac answered the question as novelists always do, insisting that Fédora was a composite. "The eyes from this one, the voice from another, the hair, skin, and temperament from another," he said. "Oh, I assure you, madame, all my characters are truly a mélange."

"And the soul of Fédora?" she asked.

"Now, madame, I can answer you with candor," he said. "The soul of a Balzac character is always supplied by Balzac."

"Is the supply inexhaustible then?"

"Quite inexhaustible," he said.

She gave him delicious China tea. They talked for another half hour of books and, casually, of politics. Balzac did not realize how skillfully the conversation had been steered into politics, nor did he notice a new intensity in the duchess's eyes when they discussed the subject.

"You are a Legitimist then?" she asked.

Until this moment, Balzac had not made up his mind. Now the issue was closed in a flash. He leaned forward and said, "From the bottom of my heart, madame, I assure you. From the bottom of my heart."

His voice throbbed with genuine emotion. Having made up his mind, he had instantly become a passionate supporter of the Duchesse de Berry and the politics of the old régime.

"Good!" said the duchess. "Then we shan't differ politically, monsieur."

"Madame, it is my profoundest wish that we differ on nothing, you and I," said Balzac earnestly.

"What a pretty speech!" she exclaimed. "You are a courtier as well as a writer, Monsieur de Balzac." She touched her lips with a pretty finger. "And now I must ask you to go," she said. "My doctors deny me my liberty, you see. I am obliged to rest as if I were an old woman."

Balzac rose.

"When may I come again?" he asked. "Tomorrow?"

She laughed.

"Of course not, monsieur," she said.

"Today a week?"

"We shall see," she said vaguely. "Don't forget, you must make allowances for one who does not enjoy your own robust health."

"I am at your disposal," said Balzac eagerly.

302

"I will send you a message," she decided.

He kissed her hand and said, "I shall not draw a breath, madame, until I open your letter."

She laughed gently and touched a bellpull that hung beside her couch. Promptly, a footman appeared to usher Balzac out of the Palace.

It was nearly dark in the street and the weather was vile. The snow was mixed with freezing rain, making the footing treacherous as wet glass. Balzac took the snow in his face and strode off toward the Observatory Quarter, laughing at himself because he had forgotten to order a carriage to take him back to the rue Cassini.

From the first meeting, Balzac's affair with the Duchesse de Castries had a quality about it that must be likened to delirium. To say that Balzac was infatuated is to be guilty of gross understatement. In everything that concerned the duchess, his reason seemed to have left him. He was obsessed with her, blinded by her beauty and the glories of her ancestry.

Quickly, he learned that she was capable of cruelty. It made no difference. He was bewitched. For Balzac, the Duchesse de Castries and the Castellane Palace, taken together, were a kind of drug. He was intoxicated by everything about her. He romanticized her illness, her past, the mystery that surrounded her.

He had been careless with money before he met her. Now his extravagance became grotesque. He ordered more clothes than he could reasonably have used up in a lifetime. He decided that it was unsuitable for a well-known writer to be seen in the Faubourg Saint-Germain in a hired carriage, so he purchased a Tilbury and a pair of English horses. Horses and harness apparently must be cared for, so he hired a little groom, nicknamed Grain-de-mil, an undersized, good-natured urchin who worshipped him.

The carriage was secondhand, but it had been repainted. The day the livery stable delivered it, Balzac ran his hands affectionately over the glossy black surface. Among the aristocracy, he realized, it was customary to have one's coat of arms painted on the doors of one's carriage. Having assumed the "de" on the strength of his speculative connection with the d'Entragues family, Balzac saw no reason why he should not appropriate their armorial bearings as well.

For a small fee, he managed to get a copy of the d'Entragues' arms drawn on parchment and illuminated by an old alcoholic professor of history, cashiered from the Sorbonne. The old fellow kept himself in drink by supplying geneological substance to members of the new rich. He was a cynical old devil with an awful breath and snuff on his waistcoat.

"A writer is better than any d'Entragues that ever drew breath," he said to Balzac. "Why don't you make up your own coat of arms? Inkpot rampant, crossed quills in the center, a blue field with a publisher, couchant and castrated."

Balzac laughed and shook his head, giving the old man double his fee.

"This one will do," he said, admiring the quarterings that he did not understand.

He had the d'Entragues arms painted on the doors of his carriage and engraved on his silverware. He knew that he was being absurd, and he did not object to being laughed at.

Alfred de Musset examined the emblazonry on Balzac's carriage and said, "Really, Balzac, your snobbery is becoming phenomenal. You know perfectly well that you have no connection with the d'Entragues."

Balzac laughed and said, "Really, Alfred? So much the worse for them, isn't it?"

He was so goodnatured about his affectations that his friends found it impossible to be angry with him. Those who were more than friends were worried. The first to warn him was Madame de Berny.

"Don't become the slave of those people in the Faubourg," she pleaded with him.

"But they are the people who count," Balzac insisted. "They receive me because they respect me as a writer."

"They care nothing about you as a writer," she said. "They are interested in one thing only—themselves. They would sell the Lord Jesus Himself to advance their cause. And the cause is lost, believe me."

Zulma Carraud was more blunt.

"Will you never get clear of this tempestuous mode of life?" she wrote to him from Frapesle. "Do you really call it literature when you write with a knife at your throat, in order to buy English carriage horses? You have important work to do. Do not squander your energy on things that do not matter. Duchesses, indeed!"

304

Balzac was blind to everything but his passion for the Duchesse de Castries. Each afternoon, his carriage drew up at the Castellane Palace. If the duchess was confined to her chaise longue, he read to her through the afternoon and evening. If her health was good, they dined together, usually at the Grand Véfour, in the Palais-Royal, then went to a concert or the theater. They heard Paganini, the fantastic violinist, whose skill was so uncanny that there were those who believed he was a musical Faust who had bartered his soul to the devil. They saw Taglioni dance. They saw the great Talma at the Comédie Française.

Balzac was exhausting himself. Each night, after he left the duchess, he went home to work, beginning at two or three in the morning, working until the pen dropped from his fingers and his head sank to his writing table. He refused to believe that he was being used and badly used at that. If the duchess withheld her favors, it was only because she was testing him. After all, he reasoned, one could hardly expect a woman of that class to tumble into bed as if she were a washerwoman.

Besides, there was the question of her health. She was not strong, perhaps the time was not right. He was confident that in the end she would sleep with him, though as yet he had not so much as kissed her.

She tantalized him with all the arts known to a skillful woman, led him on, aroused him shamelessly, then refused him the slightest intimacy. She tortured him. His life was an agony.

Chapter 31

DURING THE SPRING and early summer, Balzac was drawn more and more into the ultra-royalist orbit of the Faubourg Saint-Germain. As a writer, he began to understand it; later, he would use what he learned.

The Faubourg was neither a quarter nor a sect nor an institution, nor anything else that could be precisely defined. It was a state of mind, and one of the most influential in France. For forty years, the Faubourg had been to Paris what the Royal Court had been in other, grander days.

It was the last stronghold of the old régime, but it lacked both the brilliance and integrity of its predecessors. The men of the Faubourg were not the gallant courtiers who flashed with brilliance under the Sun King, filled with manners, honor and courage. For all their titles, they were shallow men who schemed for power and money, at heart no more concerned with greatness than the men of the rising business class that had edged them to one side.

Nor were the women of the Faubourg much like the great court ladies of the old régime. The famous beauties of the Versailles Court had engaged in gorgeous depravity with a splendid lack of concern for anything but their own pleasure, been carted off in the tumbrils, their heads held high in the air, until they were cut off.

The women of the present day Faubourg were not like that. They were neither very wicked nor very good. They were hypocritical in their passions, their eyes fixed on the main chance as steadfastly as those of the rising bourgeoisie.

It was a fake, this aristocracy of which Balzac was now enamored, and good friends tried to tell him this.

Fake or not, it was what he wanted.

He haunted the Castellane Palace, putting up with rebuffs and insults, degrading himself, playing the literary lap dog, in the hope that by some miracle the Duchesse de Castries would relent and find it in her heart to love him.

She remained what God and France had made her—a woman who trusted no one and nothing. Her passions had been once aroused—by Victor Metternich. The powers of a Faustus, a

Rabelais, a Casanova, could not have started the fires again. Sexuality—and she understood it as others understand chess—was a means to an end, an instrumentality one used as cynically as any other, for the purpose of getting or holding power.

Such women exist in all countries, in all classes, and are often described with an ugly word that one does not put into print.

When he was away from her, Balzac knew well enough what she was. With pen and ink he could have created such a creature in a few hours, and in a few hours more demolished her once and for all.

When he was in her presence, his reason went on holiday.

She could do as she pleased with him. She kept him waiting, as she had done the first time he was permitted to call. Sometimes he waited for an hour or two in the close little anteroom, only to be told by the servant that Madame la Duchesse regretted—she was too tired, or too ill, and he must go away.

When he was nearly helpless, the Duchesse de Castries sprung her trap.

One afternoon, when Balzac arrived at the Palace, the footman, instead of showing him into the anteroom and leaving him to cool his heels, took him straight up the elegant staircase and into the Duchesse de Castries's boudoir.

She was not alone.

Two elegant gentlemen stood beside the chaise longue upon which the duchess had been attractively arranged. Balzac recognized them at once. One, the taller, was the Duc de Fitz-James, uncle of the Duchesse de Castries. He was slender as a willow, impeccably tailored, holding a gold lorgnette in his hand. The other was the Duc de Rauzan, heavier than Fitz-James, more powerful, but just as much the dandy. At various times, Balzac had seen both men, in the theater or concert hall, or sometimes in the Restaurant Grand Véfour, always at a table better than his own.

Balzac was prepared to be snubbed. He knew that to these aristocrats, a man of bourgeois origin, however distinguished as a writer, soldier, statesman, was regarded as little better than a lackey. To his surprise, when the introductions were made both men bowed as though he were an equal and both assured him that they were enchanted.

"It is a great privilege to meet the author of THE MAGIC SKIN," said Fitz-James, with what seemed to be complete sincerity.

Balzac assured the Duc that the honor was his own.

307

The three gentlemen seated themselves and a pretty maid served tea. Fitz-James and Rauzan made themselves so ingratiating that Balzac's apprehension dissolved. He persuaded himself that he was actually on equal terms with the two Royalist leaders.

"My niece tells me that you support the cause of the Duchesse de Berry," Fitz-James said casually.

"With all my heart," said Balzac.

"That is a fine thing to hear," said de Rauzan. "Too few of our French writers are on the side of decency these days. Men like Hugo and Dumas seem to take perverse delight in lending their weight to the cause of the rabble."

"Dumas comes from the rabble and worse," said Fitz-James. "His grandmother was a black savage with a ring in her nose. His father was an ordinary trooper who rose from the ranks under Bonaparte."

"I should like to see Monsieur Dumas with a ring in his nose," said the duchess placidly. "One could lead him like a trained bear."

Balzac laughed with the others. Later he was ashamed of himself, but in front of his duchess he laughed.

"One reads your articles in the Girardin papers, of course," Fitz-James said to Balzac. "Excellent. Masterfully precise."

Balzac inclined his head.

"One wonders why your name does not appear in the columns of *Le Rénovateur.*"

Le Rénovateur was the most incendiary of the Royalist papers, a die-hard Bourbon sheet, reckless in its denunciation of the republicans, merciless to the so-called Citizen King who now sat on the throne of France. For a writer to contribute to its columns was to go as far to the right as one could go in France.

"I haven't been asked," said Balzac.

"Surely that is an oversight on the editor's part," said Fitz-James smoothly. "Or it may be that he hesitates to approach a writer distinguished as de Balzac. I take it you will not refuse, if you are asked?"

"On the contrary, I should be honored," Balzac said.

"The editor is an acquaintance of mine," Fitz-James observed. "I think you will be hearing from him in a few days time."

When the two noblemen had finished tea, they departed. Alone with the duchess, Balzac moved his chair closer to the chaise longue. She looked exceptionally beautiful this afternoon, reclining gracefully against an arrangement of brown satin pillows, her head and shoulders in a position where they caught a flattering ration of light that came through the high windows. Her dressing gown was of gold lamé, and this enriched her skin color in the way a gold leaf frame adds luminosity to the colors of a painting. Her daytime perfume was chypre, a mixture made to her secret formula, a heady, suggestive scent that always excited Balzac. The pupils of her eyes had been enlarged by bella donna.

"Were you impressed by my uncle?" she asked.

"A charming man. And no fool," answered Balzac.

"It was no accident that he and Rauzan were here," she said. "They wanted to meet you."

"I suppose I have them to thank for the fact that I wasn't kept waiting as usual," Balzac said.

The duchess pouted prettily.

"Do not be cross with me," she said. "You must make allowance for the fact that I am not in the most robust of health."

"And you must make allowance for the fact that I am madly in love with you," Balzac said, almost harshly.

She looked at him wistfully, then touched his cheek.

"You play with me, cat and mouse," he said angrily. "How long do you think I can stand it? I am a man with blood in by veins, not water."

"There is no need to be crude, monsieur," she said. "You know it offends me."

"I am sorry," he said. "But you expect too much."

He moved toward her and caught her hand. For a moment she permitted him to hold it, then gently withdrew the fingers. He caught her in his arms and kissed her on the mouth. She was too startled to resist him at once. When she recovered and struggled free she was furious.

"Monsieur, you forget yourself!"

She scrubbed her lips with her handkerchief, her eyes blazing with anger. Then for an instant, there was the hint of amusement. She was enjoying his discomfort, delighted with his awkward passion.

Balzac got up and strode across the room. He was humiliated and ashamed of his crudeness.

"I was carried away," he said, his back toward her. "I forgot myself."

"So it seems," she said. "Please try to remember, monsieur, that

that sort of thing disgusts me. I cannot abide to be pawed at as if I were a servant girl."

Balzac turned.

"But you are a woman!" he cried. "You go against the nature of things. Is love ugly? Are you disgusted by nature?"

She made a face.

"Do you call that love?" she asked. "I think it is vile."

She turned her face away from him, looking at the wall, so that he could not see her smiling. Bitch, bitch, bitch, he raged to himself, clenching his fists.

"I must go," he said rudely. "I am engaged for the evening."

"Truly?" she said indifferently. "Is she pretty, monsieur? A little laundress, perhaps? I do hope she makes love more skillfully than she irons your linen."

"I bid you goodnight, madame," Balzac said stiffly.

He marched out of the feminine room like a sergeant-major on parade. He brushed past the footman, trotted down the front steps and leaped into his carriage, seizing the reins from the little groom, who had been taking a nap.

"A thousand pardons, M'sieu de Balzac."

"It is nothing, Grain-de-mil. Go back to sleep, if you like," said Balzac.

He whipped up the horses, driving toward the Observatory quarter recklessly in the half-light. People in the streets screamed and shouted.

"Drunkard!"

"Fool!"

"Pig of a pig!"

"Monarchist swine!"

Nearly two years had passed since the July Revolution, but among the people of Paris discontent was still very much alive. There had been incidents in the streets, encounters between bands of working men and members of the National Guard.

Balzac slowed the carriage. When he reached the rue Cassini he pulled up, sitting on the box with the reins in his hands. It was early evening, too early to start work. He had lied to the Duchesse de Castries. He had no engagement. But now he could not face the prospect of passing the evening alone.

He turned to little Grain-de-mil.

"Drive to Montmartre," he said. "Go to the Auberge du Lion

d'Or. Find a girl called Maria. Young, pretty, blackhaired. Speaks with a strong southern accent. Tell her that Honoré de Balzac offers her champagne and a cold chicken."

"Will she come with me, monsieur?" asked Grain-de-mil, suspecting that his master was either drunk or mad.

"Of course she will come!" Balzac roared. "Would I send you all the way to Montmartre to fetch a girl who wouldn't come?"

Two hours later, Maria was in Balzac's study. He had ordered a table set near the windows. The curtains had not been drawn, and one could see the street, in heavy twilight.

There was a cold roast chicken and a magnum of Balzac's best champagne. He had changed into his dressing gown—not the monk's habit, but a black silk creation, embroidered with gold thread, fastened at the waist by a scarlet sash, a seducer's costume, out of a book.

They ate the chicken and drank the wine. The bubbles went up Maria's nose and made her giggle. Balzac wiped her fingers and mouth with the corner of a napkin, after she had eaten a wing with her fingers.

They made love in the bedroom, with the candles lighted. Balzac was tender. She was, after all, a child. He taught her the arts of love, that night and other nights, during the weeks that followed.

She was sweet, simple, kind, intelligent. She adored him. To her, he was a kind of god, to be worshipped, to whom one submitted.

He did not love her at all, but he grew fond of her and she was satisfied with this. She asked for nothing.

"What will you do with your life, Maria?" he asked one evening. "This is a blind alley for you. It leads nowhere, you understand? Nowhere."

"I shall go back to Toulouse and be married," she said, answering without thought.

"When?" he asked.

"When I become pregnant," she said.

"Pregnant!" said Balzac.

"It is almost certain to happen," she said. "We are both healthy people."

"And the young man, will he marry you?" asked Balzac.

"Of course," she replied. "He loves me."

The guilt Balzac had felt after his first encounter with Maria evaporated. He took what was offered, gave nothing in return, except his body and his presence. He offered money. It was refused.

"I get my meals at the inn," she explained. "I need no clothes. What would I do with money?"

A few of Balzac's closer friends came to know Maria. Everyone liked her. When others were present, she would sit crosslegged on the floor beside Balzac's red armchair, attentive as a schoolchild, and as silent. She waited on Balzac like a faithful daughter, bringing his slippers or his robe, attending to his slightest want.

"If you were a sensible fellow, Balzac, you would marry Maria," Alfred de Musset told him.

"Marry Maria? Are you out of your senses? She is the daughter of a draper in Toulouse, probably disowned. She earns her living as a chambermaid in a country inn in Montmartre. She hasn't a penny to her name."

"I know. I know," said de Musset, wagging his head. "Forgive me, Balzac, I was forgetting. You are a genius, and they are almost never sensible fellows."

While he was making a fool of himself over the Duchesse de Castries and finding solace with Maria, Balzac was writing a philosophical novel, based on his experience as a boy at the Collège de Vendôme.

The public was waiting for him to produce another readable romance or a sardonic commentary on manners in the style of THE PHYSIOLOGY OF MARRIAGE. Instead, he was hammering out a book that was far ahead of its time, ahead of its century, an apocalyptic novel that dealt with the dark, mysterious inner struggles of the unexplored psyche.

In LOUIS LAMBERT, Balzac explored the relationship between genius and madness. He intended to write a tale to be put on the shelf with Goethe's FAUST, except that he rejected Goethe's supernaturalism.

Like Faust, Balzac's hero craved the impossible.

Unlike Faust, he sought it without the aid of the Devil . . . sought it in the dark, terrifying corridors of his own mind. Balzac intended LOUIS LAMBERT to be a terrifying as well as an ennobling book. He wanted to work on the reader the cauterizing, cathartic effect sought by the Greek masters of tragedy.

He very nearly succeeded.

That he did not succeed was the fault of the Duchesse de Castries and of his new publisher, Gosselin, as much as of Balzac himself.

Gosselin was not interested in literature, but in money. Balzac had promised to deliver LOUIS LAMBERT in July. Goethe, with whom he competed, had worked on FAUST for sixty years. Balzac had bound himself to produce LOUIS LAMBERT in six weeks. Had he been locked in a prison cell, given nothing but food, paper, ink and coffee, he could not have done it.

The Duchesse de Castries was driving him mad. For three days after the abortive kiss, he had stayed away from the Castellane Palace. A one line note brought him running like a dog. Now he went every day at three, as he had done through the winter. He made no progress with her whatever, but she and her friends made progress with him.

He began to contribute to *Le Rénovateur*.

His friends and admirers were outraged.

Victor Hugo called at the rue Cassini, and urged him to cut loose from the Bourbons. Alphonse Lamartine pleaded with him, then offered to punch him on the nose. De Musset poked fun at the duchess and her companions.

Balzac listened to no one. He struggled on, trying to do justice to LOUIS LAMBERT, courting the duchess, turning out snide little pieces for the Royalist paper.

The mid-June heat was oppressive. Each night Balzac drugged himself with coffee, turning his work into a kind of debauch. He was coming to the end of his nervous resources and his novel was not nearly finished. The unwritten pages were in his mind, but he could not produce them on paper. The publisher, Gosselin, harried him, and threatened to sue.

One sweltering afternoon in July, he entered the Duchesse de Castries's boudoir and found her engaged in conversation with her confessor, a freelance bishop who gave his attention exclusively to the immortal souls of aristocrats.

The bishop wore a silk soutane and a crucifix decorated with rubies and pearls worth enough to pay for the building of a village church. A handsome man in his forties, he had a voluptuous mouth and a set of strong white teeth. His black hair glistened with pomade. His fingernails had been buffed with pumice.

313

Balzac was sweating like a food porter at Les Halles. His collar was like a wet dishcloth and sweat had soaked through his clothes, making dark patches in awkward places on his tight-fitting, light colored trousers.

Neither the duchess nor the priest seemed aware of the heat. Clad in a filmy peignoir of light blue crêpe-de-chine, the duchess looked serene as if she had just stepped out of an iced bath. The bishop's hair was unruffled, his tall forehead cool and dry.

Unless a man is a stevedore or an athlete, sweating always puts him at a disadvantage. Beside the bishop, Balzac felt crude as an oarsman in the penal galleys. When he was introduced, he caught a whiff of the upper-caste clerical smell, a compound of incense, candle wax, silk, and excellent, fruity brandy. The odor antagonized him. He was a Catholic, but he was his own kind of Catholic. He admired the Jesuits' toughness of mind. The selflessness of the provincial clergy inspired his respect and compassion. For this elegant, dilettante man of the cloth he had nothing but contempt.

"His Lordship wants your support, monsieur," the duchess said to Balzac.

"Monsieur Milord?" Balzac bowed.

The bishop rubbed his palms together and displayed his dental edifice.

"Like everyone else who matters in France, I am one of your admirers, Monsieur de Balzac," he said.

"Really?" said Balzac coldly. "It is gratifying to learn that the clergy interest themselves in contemporary writing. Which of my books does your Lordship find most to his taste? THE MAGIC SKIN? THE PHYSIOLOGY OF MARRIAGE?"

This drew a blush from the Bishop and threw him off his ecclesiastical stride.

"I'm afraid that my religious duties leave me no time for reading books," he said. "Except, of course, for the classics and volumes approved by the Church. My admiration has been aroused by your articles in *Le Rénovateur.*"

Balzac took out his handkerchief, shook it boorishly, and mopped his forehead.

"So?" he said.

"As one who is both a Royalist and a priest, monsieur, I am eager to see the Church restored to its splendor in France," said the bishop.

314

"I hope that the Church comes into her own, when we have succeeded in replacing this dreary monarch with a king worthy of the name."

"Do you propose that the King of France be ordained a priest?" said Balzac innocently.

"Really, monsieur, one must not speak lightly of such matters," said the bishop. "What I propose is that the Restoration, when it comes, be complete. I believe that the House of Peers should include a Bench of Bishops, as in the happier days when France was governed by stronger and wiser kings."

"Absurd!" said Balzac.

"Monsieur?" said the Bishop.

"Balzac!" cried the duchess.

"If your Lordship wants to be perfectly certain that the events of 1789 are to be repeated on an even grander scale, he has only to encourage the clergy to stick their ecclesiastical noses into affairs of state. The people will pour into the streets the moment they learn that the bishops intend to supervise the laws of man as well as the laws of God."

The bishop was white with anger. To Balzac's satisfaction, beads of sweat broke out on the immaculate forehead.

"You call yourself a Royalist, monsieur," he said stiffly. "Upon my word, you sound more like your nigger colleague, who runs in the streets with the rabble."

"If your elegant reference is to Dumas, then let me tell you something," said Balzac, tight with anger. "I disagree with Dumas on almost every question—food, clothes, wine, women, books. We are not friends. But Dumas is nevertheless a man of honor and he comes by his convictions as honestly as your Lordship comes by his own."

The bishop drew himself up to full height. The impressiveness of his figure was emphasized by his cassock. Ignoring Balzac, he addressed the duchess.

"I seem to have been misinformed concerning this gentleman's sympathies," he said frigidly. "I shall withdraw."

He swept from the room, the rich silk skirts of his cassock rustling with anger.

Balzac laughed.

"Sir, your conduct obliges me to demand an explanation," the duchess said furiously. "Have you been drinking, monsieur?"

"Only water," said Balzac pleasantly. "If madame is suggesting

315

refreshment, of course I shall be delighted. A glass of chilled white wine would be pleasant."

"Explain yourself, sir!" she demanded.

"Very well," said Balzac.

He drew up a chair and sat down without having been asked. He looked straight at the duchess.

"The explanation could not be more simple," he said. "I drive halfway across Paris, on a day when the streets are like a baking oven, to see you. Alone. Preferably in a nightgown. Preferably, ready at last to concede that you are a woman, whose body is supplied with the apparatus designed for the purpose of receiving a man."

"Sir!" she cried.

"Hear me out," said Balzac. "I drive across Paris, as I said. Do I find you alone? No. I find you attended by that perfumed fraud of a priest, all of whose ideas are absurd, except for the one he shares with me concerning a no doubt delectable but so far carefully hoarded portion of your anatomy."

The Duchesse de Castries sat up, trembling with rage.

"I command you to leave!"

Balzac bowed.

"Anger becomes you, madame," he said. "It is perhaps the only honest emotion you permit yourself to express."

"If you do not leave at once, I shall call my servants and order them to throw you into the street," she said.

Balzac bowed.

"I am leaving, madame," he said. "Do not ask me to return, until you are ready to spread your legs."

Behind him, as he left the room, he heard her gasp. He smiled. It had done him good to be blunt with her. He half wished he had taken her by force, on the chaise longue where she draped herself.

For the time being, he was freed from his obsession with the duchess. The force of honest anger had saved him, temporarily, at least. As he drove away from the palace, he felt that he was his own man for the first time in months.

Back in the rue Cassini, he made coffee and sat in his red armchair to drink it, taking stock of his situation.

He felt like a man who has just emerged from a long illness.

His adventure into the gilded world of the Faubourg Saint-Germain had been expensive. He had piled up debts—to tailors,

316

jewelers, caterers, restaurateurs, the livery stables, florists, perfumers. He had squandered what cash he had on fabulous dinners in the best restaurants. For the first time in years he had let his work go hang while he knelt at the feet of the uncompliant duchess.

He sat down at his writing table and went through the stacks of bills that had piled up in the last months. They were fastened together in batches with silver clips, engraved with the d'Entragues' arms.

Balzac cast off a rough total of what he owed.

"Two hundred thousand francs!"

He was staggered by the figure. It was more than twice what he had guessed.

"God in heaven," he thought. "I could have written two novels during the time I have wasted on that cold-blooded wench. Three, maybe, with a bit of luck."

He sat back in his writing chair, puzzling over his situation. Already the bailiffs were beginning to call, demanding payment of this bill or that one. Soon they would give him no peace. There would be half a dozen of the scoundrels on his doorstep everyday.

He could not write under such a siege.

Especially, he could not write a book like LOUIS LAMBERT. He knew that he must get away . . . away from Paris, away from love, away from the spending of money.

Again, in trouble, he went to Saché, to his beloved Touraine, where the Margonnes made him welcome and asked no questions.

For two days he slept, ridding himself of exhaustion. On the evening of the third day he sat down at the table in his bedroom, a single candle beside him. The window was opened to the summer night and the room was filled with the healthy scent of the Margonne vineyards and meadows. The smell was delicious and reassuring. Balzac sighed happily, rubbed his shoulders, then took up his pen and began to write.

He had been helpless in Paris. Here at Saché the weight was lifted from his heart. He wrote steadily and with brilliance, piling up page after page each night.

LOUIS LAMBERT was not an easy book to write, for it meant going back into childhood memory, dredging up the sequence of days passed in the prison house of the Collège de Vendôme. So

317

intensely did Balzac relive the experience that he could smell the dankness of the punishment rooms, taste the nauseating food, feel the lash on his shoulders, hear, in the still night that surrounded Saché, the priest's accusatory voice, "Balzac, you are idling!"

He took his midday meal with the Margonnes, usually at a table placed under a tree on the lawn. He drank sparingly of the Margonne wine, the good dry Saché that he loved. Sometimes, in the afternoon, he loosened his muscles with a walk through the vineyards or along a country lane.

Touraine was at its best—the Garden of France in full bloom, precious vines orderly as troops, meadowland reaching down the water, maternally green and lush. The handsome trees were like green sculpture against the washed, pale sky.

That summer, Balzac had an intense awareness of his native province. In his mind was beginning to form a conception of France in terms of contrast—province with province, province with city, city with town, class with class. He was beginning to see France as both a universe and an ant hill, heaven on earth and earth in hell.

Late in July, Balzac finished LOUIS LAMBERT and sent it off to Paris. He was sure that Gosselin would not like it, and he understood that it would baffle his own public. It did not matter. He knew that he had written a book different from any ever before written by a Frenchman.

He came out of his creative shell eager to be at work again, yet he felt that he could not stay on at Saché without abusing the Margonnes' hospitality. He had no money, and did not dare return to Paris, where his creditors were waiting for him.

Zulma Carraud and her husband were at Angoulême, where the major had been given command of a powder factory. "They are as poor as I am," Balzac told himself. "They won't mind the fact that I don't have a sou in my pockets."

He borrowed a few francs from Monsieur de Margonne and walked into the village, where he caught the stagecoach that passed through Angoulême.

Chapter 32

A<small>FTER</small> A LONG
hot journey, unannounced, Balzac knocked at the door of the little
army house on the outskirts of Angoulême, in the shadow of the
arsenal and powder house. There was a pretty garden behind a
wooden fence that had been painted white. The house looked
bright and attractive, the kind of place to which one might retire.

Zulma came to the door herself. She was dressed in an apron
and a dust cap. For an instant, startled, she stared at Balzac. Then,
as if she had been waiting for him, she said, "You are tired. And
very dirty. Come in."

She took his carpetbag and led him into the house. In the sitting room, darkened and kept cool by awnings at the windows,
she gave him a glass of chilled white wine.

"You will want to rest," she said. "Your room is ready."

Tears rose in Balzac's eyes. Months ago, in Paris, when she
was uprooted and nearly without hope, Zulma had told him,
"Wherever we are, there will always be a room in the house for
you, with a writing table and a good bed."

He finished the wine and went upstairs to the room that had
been waiting for him. It was a simple whitewashed chamber at
the back of the house, overlooking a kitchen garden in which grew
neat rows of carrots, beans, peppers, onions. There was a table
near the window, covered with green baize, supplied with a sturdy
chair. There was a wide wooden bed, the headboard painted and
stenciled with an intricate pattern of flowers. The floor was red
tile, waxed and polished, partly covered with small, bright-colored,
crocheted rugs.

Balzac took off his coat, rolled up his sleeves and washed himself. He had been in the house only ten minutes, but already he
had the sense that he had come home—an awareness of peace and
of safety, as if no one could touch him here.

He brushed the road dust from his trousers and stretched out

319

on the bed to rest, aware of the sounds of bees beneath his window, and of the fragrance of Zulma's roses, carried on the light summer breeze. He slept for a time, peacefully as a child.

At dinner that evening, Major Carraud greeted him as simply as Zulma had done when he knocked at the door. Zulma's child, Ivan, shook hands with him solemnly and told him he was glad that he had come. Everything was simple, utterly natural. Balzac was touched and grateful.

There was a roast of lamb, cooked in the southern manner, with garlic, and a tureen of white beans that Balzac found delicious. Even the coffee that followed the meal was good, not as good as his own coffee, but fragrant and strong and far better than what they had given him at Saché.

After dinner, the three of them sat in the little front parlor, Major Carraud dozing in his chair, artillery manual on his lap, Balzac and Zulma with the backgammon board between them, just as they had often sat in the room at Saint-Cyr.

"Well, Honoré?" Zulma said, in a frank tone, as if the two of them were alone.

Balzac glanced at the major. He was breathing peacefully, the pipe held in his limp fingers, his legs propped upon a hassock. Zulma smiled indulgently.

"Well, Zulma," said Balzac quietly. "I have just finished my best novel and I don't have ten francs to my name." He laughed. "The great Balzac. The same Balzac who was driving around Paris behind his own horses, a month ago, giving intimate little dinners at the cost of a mere hundred francs. Madame, your friend is a fool."

During the next few days, he poured out the story of the humiliation at the hands of the Duchesse de Castries. Zulma listened and said nothing, knowing that it did him good to talk. He could confide in Zulma with absolute faith in her honesty. There was no one else to whom he dared reveal the flaw in his temperament that had made him the victim of the Duchesse de Castries.

"You are the greatest writer in Europe," she told him. "When will you learn that nothing else matters? Money, fame, clothes, women, English horses for your carriage—all that means nothing. What is important is your work."

They were walking in a peach orchard, under trees heavy with ripening fruit. The day was still and very warm. Balzac paused and leaned against a tree.

"Sometimes I am like a drunkard," he said. "I cannot help myself."

She looked steadily at him. Leaf shadows fell on her face, made by the sunlight filtered through the peach trees.

"You are hopelessly in debt, I suppose," she said.

"Catastrophically," he admitted. "I am so deeply in debt and so besieged by creditors, that I don't dare return to Paris."

"Someone must act for you," she said. "Perhaps a lawyer?"

He shook his head.

"I know lawyers," he said. "I barely escaped being one. A lawyer would only make things worse."

"Your mother, perhaps?"

He frowned, shaking his head.

"She could do it," he said. "If anyone could do it, my mother could. But I would never hear the end of it."

"It would be worth a good deal, to start with a clean slate," said Zulma.

Balzac put his pride in his pocket and took Zulma Carraud's advice. He wrote to his mother and appealed for help, a frank letter, son-to-mother, in which he confessed his faults and expressed determination to manage things better in the future.

He tried to imagine his mother's face, when she read his plea for aid. There would be a mixture of annoyance and triumph, a sense of superiority because the great Balzac, darling of the salons, dandy, gourmet, scandalous lover, author of books that were being read in France, England, Germany, Italy, even far away Russia, must come to his mother, hat in hand.

"She will rub it into my skin," he thought. "She won't be able to resist that. But she will do the job, and do it well. And in her own odd way, she will enjoy it."

That night, he began to work, starting a novel that he called THE ABANDONED WIFE. A few nights later, he sketched out half a dozen short pieces, modeled on the tales of Rabelais. He intended to write a series of these, to be published under the collective title, ONE HUNDRED DROLL STORIES.

They were droll tales indeed, worthy of his famous fellow-countryman. . . . lusty, bawdy stories, filled with eating, drinking and loving, folk tales that went back to a time when literature was not written down, but simply talked around the fireside, stories passed from one village to the next, and down through the generations.

Balzac enjoyed the writing. Sometimes, in the dead of night, alone in his room with his candle, he would write a page, read it over, then lean back in his chair, roaring with honest laughter until tears rose in his eyes.

"They will sell, these little babies," he chuckled to himself. "The public will eat them like sweetcakes, no doubt about that."

Yet they weren't written merely to make money or to shock the bourgoisie; they were honest stories, out of the rich soil of Touraine, and Balzac believed in them.

From midnight 'til morning, Balzac worked. In the forenoon, he slept. In the evenings he amused himself with Major Carraud and the little staff of officers attached to the powder factory. There was a billiard room on the first floor of the house, and several evenings a week Balzac played with the soldiers. He was not much good with a billiard cue, but he found the game relaxing and he enjoyed making conversation with simple, unpretentious people.

He tried to get the Duchesse de Castries out of his mind, but she refused to be banished. Deep in his soul, he understood that the last hand had not been played. He could not analyze his motives, but he had a sense of inconclusion. In a moment of weakness, he wrote to her, and gave her his address at Angoulême.

When he told Zulma what he had done, she shook her head.

"You are like a monkey on a string, where women like that are concerned," she said. "Here with us you are working well, eating well, living the kind of life that is right for you, most of the time. Yet if Madame de Castries snaps her fingers, you will run to her feet like a frightened puppy."

"Never!" said Balzac, and he believed it. "That woman put me through the fires of hell. She can call from now until the day of doom, but I won't go to her."

"Then why did you write?" asked Zulma blandly.

"Simple politeness," Balzac said.

Zulma turned to him, suddenly impatient.

"For the love of heaven, Honoré, take a mistress!" she cried. "A simple girl who will love you and cause you no pain. Or marry. And not in the Faubourg either."

She was crying. For a moment, her forehead touched his chest. He held her in his arms, tenderly, then kissed her cheek. They remained motionless for several moments, touching each other. It

322

was as though time had stopped. Then Zulma stepped back and dried her eyes.

"Forgive me," she said. "I have no right to criticize that part of your life."

He made no comment.

They walked slowly back to the house, along a dusty road that was bright with sun. Balzac was troubled. He and Zulma loved each other, but it was a strange kind of love, at once intense and inconclusive, almost incestuous. And there could be no conclusion. Even if Carraud did not exist, Balzac could not imagine making love to Zulma, any more than he could imagine making love to his sister Laure.

Yet he needed her.

She had become a part of his life—permanently—and he understood that there would be passages in the years ahead when he would come to her because no one else on earth would meet the demands of his nature.

Meanwhile, in Paris, Balzac's mother made an attack on the phalanx of debt he had erected. She was appalled by his extravagance. She wrote to him nearly every day. The landlord wanted to distrain his furniture because the rent had not been paid. There was a baker's bill for seven hundred francs.

"In the name of heaven, how could a bachelor eat that much bread in a lifetime?" his mother demanded. "Have you been running an orphanage, in addition to your other activities?"

"I feed the pigeons!" Balzac replied. "Keep up the good work."

His mother got on with the job. Balzac's carriage and horses were sold. His groom and his cook were sent packing. In a fit of panic, he begged his mother to save his books and his red armchair. She heeded his wish, mostly because she understood that secondhand furniture and books brought almost nothing on the market.

She worked a minor miracle.

She haggled with creditors and cajoled them. She juggled accounts, and persuaded tradesmen to reduce their bills in return for cash payments, warning them to take what she offered or be content with nothing.

With the larger creditors, she arranged time payment schemes, fighting for low rates of interest. She besieged people who owed Balzac money, threatening, pleading, bargaining. Finally, after weeks of labor, she had managed to cut a pathway out of the financial swamp.

"Ten thousand francs in cash will see you solvent," she wrote. "It is the best that can be done."

It was a marvel and Balzac knew it. For ten thousand francs, he could purchase his freedom. He would be at liberty to return to Paris, to live without hiding. But he had no idea of where he could put his hands on the money. He was in debt to half a dozen publishers, having already been paid for most of what he would be able to write between now and the end of the year. To borrow a sum of this size was out of the question.

His mother perfectly understood that he had no means of getting the money. She was backing him into a corner. After an interchange of letters, she sprung the trap and promised to get him ten thousand francs, if he would meet her conditions.

"I agree to anything, only get me the money," he wrote.

His mother's terms were simple.

Balzac agreed, in writing, to renounce his old way of life. He promised to cultivate simplicity, thrift, economy—to become, in short, a good bourgeois, a son of whom his mother could be proud. He was to live within his means and to liquidate his debts at compound interest.

He signed the agreement in good faith and sent it off to Paris. For several days afterward he radiated the self-contentment that rewards a publically penitent sinner.

Though he was free to return to Paris, Balzac planned to stay on at Angoulême until he had written a book or two and a number of short pieces, including a few dozen of the DROLL TALES he enjoyed writing.

"I won't go back to Paris empty-handed," he told Zulma. "If I do, I will need cash and every publisher in town will take advantage of me."

"Fill your larder," Zulma said. "You can stay with us as long as you like."

Balzac settled down to work, delighted with the idea that for once in his life he would be ahead of the game and in a position to drive a hard bargain with his editors.

Then, on a bright August morning, his little world of virtue exploded. The bomb was contained in an envelope, mailed to him from Aix-les-Bains, a resort town near Geneva, in the French

324

Alps. The Duchesse de Castries was stopping at Aix, with her uncle, the Duc de Fitz-James. The scenery and the air were lovely. If Balzac was in the mood for a holiday, nothing would please them more than to see him.

The note was innocent as butter. It was as if he and the duchess were good friends, nothing more. He sat with the letter in his hands, remembering his last words to her, vulgar words that had the truth in them. He reread the lines she had written. There was nothing. She promised him nothing. She simply asked him to come to Aix, no more.

He crumpled the letter in his hand, angrily. Then he smoothed it out and smelled the paper, certain that he could detect a hint of her perfume that had survived through the mails.

The infatuation, strong as ever, came into his blood like a drug. He knew that he was going to Aix, yet his sense of form obliged him to put up a token resistance.

He showed the letter to Zulma.

"What shall I do?" he demanded.

She refused to give him advice. He plagued her with the question. For a week, they talked of nothing else. Balzac poured out his heart.

"Of course you must go," she said, finally. "It is obvious that you will have no peace, unless you go."

He kissed her hands and thanked her. Zulma looked at him and marveled. He was a man with the will of a lion where work was concerned, yet he could be reduced to impotence by a few lines written on a scrap of perfumed paper. What was the source of the weakness, she wondered. Or was it a part of his strength, grotesquely disguised?

Chapter 33

THREE DAYS LATER, Balzac was on his way to the Alps, having borrowed two hundred francs from Major Carraud.

The keynote of the adventure was struck long before he reached Aix-les-Bains. At the stagecoach stop outside Lyons, while the horses were being changed, one of the animals started in the shafts. Balzac was thrown from the top of the coach. He fell against the iron step and cut the flesh of his calf to the bone. For a few seconds he lay on the ground, stunned by the fall.

"By the Lord in Heaven, he is dead!" one of the passengers shouted.

"You exaggerate grossly, my good friend," Balzac said, through his teeth, feeling the pain of the gash all at once. "Help me up, someone, and I'll come back to life."

The wound was clumsily bandaged. Balzac rode into Lyons on the floor of the stagecoach, sick with pain, the leg throbbing.

Another man would have waited until his leg was properly healed. Not Balzac. He was on his way to see his duchess and cutting off his head would not have stopped him. He found a doctor in Lyons and bit on a bullet while the man sewed up the wound with a dozen stitches, warning him, while he sewed, that he must take to his bed.

"There is the danger of putrefaction, do you understand, my friend," the doctor told him. "Unless you are careful, it will be quite possible to lose the leg."

Balzac paid him and limped out of the surgery. He put up at a third-class hotel and passed a night in misery. The next morning he bought a cheap cane with a rubber tip and continued on his way, weakened by loss of blood, sickened by pain, but as determined to cross the Alps as ever had been Hannibal of Carthage.

The stagecoach lumbered into Aix-les-Bains and drew up before a café in the public square. Balzac got down clumsily. His leg was stiff and he leaned heavily on his cane, but the pain had slackened off. He hobbled into the café and ordered brandy and water, thinking that the spirit would cut his fatigue. Unable to move for the time being, he sent a boy to the hotel to tell the duchess that he had arrived.

In twenty minutes, she reached the café, riding in an open gocart drawn by a short-legged mountain pony. Balzac got to his feet, trying to conceal his infirmity. She came toward him, looking radiant. He bowed to kiss her hand, lurched, then staggered and nearly fell.

"You are ill!" she exclaimed.

He caught the edge of the table, winced, then sank to his chair.

"It is nothing," he muttered. "Nothing."

She was all concern. He must see a doctor. He must rest. Perhaps warm baths would help.

"I've taken a room for you," she said. "When you can manage I will drive you there in my little Savoyard gocart."

"Am I not at your hotel?" he asked.

"Unfortunately, there was not a room to be had," she said. "But you won't be far away."

The room she had taken for Balzac was in a small hotel on the outskirts of Aix. She left him there, refusing to come up.

"But we will dine together," she promised. "At my hotel, at seven-thirty."

Painfully, Balzac negotiated the narrow staircase that led to his room. The room was small and rather damp, but there was a magnificent view of the lake and the mountains and the rent was only two francs a day, a blessing considering his exchequer.

By this time the wound in his leg felt as though it were on fire. He was feverish and exhausted. The infection was in his blood and the poison made him dizzy. He pulled off his shoes, loosened his collar, and stretched out on the eiderdown mattress, intending to rest for an hour and then to get ready for dinner.

The moment his head was on the pillow, he fell into a drugged sleep. He woke up sometime after midnight, aware of the sharp Alpine cold. He sat up and rubbed his eyes, realizing, after a moment, that he had slept through dinner. He was angry with himself; it was a bad beginning. He rubbed his shoulders against the cold, groaning as he moved his leg too quickly. Then he shrugged helplessly, pulled the quilt over himself, and went back to sleep.

327

When he woke up in the morning he was refreshed and his leg was somewhat better. He rang for a servant and ordered breakfast. The coffee was delicious and he made some comment.

The serving girl looked at him slyly. She was a young Savoyard, dressed in provincial costume, black wool skirt, rich with embroidery, black headdress trimmed with gold, felt slippers, crisp white apron.

"It is not our usual coffee, monsieur," she told him. "It was sent to monsieur this morning from the Grand Hotel."

"Truly?" said Balzac.

"Of an absolute certainty, monsieur."

Balzac was encouraged. Never before had the Duchesse de Castries made such an intimate gesture. Perhaps she has really had a change of heart, he thought, shaving himself with special care and giving his clothes a good brushing before he set out for the Grand Hotel.

It was an impressive establishment, with a stone façade and an entrance foyer that was lushly carpeted and fitted with a number of full length mirrors, reflecting a crystal chandelier. Balzac asked for the duchess and a porter in uniform gave him a note.

He read it standing in the foyer, uncomfortably aware of his multiple reflections, given back by the mirrors. She understood that he had been too tired for dinner last night. And she regretted that she could not see him before five in the afternoon. It was too stupid, but her doctor insisted that she rest during the day.

He was disappointed. Then he realized that if his days were free, he could work here in Aix as easily as elsewhere. He went back to his modest hotel and laid out his writing things—paper, quills, dusting sand, traveling inkpot. These were all the tools he needed. The rest of it was in his head.

In Paris, Marie de Castries had played cat and mouse with Balzac. Here in the Alps she played with him as if he were a hooked fish on a line.

Each night Balzac dined with the duchess and her uncle in the restaurant of the Grand Hotel. Fitz-James was suave and polite. The duchess was charming. Her daytime sleep refreshed her and the ardent air of the high mountains quickened her beauty. Balzac found her enchanting. Again he was bewitched and utterly helpless.

328

Sometimes he persuaded her to walk with him on the promenade. On fine days, in a hired carriage, they drove to the Grande Chartreuse and to Lake Borget, enjoying what is probably the most gorgeous scenery in the world.

He made no progress with his romance.

One afternoon, on a rustic bridge that spanned a waterfall near the Grande Chartreuse, he lost patience and seized her roughly. He drew her to him and kissed her passionately. For a few seconds she seemed to respond. Her lips parted and she permitted him to go on with the kiss, trembling a little, as if she were really aroused. Balzac sought her breast with his hand. He was out of control. When he loosened his embrace, she stepped back, flushed, taunting him with a smile.

"Surely not in public, monsieur!" she said reproachfully.

"In public?" Balzac cried. "We are in the wilderness, miles from anywhere."

"On the contrary," she said. "Unless I am mistaken we are very much in view."

Balzac turned. A party of English tourists were approaching, pointing with their sticks and babbling in their atrocious language.

"You play with me," he said sullenly. "You make me feel like a young bull, then you expect me to behave like a eunuch."

She tapped his cheek with her glove.

"My dear Balzac, surely the author of THE PHYSIOLOGY OF MARRIAGE understands that one does not treat all women in the same way."

"I adore you," he said, taking her hand, kissing it.

She laughed and said, "It is extraordinary that the man whose books have revealed the secrets of French womanhood, actually makes love like an inexperienced schoolboy. You have no finesse, monsieur. You are crude."

He trembled with rage. A part of his nature urged him to turn on his heel and leave her where she stood. It lost to his embattled vanity and to the power of sexual frustration.

"You must forgive me," he said hoarsely. "After all, I was born in Tours, not in the Faubourg Saint-Germain."

"A man with the blood of d'Entragues in his veins should not find it difficult to learn the ways of another world," she said blandly.

He stared at her, taken off guard, wondering how much of the truth she knew about his ancestry. Her face was guileless. She smiled at him as prettily as if no words had passed between them, took his arm, and said, "We must go."

They walked back to the valley road where the carriage was waiting for them. Balzac sulked like a schoolboy, cursing himself, knowing that he lost the advantage, but unable to muster a spark of wit with which to repay the duchess in kind.

In his pursuit of the Duchesse de Castries, Balzac was no longer governed by intelligence or good judgement. That night, in his room, he copied out a love letter from the proof sheets of LOUIS LAMBERT, which he was correcting. It was a reckless and passionate letter, filled with the fire of youth in love. He gave it to the duchess the next day, pretending to want her opinion of it as part of a work of fiction.

She promised to read it that night.

The next evening, at dinner, he asked for her judgment.

"It is good, perhaps too good," she told him. "One gets the impression that the boy is unbalanced, as well as being sick with love."

She is impregnable! Balzac thought. There is no way to break through this shell of ice she wears. Yet he could not get rid of the idea that she was capable of passion. There was an undercurrent that he could not reach. It tortured him.

She handed back Louis Lambert's letter. At this moment, the Duc de Fitz-James joined them at the table.

"What a glorious country this is!" the duc exclaimed cheerfully. "If only one could forget the world and lose himself in these mountains." He sighed, took a bite of the mountain trout that had been placed before him, and said, "Unfortunately, one has duties." He looked at Balzac, then said casually, "Are you preparing another article for *Le Rénovateur,* my friend?"

"I have something in mind," said Balzac.

"You won't regret doing your part," Fitz-James promised him. He glanced at his niece mysteriously, then said, "Shall we tell Monsieur de Balzac what his reward will be?"

"Not to tell him is unfair," the duchess replied.

Fitz-James leaned forward and shifted into a conspiratorial tone of voice.

"De Rauzan and myself have had the honor to talk with the Duchesse de Berry," he said. "She has promised that when her son takes power, you will be given a post in the cabinet."

330

"The cabinet?" said Balzac.

He was astonished. His vanity would not permit him to see the absurdity of Fitz-James's statement.

"The cabinet," Fitz-James repeated. "You are the only important writer in France who supports our cause. It is simple justice that you be proudly rewarded."

Balzac left them walking on air. He went to his hotel room and wrote three articles for the Royalist paper, knowing that when they were published the wrath of Zulma, of Victor Hugo, even of de Musset would descend upon him.

The bout of work sobered him up. Standing at his window the next morning, tired after six hours writing, he looked into the mountain dawn and realized that he was a fool to take Fitz-James seriously. The Bourbons would never be restored; their cause had been lost with Charles X. He turned back to his writing table and glanced through the articles he had written for the Royalist paper. What he had written was nonsense. He tore the pages once across, folded them and tore them again, then dropped them into a wicker basket that sat beside his table.

Fitz-James's colleague, the Duc de Rauzan, arrived in Aix from Paris and that evening he joined them at dinner. He looked vigorous and athletic, and Balzac found himself growing peevish when he observed that the Duchesse de Castries brightened in his presence.

After a little, she turned to Balzac.

"We are all going to Italy!" she said. "To the lakes. Will you join us?"

"By all means, Balzac, you must come," de Rauzan said.

"It is a very romantic country," the duchess said coquettishly. "In Italy, anything can happen."

Balzac hesitated. He was eager to go to Italy, but he had no money. When they had finished dinner, the Duc de Fitz-James took him aside.

"If it is a question of money, my dear chap," the duc said carefully, "please put your mind at rest. I shall be happy to advance what you need. After all, you are serving a cause."

Balzac agreed to go.

A few days later, the party of four set out from Aix for Geneva, which was to be the first stop on the journey south. Fitz-James had hired a mountain carriage, drawn by a team of four horses, luxuriously fitted inside. Balzac was apprehensive. He had the feeling that he had been kidnaped.

They rolled into Geneva early in the evening. The city was bathed in clear gold light. The evening sky was pale and washed. Everything was orderly and clean, as if the streets had been scrubbed with brushes. The city was imperturbable and Balzac missed the sense of life one is used to in France.

"A nation of hotel keepers," Fitz-James said, as if he read Balzac's thoughts. "Still, they make one comfortable."

Since they planned to leave Geneva at dawn, the party retired early. The Duchesse de Castries and Fitz-James had adjoining rooms. De Rauzan was near them. Balzac's chamber was some distance off, down a corridor, at the end of which was a stone balcony, from which one had a superlative view of Lake Geneva and the Swiss Alps.

It was a bright, moonlight night. Balzac had gone upstairs with the others but he had no desire for sleep. He sat in his room for an hour and read. Then, feeling restless, he tiptoed down the corridor and went out onto the balcony.

The moon was full.

The lake and the mountains, the city's rooftops, all were coated with shimmering silver. The silence was dense. Balzac rested his arms on the stone parapet, enchanted by the sense of mystery.

After a little he became aware of the sound of voices, low-pitched and intense. He leaned out over the parapet and discovered that he could see into the room that adjoined the balcony. The chamber was flooded with moonlight. On the bed, a man and woman were making love. The wet, seductive moonlight played on their bodies. Balzac watched, hypnotized, unable to pull himself away.

The lovers moved and he saw their faces. It was Marie de Castries and the Duc de Rauzan. Balzac struck the stone with his fists and suppressed the cry of rage that formed in his throat. He was too stunned to move. He watched them until at last their bodies slowly came apart and the two-backed beast was destroyed.

His duchess lay with her head on the bolster, her hair in a glorious cascade. For the first time in his life, Balzac saw her body. She stretched herself voluptuously.

"You are magnificent," said the duc, raising himself on an elbow, gazing down at her, then quietly kissing her breast.

332

She sat up in bed, her chin on her knees.

"How much longer am I to put up with that insufferable Balzac?" she demanded.

The Duc de Rauzan shrugged.

"As long as he is useful to us, my dear," he said. "He may be a baboon in a boudoir, but people read what he writes. And he is the only writer we have. The other scribblers, Dumas, Hugo, and the rest, are bitterly against us."

The duchess made an impatient gesture.

"It is all very well for you," she said. "I am the one who puts up with him."

He touched her cheek playfully.

"My darling, you complain too much," he said. "After all, it's not as if you were obliged to sleep with him."

"Don't be disgusting!" she said.

"Other women have done as much, for a cause they believed in," said the duc.

Balzac retreated to his bedchamber and stood in the center of the room, trembling. He felt like a cuckold. He was sick with humiliation. His stomach writhed and he tried to vomit, standing over the washbasin, retching as if he had been poisoned. He sank to the bed, shuddering, and wept.

When he had finished crying, he dressed himself, packed his bag, and crept out of the hotel like a thief, passing the sleeping hall porter and going into the street.

He did not trust himself to face the duchess in the morning. In all his life he had never committed an act of violence, but in this moment of degradation he was unsure of his sanity. If she produced the wrong gesture, the wrong word, it was possible that he would strangle her.

It was three o'clock in the morning and the air was chill. Balzac walked until he came to a public square, with trees, benches and a statue. He sat down, his bag at his feet, and turned up the collar of his coat.

He sat in the little park until dawn, then got up, his legs aching from the cold, and wandered through Geneva until he found a café, where he ordered coffee and a roll. At eight o'clock, he climbed aboard the stagecoach that would carry him back to France.

He was hurt, bitterly hurt, but he was a writer to the bone. Already, his cheek against the window of the stagecoach, he was planning the book he would write about the Duchesse de Castries, a book that would tear her to shreds and give him his revenge.

Chapter 34

"MADAME DE CAS-
tries has shattered my life without giving me a new one in its place," Balzac complained to his friends. "She leaves me in a vacuum—without love, without job. I am sustained by my work, nothing more."

The vacuum was soon filled, though not, for the moment, by a woman of flesh and blood.

While he had been in hot pursuit of the Duchesse de Castries, Balzac had received an admiring letter posted in the Tsarist Polish Ukraine, an intelligent and flattering letter, written on notepaper thick as bark, engraved with a noble crest, signed simply L'Étran-gère—The Foreign Lady.

During the months that followed, there had been more letters from the same correspondent, signed always in the same way: L'Étrangère. Balzac had been intrigued by the tone of the letters, by the gilt crest, and most of all by the fact that they came to him from Imperial Russia, from somewhere on the stark plains in front of Moscow, where the French Emperor and his Grand Army had fought, frozen, and died in large numbers.

As the letters from the stranger piled up, Balzac became more and more intrigued, then frustrated because he had no means of answering his aristocratic admirer. They were letters that yearned for answers, yet they came from the void.

Then came a break in the clouds.

A missive from Poland arrived in November, containing the following words: "A line from you, published in *La Quotidienne*, will assure me that you have received my letters and that you want me to continue to write."

Balzac scribbled a message on a sheet of manuscript paper and sent it off to *La Quotidienne* in the hands of Auguste.

"Hurry," he insisted. "Run all the way. Perhaps there will be time to get it in tomorrow's issue."

Auguste was used to the impetuous ways of the master he had come to worship. He asked no questions, but tucked the message into his stocking and raced through the back alleys of Paris to the office of the newspaper.

A day later the notice appeared in the columns of *La Quotidienne*. Balzac waited impatiently, searching his mail each day, looking for a letter from Poland. When it came, he was disappointed. The Unknown, as he had taken to calling her, thanked him for the note he had put in the paper, but the signature was the same as before, simply l'Étrangère.

Balzac put a second notice into the columns of *La Quotidienne*. "L'Étrangère, tell me your name, I beg of you, so that I may reply. H. de B."

In her next letter, the lady refused. It would not be seemly, she told him, for her to receive letters from de Balzac. She was married—to an older man, it was true, but nevertheless, married. She was the mother of a young child and, moreover, a religious woman. No, it was certainly far more appropriate that she preserve her Slavic anonymity. She praised his work, as she always did, and thanked him profoundly for the high privilege of being permitted to write to him.

These fragmentary details concerning her life merely served to excite Balzac's curiosity. He was determined to know her identity. Each day he placed a notice in *La Quotidienne,* imploring the stranger to make herself known.

The situation, of course, precisely suited Balzac's temperament.

It was romantic as the plot of one of his early potboiling novels, based on the stories of Mrs. Radcliffe. Here was the famous novelist, injured in love, living a life of celibate fame. There was the beautiful foreigner (he was positive that she was beautiful, certain that she was rich) living in a bizarre part of the world, the Faraway Princess of the story books, starved for love and ideas and excitement, chained by the vows of Holy Marriage to a doddering, impotent nobleman. There was the cryptic, one-sided correspondence, the cabalism of the newspaper notices.

Even during the opening passages, Balzac thoroughly enjoyed himself. For a long time now, he had been trying to make a love story out of his own life. He had failed with Madame de Berny because of the difference in age between them. For Zulma, his love was not romantic. The Duchesse d'Abrantès had been nothing more than a fiery episode. With the Duchesse de Castries, he had met disaster. Now, in the crested letters that came to him from the forests of the Polish Ukraine, he felt the rustlings of his destiny. He consulted a fortune-teller, then a famous trance medium. Both of these mystics assured him that the hand of his fate was moving from the East.

The letters from Poland became more intimate, even almost passionate.

"When I read your books, I feel that there is an affinity between us," she wrote, in perfect, but somewhat stilted French that delighted Balzac. "When I am alone in my room, late at night, reading your words by the light of one small candle, sometimes I am overcome by the conviction that what I read was written for me alone. All other writers are pale beside you."

These letters from beyond the Russian frontier had a strange and fateful story behind them, a story worthy of Balzac's most ingenious invention. The "Foreign Lady" (whose name he was not to know for months) was, in fact, everything that he imagined, and more.

She was the Countess Evalina de Hanska, born the Countess Evalina Rzewuska, of the proudest and most fateful blood in Poland, that tragic, moody, unhappy country, then a part of the Tsar's domain. As a girl, she had been given a first-rate education. In addition to Russian and Polish, she spoke and read with ease French, English and German. She yearned for the brilliance of the western world, from which she had been cut off in youth by her marriage to Count Hanski, who was twenty-five years her senior.

She lived in Wierzchownia, a vast palace in the midst of the steppes, in the isolated province of Volhynia, which meant that she lived in the Middle Ages. Poland was a century or more behind the rest of Europe, and Volhynia was behind Poland. The Count Hanski was a feudal lord, with powers that would have been unthinkable in the more advanced countries of the West.

The palace of Wierzchownia was surrounded by hundreds of miserable hovels inhabited by Count Hanski's serfs, unfortunate people who, like Hanski, acquired at birth unalterable social status. Not quite slaves (they could not be bought and sold like horses, cattle or the Negro slaves in America) they were nevertheless bound to the soil and to the feudal master whose land they worked.

Count Hanski's palace was placed in the center of his vast do-

337

main, completely isolated, even from the backward world of Poland. There was no town, not even a village, but only the thatched huts of the serfs, the thousands of acres of cultivated land, plowed and planted in strips, so that the landscape looked like a patchwork quilt. Beyond the farmland was the endless, brooding virgin forest, filled with small game, wild boar and deer.

The palace contained every luxury. There were gorgeous Persian carpets, French tapestries from Bayeux, paintings to rival those in the Louvre, gleaming silver from England, priceless porcelain from Limoges, from China, and from the German potteries on the banks of the Volga.

Most important to the Countess Hanska was the well-stocked library that contained the famous books of the world, indexed and catalogued twice a year by a student sent down from the University at Warsaw. These books, together with the French and German periodicals that came to her by post, literally were the instruments that preserved Eve de Hanska's sanity.

She detested her life at Wierzchownia, she was bored with her husband, and she hungered for contact with the outside world, for the culture of the forbidden West, to which she had been introduced as a child.

The monotony of rural life affected Eve's soul in the way a cancer affects the tissues of the body. She had the grim conviction that her youth was falling away, the years falling tragically like dead leaves from a tree. Even the solace of physical love was denied her. Count Hanski was already an old man, ill and nearly impotent, uninspired by his young and passionate wife.

For half the year, central Poland was blanketed with snow. Eve hated the implacable, imprisoning whiteness that emphasized her isolation. In the spring, when the roads were passable again, she and Count Hanski went to Kiev, where they danced at a dreary provincial ball, paid courtesy calls on their fellow members of the nobility, did some desultory shopping and returned home. Once every three years they went to St. Petersburg, where the Count renewed his allegiance to the Tsar of all the Russias.

These were their only contacts with the outside world. Otherwise, Eve was condemned to unremitting boredom. The single exciting event of the week, aside from Mass on Sunday mornings, was the arrival of the post from the West. The mailman's sledge or wagon brought her the latest newspapers from Paris . . . three

338

weeks late, but nevertheless a treasure chest of amusement, information, ideas.

A bookseller in Paris had standing instructions to forward the latest novels of importance to Wierzchownia, and Eve devoured them, sometimes, in the winter months, racing through three or four volumes in a day. She was bursting with ideas, with questions, with speculation, eager to talk with a kindred spirit.

There was none.

Count Hanski was interested in nothing except amateur ornithology. He was a bird-watcher, pure and simple. He did not care for the earthy pursuits that diverted his fellow members of the Polish aristocracy—pig-sticking, prodigious drinking, wenching with the daughters of the serfs, gambling.

Henriette Borel, the Swiss governess who looked after Eve's child, Anna, was a good creature and loyal, but fanatically religious and at root as dull as any peasant. Anna herself was too young to be more than an amusement. There was no one within a thousand miles of the palace of Wierzchownia with whom the lonely countess could talk about the things that were close to her heart. She yearned for a friend like Voltaire; she was condemned to a silence deadly as the silent snow.

Then one winter evening she began a new French book, taken at random from a batch that had just arrived from Paris. It was Balzac's latest work, SCENES FROM PRIVATE LIFE.

When she had read twenty pages, the Countess Hanska was immersed in Balzac's world. When she had read fifty, she had become a part of that world. Never before had she encountered a writer whose meanings were so precise to her. Here, in Balzac's pages, living and breathing, was the world of which she yearned to be a part.

She finished the book and sat down at her little marquetry desk, writing to her bookseller in Paris.

"Send me, and at once, everything that has been written by the novelist, Honoré de Balzac."

For weeks, Eve de Hanska read nothing but Balzac. She was enthralled. Surely, she thought, no other writer has understood with such blinding clarity the agonies of a lonely woman—deprived of love, of hope, almost of life itself.

"He might be writing about me," she said to herself with awe. Then with a sense of terror she said, "He *is* writing about me!"

339

For some months she struggled with her conscience.

She wanted to write to Balzac, to pour out her heart to him, but she hesitated. She had heard from an old aunt that he was a young man, and that his relations with women were notorious. She had been strictly reared, as a Roman Catholic and as an aristocrat. To enter into correspondence with a stranger, whose morality was doubtful in spite of his genius, was to her mind unthinkable. Yet she burned with the need to communicate in some way with this writer who had touched the most secret parts of her soul.

"Perhaps if I do not reveal my name, the sin will be merely venial," she thought.

Torn by doubt, trembling, she composed the first anonymous letter and sent it off to Paris.

After the first letter, she gained confidence. In the messages that followed, she poured out everything that was in her heart, revealing all except her identity, confiding in Balzac as she could confide in no one else on earth, protected, as she thought, by the fact that she would always remain as she signed herself . . . L'Etrangère.

After several months, however, she found it unbearable to send her letters into the void, with no way of knowing whether or not Balzac received them. Finally, she hit on the idea of asking Balzac to insert a few words into the columns of *La Quotidienne,* one of the French papers to which she subscribed.

Balzac, of course, would not rest until he found some means of writing to her. He heightened the tone of his daily messages, begging the Unknown to reveal her name.

She did not dare.

A letter from de Balzac, arriving at Wierzchownia, was certain to create a sensation. The Count Hanski had no passion for his wife, but he had great pride in his family name, which had never been touched by so much as the breath of scandal. He would not approve of his wife's correspondence with a stranger, let alone with a stranger like de Balzac.

Eve cudgeled her brain and at last hit on an idea. Anna's governess, Henriette Borel, sometimes received letters from relatives in France. De Balzac could send his letters to Henriette, who would pass them on to her mistress.

Henriette was a devout Protestant, fierce and fundamental. She was on her knees in prayer whenever she had a moment to spare from her duties. She was also intensely loyal to her mistress, whom she adored. With misgivings and a promise to say a prayer for Eve, she agreed to act as cover.

From the moment he posted the first letter to the innocent Henriette, his correspondence with Madame de Hanska assumed an importance in Balzac's life that was second only to his work itself.

For Balzac, the situation was made to order. He was able to create his own romance. It thrilled him as a man and comforted his ego as a writer conscious of his position. Bizarre romances were the fashion for writers, artists and musicians. There had been Lord Byron's tempestuous affair with the Countess Guiciolli. There had been Liszt and Madame d'Agoult, Chopin and George Sand, Dumas and God knows how many women. Recently, the great Victor Hugo himself had begun an open affair with an actress of the Comédie Française.

Now there was Balzac and his Unknown—"La Princesse Russe, ou Polonaise,"—as he described her to his sister Laure.

Balzac was beginning to act in life with a nod to his future biographers. He sensed almost from the first that his letters to Madame de Hanska would become famous. He wrote to her several times a week, filling the letters with detail concerning his personal life and his work, as well as with observations of the social scene in Paris.

Very soon after he began to write, he openly protested his love. "You are the subject of my most delightful dreams," he wrote, bringing a blush to the cheeks of a woman too long deprived of the delights of love.

The Faraway Princess in Poland was both flattered and disturbed. Dormant passions were aroused by Balzac's frankness and the power of his prose. Eve was pursued by hot longings, prodded by a strange recklessness.

Count Hanski was too immersed in his boredom to be aware of the change in his young wife, but the governess, Henriette Borel, understood that what brightened the eyes of her mistress was more than a literary interchange with a distinguished writer in Paris. Herself the instrument by means of which the correspondence was carried on behind the back of the master of the house, the good soul was besieged by guilt and a vicarious awareness of sin, torn between her sense of duty and her love for her mistress. She conceived a morbid distrust of Balzac and convinced herself that Balzac had somehow cast a kind of spell on Madame de Hanska's soul.

In one sense, the loyal servant was not altogether wrong.

In his letters, Balzac painted a picture of himself that was romantic and appealing, if not strictly accurate. He revealed himself as the lonely artist, single-mindedly devoted to his craft, indifferent to fame, flattery and money.

"I live like a monk," he promised the countess. "I have nothing but my work and your letters."

He was devoted to his craft. That was true enough. He was also keenly aware of the fact that the great Goethe, at Weimar, was discussing his work with Eckermann. He realized that the name of Balzac was becoming one of the most famous in France. As for his indifference to money, he was driving his publishers out of their senses, making the toughest contracts of any writer in Europe. As for his loneliness—it was a matter of the spirit more than of the flesh.

For a few months after his return to Paris, Balzac had tried to live up to the agreement he had made with his mother—to live frugally, as an honest and temperate bourgeois, at least until his debts were paid and there was a backlog of money in the bank.

It was not in his temperament.

The need to spend money was a passion with him and he soon slipped back into the way of life he had adopted during the first months of his infatuation with the Duchesse de Castries.

Having planned to keep only the faithful Auguste, his valet de chambre, he weakened quickly and hired a cook, then a maidservant.

"She can do my laundry," he told his friends. "That will be a saving right there."

He indulged himself with a new wardrobe, having grown tired of the clothes he owned, though nothing had been worn out and some of the things had been worn not at all.

Fortunately, his tailor, Buisson, regarded Balzac as the first flower of French letters and considered it an honor to dress him even if he didn't get paid. He made Balzac what Balzac wanted . . . bright-colored coats with gilt buttons, saffron-colored pantaloons, brocaded waistcoats by the dozen.

Sartorially, Balzac no longer tried to ape the dandies of the

Faubourg Saint-Germain. He was out to impress the crowd and impress them he did. His public life was a harlequinade. He had no intimate friends in Paris, but suddenly, as his fame spread and his legend grew, he seemed to know everyone in the capital.

He was a fixture at the great restaurants—Véry's the Grand Véfour, the Café de Paris. He sat in a box at the Italian Opera and listened to the music while he watched the crowd and the crowd watched him. On the street, in theater lobbies, in the cafés, he was stared at, whispered about, laughed at, talked about.

He was Balzac.

Mad Balzac.

The Great Balzac.

He entertained in his rooms in the rue Cassini, giving notable dinner parties, sometimes sitting at the head of his table dressed in his white cashmere robe, paper shears dangling from the gold chain drawn tightly around his waist.

One of his acquaintances, almost a friend, was the novelist George Sand, who came to Balzac's rooms, wearing her trousers and her lover, the unfortunate Jules Sandeau, for whom she had abandoned her husband. She had published INDIANA and gained a certain notoriety, but her real fame was still in the future. Balzac liked her, though he thought nothing at all of her work. He made fun of her trousers and called her frère George. She regarded Balzac as the great pioneer and sometimes addressed him as Master.

She and her lover arrived one night just as the Carmelite bells were striking. Balzac greeted them, wearing his robe, his fingers smudged with damp ink from the proof sheets he had been reading. He kissed frère George on the cheek, shook Sandeau's hand, and led them straight to the table, which was waiting for them.

"I am a laboring man," he insisted. "Like any good French workman, I want my dinner when the day's work is over."

George Sand admired the china with which Auguste had laid the table—thin porcelain plates, edged with gold, decorated with the d'Entragues coat of arms.

"Made to my order in Limoges," Balzac said proudly, holding a plate to the light to prove how thin was the porcelain. "The finest quality obtainable. There is nothing better made in France, or more expensive."

"Does it improve the taste of the food to be eaten from the costliest plates in France?" Sandeau inquired mildly.

"Demonstrably!" thundered Balzac good naturedly. "Demonstrably, my good friend, Jules."

He could always laugh at his own absurdities, even though he could not suppress them.

"Auguste!" he bellowed. "Serve dinner at once. My guests are famished. They have not eaten for three days."

He gave them oysters by the dozen, accompanied by slender bottles of slightly chilled wine from Saché. The oysters were followed by a tenderloin of beef stuffed with truffles, beautifully cooked, redolent with fine brown juices. There was a plateau of cheese and a bowl of fruit, carefully arranged.

Then Auguste brought boiling water and a spirit lamp. Balzac made the coffee himself, giving a lecture on the beverage as he handled the pot and decanter.

"Tobacco is an evil," he warned George Sand, whose penchant for strong black cigars was notorious. "It attacks both mind and body and makes whole nations dull-witted. By means of tobacco, the Americans hope to bring us to our knees."

"And coffee?" asked frère George. "It is not a drug, one supposes?"

"A drug?" said Balzac, measuring carefully, squinting at the simmering water to make sure it was absolutely clear. "Properly made, coffee is the nectar of the gods, the fuel of talent. For work, it is the only thing. It is as necessary to me in my trade as holy water to a priest in his own."

As he poured the water, carefully as a chemist, a delicious aroma rose from the pot, filling the room. A few minutes later, beaming with pride, he served his guests.

"Taste it!" he commanded. "Admit that it is the best coffee that has ever passed your lips."

George Sand confessed that Balzac's coffee was the best she had ever tasted. Balzac gave his friends brandy and sat down in the red armchair that was perfectly shaped to his body. He sighed with contentment and patted his stomach.

"Well, frère George, are you still determined to find beauty even in defecation if necessary?" he asked good naturedly.

George Sand sat up straight, her dark eyes flashing with interest. She loved to talk about literature and she had theories.

"It is right to idealize life in a novel," she said. "It is the novelist's duty to make love noble."

"Even when it is degrading?" Balzac asked.

344

He was turning his affair with the Duchesse de Castries into a novel, and he saw nothing noble in the torturing kind of love that had brought him gross humiliation.

"If it is love, it cannot be degrading," George Sand said stubbornly.

"I am all for love," Balzac said. "Next to coffee and sex, I adore love. It is almost as important to me as money. But I tell you, George, it can turn a man into a worm."

"In a novel, it should not," she said.

"You like roses," Balzac said. "You fill your books with them. I like roses too, but I don't forget that there are cabbages in the garden too. And stinkweed in the field that's just outside."

George Sand shook her head and said earnestly, "You are the first writer of the age, but you are a cynic."

"I? A cynic?" said Balzac. "Never. My faith is boundless."

"You degrade love at every turning," she said. "You turn it into something ugly and selfish."

"There is a difference between us," Balzac said. "You write about man as you think he ought to be. I am content to take him as I find him."

"Isn't that a job for history?" Sandeau asked. "To put down things as they actually are . . . that doesn't make a novel."

"It makes the only novel worth reading!" Balzac said with some passion. "If one must steal from history to make a good novel, well and good. What is important is life. And truth."

When George Sand and her lover had gone, Balzac sat for a long time at his work table but he could not concentrate. He had a sharpened quill in his hand, blank paper was in front of him, but he wrote nothing. He was haunted by an aftertaste of the conversation with George Sand. He did not agree with her theories at all, but frère George was no fool. She had challenged his own method and his spirit rose to defend it.

Ever since he had written THE COUNTRY DOCTOR and THE CURÉ OF TOURS—stories about simple people—he had become aware of a striking difference between himself and other writers. He could make fiction out of anything. A love affair, a parish priest, a peasant girl, a master printer in the provinces, a Paris whore, a cat in the wet darkness, crossing a cobbled street, the smell of good French bread a'baking . . . these things he understood and could turn into passionate words.

"Let Hugo and Dumas and the others search for their stories in the dim past or in faraway, exotic places. Let them disguise life by putting it into costume. As for me, from now on, I intend to portray France as I find her, to paint my country and my compatriots the way Cromwell asked to be painted—'warts and all.' "

He scratched on the paper with the dry pen.

"The fact is, I am not writing individual novels, as are Hugo and Dumas," he said to himself. "I am really writing one great book. If I can bring it off, it will be for nineteenth century France the one great history of manners."

He found the conception staggering, once it had been formed in his mind. To be the historian of his age, nothing less. To omit nothing, conceal nothing, to reveal every facet and layer of life in a series of books, each of which would be part of the other. That was the assignment the Good God seemed to have given him.

He dipped the pen into the inkpot, hesitated, then headed a page: STUDIES OF XIXTH CENTURY MANNERS.

Under the title he drew up a ground plan for the work that was to occupy the rest of his life, a series of interlocking novels and stories that would cover every phase of French life, every variety of the human species, every type of human behavior, public and private. Artist, lawyer, doctor, thief, pimp and prostitute, master and slave, king and peasant, private and general, man and woman, virgin and trollop, saint and sinner—each would have a place in Balzac's fictional scheme of things.

"I shall be Walter Scott, plus an architect," Balzac told himself, looking over what he had written, wondering how all this was to be done by a man already in the decade between thirty and forty.

He woke up the next morning, bursting at the seams with his new idea. The conception was magnificent and he knew it. To find anything more mighty, one had to go back to Shakespeare.

In his grand design, Balzac found the literary security for which he had always yearned. His work—past, present and future—became his fortress. From this point on, he was determined to bargain with no one, editor, publisher, critic, and he refused to cut his cloth to suit the convenience of newspaper editors.

"They are nothing but lice, these critics," he told his friend Borget, the painter, who had recently come back to Paris. "They

346

are people who can't write themselves and who seem to think that their lack of talent gives them a license to shoot at anyone who has the energy and courage to sit down and write a book."

Borget nodded agreeably, looking up from his sketch pad. He was making a drawing of Balzac's workroom that Balzac intended to send to his Unknown in Poland.

This year, Borget was as close to being an intimate friend as any man in Balzac's acquaintance. He was a simple straightforward fellow, who smoked cheap tobacco and wore workmen's shirts. Balzac enjoyed masculine company and he was on good terms with dozens of men in Paris, but all of his life his intimates had been women. With Borget, he was at ease. The two men often shared a meal in Balzac's house or enjoyed a glass of wine in the café on the corner. Balzac found he could let down his guard and relax. The little painter was not a competitor, like Dumas, Hugo, Soulié and the others, or a disciple, like George Sand, or a jealous tyro, like the scores of young men who besieged Balzac in the cafés, hoping for a scrap of advice or a note to an editor, fawning on the great man to his face, then giggling at his costumes when his back was turned.

Balzac's experiences in the literary world of Paris had toughened his fibre. With editors, publishers, critics—even with fellow writers—he was always ready to raise his steel.

"Some day I am going to write a book about that crew of human scorpions," he promised Borget. "I will expose the publishers for what they are, lice who crawl on the backs of writers and live on the sweat of honest labor performed by someone else."

Borget puffed at his pipe and nodded; he never got on Balzac's nerves.

Meanwhile, ignoring the midsummer heat of Paris, Balzac began work on a book that was to become one of his greatest novels.

This was EUGÉNIE GRANDET, a story of provincial France.

Balzac was sure of himself when he sat down to write. He struck the great note at once, in prose as prophetic as the tolling of an ancient and important bell:

In certain country towns there are houses whose aspect inspires a melancholy equal to that evoked by the gloomiest cloisters, the most monotonous moorland or the saddest ruins.

347

Perhaps, in these houses, there are at once the silence of the cloister, the barrenness of the moorland, and the bones of the ruins. Life and movement are so tranquil in them that a stranger might believe them uninhabited, if he did not suddenly see the pale, cold gaze of a motionless person whose half monastic face leans over the casement at the sound of an unknown step.

From the first page to the last, there is in EUGÉNIE GRANDET not a faltering or a false note. The story, the language, the scene, the form, are all as one and inevitable as the shape and form of a great mountain range. In the story of the old miser Grandet and his daughter, Balzac brought to life the dark passions of a provincial town. EUGÉNIE GRANDET is not simply a story, it is provincial France of its time, imprisoned in prose, truer than life itself, because the genius of Balzac had seized it and caused the flow of life to stop under his microscope.

Even the critics—those "human scorpions"—for once in their lives recognized a masterpiece when it was placed under their noses. EUGÉNIE GRANDET was a triumph. Everyone praised it and everyone read it. It became the cornerstone of Balzac's edifice. Had he dropped dead on the day it was published, he would still , have to be counted among the great men of France.

Among those aware of Balzac's new importance after EUGÉNIE GRANDET appeared was the shrewd-eyed publisher, the Widow Bechet, one of those French women of business who sometimes startle their men by outplaying them at their own game.

Rumors of Balzac's grand design were circulating in the literary salons and cafés. Everyone wondered what he was going to do next.

The Widow Bechet knew a good thing when she saw it, or even when she merely smelled it. She sent for her editor, Edmund Werdet and ordered him to get exclusive rights to Balzac's future novels.

"Pay through the nose if you have to," she said. "But don't come back unless you get an agreement."

Werdet was young, hard-working, intelligent. He had taste, and for a publisher, he was comparatively honest. He called on Balzac in the rue Cassini, having prepared himself for the interview by reading a dozen of Balzac's novels.

Balzac, as usual, needed money.

He had been piling up debts again, depending for ready cash on the discounting of editors' notes, given in payment for work he had not yet written. He received young Werdet with the guarded courtesy of a careful father giving an audience to a prospective son-in-law, about whom not enough is known.

Werdet accepted a glass of wine and praised Balzac's novels. Balzac questioned him closely. He was used to being called a genius by frauds who had not read a line of his work. When he was satisfied that Werdet actually was able to read, he asked the young man why he had come. Werdet informed him that the Widow Bechet would like to become the sole publisher of Balzac's work in the future.

"My dear young man, that is no distinction," Balzac said, with a wave of the hand. "So would every other publisher in Paris."

"Quite true, monsieur," Werdet agreed politely. "But are the others prepared to pay substantially in advance, as is the house of Veuve Bechet?"

Balzac's nose came up, like a bird dog's on scent.

"Pay in advance?" he said. "In notes or in cash?"

"In cash, of course," said Werdet easily. "In gold coin, if that is what you want."

"It is my favorite color," said Balzac. "Perhaps we can reach an understanding, you and the Widow Bechet and I."

They discussed terms.

Werdet had been authorized to commit his firm to a cash advance of thirty thousand francs. . . . "as a last resort, mind you!" the Widow had told him. Werdet opened with an offer of twenty thousand.

Balzac laughed at him.

"We might manage twenty-five," said Werdet.

Balzac laughed again and told him it wouldn't pay his tailor's bill.

At thirty thousand, Balzac became interested. At thirty-five, he was won over, but he insisted on an extra thousand, to prove to this young publisher that he was as expert at bargaining as at writing novels.

"Now as to exclusive rights," he said. "Actually, I don't mind, but I think as a matter of principle the agreement should be conditional."

"Conditional?" Werdet asked.

"Let us say that I agree in principle to give the Widow Bechet exclusive rights to future volumes of that part of my work that I call STUDIES IN XIXTH CENTURY MANNERS," Balzac explained. "To safeguard both sides, let the agreement be subject to review when I have delivered twelve volumes."

For a man in Balzac's trading position it was a not unreasonable hedge. Werdet agreed, subject to the Widow Bechet's approval, aware that he had gone six thousand francs over the Widow's top figure.

"One thing more," said Balzac. "The agreement of course will be public knowledge, but the amount of the advance must be kept absolutely secret. You see, Werdet, most of my friends are writers. If they were to find out how much I'm getting it might make for bad feeling."

Actually, Balzac was not concerned with his writer friends, but with his creditors and his mother. If word got around that he had thirty-six thousand francs, half of Paris would be on his doorstep in the morning. His mother would be first in the queue.

Somewhat to Werdet's surprise, the Widow Bechet accepted Balzac's terms.

"You have not done badly," she told the editor. "The extra thousand? It is for his vanity, one suspects?"

Werdet nodded.

A week later, Balzac possessed thirty-six thousand francs in gold. It was the largest sum of money he had ever controlled free and clear, but it was not unlimited wealth, though Balzac acted as if this were the case. When he had money, even a little, he was always sublimely self-confident. Now that he had quite a lot, his faith in himself was boundless.

"I always knew that I would be rich, but I didn't expect it quite so soon," he told Borget.

Borget nodded sagely and a few minutes later refused the loan of a thousand francs, though Balzac knew that he had scarcely enough money with which to buy canvas and paints.

"Take the money," Balzac insisted.

Borget shook his head.

350

"No, 'Noré, thank you," he said. "I only borrow from my enemies, never from my friends. It is a matter of principle, you see."

Others were less troubled by principle than Borget. Suddenly, Balzac discovered that he was a good fellow, immensely popular in the literary cafés and restaurants. Wherever he went, his table was always crowded with well-wishers and admirers, most of whom managed to leave just before the bill was presented.

The Widow Bechet's advance simply melted away.

Balzac was enjoying his fame with all the reticence of a gold miner fresh out of the arctic wastes. He gave dinners for thirty people at restaurants like Véry's. He tipped with absolute abandon. He bought jewels and furs for women who meant nothing more to him than a body to be used for the night.

Meanwhile, in the letters that he wrote to Poland, he was creating a romantic myth. Already, in the extravagance of his own imagination, he believed that he was madly in love with the anonymous Slavic beauty, to whom he revealed himself as a celibate, solitary genius.

"But it is absurd to think you are in love with a woman whose face you have never seen," his sister Laure declared.

"I have seen her face a thousand times, in my heart," Balzac answered rather smugly. "I have heard her voice a thousand times, with the ear of my soul."

Laure snorted indignantly.

"The ear of your soul indeed!" she said. "My darling brother, you are preposterous."

She was wrong.

Balzac's success in love had never been as great as it was now, when the woman he loved was almost altogether a product of his own imagination. He literally adored his Unknown Princess. She was his own creation.

Chapter 35

As the pas-
sionate tone of Balzac's letters rose in pitch, so did the Countess
Hanska's response. It could hardly have been otherwise. Here was
a lonely, warm-blooded woman, tied to an impotent husband, assaulted almost every day by letters that were a burning challenge,
composed by one of the greatest living masters of romantic prose.
To have resisted the infatuation, the lonely and beautiful Slav
would have wanted the powers of Saint Theresa.

Eve de Hanska was not a saint. She was a young woman bursting with eagerness for life. Eventually, the time came when mere
letters no longer satisfied her. The need to see Balzac, touch his
hand, to hear his voice, to know the color of his eyes, became as
demanding as the need for food, water or air.

When the winter snows began to melt, she suggested to her
husband that both of them needed a change of scene and air. The
Count Hanski shrugged indifferently, looking up from his bird
book.

"We shall be going to Kiev soon enough," he said. "If you like,
we can go to Petersburg. Perhaps even to Moscow."

She shook her head.

"I mean a real change," she said. "It would be refreshing for
you to see Vienna again."

Count Hanski's face brightened a little. His student days had
been passed in Vienna, a city that has always rivalled Paris in its
attraction for the Polish aristocracy.

"Vienna," he said. "I don't know."

She pressed the issue no further, but in the weeks that followed
she kept the idea of going to Vienna alive in his mind, feeding it
carefully, never permitting him to suspect that he was being
manipulated into a position. By the time the roads were clear of
snow, he had persuaded himself that an expedition to Austria had
been his own idea. Then it was a simple matter to convince him

352

that a side trip ought to be made to Neuchâtel, in Switzerland, the home of Henriette Borel's parents.

"It's only fair," Eve pointed out. "The poor thing hasn't seen her family in years. Besides, it will be very good for Anna's French. The next best thing is going to France."

Subjects of the Tsar were not permitted to go to France without special permission. Even Switzerland was doubtful, but Eve was willing to risk it.

"Very well, we go to Neuchâtel," Count Hanski agreed, turning back to his bird study.

Trembling with anticipation, though the actual meeting was months in the future, Eve wrote to Balzac and told him the news. When the letter had been handed to the postman, she was overtaken by rich, delectable guilt. She put on her sable coat and hood and hurried through the cold to the de Hanski private chapel, where she fell on her knees and prayed, imploring the Blessed Virgin to intercede and protect her from the lustful desires that were so hateful, strange and delightful.

"Holy Virgin, give me strength to resist him," she prayed. "Protect my marriage vows."

When the news reached Balzac, he was delighted but not surprised. He had not gained his reputation as an analyst of women for nothing. In composing his letters he had been calculating as any courtesan.

He could not resist bragging to Laure.

"Admit that I am a gay dog," he said. "Don't you think it is a pretty piece of work, to tear a husband from his lair in the Ukraine and make him travel fifteen hundred miles, simply to oblige his wife's lover, who must travel only four hundred?"

"But you are not her lover," Laure protested.

"I shall be," said Balzac. "I have consulted a fortune-teller, one who is never wrong."

She laughed at him.

"You and your fortune-tellers!" she said. "Suppose she is forty and fat as a sow?"

"Blasphemy!" cried Balzac. "My fortune-teller assures me that she is young, beautiful and rich. Why else would I be going to Switzerland?"

Balzac joked about his fortune-tellers, yet he was certain there was something in it. So intense was his own power to draw on the unconscious mind, he believed there must be a whole country of the mind, hidden beneath the surface. Given the time and the money, he would have plunged into a study of psychic phenomena. As it was, he contented himself with dabbling in the subject. What really fascinated him was the working of the human mind. What goes on in the darkness of the brain? he demanded of himself. That was the question he was asking, when he consulted hypnotists, trance mediums and others.

At the end of August, Balzac left Paris, having provided himself with new clothes and a new set of luggage, made to his order from the best English coach hide, buffed to the color of wild honey, stamped with the arms of d'Entragues. On the way to Switzerland, his mood of high confidence wavered a little.

"What if she finds me unattractive?" he asked himself, glancing at his jolting reflection in the stage-coach window.

"Suppose she is revoltingly ugly?" he thought. "After all, it is possible for a beautiful soul to inhabit a repulsive body. God often plays such tricks. They seem to amuse Him."

The stagecoach climbed into the Alps and entered the province of Neuchâtel, in Western Switzerland. The sight of the snow-capped peaks, like a stab in the heart, brought into focus sharp memory of the last occasion on which he had visited this country. He closed his eyes and for an instant he was on the hotel balcony in Geneva, aware of hot blinding shame. He opened his eyes and looked at the picture-book landscape around him.

"It is a wound that will never quite heal over," he said to himself, resting his forehead on the frame of the window.

As they approached Neuchâtel, he was nervous as a young soldier going into battle. The Faraway Princess was about to be brought to life by the Good Fairy, and he was frightened.

Eve de Hanska was not without a flair for the theatrical. If she were going to deceive her husband, even on this conjectural basis, the thing must be done with proper attention to the demands of romantic form, as she had come to understand them after reading a hundred novels that centered on clandestine lovers.

The de Hanskis had rented the Villa André in Neuchâtel, and Eve had instructed Balzac to take a room at the Hotel de Faubourg, which was nearby. When he reached the hotel, a letter was waiting for him, addressed in the now familiar hand: "Monsieur:

354

Be on the promenade between the hours of one and four, on the twenty-sixth of September."

Balzac consulted a calendar on the hall porter's desk. The twenty-sixth was tomorrow. He wasn't sorry. After four days traveling without a break, he was filthy, bruised and exhausted. He had a bath and a light meal and got himself early to bed, falling asleep with surprising ease.

The next day, the curtain went up on the first act of Balzac's romantic drama. A more appropriate setting could hardly have been devised by Mrs. Radcliffe herself. The promenade at Neuchâtel was one of the beauty spots of Europe. It had been the scene of noble, even royal intrigues of the heart. In September, the air was thin, but stimulating as a good dry wine.

The promenade had the pretty town behind it, a cliff in front. Across the valley were the gorgeous mountains, colored pasteboard cutouts in the astringent Alpine air. There were public benches between the flower beds and well groomed bushes along the public walk. Nowhere else in the world was nature presented more elegantly to those who enjoy good fortune.

Balzac, for once in his life, was early for an appointment. At a quarter to one he was on the promenade. He was almost alone. An old gentleman sat on a bench, reading a German newspaper, the page held close to his nose. Around him was a pleasant aura of wealth. A pair of immaculate children played some game of their own invention. Otherwise, the promenade was deserted. Most of the hotel guests were devoting themselves to the customarily enormous midday meal.

At two o'clock, heavy with food, they began to filter down from the various hotel dining rooms, well-dressed, self-confident people, enjoying the fruits of wealth.

Like a detective tracking a fugitive, Balzac scrutinized every face. There was not a sign of anyone who could possibly be his Unknown. He waited nervously, his ego on guard against a trick. He paced the length of the promenade like a soldier on sentry duty.

At three o'clock, Eve de Hanska made her appearance, accompanied by Henriette Borel. Balzac saw them at once. For a moment, his heart sank. What if the older, worn-looking one turns out to be the Unknown? Then, as he drew near them, he saw that the older woman wore the clothes of a lower bourgeoise, while the younger was dressed in the height of fashion.

Eve had selected her costume with care. She wore wine-colored

355

velvet, cut by the best dressmaker in Vienna, shaped to her figure, emphasizing the soft curves of her body. She was emphatically feminine, delicate without being fragile. Her small hands were protected by gloves of white doeskin. She wore a large stylish hat that placed a part of her face in shadow. Balzac had only a glimpse of her glorious, blue-black hair.

In her hand she carried a book. As he drew close to her, Balzac saw that it was a copy of his own THE MAGIC SKIN. It is she! he realized. It must be she! He stopped for a moment, drew in his breath, then stepped forward, raising his hat.

"Madame. . . ?"

The voice that answered him was delicious, perfect French, school taught, brushed with the faintest of accents.

"Monsieur de Balzac? I am Evalina de Hanska."

Balzac bowed again and assured her that the honor was overwhelming. Henriette Borel was introduced. She gave Balzac a half-curtsy, muttering "Monsieur," as if it were a curse, her shoe-button eyes filled with suspicion of this notorious author who had caused her mistress to forget her position in life, her obligations, even the Lord God Himself.

For a few seconds, the three of them stood like a group of awkwardly arranged statues. Then Balzac glanced at a bench and suggested that they sit down, feeling desperately awkward. The afternoon sun was warm and there was only a light breeze, but the Countess Hanska shivered and announced that she was aware of a chill in the air.

"Lirette, my darling, be an angel and fetch my scarf," she said, touching the governess on the cheek affectionately.

Lirette glared at Balzac, then bowed to her mistress and was off on her pointless errand. Eve laughed indulgently, a delectable, musical laugh.

"Poor Lirette. I'm afraid she disapproves of you, monsieur," she said, smiling at Balzac. "She prays for my soul, morning and night."

Balzac sat staring at her. He was stunned. The Faraway Princess had come to life and she was precisely as he had predicted. She was young, in her twenties, certainly. She was beautiful. She was pulsing with life and the yearning to love.

"Evalina," he said, tasting the syllables. "Eve."

Their eyes met. In silence, they sat together, constructing between them the last section of the romantic bridge that had been started with the long interchange of letters. Finally, Balzac broke the silence.

"You are beyond my dreams," he said.

He was speaking from the heart, with profound honesty. She felt it and her lips trembled. She could not resist his eyes. He touched her hand for an instant, his finger moving on the soft doeskin. The color rose in her cheeks.

"Eve," he said softly. "We must be alone."

"We must," she said desperately. "But how? There is my husband. There is the child. There is Lirette, who watches me as if she were a sentinel."

"We must be alone, and soon," said Balzac flatly, as if he were stating the time of day.

He seemed calm, but he was exultant. From the instant he had set eyes on Eve, a great relief had flooded through his being. This time he was sure that God had not played him a trick. This was the woman intended for him by fate. There was not the slightest doubt in his mind that he would possess her. He felt no urgency, no need for immediate conquest. There was no need to prove anything, for all had been proved in the first interchange of glances between them. For the moment, it was enough simply to sit here beside her, aware of the softness of her body, the translucence of her skin, aware of her proud, voluptuous mouth, conscious of the romantic odor of her perfume.

The two of them sat together, oblivious of the people around them, ignorant of the scenery, of the passage of the sun. For all their awareness of anyone but themselves, they might have been sitting on the surface of the moon. They did not notice the tall figure who came toward them, stood for a moment watching them, then coughed politely and said, "Madame. . . ."

It was Count Hanski, with his wife's scarf carried over his arm. Balzac got to his feet, feeling no embarrassment.

"My husband, the Count Hanski," said Eve. "Monsieur Honoré de Balzac."

"Balzac? Balzac?" the count said, rubbing his chin. "Not the French writer chap that everyone in Neuchâtel is talking about?"

"I'm afraid I must plead guilty," Balzac said gracefully. "I had hoped to remain incognito in Switzerland, at least for a day or two, but that's not always possible." He picked up THE MAGIC

357

SKIN and riffled through the pages. "Your wife chanced to drop this book and I had the honor to recover it, monsieur. When I saw the title, I could not resist the temptation to introduce myself."

"Most natural. Most natural," Count Hanski said.

He must be nearly sixty, Balzac thought. Probably he was never a match for this woman he had married. If Balzac had felt the slightest qualm at the prospect of committing adultery, this would have vanished the moment he set eyes on the count. By all the laws of common justice, Hanski simply had no right to this lovely and passionate creature.

Unfortunately for Balzac, the adultery had to be postponed.

Count Hanski read very little and that little did not include French novels, but he had a provincial's respect for fame. He was impressed by the fact that Balzac's name carried such weight with the fashionable crowd at Neuchâtel, and it flattered him to be seen in the company of the famous writer.

It was impossible to shake him off.

Only once was Balzac alone with his Eve long enough to snatch a kiss. They were in the public gardens, shielded from view by massed shrubbery. Count Hanski had wandered off, attracted by the plumage of some unusual bird. Balzac seized the moment. He drew Eve to his breast and kissed her expressively.

"My darling," he whispered.

She clung to him, her cheek pressed against his, her small soft fingers on his neck.

"I am damned," she whispered. "Eternally condemned. But I love you, Honoré. May God forgive me!"

"He will forgive you," Balzac said generously.

He kissed her again, then, reluctantly, he released her. A few seconds later, Count Hanski returned, swinging his stick enthusiastically.

"What an extraordinary bird!" he exclaimed. "We've nothing like it in Poland. Nothing remotely like it."

They walked back to the Villa André, where Balzac was dining as the count's guest. All through dinner, he and Eve exchanged dangerous glances. After dinner, in the drawing room, they waited in the hope that the count would excuse himself and go upstairs to bed. It was hopeless. Count Hanski gurgled brightly about the birds of Switzerland and it was Balzac who became sleepy.

"Neuchâtel is too small," he said to Eve the next day. "One might as well be in a village. We must meet in a city, my darling. In a city anything can be managed."

"Where shall it be?" she asked eagerly.

For Balzac, only one city was appropriate.

"Geneva," he said promptly. "Since you cannot cross the French frontier without the Tsar's permission, it must be Geneva. Can it be managed?"

"I will manage it somehow," she promised him. "But Honoré, darling, it won't be easy. You must give me time. It's not only Wenceslas, you see. I must not permit Lirette to suspect how far things have gone with us."

"A month?" he said.

"Two," she said. "But depend on me. I will manage it somehow."

He touched her hand.

"Every day will be a year," he said.

A few days later, Balzac left Neuchâtel, unable to bear the strain of being with Eve in her husband's presence. He reached Paris in a state of extraordinary exhilaration and plunged into his work at once, ignoring the effects of a four-day journey over rough mountain roads.

He needed money.

The journey to Switzerland had almost finished off the thirty-six thousand francs he had got from the Widow Bechet. He was under the whip again, forced to work like a galley slave in order to pay his running expenses, meet the interest on his notes, and put by enough cash to underwrite the expedition to Geneva, to which he looked forward as a turning point in his life.

The prospect of Geneva was the fuel that fed his fire. He worked at a pace that was alarming, even for the great Balzac, driving himself fourteen, sixteen, eighteen hours a day, turning out magazine pieces and a few short books.

Laure was worried about his health. She and her husband had moved into Paris, to a house in the Faubourg Poissonière, and she came to the rue Cassini two or three times a week, bringing Balzac a tureen of soup or a bowl of ragout and a long loaf of fresh bread.

"You must eat, Honoré, she insisted. "Keep up the way you are going, and you will go to Geneva not as a lover but as a corpse."

359

When he refused, she badgered him, threatening to feed him with a spoon, like a child. But for Laure, he would have eaten almost nothing and tried to live on coffee, as he did nowadays when he was engaged with a sustained bout of work. When he was headlong into a novel, the thought of food was abhorrent to him. It was afterward, when he came out of the creative shell, that he devoured the Gargantuan meals for which he had become famous.

He was astonished by his own energy this year, and believed that it came from the circumstance of being in love.

"I tell you, Laure, I am a man who needs love in the way other men need food and drink," he said. "It is my ammunition."

Laure nodded. He saw that she was crying.

"What is the matter?" he asked.

"Nothing," she said. "Everything."

Things were not going well with Laure. De Surville was having bad luck with his profession. There was not enough money, and the de Surville house was filled with the grim atmosphere of defeat.

"If it's a matter of money, perhaps I can put my hands on some," Balzac said.

"That is unnecessary," Laure said tersely.

"If I were to talk with Eugène. . . ."

She flared up.

"I forbid you to speak with him!" she said. "We will manage, as we have always managed."

A few days later, Balzac was working on a set of proofs when his doorbell rang with a challenge. "It sounds like a process server," he thought. He paid no attention. Auguste had become most efficient at getting rid of bill collectors, unsolicited females, curiosity seekers and the various others who inflict themselves upon a celebrity.

This visitor, however, was one with whom Auguste could not deal. The door to Balzac's study was opened with some force. He looked up from his table and found himself face to face with his mother, whom he had not seen in months.

"Well, Honoré?"

He got up awkwardly, stiff in the neck, and kissed his mother's cheek. She touched the fabric of his monkish robe and sniffed disapprovingly.

360

"This absurd masquerade," she said. "You still wear it, I see."

"It suits me," said Balzac, patting his stomach. "What would you have me wear when I work? A suit of armor?"

"Most men find it possible to work in a pair of trousers," his mother said tartly. "But I haven't come all this way to discuss your peculiar taste in dress."

"Evidently not," Balzac conceded.

He gave her a chair and offered her tea, which she refused. He sat down at his work table.

"I will come straight to the point," his mother said. "I am here to talk about money. Since you ignore my letters, I am obliged to come in person."

"I send you an allowance," Balzac said defensively.

"A pittance!" she said. "Do you realize that your 'allowance' as you call it, amounts to less than the interest on the capital sum you owe me?"

"I am not an accountant," Balzac said. "I do what I can."

"It is not enough," his mother said. "When you were faced with bankruptcy, five years ago, you were glad to have my help and filled with promises that the debt would be paid, no matter what sacrifices you were obliged to make. That was five years ago, nearly six, and you have paid me nothing, not even the interest on the money."

Balzac muttered something about not getting blood from a stone. His mother shook her head.

"Honoré, I am not a fool," she said. "You are one of the most successful writers in France. One sees your books everywhere, in edition after edition. You have never been the man to work without being paid. Can you tell me honestly that you've earned nothing, these last three years?"

"It is necessary to make an appearance in order to make progress," he said lamely. "If editors think you are without funds, they take advantage of you. One must make an impression of prosperity, even if it's only a shell."

His mother rejected this with a short, humorless laugh.

"Your extravagance is almost as famous as your lack of morals," she said. "I may be a simple middle-class woman, but I am not unaware of what Paris is saying. Your dinner parties, your ridiculous clothes, your carriages, your women . . . that's where your money goes, and don't try to deny it."

"I don't deny that I've spent money," Balzac said. "But it has been with an end in view, not simply out of vanity." He sighed and assumed a wistful expression. "I had planned to keep it a secret," he said cautiously. "But I suppose I must tell you." He leaned forward and lowered his voice. "The fact is, before very long we shall all be rich, you, Laure and I. Worry about money will be a thing of the past with us."

"You have discovered a way to manufacture gold?" his mother said cynically.

"What I am going to tell you must be kept absolutely secret," said Balzac, his voice just above a whisper. "At this point, the breath of gossip could ruin everything. I am in the process of arranging a rich marriage, marriage to a woman whose fortune is reckoned in the millions, whose lands are beyond measurement."

He went on to describe the Countess Hanska, her beauty, her wealth, her vast estates in Poland.

"What is the obstacle?" demanded his mother.

"She is married," said Balzac. "Her husband is a dying man, incurably ill, in anguish, waiting for the Lord's mercy. It is simply a matter of time, you see, yet one must observe a decent respect for the marriage vows."

"For you, this is a new departure," observed his mother. "In the past, as I remember, marriage vows were never permitted to interfere with your desires."

"A man grows up," said Balzac. "In any case, you know my secret. Sooner or later, but with certainty, I shall be the possessor of a large fortune."

"And in the meantime?" she asked.

"In the meantime, I will do what I can," Balzac promised.

His mother stood up, smoothing her skirt. She made a smart appearance and looked closer to forty than fifty. She was still sharply aware of style.

"I have no choice but to take your word," she said bitterly. "I cannot take my own son to court. I am obliged to depend on your sense of justice."

When she had gone, Balzac sat in his armchair, brooding over what he had told her. He had been eager to put her off, and had said what came first to his tongue, without regard to truth or false-hood . . . anything to get rid of her so that he could go back to

362

work. Yet he realized that what he had said was not far from what was in his mind. He was determined to marry Eve. Certainly she was enormously wealthy, a circumstance that did not make her less attractive. Count Hanski, if not precisely in anguish, was nevertheless an old man, whose remaining years were within counting.

Balzac had no sense of shame at counting his matrimonial chickens before the eggs had been laid. He loved Eve for herself. Her vast wealth would simply make it possible for love to find its full expression.

Yet if he and Eve were to share Count Hanski's leavings, Eve must be protected from herself, from the recklessness that would certainly invade her spirit when their love was consummated in Geneva. Hanski must not be permitted to suspect that she was unfaithful, or the sparkling future might be spoilt.

Balzac blessed his good fortune. "God has given me love," he said, "and thrown in the money for lagniappe."

He saw himself living in a bright future, where marital and economic bliss would be combined. He glowed with anticipation, a man who saw on the horizon the brilliant shape of his own reward.

In November, Balzac canvassed every editor in Paris and collected advances wherever he could, promising to deliver articles on every subject he could think of, from politics to hypnotism. To a magazine editor, these days, he was the best name in France, an absolutely certain drawing card. An article by Balzac, on any subject, meant that the issue would be sold out on the day it came from the press.

Balzac knew the value of his name and demanded high prices, even for work that had not been written. He got them. He had no difficulty in collecting enough cash to finance his trip to Geneva. He considered sending his mother a token payment of a thousand francs, then decided against it.

"She has no real need of money," he said to himself. "And once she tastes blood, she will give me no peace."

Shrewdly, Balzac prepared the ground for his conquest in Geneva, which by now had taken on symbolic meaning. He wrote priapic letters to Eve, addressing them to Henriette Borel as before, but he also wrote other letters, unexceptionable in content, the friendly words of a distinguished man of letters to an aristocratic admirer.

These were meant for the eyes of Count Hanski.

Balzac intended to establish himself as a friend of the family, so that his presence in Geneva would seem perfectly natural. The final paragraph of the formal letters always included his felicitations: "To your esteemed husband, the Count, to little Anna, and to the estimable Mademoiselle Borel."

The cynical reader must not conclude that Balzac's behavior was insincere. He felt that he was protecting the elderly count from unnecessary discomfort and guarding his Eve from embarrassment that could serve no useful purpose.

He was not yet ready to reveal his romance to Zulma Carraud or to Madame de Berny. He dreaded Zulma's sarcasm and he could not bear the thought of hurting Madame de Berny, whose health of late had not been good. He wrote to both of these women who loved him, and indicated that he was going to Switzerland to gather material for a new book. O classic excuse of authors! Simple, virtuous, incontestable.

In the midst of a minor blizzard, Balzac left Paris, wrapped in a heavy, Napoleonic cape. In one of his bags was the manuscript of THE DUCHESS OF LANGEAIS, the bitter novel that was to be his revenge on the Duchesse de Castries.

Chapter 36

On Christmas
Day, Balzac reached Geneva. He booked a suite at the fashionable
and expensive Hotel de l'Arc. His object was matrimony and he
intended to make an impression on Eve, not only as a lover, but
as a prosperous, knowledgeable man of the world. His good spirits
were raised higher a few minutes after his arrival. The hall porter
handed him a small package and said, "This was left for monsieur
by the Countess de Hanska."

In his room, still wearing his heavy cape, Balzac tore the
wrappings from the package. There was a jeweler's velvet box,
containing a handsome gold ring of what he took to be Florentine
workmanship. The ring was heavy and valuable. A note in the box
commanded him to open it. He found the concealed spring and
the jeweled seal flew back. In a secret capsule was a tiny lock of
Eve's gorgeous blue-black hair.

Balzac kissed the ring and slipped it on his finger, vowing never
to take it off. He stood in front of the mirror, admiring himself
and his new jewelry. Then he rang for the maid and ordered a bath,
soaking himself in the tepid water, easing the muscles bruised by
the journey.

If Balzac's visit to Neuchâtel had been in the nature of a re-
connaissance, his expedition to Geneva was a frontal attack in
force. At Neuchâtel he had been tentative, feeling his way. This
time he was determined to be forthright, taking his privileges for
granted, placing his trust in the preparation he believed his letters
had made with the count.

The day after Christmas he called formally on the Hanskis. He
drank tea with the family and ingratiated himself with Eve's daughter, Anna, a poetic child with long gold braids and delightfully
serious eyes, dressed in white serge. He went out of his way to be
charming to the count, having skimmed through a book on birds in
preparation for the meeting. He seemed almost to ignore Eve.

When it was time for him to leave, he played his first risky card.

"Geneva is famous for its art gallery, which I have not had the good fortune to see," he said. "Perhaps you and Madame de Hanska would do me the honor of coming with me."

"Ah yes. Art," the count said, polishing his monocle. "Not quite in my line, I'm afraid. I'm interested in birds, you see, and the winter birds are extraordinary here." He looked at Eve. "Of course, my wife likes art."

"I should love to see the pictures," Eve said blandly.

Balzac bowed and said, "Perhaps, then, with the count's permission. . . ?"

Count Hanski waved a careless hand.

"Of course, my dear chap. Of course," he said. "By all means. Enjoy yourselves."

Balzac bowed to the countess. Their eyes met.

"Shall we say tomorrow?" he asked. "At one?"

"At one," she agreed.

Even on the threshold of the most passionate love affair of his life, Balzac remained the slave of his pen; it was understood that the hours between midnight and noon were sacred to his writing.

The following day, for the sake of form, Balzac and his Eve passed an hour in the gallery, pretending to look at the pictures. Then they drove through the sparkling city to his hotel. He was both thrilled and disappointed. They embraced in private for the first time. They kissed, passionately. But when he tried to loosen the bodice of her dress, she drew back.

"No," she said, arresting his hand.

"But why?" he demanded, baffled. "You love me. Why do you refuse to make me happy? Why do you deny yourself?"

She sat on the edge of his bed, the dark hair that he admired slightly loosened, her cheeks flushed from the preliminary love-making.

"I don't want to be a fool," she said. "I love you, it's true. May God help me!"

Balzac spread his hands.

"Well, then, what else matters?" he said.

"For you, it is nothing," she said. "Another woman. For me, you understand, it is a fatal step."

"It is a step you can take with confidence," he said.

366

"You are a famous man," she said gravely, raising her head. "Do you imagine that your way of life in Paris is a secret from the world?"

"What are you saying?" he demanded.

"I will not share you with others," she said.

"But I have told you a hundred times that I live like a monk," he protested. "My life is blameless as that of a virgin girl."

"There were some French people at Neuchâtel," she said. "They talked of nothing but your affairs, your extravagances, of the dozens of women who are nothing but playthings to you."

"Name one!" he challenged her.

"They mentioned Madame de Girardin," said Eve.

Balzac roared with laughter.

"Delphine? She would be amused, I assure you," he said. "Delphine's lovers are all boys who have just begun to shave."

"The Duchesse de Castries?" Eve said.

Balzac's lips turned white. He gripped the bedstead.

"I detest the Duchesse de Castries!" he said violently.

"The wife of an officer, a certain Madame Carraud?" Eve asked.

Balzac clenched his fist and struck the palm of the other hand.

"My God in heaven, is nothing sacred?" he demanded. "She is a friend. A second sister. A woman pure as a saint."

He dropped to his knees beside the bed and took her hands in his own.

"Eve, my darling, believe me," he said. "I love you and no one but you."

She kissed his forehead and whispered, "I want to believe you. I must believe you, or my life will turn to ashes."

He kissed her full on the mouth. She clung to him.

"You must give me time," she said softly. "For a woman, it is not a light thing. She must come with a free heart."

For a week, Balzac courted his Eve. He bought her little Swiss bouquets. He copied lines from Byron's verse and pressed them into her hand. He was attentive, ardent, persuasive, and his field was clear. Count Hanski passed his time with his birds, leaving his wife to be entertained by that writer chap, de Balzac, a capital fellow.

At the end of a week, Eve was ready to drop like a sweet sun-ripened peach.

367

They went to the Villa Diodati, which had witnessed the love of Lord Byron himself. They held hands and exchanged endearments. Then they drove to the Hotel de l'Arc. Outside, the day was brilliantly cold. The sitting room was seductively warm. Balzac drew the heavy curtains, shutting out the light. The coal fire burned discreetly, casting a romantic glow into the darkened room, falling on Eve's face, which was framed in the collar of her sable coat.

They embraced without speaking, passionately.

"How can you doubt me?" he whispered.

"I don't doubt you, my darling," she said. "Take me, I beg you. Take me!"

Her dress was fastened with gold clasps. Balzac undid them slowly, making a kind of ritual of it.

"Hurry!" she commanded. "Hurry!"

"We have a lifetime, my darling," he whispered.

She stood in the soft poetic firelight, a column of white satin, when the dress had been removed. Making a rustling sound, she drew her petticoats off.

"Be kind to me," she begged. "It has been so long."

He drew her close.

"Mother of God, save me!" she cried.

Spent, both of them, they sank into a delicious lassitude. The firelight flickered on their bodies. Finally, Eve stirred.

"I am condemned," she said, mechanically, as if she had announced that she had a cold.

Balzac sat up in the bed; never before had he made love to a truly religious woman. He crossed his forearms on his knees and consulted the fire.

"You are my wife," he said soberly. "From this moment, you are my wife of love."

"I have a husband," Eve said.

"If these things are ordered in heaven, we are meant for each other, you and I," Balzac said positively.

"It is a mortal sin," she said.

"A woman who loves with all her heart will be pardoned by God," said Balzac.

They dined together in Balzac's sitting room, at a table set up in front of the fire. Eve was relaxed and charming. Balzac was

368

delighted with her. She reached across the table and fed him African grapes. They laughed together. They were happy.

At midnight, when Eve was gone, Balzac changed into his robe and sat down to work, manuscript on the table before him. The taste of Eve's kisses was on his lips. The room was heavy with her scent. Balzac took up his pen and began to write the final chapters of THE DUCHESS OF LANGEAIS, unable to suppress his triumph. Here in Geneva, the scene of his greatest humiliation, he had possessed a woman whose beauty, wealth and rank placed her above the Duchesse de Castries, and here in Geneva he was finishing a book that would show the Duchesse de Castries for what she was—a soulless hypocrite, incapable of an honest act or emotion.

He was taking his revenge, yet he believed himself to be in love. He was unconscious of the disease inflicted on him by his mother, that made it impossible for him to love with health and without reference to the wound in his ego.

During the next three weeks, Balzac and Eve de Hanska moved into an area of the most delightful intimacy. The room at the Hotel de l'Arc, with its big bed and fireside table, became the first home of their love. They made love fiercely, and without shame. They passed hours together, enchanted with one another. Count Hanski was forgotten. He was nothing more than an inconvenience, soon to be removed.

"Poor man, his lungs are weak and I believe it has affected his heart," Eve told Balzac.

"May God give me the strength never to wish for his death," said Balzac. "Still, if it must come, it must."

In the darkened hotel room, they adopted as a motto the sacramental phrase, *adoremus in aeternum,* pledging their eternal love. It was agreed that they would marry as soon as Count Hanski was thoughtful enough to depart this earth.

"Until then, my darling, we will grasp at happiness when we can," said Balzac.

They were madly in love by now, but it did not occur to either of them to sacrifice Eve's position or fortune for the sake of love. A modest, illegal life in Paris did not appeal to Eve's temperament. She loved Balzac, but she also loved the luxuries that great wealth offers. As for Balzac, he had always felt that his genius gave him the right to "une femme et une fortune." He saw no point in behaving like an idiot, when a few years of patience would bring wealth as well as conjugal bliss.

In February, Balzac left Geneva. He would have stayed on through the spring, but he was down to his last few hundred francs. He parted from Eve in a mood that must be described as blissful, and drove in a hackney carriage to the stagecoach terminus. He stood under a big clock, ready to board the stage for Paris, when he was struck by a curious telepathic sense of danger, aware of a prompting voice that came from he knew not where.

He changed his seat for one on a coach that would take him through Nemours, to La Bouleaunaire, the country house to which Madame de Berny had retired.

It was midmorning when he reached La Bouleaunaire, a grey, merciless winter's day. An old servant let him in.

"Madame has taken to her bed," she told him. "The doctor is with her now."

Balzac went up the stairs. At Madame de Berny's beside sat his own physician, Nacquart. Balzac's chest tightened. If she had sent to Paris for Nacquart, she must be seriously ill. He nodded to Nacquart, then knelt beside the bed and kissed her cheek. She turned her head. When she saw him her eyes brightened.

"Honoré," she murmured. Her voice was weak.

"I am here," he said.

Nacquart stood up.

"I will be downstairs, 'Noré, if I am needed," he said.

For an hour, Balzac sat with Madame de Berny, holding her hand. She was too weak to talk. When she fell asleep he withdrew his hand gently and went downstairs. Nacquart was sitting in an armchair, staring at the fire.

"Well, 'Noré, there is no need to tell you what you have seen for yourself," he said.

Balzac sat down in a straight chair. He was oddly calm.

"There is no hope for her then?" he asked.

"None," said Nacquart. He shrugged. "It is in God's hands. She may live for a week, a month, even several months. She may not live through the night."

Balzac passed a hand in front of his eyes. He made no sound. Nacquart got up, poured a glass of brandy and gave it to Balzac. Balzac drank it at a gulp and shuddered. It steadied his nerves.

"She is my creator, Nacquart," he said. "Whatever I am, as a writer, as a man, is because of her."

For a week, Balzac remained at Madame de Berny's bedside. He carried her meals to her on a tray, read to her when she was well enough to listen, sat for hours holding her hand.

She seemed to draw life from him.

It was a miracle. At the end of a week she was so improved that Nacquart was astonished.

"I am only a doctor," he said. "I am not God. But she must be careful from now on. This last attack, it was a near thing."

"She will not die," said Balzac stubbornly. "It is not time for her to die."

When Balzac reached Paris, a letter from Eve was waiting for him, a quick note mailed from Geneva. She had persuaded the count to take her to Italy, to the lake country for the spring.

A week later, she wrote from Tuscany.

"Why must you be in Paris, my darling? I have a bedroom with a balcony that looks across the lake, a bed the size of a tennis court, and no one to occupy it but myself."

"Patience," counseled Balzac in his reply. "We have a lifetime before us, my darling."

He was back at the oar of his galley again, trying to make up for the time lost at La Bouleaunaire, when his concern for Madame de Berny had not permitted him to work.

There were still five volumes to be written of the twelve for which the Widow Bechet had paid thirty-six thousand francs now gone. Magazine editors who had given him various sums on account plagued him for copy.

He met the demands as he always had done, but Nacquart, who called with news of Madame de Berny, warned him that overwork and coffee were putting an unconscionable strain on his heart.

Balzac thumped his chest.

"I am as strong as a lion, Nacquart," he said. "I have inherited my father's constitution, and I certainly intend to live at least as long as he did."

"Even lions die, my boy," Nacquart reminded him. "And sometimes they die young, just as people do."

"Are you trying to tell me that I am ill?" Balzac demanded. "I tell you, I am fit as a prize bull."

"I am trying to tell you to relax," Nacquart said patiently. "And to drink less coffee."

Nothing short of complete collapse would have enabled Balzac to have altered his way of life as Nacquart suggested. It was not in his nature to relax. He was a machine, a factory, almost an industry in himself, an open-hearth furnace of literature that could not be shut down unless the fires were drawn completely.

When he put "The End" to the manuscript of THE DUCHESS OF LANGEAIS, Balzac thought he had also put an end to the disastrous affaire de Castries. He had underestimated the resiliency of those who inhabited the Faubourg Saint-Germain. Late in the spring, a short note asked him to call at the Castellane Palace.

"I am ill and condemned to my couch," the Duchesse de Castries wrote. "Please do me the honor of paying me a visit."

He went out of curiosity and took with him the proof sheets of THE DUCHESS OF LANGEAIS. This time he did not cool his heels in the anteroom for an hour. The servant who opened the great carved doors had instructions to take him straight upstairs to the familiar private sitting room, where the duchess rested on her chaise longue.

She was certainly ill, but it was an illness that did not affect the beauty of her face. She was like a miniature painted on porcelain, fragile and delicate, a superlative example of decadent beauty.

Balzac was mildly amused by his own indifference.

"She is simply an ornament," he told himself. "A bangle. No more authentic than a piece of paste jewelry of the kind women sometimes have made to conceal the fact that the real ones have been pawned."

He kissed her hand, getting a whiff of the perfume that once had driven him to distraction.

"You are kind to visit an invalid," she said.

"I am the soul of kindness," he answered, bowing ironically, wondering what on earth she wanted. It wasn't politics this time. Certainly she wasn't moved by passion. It must be that she had heard of his new attachment and, womanlike, resented another's having what she did not want.

372

She gave him tea, praised his appearance, asked about his work. It was all as formal as a court visit. In an hour, Balzac rose to go, offering her the page proofs of THE DUCHESS OF LANGEAIS. She thanked him and promised that she would begin the book that very evening.

Balzac went down the marble staircase, humming a tune, pleased with himself. The Duchesse de Castries had given him the chance to bring his revenge to her doorstep. He chuckled, speculating on the rage that would be produced when she read his book.

She surprised him. He had expected her to be furious, to denounce him, perhaps even to persuade the Duc de Fitz-James to challenge him to a duel. Instead, he got a polite note that praised his book and asked him to call again at the Castellane Palace.

He obeyed the summons and passed an hour with the glamorous invalid. No longer in the least infatuated with her, he discovered that she could be amusing and very clever. She was a fraud, but there was a strain of magnificence in her masquerade. He fell into the habit of going to see her once a week for an hour, drinking tea and bringing her the gossip of literary Paris.

Then, late in the spring, came a bombshell from Italy.

"One hears that Paris talks of nothing but your liaison with the Duchesse de Castries," wrote Eve de Hanska, in her angry, slanting hand. "One hears that you are a daily visitor, that you shower Marie de Castries with gifts and wait on her as if you were a servant. One even hears—worst treachery of all!—that you bring her proof sheets of your books. After what passed between us in Geneva, after your solemn promises, your protestations of love, how can you be so false?"

Balzac was stunned, then outraged. He reread the letter, carefully, then realized that the gossip that had reached Eve in Tuscany had been put on the road by the Duchesse de Castries herself, deliberately, as part of a scheme to compromise him. No one but the duchess herself knew that he had carried proof sheets to the Castellane Palace. He had been nicely taken in again by that treacherous woman.

He wrote to Eve, protesting his innocence.

"Madame de Castries is dying," he told her. "Hopelessly paralyzed. Her beauty has entirely disappeared and she inspires only one emotion—pity. As for love, even if I desired it, that is absurd and impossible. She is packed in a plaster cast that extends

373

from the nape of her neck to a point below her hips. I defy you to find in the Cluny Museum a more effective chastity belt."

Balzac mailed his letter, hoping that it would convince Eve; he had neither the funds nor the time for a trip to Italy at the moment. He decided to ignore the Duchesse de Castries, to treat her shabby trick with contempt.

In two weeks he had a plaintive message from the Castellane Palace; she was being ignored. Had she offended? What had she done?

He sent a stiff little note in reply.

Perhaps for the first time in her life, the duchess turned the other cheek. She wrote him a long, abject letter. She begged for a word of kindness from him. She reminded him that he had loved her and hinted that she loved him.

Balzac read the letter with a feeling of disgust. She must be delirious, he thought, demented. Certainly she is not sincere.

He ignored the letter and saw no more of the Duchesse de Castries, but he could not prevent himself from speculating on what his present life might be like had he received such a letter before the fatal night in Geneva. Quite possibly he would have paid no attention to the anonymous letters from the Ukraine and thus never have set eyes on Eve.

Eve had not yet answered his letter of explanation. He was worried. He went to his favorite fortune-teller and asked the man to search Eve's mind. He was reassured. The medium promised he would have a letter before the next full moon.

A week later, the letter from Italy reached him. There was a certain chill in the lines, but the Duchesse de Castries was not mentioned. Within a month, the correspondence was back to normal, but Balzac was on his guard. He had caught a glimpse of the fierce strain of jealousy that was a part of Eve's character. It was a dangerous thing, and something he must always keep in his mind.

Chapter 37

THE WIDOW BECHET was pressing Balzac for delivery of the remaining volumes of his STUDIES IN XIXTH CENTURY MANNERS. Werdet had quarreled with the Widow and left her employ, so that Balzac was obliged to deal with the irascible businesswoman in person. He developed a hearty dislike for the sharp-eyed Widow and called her "the Old Crone of Publishers' Row." He was determined to leave her. Bitter experience, in any case, had taught him to regard publishers with enlightened suspicion. He did not think it was sound practice to remain with one publisher over a long period of time.

"They are like young students in love, these publishers," he told his companions in the cafés. "They are filled with enthusiasms and promises of undying affection until the contract is signed and they have you on the hook. Then they are off in hot pursuit of some other writer. You are forgotten, the same way the young student forgets his girl, once she has taken him into her bed."

While Balzac was fighting with the Widow, young Werdet decided to go into business for himself. The first writer he approached was Balzac. He had the good sense to know that Balzac, alone, could be the making of an infant publishing house.

When Werdet called at the rue Cassini, Balzac pretended a haughty indifference.

"What makes you think you can afford me, Werdet?" he asked. "The man who wants to publish Balzac should be well-supplied with capital. I often need rather large advances."

Werdet took out his pocket book and withdrew six five-hundred franc notes, placing them, one by one, on the table under Balzac's nose.

"There is my entire capital," he said. "It is yours for one book. Any book you care to write."

Balzac smiled. He picked up the notes, folded them neatly, and placed them in Werdet's hand.

"You should know better than that, Werdet," he said sadly. "It was you who arranged the contract with the Widow Bechet, when she paid me thirty-six thousand."

"Quite true, monsieur. Thirty-six thousand," said Werdet steadily. "But that was for twelve books."

"One book, twelve books, it's all the same with me," Balzac said, with grandiose illogic. "Besides, you seem unaware of the fact that Buloz, of the *Paris Review*, pays me five hundred francs a sheet for copy. You are fishing in water that is over your head, my dear Werdet. Come back and see me when your bank account is the same size as your ideas."

Werdet shook hands and departed, taking with him his three thousand francs. He was not in the least put off by Balzac's rebuff. Werdet had a keen understanding of authors' economics, and he was familiar with Balzac's personal situation, which was far from being a well-kept secret. He had baited his hook with cash, the bank notes that Balzac had pretended to despise. Cash has a compelling effect on a man who needs money; three thousand francs in cash, that can be held in the hand, are more persuasive than ten thousand in the form of notes or promises. Werdet believed that he had only to wait.

He was not mistaken.

Three days after his visit to the rue Cassini, he had a note from Balzac:

"Sir: The other day when you came to see me, my mind was preoccupied by a piece of writing and I'm afraid I may have missed the drift of your remarks. Today, my mind is freer. Do me the honor to call at four in the afternoon, and we can discuss the matter more intelligently. de B."

Werdet sent his regrets, pleading the pressure of business. Now it was Balzac's turn to wait.

A week later, casually, Werdet appeared in the rue Cassini. For the despised three thousand francs, Balzac gave him the right to reprint a revised version of THE COUNTRY DOCTOR, as well as an option on his first novel after the Widow Bechet had eaten her pound of flesh. When he left Balzac's house, Werdet was in business.

Zulma Carraud reproached Balzac for selling himself too cheaply.

376

"A writer of your status should be in command," she said. "But your reckless extravagance and lack of judgment puts you in the power of publishers, editors and critics. You should be above the battle, yet you are forced to march like a private in the ranks."

"Publishers, editors, critics!" he replied. "In the end, my dear, I shall drink from their skulls."

The skull that he drank from was his own.

He had laughed at Nacquart's warnings, pounded on his chest, and boasted that he had the strength of a bull, but as the heat of summer closed in on Paris he began to feel the strain. Several nights during August he was seized by attacks of vertigo. One night, when the heat was damp and particularly oppressive, he began to tremble, as if he had been taken with a fit. He shook helplessly for perhaps an hour, then his head dropped to his arms on the table. Auguste called Borget from his studio nearby. Both of them urged Balzac to see a doctor.

He refused.

"I know a hypnotist in the Latin Quarter who will put me right for three francs," he insisted. "Doctors are all very well when it comes to the diseases of women. They have no understanding of the problems that afflict a man of talent."

He went on with his work, ignoring the warnings of his over-taxed body. He sat at his writing table, bathed in a cold, unnatural sweat, shivering with sudden chills, though the nights were in-humanly warm. Any sensible physician would have sent him to a nursing home at once and he knew it. He refused to see Nacquart.

At last he pressed himself too far.

One hot night in September he attempted to rise from his work table, intending to go to the kitchen and make fresh coffee. His muscles would not respond to his mind. He felt no pain, only a kind of numbness, as if he were frozen. He attempted to call for his servant. He was unable to utter a sound. After a little he made a supreme effort of the will and succeeded in standing almost erect. Then the full force of the attack struck him. He swayed for a moment. His vision failed. There was a stabbing pain be-tween his shoulderblades. It radiated to his arms. He fell to the floor like a doomed tree.

He was still unconscious when Auguste found him, nearly five hours later. For a moment, Auguste was certain that his master was dead. He drew the heavy curtains back, flooding the room with morning light, irrationally reminding himself that it was the first time he had touched the curtains without a direct order from Balzac.

Auguste knelt beside Balzac and opened the monk's robe, placing his ear against the still chest. There was a heartbeat, faint and irregular, like the sound of inexpert chopping heard from far away. Auguste crossed himself, made a brief appeal to God, and ran to fetch Borget, Balzac's nearest friend.

In a few hours, Nacquart was there. Balzac had been moved into his bedroom and his breathing was beginning to return to normal, though his lips were blue and the skin of his face was the color of ashes.

Nacquart shook his head, massaging Balzac's chest gently, chafing his wrists and ankles. Balzac stirred on his pillow. Slowly, consciousness returned and his tremendous will to live asserted itself. His heart responded to his will.

"Well, Nacquart?" he said, managing a half smile.

"Well, 'Noré, this time you have managed it, it seems. But only just," said Nacquart. He reached for Balzac's wrist, a big gold turnip of a watch held in the other hand. "Another time God may not be so indulgent, my boy."

"It seems that I fainted," Balzac said. "Altogether out of character for me. Heroines are supposed to faint, not authors."

"You fainted certainly, that much is clear," said Nacquart, snapping shut the case of his watch. "The important thing is, you are ill. Seriously ill. You have had an attack of the heart, a stroke, if you like. It is not a thing to be trifled with by a man who wants to go on living."

"I can't be ill," protested Balzac. "I haven't got the time to spare for it."

"Listen to me, Honoré," Nacquart said severely. "Get up from that bed, cross the room, go down the stairs to the street, and try to walk as far as the bistro on the corner. You will not make it. Somewhere between the bed and the bistro you will find that you have been overtaken by death."

Balzac smiled feebly and raised a hand in surrender.

"As a matter of fact I don't feel in the mood for a drink," he said. "So there's no point in going to the bistro, is there, old friend?"

378

"The only real medicine for what you have got is rest," Nacquart advised him. "Absolute, total, complete rest. You must not move from that bed, even to make pee-pee. I will leave instructions with Auguste. Borget has offered to help out. Between them, they'll look after you, if you will give them the chance."

"How long am I condemned to make pee-pee in my bed?" asked Balzac.

Nacquart shrugged.

"Until the wound in your heart is healed," he said. "Two weeks at least. Maybe three."

"Three weeks!" Balzac protested.

"Be thankful you're alive," Nacquart told him.

Balzac remained in bed for the full three weeks. Borget and Auguste fed him and bathed him and looked after his other personal wants. For all his bluster, Balzac was sensible enough not to defy Nacquart's orders this time.

He made Borget promise to say nothing of his illness. The thought of being nursed by his mother was appalling. Madame de Berny was too ill to leave her house. Zulma Carraud was expecting a child. As for his acquaintances in Paris, Balzac felt that the less they knew about his attack the better. He had no intention of dying or of becoming an invalid, but he knew that the average magazine editor would think twice before he paid over a fat advance to a man who had been brushed by the wings of death.

Nacquart came every day. Balzac was more than a patient to him. Aside from the fact that he had known him since birth, taught him to read, befriended him in childhood, Nacquart had a high regard for Balzac's genius.

"You have no right to abuse yourself," he told Balzac. "It is your obligation to survive and to use the gifts God gave you."

Balzac was sitting up in bed. His color had returned to normal, his eyes were clear. Only the loss in weight betrayed the fact that he had been ill.

"Exactly my idea," he said. "I feel fine. When can I get up? Unfortunately, I can't earn my living in bed. I am the wrong sex."

"You can get up tomorrow for a couple of hours," Nacquart decided. "Day after tomorrow, for twice that. By the end of the week, if nothing happens, you can resume normal living."

"Good!" said Balzac.

379

Nacquart raised a warning hand.

"I said 'normal living,'" he observed dryly. "Definitely, that does not mean that you can go back to your old ways, as if nothing had happened."

"I am listening," said Balzac.

"First of all, you are overweight, despite what you've lost this last three weeks. Carrying all that lard about puts a strain on your heart. You must eat less, especially you must eat less rich food. Secondly, you must have a stated amount of sleep each night—ten hours, in the beginning, then eight. Never less."

Nacquart paused, made a bony steeple with his fingers, and sighed before he went on.

"Third, we come to the matter of coffee," he said.

"A noble beverage!" Balzac insisted. "I won't hear a word against it."

"As you say, a noble beverage," Nacquart agreed. "For most people. With you, Honoré, it is a vice. Some men make a vice of tobacco. Others, of alcohol. There are those who eat hashish. You are unique. You make a vice of coffee drinking."

"I can't give up coffee," said Balzac flatly.

"But you can cut down," said Nacquart. "Let us say, three cups a day."

"Impossible!" said Balzac.

"Very well then, four," Nacquart conceded. "But stop using a pound of coffee to get six small cups."

Balzac laughed and said, "You know all my secrets, Nacquart."

"Not all of them," said the doctor. "But I've had your coffee. It is delicious, but it is also a poison. Slower than arsenic, but just as deadly in the long run."

Balzac stared at his thumbs. He knew that Nacquart meant what he said and wasn't simply trying to frighten him into being a good boy.

"So that is the verdict," he said. "No food. No coffee. Sleep half the time, as if I were an infant. Anything else?"

"Yes," said Nacquart. "As soon as you are well enough to travel, you must get away from Paris for a few months. Go to the country, somewhere where you can find rest and peace and get away from editors."

Balzac shrugged.

"I insist on it, Honoré," Nacquart said. "You aren't well yet, you know. You are a convalescent. In order to recover you must lead a quiet life and that can't be done in Paris."

The first week in October, Balzac set out for Saché, where he knew that the Margonnes would make him welcome again. His heart beat was normal. Aside from a certain weakness in the knees he felt as well as he had before the attack.

In his carpet bag were his coffee machine and six cloth bags of his private blend, as well as several reams of paper and a good supply of ravens' quills. He had promised Nacquart to go slowly, but he didn't take that to mean that he was obliged to live the life of a turnip. He had been idle too long; he was literally itching to write, an itching that he could feel in his fingers.

There had been a sharp, early frost in the Valley of the Loire and the leaves of the hardwood trees had turned color, so that all of Touraine was ablaze. In the sun the air was warm, but very clear, free of the morbid summer haze. The fine nostalgic smells of autumn rose from the decorated countryside, rousing memories of childhood, evoking a mood of bitter-sweetness. Balzac tingled with anticipation.

"Go to the country," Nacquart had said. "Sleep. Read nothing. Write nothing. Talk only with the animals."

On top of the post-chaise, with the sun of Touraine in his face, Balzac smiled, remembering the bony, warning finger.

"I am sorry, my dear Nacquart," he said to himself. "I have other fish to fry."

The Margonnes knew nothing of his heart attack. They embraced him warmly and gave him the room in which he had written the greater part of LOUIS LAMBERT. He was told that he could do as he liked about joining the family for meals.

"You will always hear the bell," said Monsieur de Margonne. "And there will always be a place laid for you. When you care to join us, you will be welcome. When you prefer a tray in your room, we will understand."

For three days, Balzac rested. On the fourth he began to work, his coffee machine set up over a spirit lamp on the table beside his bed. Each time he brewed up, using his old and tested measurements, he made mental apology to Nacquart.

"It's just until this book is finished, old sawbones," he muttered, as he poured out the thick, aromatic concoction. "Then, if you tell me to do it, I will swear off the black stuff forever."

Over the years, Balzac's coffee had become stronger and stronger. Now it was like syrup. It was essence of coffee. To drink it by the pint, as he did, was, for a man who had had a heart attack, deliberately to risk his life.

The book for which he was risking his life was PÈRE GORIOT. It was a book conceived, started, and finished as a masterpiece and nothing less. Balzac had come a long way from THE LAST CHOUAN. He was not even related to the youth who had written pseudonymous and borrowed trash. He had seized a whole area of life, made it his own, and perfected the technical instrument by means of which this world was to be turned into literature. PÈRE GORIOT was to be a cornerstone of his structure; had he given up his life for it, the sacrifice might not have been too great.

Balzac had a story to tell that was simple as a hillside in its outline, but supercharged with understanding of the human heart and recognition of the baffling identity of good and evil in the property box of character.

Balzac's directing theme was the tragedy of obsession with an idea. The theme grew from roots deep in his own soul. He was himself obsessed by the twin ideas of love and fame.

Old Goriot loves his daughters. He loves them more than he loves God, more than he loves his own immortal soul. He strangles himself on love, hammers himself to the cross for love.

In his room at Saché, through the window of which by day he saw a curtain of chalk-blue sky, by night a flat adornment of stars, Balzac became Old Goriot more completely than he had ever before stepped into the body and soul of a character.

Goriot, facing his death on a rooming-house bed, cries for the daughters that he loves.

"My daughters! My daughters! I want to see my daughters! Send the police to fetch them! Compel them to come! Justice is on my side. I have everything on my side, nature and the civil code!"

It was Balzac demanding the love of his mother, it was Balzac demanding the love that he lacked. It was Balzac in ecstasy and agony, Balzac obsessed.

He wrote with the sense of utter conviction with which a saint may be supposed to pray. He did not falter. He was sure of himself.

In six weeks, he was finished.

He was haggard from lack of sleep. Coffee had made his nerves raw. The muscles of his neck and shoulders ached as if he had been stretched on the rack.

He was satisfied.

He knew that he had succeeded; it was not necessary even to glance at what had been written.

He threw himself on the unmade bed and stared at the ceiling, all at once aware of the protests of his empty stomach.

"At least I've kept one of your rules, Nacquart," he said, addressing the ceiling. "I haven't been overeating these last six weeks."

He had eaten almost nothing while he was writing PÈRE GORIOT —a little cheese, a boiled egg, a bit of grilled fish, a crust of bread. When the servants had come, bearing trays and silver covered dishes, he had sent them away, unwilling to break off work for a meal. Now he was ravenous as a peasant just in from the fields.

When the dinner gong rang he went downstairs just as he was, unshaven, his hair touseled, his shirt wrinkled and quite dirty. He was not being thoughtless or rude; it was simply that he had not altogether emerged from the other-world of his novel.

A stranger would have taken him for a chronic drunkard, just coming off a monstrous debauch. The Margonnes were not strangers. For all the notice they took of his appearance, he might have been dressed in evening clothes, as was Monsieur de Margonne.

He sat down and began to spoon up the soup that a servant placed before him. When the plate was empty he raised his head.

"I have finished my novel," he said quietly.

"Are you satisfied with it?" Margonne asked.

"It is a work of genius," Balzac replied dispassionately.

Chapter 38

Early in 1835, the mysterious Widow Durand took up the lease at No. 13, rue des Batailles. The negotiations were conducted by the widow's nephew, a vigorous man in his mid-thirties who seemed to know just what his aunt wanted.

The Widow Durand was Balzac.

For a long time now, he had played with the idea of renting a flat some distance from the Observatory District, where he had become a fixture. He wanted a refuge to which he could flee when bill collectors, editors, aspirant mistresses and simple well-wishers made life unbearable and work impossible.

"A man who lives my kind of life needs a second set of lodgings," he told his publisher, Werdet. "I am volatile. I thrive on change."

There was another reason. A few months earlier, the King of France had decreed that every able-bodied citizen of Paris was to be obliged to perform token service with the National Guard. Balzac had no intention of shouldering a musket when France was not at war.

"Before they turn me into a soldier, they will have to find me," he announced.

Not much later he rented the flat in the name of the Widow Durand. The rue des Batailles overlooked the Seine. From his new windows, Balzac had a view of the river, of the Champ de Mars, the Ecole Militaire, and, dominating all of this, the splendid gilt dome of the Invalides.

He could not bring himself to give up his establishment in the rue Cassini, a place he loved in the way a man loves an old friend. The furniture and most of his books remained where they were and so did the cook, left behind to look after the place and to serve him a meal whenever he was inclined to work in his old familiar study. He took the precaution however, of hanging a sign on the front door announcing that the house was to let.

384

The flat in the rue des Batailles was in an old but impressive building solidly built of grey stone. There were a number of small rooms. Balzac wanted larger ones. He hired a battalion of carpenters and had the partitions torn down. When the workmen were finished, his new quarters consisted of four commodious chambers, a kitchen, and a marble bath.

No expense was spared.

In these opening months of 1835, Balzac was flushed with triumph. PÈRE GORIOT had been published as a serial in the *Paris Review* and greeted with universal acclaim. Even Balzac's bitterest rivals were obliged to pronounce it a masterpiece.

In book form, the first edition was sold out in four days. For Balzac it was a triumph. No one could now deny him a place in the absolute front rank. Not yet in his forties, he was already immortal.

He was also in funds.

He amused himself by furnishing one of his new rooms as exotically as the boudoir of a mysterious and not quite respectable Turkish beauty.

One wall of the Turkish room was gracefully curved. Balzac instructed his upholsterer to construct a divan to fit the curve. This couch, in the shape of an enormous serpentine pouf, was covered with the best white cashmere, held in place by bows made of black and flame-colored satin.

The wall that faced the extraordinary couch formed a straight line, broken only by a chimneypiece made of milk-white Italian marble, carved to Balzac's order, with a chaste design picked out in gold.

The walls were hung with three hundred yards of raw silk, crimson in color, falling in lavish folds. Over this background were wall hangings of fluted white Italian muslin. Under artificial light the red struck through the semi-transparent muslin, producing a seductive rose color.

Six silver sconces, holding black candles, were fixed to the wall behind the Turkish divan. The ceiling was painted dazzling white and suspended from it was a lustre chandelier, fitted with four dozen wax tapers. There was a white marble clock with a corrupt and painted face, and a table covered with white cashmere. There were a dozen large vases that Balzac intended to keep filled with dark red roses.

"You mean to work here?" Borget demanded, when he saw the place. "Balzac, you are out of your mind. It is impossible to imagine this room being put to any purpose but one. It reeks of fornication."

Balzac grinned sheepishly.

"You are right, Borget," he admitted. "It is a room straight out of a whore house. But a rich whore house, you must give me that."

There was an attic room vacant, and he rented that to use as a study, furnishing it with a rough table and chair and a simple cot. He thus felt justified in describing his new quarters to Eve as "a simple artist's garret."

Balzac yearned to see Eve. His "wife of love," as he now called her in his letters, had somehow persuaded her husband to remain in Europe. On the way home to Poland, later in the year, the de Hanskis planned to spend a few months in Vienna.

Balzac was determined to join them.

"Vienna is the star that I steer by," he told his Eve. "I live in utter solitude, sustained only by the glorious fact that in Vienna I shall see you, touch your hand, touch your beloved lips."

Meanwhile, in Paris, he worked, dodged creditors and the National Guard, and slept with several dozen women who happened to cross his path. He was a Frenchman of his time. He saw no disloyalty to Eve in these adventures, that to him meant no more than answering a call of nature, but he had been scorched by the Duchesse de Castries's trick. He worried about the gossip that might reach Eve's pretty ears.

As a hedge against gossip that might rouse dangerous jealousy in Eve, Balzac complained to her that he was besieged by women and professed to be shocked by the fact that unscrupulous females went so far as to seek cheap notoriety by pretending that he was their lover.

"There are women in Paris who will stoop to any deception in order to attract attention," he informed Eve. "Believe nothing that you hear about me, for you will hear nothing but lies. I live as chastely as a young girl. I wait only for our meeting in Vienna."

An accident nearly spoilt Balzac's reunion in Vienna.

Eve became ill at a moment when the governess, Henriette, chanced to be visiting her family. Two of Balzac's ultra-private

386

letters fell into the hands of Count Hanski, who was attending to the household correspondence during his wife's indisposition. He read the letters with incredulity, then with shock, then with splendid patrician outrage.

Nothing equals the family pride of a Polish aristocrat.

Balzac's passionate letters caused Count Hanski's adrenalin glands to function for the first time in forty years. It did not occur to him that Eve could be in any way involved. After all, she came from a family even more distinguished than his own. It was a case of this bounder Balzac forcing his attention on a high born and innocent lady.

Count Hanski sat down with trembling fingers and wrote Balzac a fierce little letter, demanding an explanation. Then he put on his top hat and went out to shop for dueling pistols, an item of gentlemanly equipment he had neglected to bring with him from Poland.

Count Hanski was a man of honor, but he was no match for Balzac when it came to ingenuity.

Balzac replied to the challenge at once, explaining the compromising letters as easily as he would have solved a simple problem of plot in a novel. The whole thing was a misunderstanding, he assured the count.

"As you know, your dear wife is a perceptive critic of literature," Balzac wrote. "In the past she has done me the honor to correspond with me about my own work. Some time ago (she may have forgotten by now) she asked me to send her samples of the kind of letter a not very admirable character in fiction might be expected to write to his beloved. These, my dear sir, are the documents you chanced to read—literary exercises, nothing more. That they have offended you, my dear sir, is an unfortunate accident that I shall always regret. That they have offended your wife— that purest of beings!—causes me unbelievable anguish. If I have not completely forfeited your friendship, I entreat you, as man to man, to intercede for me with the countess and give the backing of your authority to my humble apologies, which are already on their way to her."

By nature, Count Hanski was a peaceful soul. He had never fought a duel and the prospect discouraged him. Besides, he had been flattered by his wife's connection with Balzac, whose name seemed to command respect wherever it was mentioned, but especially here in Vienna, where the count had many friends on the highest levels of society and government. Their connection with

Balzac had given the de Hanskis entrée everywhere in the Austrian capital and added enormously to their own quite modest prestige. Even Prince Metternich himself had expressed a desire to meet the novelist, when Balzac visited the de Hanskis.

It would certainly be a pity to disappoint the first statesman of Europe, Count Hanski reflected.

Without too much self-debate, he persuaded himself to accept Balzac's explanation of the love letters. He wrote to Paris, accepting Balzac's apology, and returned the dueling pistols to the shop. He got back what he had paid for them, less ten per cent, and he was happy to have them off his hands. As soon as Eve's fever abated, he intended to put in a word for Balzac and assure her that the good fellow absolutely had meant no offense.

As for Eve, womanlike, she was furious with both of them. She was impatient with her husband for his gullibility and cross with Balzac for his impudence. Somehow, in a day or two, one emotion seemed to cancel out the other and she began to make plans for Balzac's visit, aware that they would have to be especially careful after the incident of the letters.

Balzac, the strategist of love, regarded the expedition to Austria as critical in the great campaign that was to be concluded with marriage to a titled, wealthy and beautiful widow. Passion and intellect, such as he had offered, were not enough to hold Eve firmly during such time as the count continued to be an obstacle. Balzac felt that he must also impress her with his prestige as a man of society, whose lineage was not to be despised.

"A man of my status should not travel in the common postchaise," he told Werdet, from whom he was getting most of the money needed for the journey. "I have decided to hire a carriage."

Werdet exploded.

"Hire a carriage to go to Vienna?" he cried. "Honoré, you are out of your mind. It will cost. . . ."

"Five thousand francs," said Balzac. "A pittance. A third of the sum my next book will earn."

"Where will you get this pittance?" asked Werdet suspiciously.

"From you, of course, where else?" answered Balzac cheerfully. "After all, old boy, you are my publisher, are you not?"

Werdet groaned and protested, "I am a publisher, not a banker."

Nevertheless, he produced the money. He had no choice. With-

388

out Balzac, Werdet was nothing, another of several hundred people who lived on the fringes of literature, digging like moles for a few francs.

Balzac hired a glistening carriage, drawn by a pair of glossy, arrogant horses, and driven by an Irish coachman who spoke French with a charming brogue. The Irishman drove like an angel and made a splendid appearance; sitting on the box, he looked like a guardsman and he regarded everything around him with gorgeous contempt.

Balzac had the d'Entragues's arms painted on the carriage doors. The driver he took to Buisson, his own tailor, to be measured for a suit of livery, the buttons of which were to be engraved with crossed quills and the monogram "deB."

The coachman was delighted with his new rig.

"It must be a lady your lordship is goin' to visit in Jairmany," he said to Balzac respectfully, with just the hint of a gleam in his eye.

"More than a lady, O'Donohue," Balzac told him. "An angel." He looked at the Irishman for a moment, then added, "Unfortunately, the angel is married."

The Irishman's eyes brightened at the prospect of secret meetings at country inns and wild gallops in the night.

"Ah, you've hired the right man for the job, your worship," he said. "There's not a trick in the book that I don't know and your lordship can depend on that. Didn't I give the English the slip, when they were after arrestin' us harmless rebels and hangin' poor Robert Emmet, God rest his soul in heaven?"

Balzac laughed and gave the coachman a gold ducat. He had a soft spot in his heart for the Irish and an inbred, Gallic dislike for their English landlords, regarding it as one of God's blunders that this nation of mutton-eating shopkeepers should possess the most splendid literature in Europe.

Balzac was unprepared for his reception in Vienna. In France, he had a great reputation. He was famous, but he was a mortal, at whom it was permitted to throw mud on occasion.

In the brilliant, easygoing Austrian capital he found himself placed beside Shakespeare and Goethe. Perhaps the massiveness of his structure, becoming implicit in his recent work, appealed to

389

the Teutonic imagination. Whatever the reason, in Vienna Balzac was a lion and it was appropriate for him to roar.

He roared.

The de Hanskis were living in a grey stone mansion in the fashionable, diplomatic quarter of the city, and Count Hanski had booked a suite for Balzac at the *Hotel zur goldenen Birne,* which was conveniently nearby.

The moment he entered the hotel, Balzac was made aware of the way in which he was to be idolized in Austria. No mere majordomo greeted him at the *Hotel zur goldenen Birne.* It was the proprietor himself, in a frock coat, wearing his decorations for the occasion, who made him welcome with a deferential bow and the gift of a huge bouquet of roses.

"My hotel is honored to have the great de Balzac under its roof," he said. "I and my staff are yours to command."

Balzac was delighted. The adulation of the Viennese made up for the snubs he had received in the Faubourg Saint-Germain, and for the sarcastic barbs of people like the critic, Sainte-Beuve. He made a note to be sure that Dumas learned of his Austrian triumph. "Alexandre will be green with envy," he told himself with some satisfaction.

Fame, of course, has its complications. The Lion of Vienna found it difficult to be very much alone with his Lioness. From the moment he entered the Austrian city, Balzac was almost constantly on public view. It was impossible to snatch more than a few minutes alone with Eve.

Part of this was Eve's fault. She was proud of her captured lion and kept him on constant exhibition, at luncheons, teas, dinners and soirées. He was her personal property, and the source of her own prestige.

"We are never alone," he complained, a week after his arrival.

"It is the price of fame," she said, smiling at him.

She was ravishing. The months in Europe had brightened her eyes, and life in important drawing rooms had taught her to make full use of her beauty. Balzac was wildly in love with her and frustrated because she seemed more interested in showing him off than in making love.

O'Donohue, the Irish coachman, gave Balzac one of his few opportunities to be alone with Eve.

Eve had agreed to drive in the Prater with Balzac on a splendid morning in May. O'Donohue had outdone himself. Not a speck of dust marred the patent leather surface of the carriage. The d'Entragues's arms gleamed in gilt. The flanks of the horses flickered in the sunlight. The brass fittings of the harness were like gold. O'Donohue was filled with subservient charm.

As they trotted through the pretty park, Balzac was so occupied with Eve that he paid no attention when the carriage turned out of the drive and made its way along a high road, leading out of the city. They were a half mile out of Vienna before he realized what had happened. He rapped on the glass with the nob of his stick.

"Where on earth are you taking us, Patrick?" he demanded.

"Why sure and to the inn, where your worship ast to be taken," the Irish conspirator answered, not slowing the horses.

Balzac subsided, placing himself in his coachman's hands. In a few minutes, O'Donohue pulled up in the courtyard of a charming country inn, a picture-book house made of logs, with tables placed under the trees.

Balzac and Eve got down from the carriage. Seizing his moment, O'Donohue whispered, "The room is waitin' for your lordship, an' in my name, mind you."

"God bless you, Patrick," Balzac replied.

The room was delightful, with leaded windows that opened to the forest behind the inn, so that the branches of trees almost came into the house. There was an enormous bed, covered with a bright colored peasant spread. A servant brought cold meat and a bottle of innocent Austrian wine that had been cooled in a spring house.

If Eve was annoyed, she was too intelligent to show it. She opened the top of her dress, nibbled at the cold meat with relish, and asked Balzac to order a second bottle of wine. They made love on the big bed conclusively, as animals mating.

"We are alone," said Balzac. "It is heaven."

"Heaven," she said drowsily.

She has changed since Geneva, Balzac thought, watching her as she lay asleep, after they had made love again. In Geneva, she was tentative. There was fear mixed with her passion and a hideous awareness of sin. Now she seems unaware of fear, careless of the idea of sin.

She stirred in her sleep and moved closer to him. Her arm came up to his shoulders. Her hips moved close to his body. His speculations were dissolved in the moistures of love.

391

"Let us stay for the night," Balzac begged, when it was late afternoon. "The room is charming. We can get dinner. We can be alone."

"You know I would adore it," she said, hairpins in her teeth. "But it's impossible."

"Why?"

"Surely you haven't forgotten who is dining with us tonight?" she said, turning, her hair in a fall down her creamy back. "My Aunt Rosalie. The Potockis. The Russian ambassador to Austria. And Count von Haenfstaengel, from the Palace."

Balzac groaned.

"Another dinner party," he said. "I feel like an animal in the zoo, or maybe a clown in the circus."

She turned away from the mirror in front of which she was fixing her hair. There was no humor in her face.

"I don't mean to be offensive," she said bluntly. "But sometimes you seem to forget that when one has a certain position in society, one has certain obligations. I am the Countess de Hanska of Wierzchownia. I am expected to entertain."

"I prefer it when you entertain Balzac, as you have been doing these last few hours," Balzac said good naturedly. "Ah, well. There's nothing for it," he grunted.

He got up from the bed, naked, and stretched himself, then scratched the hair on his chest and stomach and yawned, making a noise. It was a vulgar series of gestures, too earthy for Eve's taste.

"Ugggh!" She made a face. "Sometimes you are boorish as a mujik."

Balzac laughed. He was looking at Eve's delectable backside, flattened out by the bench she sat on. Nothing would have pleased him more than to have slapped her bottom playfully, then to have kissed it, then to have carried her back to the rumpled bed.

He had too much judgment for that. For all her sexuality, Eve insisted on being treated as a countess. He went to her, lifted the weight of her hair, and kissed her shoulder.

"Of course you are right," he said. "We must go back to Vienna at once."

He dressed himself quickly and went downstairs to pay the innkeeper's bill, leaving Eve to finish dressing. He found his coachman in the kitchen, making eyes at the scullery maid who had given him something to eat.

392

"Patrick, you are wasted as a coachman," he said. "You should be an ambassador."

He counted five gold pieces into the good fellow's hand, thanked him again, and told him to get ready to leave for Vienna. O'Donohue was hurt.

"Not stayin' the night, your lordship? An' that lovely room an' all?"

Balzac glanced at the scullery maid, a pretty little thing with yellow hair and bright blue eyes.

"I shan't need you tonight, Patrick," he said. "Surely you can drive into Vienna and back before it gets dark."

"The blessings of a thousand saints on your worship," said the delighted Irishman, tossing one of his well-earned gold pieces into the air.

That night, at the dinner party, Balzac gave a brilliant performance. He charmed the Russian ambassador. He impressed the Emperor's young aide. He flattered an ancient baroness. He made Count Hanski feel important.

One person was unimpressed. That was Eve's Aunt Rosalie, who lived in Vienna. She was a petulant old maid aristocrat, heavy with garnets and lace. Her drawing room was a clearing house for gossip from Paris, Rome and London. She detested Balzac and made no effort to conceal her feelings from him or from Eve.

"He is a guttersnipe and a fortune hunter," Eve was informed by her aunt. "If you knew what decent people think of him in Paris you would not have him at your table."

She was a dangerous enemy and Balzac knew it. He tried to win her with charm, with wit, with flattery, but she was immune to every attack. Balzac consoled himself with the thought that Eve would soon be back in Poland, out of range of her aunt's sniping.

Balzac found Austria enchanting. Each day he drove through the streets lined with aspen and linden trees, cheered by the passersby as if he were a king or a conquering general. He was recognized everywhere in Vienna. People who had never read a book in their lives raised their hats to him in the street. He loved to sit at a café table, sipping chocolate mixed with coffee and topped with a dollop of whipped cream, listening to the well-groomed music of Schubert played by an able string quartet of which in Vienna there seemed to be thousands. He loved the brilliant ballrooms, filled with admiring, glittering people. He surrendered to the famous Viennese charm, less sophisticated than the French, but also less demanding. Paris can be astringent; Vienna was sweet, sweet as the whipped cream on the coffee and just as delicious.

Balzac went to the opera with the de Hanskis and arrived twenty minutes late. They had held the curtain for him, a thing that had been done in the past only for the Emperor and Prince Metternich himself. When he appeared in the gilded box, the audience rose to their feet, faced him, and bowed.

Standing beside him, Eve swelled with triumph. Her eyes flashed with pride. Everyone in Vienna, excepting Count Hanski, took it for granted that she was the great man's mistress. She was bathed in Balzac's glory.

After half a lifetime passed in the desolate forests of Poland, all at once Eve found herself admired and envied by the most famous and glamorous women in Europe. She knew that hundreds of beautiful women gladly would have changed places with her. She was thrilled with herself. Balzac was more than a lover to her; he was her passport to fame.

She was jealous of Balzac, obsessively jealous. She had permitted him to take her in adultery and she demanded payment in full. She was satisfied with nothing less than absolute possession. If he was a bit too attentive to another woman, she came and dragged him away. He was invited to almost every one of the great houses in Vienna, but forced to decline two thirds of the invitations because Eve objected to his going where she had not been invited. She was suspicious as well as jealous. When Prince Metternich asked Balzac to call, she insisted on seeing the invitation.

"Surely you don't suspect me of a liaison with Metternich?" said Balzac, trying to laugh at her.

She glared at him, crushing the gilt invitation in her hand.

"Everyone knows your reputation," she said. "I warn you, I will not be deceived by you."

"It will do you good to get away from your Aunt Rosalie," Balzac said with a sigh.

"Aunt Rosalie is no fool," said Eve.

394

The aging Prince von Metternich received Balzac as an equal, gave him jewel-like wine from the Rhine Valley, praised his books. Before Balzac took his leave, the old Chancellor wrote a note to Baron Rothschild in Paris.

"Rothschild is a good person to know," said the shrewd old statesman. "He represents Austria in France, where financial matters are involved. Where such things are concerned, his opinion is the most valuable in Europe."

Balzac swelled with pride. He would begin to make investments the moment he got back to Paris. With the great Rothschild to advise him, how could he not get rich?

At the end of a fortnight Balzac was exhausted by the pressures of being famous and he had spent every penny of the money Werdet had advanced him. The trip to Vienna, including rental of his carriage and horses, had cost him fifteen thousand francs. He was obliged to return to Paris, where he could earn more money.

He persuaded Eve to drive out to O'Donohue's inn, so that they could be alone for a few hours before his departure. Balzac half expected that she would beg him to stay on. He was disappointed. She accepted his going without protest.

"When will we be together, you and I, permanently, openly, before the world?" he asked moodily.

She shrugged her pretty shoulders.

"Who knows?" she said brightly. "One thing is certain, however. Wenceslas cannot live forever."

The next day, early in the morning, Balzac started out for Paris. Eve sat in her boudoir, admiring the gloss of her hair. She was relieved that her lover had gone. She loved Balzac in his absence more than in his presence. Except in the most intimate moments, she found his vitality overwhelming, almost suffocating.

In his books, Balzac penetrated the souls of his women as had no other writer before him. He did not penetrate the soul of his Eve. He had no idea of the shrewd detachment with which she was able to analyze her contradictory responses.

She wrote to her brother, Adam Rzewuska, who had been in her confidence since they were children together:

"You remember how you predicted that he would eat with his knife and blow his nose on his table napkin? Well, he has not committed the second of these crimes, but he has been guilty of the first. It is embarrassing to see him behave like any petit bourgeois, and one wonders why his napkin is not tied about his neck as he addresses his food with all the delicacy of a hungry mujik plunging into his cabbage soup. No, my dear brother, he cannot be described as a gentleman. Yet he does have a quality that sometimes seems more important than good manners or bad. He makes a woman like me aware of what has been lacking in my life. I suppose you will call me exaltée, but I think you will be wrong. I find his crudeness revolting. Often he bores me. Yet at other times he lifts me up to the highest realms of the spirit."

It was in this mood of equivocation that Eve prepared to return to her luxurious prison in Poland. She had no means of knowing when she would see Balzac again, yet she wanted him on a short leash. Paris was filled with Polish aristocrats, émigrés and expatriates. They would know how faithfully the impetuous Balzac lived up to his promises of fidelity.

To the Countess Potocki, in the Faubourg, Eve wrote a casual note.

"I worry about Balzac," she said. "He drives himself too hard and I fear for his health sometimes. If it is not too much trouble, my dear, please let me know from time to time (confidentially, you understand) how he is getting on, what people he sees, where he dines and so on."

The Countess Potocki was a woman of the world. She would understand what it was that Eve wanted to know. As she sealed the letter, Eve smiled. Balzac would find it more difficult to dodge the countess than to avoid the National Guard or the bill collectors, she thought.

Chapter 39

Eve de Hanska's agents in Paris soon had something to report. Balzac, as usual, was living three lives. He plunged back into his work and into society, and he kept up his game of hide-and-seek with his creditors and the National Guard.

Not long after he returned from Vienna, Balzac received an impressively engraved invitation to a ball at the Austrian Embassy.

"Ah ha!" he exclaimed. "It does one good to be on friendly terms with Metternich!"

He accepted immediately and ordered a new dress suit from Buisson, brushing aside the fact that he did not have the price of a pound of beans in his pocket. Nothing short of death would have kept him from making his appearance at the Embassy.

For the time being he had decided to keep the rented carriage and driver, and he needed money to pay the livery stable and to buy feed for the horses. When he asked the long-suffering Werdet for a thousand francs, the publisher nearly exploded.

"Balzac, you are trying to drive me into bankruptcy," he complained. "You may enjoy being in debt, but I don't. It does not exhilarate me to dodge bailiffs."

"Be quiet, man," said Balzac calmly. "You know that Honoré de Balzac is the best investment in France."

"Why don't you offer shares of stock to the public?" Werdet suggested ironically.

"A splendid idea! I will speak to my friend Rothschild about that," Balzac said. "In the meantime, if it is convenient, a thousand francs from you will put bread in my mouth, oats in the mouths of my horses, and enable me to write a novel that will make us both rich."

"It is not convenient," said Werdet firmly.

Balzac glared.

"But one presumes it is unavoidable," Werdet said.

397

"Completely," Balzac agreed.

Werdet handed over the money—ten one hundred franc notes. Carelessly, Balzac stuffed them into a pocket of his waistcoat. With some affection, he patted the little mound on his stomach made by the wad of money.

"Now Werdet, come along with me," he said cheerfully. "I am going to buy you a first-class dinner, to prove that de Balzac knows how to be grateful."

"Just give me back the price of the meal out of what I just handed to you," Werdet suggested hopefully.

"Nonsense, man!" roared Balzac. "How do you expect people to know that you are the first publisher of France unless you are seen in the right places?"

"I am not the first publisher of France," Werdet objected.

"Absurd!" said Balzac. "You are my publisher. That establishes the fact. Now put on your hat and come along."

They went to Véry's, the most expensive and fashionable restaurant in Paris. A fountain played in the center of the glittering dining room, which was filled with well-dressed clients and noiseless, impeccable servants. The windows were hung with winecolored velvet. There were paintings on the walls. The candlelight was flattering.

"I am hungry," Balzac decided, when they had been given a table.

Werdet groaned. He knew Balzac's gastronomic habits—either a crust of bread and a bowl of broth, or a meal of Gargantuan proportions. Apparently, Balzac had not come to Véry's for a bowl of broth.

"To begin with, gentlemen?" purred the immaculate headwaiter.

"A hundred oysters!" Balzac said casually.

"Monsieur????"

"A hundred oysters," Balzac repeated. "Let them be brought in batches of two dozen."

Werdet ordered thin soup and half of a grilled chicken.

"I am a publisher, please remember," he said to Balzac. "I suffer from a delicate stomach."

The oysters were brought. Balzac beamed. By this time, he had attracted a good deal of notice from the other diners. He was enjoying himself and playing a part.

The oysters were delicious, small, firm and pleasantly idodinic.

398

By the time he had devoured fifty of them, Balzac had captured his audience. Diners and waiters alike looked on with admiration. When the hundredth oyster slipped down Balzac's throat there was a round of brisk applause.

Balzac rose and bowed.

He ate twelve grilled chops, a roasted duckling, a pair of partridges, a sole. He drank four bottles of Vouvray and three of Chambertin. For dessert he had six wax pears, followed by a sampling of various cheeses. With his coffee he had a small flagon of Chartreuse Vert.

The proprietor of Véry's offered his congratulations.

"Not since the days of Louis XIV has such a meal been eaten," he said admiringly.

Balzac snapped his fingers and touched his mouth with his serviette.

"Louis Quatorze?" he said. "You are wrong, monsieur. Not since the days of my own countryman, Rabelais."

With some respect, the bill was presented. One hundred and fifteen francs. A staggering sum for a meal. Balzac glanced at the addition. He was unperturbed.

"Give me twenty francs, Werdet," he said. "I have no change."

Mystified, Werdet gave him the money.

Balzac handed the coins to the waiter, scribbled something at the bottom of the bill, and said in a voice that must have carried to the kitchen, "Tell the cashier that I am Monsieur Honoré de Balzac, the novelist."

With Werdet in trail, Balzac made his exit amid admiring glances. The cashier looked at the bill, shrugged and put it on her spike.

When they were in the street, Werdet said, "Balzac, you are a great writer. Why must you play the fool?"

Balzac clapped him on the back, not in the least offended.

"You don't understand publicity, Werdet," he told him. "By tomorrow, by midnight tonight, half of Paris will be talking about the extraordinary meal that was eaten on credit at the best restaurant in Paris by that famous rogue de Balzac. How can Frenchmen resist reading a book by a man who can eat like Rabelais?"

He sighed, rubbed his stomach, and belched delicately.

"Besides, Werdet, I was hungry," he said.

To make an impression on the Austrian Embassy, Balzac ordered a new cane from his favorite jeweler, Lecointe. Only Balzac would have gone to a jeweler for a walking stick, but Balzac knew what he wanted.

"I want the most impressive cane in Europe. The most impressive cane in the world," he told Lecointe. "Here is a sketch I have made. Follow it, and spare no expense."

No expense was spared.

Balzac's new cane had an ornate gold head, encrusted with sapphires, rubies and diamonds. The head was hollow and fitted with a hinge. Into this secret compartment went a lock of Eve de Hanska's hair, together with a slim gold chain she had worn as a child and given Balzac as a keepsake.

The cane became famous at once.

Dantan, the comic sculptor, did a plaster caricature of Balzac, dressed as a dandy, leaning on the jeweled stick. Delphine de Girardin was inspired to write an amusing novel called THE CANE OF BALZAC.

"I have started the cult of the cannophiles," Balzac boasted delightedly. "Everyone imitates Balzac."

Balzac went to the Austrian Embassy intending to exhibit himself and to observe at close quarters the diplomatic set of Paris.

He came away involved in another infatuation.

The glittering grand ballroom was crowded with royalty and nobility, brilliantly lighted, adorned with flowers. Lackeys in powdered wigs moved to and fro. In full dress uniforms, there were the officers of every nation on the face of the globe. There were enough diamonds on display to have ransomed the Emperor of China. Balzac recognized a dozen princes of the blood. He was gratified to discover that he was the only writer in evidence.

Wearing his new dress suit, he stood on the sidelines and watched the dancing. He had long since decided that he had no talent for the dance; after being received by his distinguished hosts, he had joined a contingent of ancient dukes and duchesses in a cluster of gilded chairs.

An old grande dame with an ear trumpet took him for the Crown Prince of Sweden and insisted on speaking to him in German, a language with which he was unfamiliar. He made a series of appropriate grunts that were accepted as Swedish, and moved away from the ear trumpet. He was faintly bored and looked forward to the break in the dancing, when a buffet supper would be served.

After a little, he became aware that he was being stared at by the most beautiful woman in the ballroom, a tall ash blonde, with a proud mouth and witty dove-grey eyes of piercing intelligence. Was she admiring him or mocking him? He could not tell. He looked around him, searching for an acquaintance who might know her name. There was no one. He stared back and ventured a smile. At this moment, his blonde beauty was whisked away by a young Frenchman with polished hair and a waist slim enough for a girl.

"Who can she be?" he asked himself. "Who is the pipsqueak she dances with?"

Later, in the dining room, under the blazing chandeliers, he stood with a plate of lobster in his hand and watched her move through the throng of guests with the assurance of a queen.

Balzac, like nature, abhorred a vacuum.

He adored his Eve, his "wife of love," but Eve was a thousand miles away, buried in the wastes and wilds of Poland. Once again, for Balzac, she had become the Faraway Princess. Until the Count Hanski was good enough to die, he needed a flesh and blood mistress, and some instinct suggested to him that this blonde stranger might be a candidate.

He was not wrong.

Toward the end of the evening, Madame Apponyi, wife of the Austrian ambassador, approached him with the beautiful blonde in tow. Madame Apponyi was short, bejeweled and witty. She looked at Balzac with some amusement.

"Ah, my dear Monsieur de Balzac," she said. "My good friend the contessa has expressed a desire to meet the author of PÈRE GORIOT."

"I am honored," said Balzac, bowing just a bit too low as he kissed her hand.

She was the Contessa Guidoboni-Visconti, Madame Apponyi announced. Balzac was delighted. All that reckless beauty, and a countess to boot. She gave him a slow, tantalizing smile; instinctively, he liked her.

"So this is the man from whom we women have no secrets," she said.

"An exaggeration, madame," Balzac assured her. "Whenever I think I have learned a little about women, I meet someone like yourself and realize that I know nothing."

She met this with a pleasant, rippling laugh. "How old can she be?" Balzac asked himself. "Not more than thirty, certainly." He wondered, from her blondeness, if she were a Florentine.

"But are you Italian?" he asked.

"Italian? Don't be preposterous," she said. "I'm English."

"Of course," he said. "You could be nothing else. It was stupid of me."

At this moment they were interrupted by the young man who had been the contessa's dancing partner for most of the evening. His handsome, rather vacant face was flushed with annoyance.

"I've been looking for you everywhere," he complained peevishly. "Must you always disappear?"

"Calm yourself, Lionel," said the contessa, treating him like a puppy on the leash. "Monsieur de Balzac, this rude young man is the Seigneur Lionel de Bonneval, who enjoys every advantage in life except intelligence."

De Bonneval's eyes flashed with anger but he suppressed the objection that formed on his lips. Balzac bowed and shook hands, betraying no emotion; experience had taught him that it is bad tactics to take public satisfaction from a rival's discomfort, and he had decided on the instant that young de Bonneval was very much a rival.

"We receive on Wednesdays," said the contessa, looking at Balzac with candor.

"I shall be honored," Balzac said.

He watched her move across the room on young de Bonneval's arm. From the ballroom came the scraping of fiddles as the musicians tuned up. Balzac drifted with the crowd into the brilliantly lighted arena. He stood with the dowagers again and watched the dancing.

Whatever his intellectual deficiency, de Bonneval was a first-class dancer, Balzac realized. Skillfully, he guided the lovely contessa through the intricate movements of a quadrille. Balzac sighed with envy and turned away, searching for his hostess, so that he could pay his respects and depart. He was finished here; the next move would occur on Wednesday, when the contessa received him.

The ambassador's wife squeezed his hand and gave him a wicked smile. A woman of impeccable morality, she nevertheless loved scandal.

"So even the great de Balzac is not immune to the Visconti charm," she said teasingly.

"Only a man made of bronze could be immune," said Balzac absently.

The next day, he looked up Alfred de Vigny, certain that de Vigny would know all that was to be known about the Contessa Guidoboni-Visconti.

"Her name was Sarah Frances Lowell," de Vigny told him. "She comes from one of those brilliant, eccentric English families."

"Does her eccentricity extend to love?" asked Balzac.

"My dear chap, one is given to understand that she had her first child by her own mother's gardener," said de Vigny with some distaste. "And she's only just had another by that old hell-devil, Prince Koslovsky."

"Splendid! Splendid!" Balzac said.

He was delighted by what de Vigny told him. He wanted a liaison with a beautiful and charming woman, but he did not want to go through the rigamarole of a romantic affair, with all its pretense and self-deception. He maintained such an affair by mail, with Eve. He had no energy for courtship in another theater.

During the season, the Guidoboni-Viscontis lived in a mansion on the Champs-Élysées. It was a big house that gave the impression of a palace in a park. There was a long, curved driveway that led under trees to a magnificent entrance with an ornamental stone porch with columns.

With the infallible lack of judgment that characterized his romantic overtures, Balzac arrived at the Guidoboni-Visconti establishment dressed to kill. He wore nankeen trousers, orange socks, patent leather shoes tied with wide silk ribbons, a white waistcoat with coral buttons, a blue frock coat with a collar made of saffron-colored velvet. He had forgotten his gloves and he had also forgotten to clean his fingernails. His hair had not been trimmed for weeks and hung down his neck in a shaggy mane. He refused to give his jeweled stick to the servant who took his hat, and carried it into the drawing room, where the contessa was receiving.

403

The contessa was appalled. She gave Balzac thirty seconds, told him he could get tea in the next room, and turned her back on him, giving all her attention to de Bonneval.

Balzac was depressed. With his curious sartorial blindness, that was the despair of his friends and the delight of his enemies, he could not imagine what he had done to offend the contessa. In desperation, wearing the same costume, he called at the Austrian Embassy and begged Madame Apponyi to advise him.

Madame Apponyi liked Balzac and detested de Bonneval.

"See a barber," she suggested. "Wear a black coat, if you have one, and burn that shocking waistcoat. You are dealing with an Englishwoman, my dear. They are quite conscious of men's clothes."

Balzac looked at the elegant waistcoat, for which he had paid a hundred francs, and wondered what was the matter with it.

"Perhaps I've ruined everything," he said morosely. "She may refuse to see me."

"Courage, de Balzac," said Madame Apponyi. "I suggest that you try again. I have a certain influence with Sarah."

"You are an angel," Balzac assured her.

He was received for a second time at the great house on the Champs Elysées. He wore the black coat that Madame Apponyi had suggested. He had also seen a barber, and in his hand, in a little velvet box, he carried one of the strong black locks that the barber's shears had removed. This he presented to the contessa, saying, "I am not much of a Samson, it is true, but you are a magnificent Delilah."

She was amused. She laughed and Balzac's stiffness fell away. He was offered a chair beside her and when they began to talk he was at his ease, as if he had known her for a long time. For certain people, Balzac had extraordinary warmth and charm. The beautiful Sarah was one of them. Within twenty minutes they were friends, discovering, all in a rush, a dozen things in common.

"What? You go to séances?" Balzac demanded. "I know a somnambulist in Saint-Sulpice who is extraordinary. Simply fantastic. Will you do me the honor of coming with me to her next séance?"

"It is my greatest weakness," she confessed. "Or perhaps I should say my second greatest."

"And the first?" asked Balzac innocently.

"Love, of course," she told him.

404

They visited Balzac's fortune teller, a doubtful gypsy in the rue Saint-Sulpice who predicted that Balzac would soon be wealthy. They went to the opera and sat in the Guidoboni-Visconti box. They drove through the Bois de Bologne in the Guidoboni-Visconti barouche, behind a pair of superb black horses. They dined in the mansion in the Champs-Elysées and Balzac met the contessa's husband.

I have been lucky with husbands, he reflected. Monsieur de Berny was a chronic invalid. General Junot was dead. Count Hanski is a bird-watcher rather than a wife-watcher.

The Count Emilio Guidoboni-Visconti was an amateur pharmacist, whose greatest delight was in washing bottles and pasting cryptic labels on them. His second passion was music; he often played the fiddle with various orchestras in Paris or at Versailles, where the Viscontis had a summer house. He was bored by society and seldom went out, except to the opera. He had long since realized that he was no match for his wife's vibrant sexuality, but he had not a trace of jealousy. He was, in fact, rather proud of her conquests, and not at all displeased to see the famous Balzac supplant the nonentity de Bonneval.

For some weeks, the contessa wavered between Balzac and the younger man, to neither of whom had she as yet surrendered her final favors. She found Balzac amusing and vital, a challenge to her own metal, and she was thrilled by the cloud of fame with which Balzac was surrounded, so that wherever one went on his arm, one was the center of attention.

On the other hand, there was a streak of the frivolous in her nature and she was fastidious by instinct. De Bonneval was a superlative dancer. When he was not being childish and sulky, he had the pretty manners of a courtier. His clothes were elegant enough to rival those of George Bryan Brummel himself, and he wore them well. He was young and extraordinarily handsome and according to his reputation, he was an athletic and versatile man in bed.

So "la belle Anglaise," as Balzac called her, kept the novelist and the young dandy dangling on a silken string. Balzac had the advantages of age, intelligence and experience. He regarded the affair with self-confidence, certain that the outcome would be in his favor.

De Bonneval was nervous.

Until Balzac appeared on the scene, he had been making excellent progress with the enchanting Englishwoman, who had just dismissed her last lover, the notorious slavic libertine, Prince Koslovsky, who dominated the rather licentious colony of Russian aristocrats in Paris. For de Bonneval to lose out at this point would not only be frustrating. It would be a matter of public humiliation . . . something even more distressing than sexual deprivation.

Being both nervous and not very bright, de Bonneval overplayed his hand, deprecating his rival in the wrong way and for the wrong reasons.

"The chap is really a bounder, you know," he insisted. "His clothes are the joke of Paris. And he gives himself such absurd airs. A mere scribbler! I'm afraid he's no gentleman."

"I beg your pardon?"

"I said this fellow Balzac is not a gentleman," de Bonneval repeated.

Sarah was English. To the English way of thinking, the production of gentlemen is an enterprise confined to their own green island. Anything produced elsewhere is approximate and of no importance. When de Bonneval insisted on emphasizing the fact that Balzac was not a gentleman, Sarah laughed in his face, and told him that his cravat was imperfectly folded, an untruth that baffled young de Bonneval later, when he stood before a mirror and tried to find the fault.

De Bonneval's final tactical blunder would not have been made by a schoolboy of normal intelligence.

"Balzac is somewhat notorious, you know," he warned the contessa. "An affair with a man like that could be very damaging to your reputation."

"My what?" asked Sarah innocently.

"Your reputation," de Bonneval repeated.

Sarah kissed his cheek and said, "You sweet, innocent boy." Then she laughed merrily and sent him away. That afternoon, she made up her mind to become Balzac's mistress.

Sarah craved the spice of life. She behaved with a splendid equestrienne recklessness and total scorn for the formalities. Once she had decided to sleep with Balzac, she was quite prepared and even eager to dispense with the preliminaries that a well-born French woman would have demanded as a matter of course.

Three nights after she had laughed at de Bonneval's concern

406

for her reputation, she sat with Balzac in a box at Les Italiens. She was dressed in white peau de soie, a gown that was cut to reveal her bosom. Her pale hair was piled high. Her head was magnificent. She was easily the most beautiful woman in the brilliant, well-dressed audience.

Between the first and second acts, Balzac murmured the graceful trivialities women are supposed to find delightful and to horde as a squirrel hordes nuts. Sarah turned and regarded him candidly with her superb grey eyes. They were remarkable eyes, honest as a pool of clear water.

"I am sick of this turtledove sighing, Balzac," she said bluntly, as if she addressed a groom in the hunting field. "Also, I am bored with the music and the story is dull. Let us go to your famous boudoir in the rue des Batailles and find out whether we can manage a better performance than what's being given on the stage here."

Balzac was equal to this. Without a word or a change of expression, he rose, helped Sarah with her wrap, offered her his arm, and escorted her through the corridors of plush and velvet to the marquee of the theater, not far from which her carriage waited.

It was an evening carriage, the cushions upholstered in black velvet, the hand-holds of gilt cord. There was a white fur lap robe, which Balzac offered to Sarah.

"Sit back and be quiet," she said. "I loathe talking in vehicles."

She was the first woman to visit Balzac's boudoir for the purpose for which it had been designed. Balzac gave her a chair, then ceremoniously touched a taper to the candles in the silver sconces. Slowly, as the candles burned up, the eccentrically furnished room came to life. Sarah looked around her, gazing at the curved wall, with its Turkish divan, at the incense pots Balzac had lighted when he was finished with the candles, finally at the white fur rug, reflected in a great flat mirror that went from ceiling to floor.

"Balzac, it is obscene!" she cried in sheer delight. "It is magnificently obscene. Beyond belief. I adore it!"

Balzac beamed like a praised child and rang for Auguste.

"Champagne," he ordered. "And some of those tasteless cakes."

They drank a bottle of iced champagne and nibbled at the dry little wafers. Then Sarah put down her glass and crossed the room,

407

bending to kiss Balzac's mouth. It was a shocking kiss, that went through Balzac like a charge of electricity.

Balzac was thirty-seven. He had loved two women and made love to two hundred but during the thirty seconds that elapsed in the course of Sarah's kiss, he began a new education, the first lesson of which took place during the next four hours.

Sarah Visconti was not quite thirty. Her body had reached a full, glorious maturity. Her thighs were lovely. The hair on her body was ash blonde, and almost invisible. Her skin was creamy, soft, with a delicate pinkish underglow. Her throat and shoulders were magnificent.

Her passion was African, almost frightening.

She was unique.

Balzac had the sensation that he was not being loved but devoured.

Actually, Balzac did not love Sarah at all in the way he loved Eva de Hanska. He enjoyed her. She delighted him. She never gave him an instant's pain. They were friends, firm friends, who shared one another physically. It was a rare thing, precious to both of them.

They went everywhere together, to the opera, the theater, to Véry's, the Grand Véfour, the Palais-Royal. They created magnificent gossip. Sarah enjoyed being talked about. So did Balzac. The Count Guidoboni-Visconti was busy with his fiddling and his pharmaceutical bottles, and in any case would not have cared.

"For a descendant of the Condottieri, your husband is a mild man," Balzac observed.

"He is an absolute darling," said Sarah. "Sometimes I am rather hurt because he takes no interest in me as a woman. For a long time after we were married, I used to flirt with him, but I gave it up. One might as well have tried to flirt with the pope."

"What is it that he likes?" asked Balzac. "Boys? Young men?"

"Oh dear no! He's perfectly normal," Sarah assured him. "Once a month, by the calendar, he goes to the best brothel in Paris."

"But why in the name of God does he do that, when he is married to the best trollope in France?" asked Balzac.

"I asked him that once," said Sarah. "He told me that he didn't think it would be fair to disappoint me."

Balzac laughed heartily.

"He is a wonder, this husband of yours," he said. He looked at her intently. "I promise you, if I were your husband you would soon learn what jealousy is like."

"But you are not my husband, you are my friend," she reminded him. "And you must never be jealous of me."

The extraordinary thing was that Balzac felt no jealousy. They were as frank as old soldiers, discussing love affairs of the past with candor and high amusement. It was a thing that Balzac could have done with no other woman.

"Do you know, Balzac, that I am the only really normal member of my family?" she said to him one day.

They were in the boudoir in the rue des Batailles, resting after having made love. Balzac lay on the bed, contemplating the ornamental ceiling.

"You are normal if nothing else," he murmured lazily.

"My mother killed herself when she was thirty-five, because she thought her looks were going. One of my brothers did the same because he thought he was becoming impotent. Another brother died of drink. French drink. Absinthe. My sister, Arabella, is completely mad—a religious fanatic who scourges herself with whips in order to atone for imaginary sins."

"And the father of this extraordinary litter?" Balzac asked.

"He had the wit to go to Australia. Hasn't been heard of since," Sarah replied complacently.

There was absolutely no strain between them. To Balzac, after the stormy sessions with Eve in Geneva, it was a relief to have a companion with whom he could always let down his guard. He had no obligation to her, except that of being her friend.

Chapter 40

Nᴏᴛ ᴇᴠᴇʀʏᴏɴᴇ of Balzac's acquaintanceship was permitted to call at No. 13 rue des Batailles. Only a trusted few ever set eyes on the famous and fabulous boudoir that so delighted Sarah Visconti.

To gain entrance to Balzac's inner sanctum, it was necessary to be familiar with an elaborate system of passwords and countersigns. The Widow Durand was well protected; without the open sesame no one passed her defences. On certain days, the concierge at No. 13 would respond to the words: *"The Plums are Ripe!"* and permit the aspirant visitor to cross the threshold into the public stairwell.

At the foot of the stairs, Balzac's trusted valet de chambre, Auguste, would give way only to those who lowered their eyes and announced, *"I am bringing the lace from Belgium."*

The door of the flat was opened only to one who said, in a conspiratorial tone, *"Madame Bertrand continues to enjoy the best of health."*

Balzac enjoyed this rigamarole, and insisted on absolute observance of the protocol he had established.

It appealed to his sense of the melodramatic, and in a way it served his purpose. With the passwords and countersigns, and by shuttling back and forth between the rue Cassini and the rue des Batailles, he made himself a difficult man to find, unless one was in his confidence. Hundreds of people were looking for him in one way or another. A dozen editors wanted copy that had been bought and paid for. There was hardly a bailiff in Paris who was not trying to serve him with a notice of distraint. Moneylenders pursued him, with offers to lend at usurious rates and fierce demands for payment.

He was also engaged in what it amused him to regard as a personal struggle with his majesty, Louis-Philippe, King of the French, who had the effrontery to demand that Balzac serve for two days each month with the National Guard.

410

Balzac refused to serve.

"I am a Legitimist," he insisted. "I take no orders from this bourgeois king. Besides, I am too busy enriching French literature to play at being a French soldier."

"You have had a heart attack," Nacquart reminded him. "I will give you a certificate that will say that you are medically unfit to serve and that will be the end of it."

"No thank you," said Balzac. "For one thing, the certificate would be a fraud and an indictment of your status as a physician. I am fit as a lion. Also, I refuse to dignify these popinjays in gold braid with any excuse whatsoever." He snapped his fingers. "If they want to make a soldier of Balzac, let them come and get him!"

Three times he was summoned for service and three times he ignored the summons. The Tribunal of the National Guard, which had the powers of a Summary Court Martial, sentenced him, *in absentia,* to eight days imprisonment.

When he was informed of the sentence, Balzac put his hands on his hips and bellowed with defiant laughter.

"Balzac in prison!" he roared. "What impertinence!"

"It is not a joke, monsieur," Auguste said anxiously.

"Very well, let them find me!" Balzac declared.

They found him, after a few days more of hide-and-seek, and marched him out of his workroom in the rue Cassini into the green prison van that was waiting in the street. Balzac took it as a personal insult that the sergeant-major who arrested him was a dentist in ordinary life.

"At least they could have sent a regular doctor," he complained loudly. "Imagine it! The great Balzac, arrested by a puller of rotten teeth!"

"Keep quiet!" growled the uniformed dentist. "One more word, and I'll pull your teeth with the butt of my pistol."

"Dentist!" said Balzac disdainfully, as if the word in itself were a curse.

The prison van started with a jerk and Balzac was on his way to the cells.

Draft defaulters served their terms in the prison of the Hôtel de Bazincourt, nicknamed the Hôtel des Haricots, because the only dish served the prisoners was a porridge made of spoiled beans. Most of the draft evaders were Paris workingmen, artisans and

411

laborers, who objected to the loss of pay involved with service, and who went to jail for a principle, often with a bit of red ribbon defiantly pinned to their blouses. People of Balzac's class either served good-naturedly, making a lark of the thing, or got out of it altogether by means of influence or bribery.

Balzac, once captured, treated the affair as an enormous joke. When the dentist arrested him, he had been wearing his Carmelite's robe, and the toothpuller had refused to give him time to change into trousers. He was marched into the prison yard and the inmates who saw him were outraged, taking him for a priest.

"The bastards have put a monk into jail," they shouted. "A man of the cloth. They will stop at nothing, these greengrocers turned into noblemen."

Balzac bowed to right and left, making the sign of the cross.

"God bless you, my children," he said piously. "We are put on this earth to suffer and Louis-Philippe is determined that we shall not forget it."

Balzac was placed in a cell that was six feet square, furnished with nothing but a straw pallet and a waste bucket that had not been emptied. The whole prison smelt like a vast latrine. The floors were slimy with damp.

Balzac had no money, but he managed to persuade one of the guards to carry a message to Werdet, demanding cash, paper, ink, and trousers, promising the turnkey a large tip when the publisher arrived.

During the day, the cell doors were left unlocked and the prisoners were free to walk in the corridors. Balzac wandered out into the long, barred runway, at either end of which stood a National Guardsman in full uniform, armed with a musket and fixed bayonet. Most of Balzac's fellow prisoners were working men in smocks and sabots, but at the other end of the corridor he spied an elegantly attired figure, wearing silk stockings and a brocaded cravat, walking with stately indifference to his surroundings, carrying a thin dress cane.

It was the novelist, Eugène Sue. With Balzac, Dumas and Victor Hugo, Sue was a member of the Big Four who dominated French literature.

The two writers approached one another tentatively as a pair of watchdogs. They were colleagues, but they were also bitter rivals. Sue envied Balzac his prodigious energy. Balzac was jealous

412

of Sue's personal fortune that made him independent of publishers and their demands.

When he recognized Balzac, Sue raised an eyebrow at the Carmelite's robe, then bowed stiffly and raised his cane in salute.

"Monsieur!"

Balzac returned the courtesy, feeling rather ridiculous, bowing in his monk's dress.

"Monsieur!"

The two men passed one another, formal as a pair of dowager duchesses promenading on the Champs Élysées. Thirty minutes passed. An hour. As he approached Balzac, Sue seemed to hesitate. Then he stopped and bowed.

"I have asked the Grand Véfour to send in dinner, monsieur," he said stiffly. "I intend to dine in my cell. Perhaps you will do me the honor to join me."

Balzac hesitated, torn between hunger and the desire to appear indifferent. Hunger won. He bowed again and accepted Sue's invitation.

He and Sue dined on a pâté of hare and a roasted chicken, washed down with vintage wine. The meal was ostentatiously served by four of Sue's servants, who had brought linens and silver from the novelist's house.

Sue was Balzac's age, but he looked somewhat older because of the aura of chronic boredom that surrounded him. There was a self-centered quality about Sue that Balzac found almost terrifying. A healthy ego was one thing; Sue was almost inhumanly egocentric.

"I have given up writing altogether," Sue said, daintily spearing a bit of chicken. "The French public is a great beast. I consider it beneath my dignity to attempt to entertain or to edify such cattle."

"You speak from the heights of a private income," said Balzac, gnawing on the leg of a chicken. "As for me, I write for money."

Sue smiled ironically.

"That kind of bluster may be all right for non-writers, my dear Balzac," he said. "I know better. Dumas writes for money. Hugo writes in defense of various causes that seem to preoccupy him nowadays. When I wrote, I wrote for amusement—my own amusement, I mean, not that of the mob."

"And I?" said Balzac, wiping his mouth with one of Sue's silk table napkins.

"Oh, it is clear that you expect your books to make you immortal," Sue said insolently. "It is a battle that is lost before it is joined."

Balzac wished he had made his dinner of the bean porridge supplied by the prison. Sue depressed him.

When they finished dinner, Balzac complained of a headache and retired to his cell. He lay on the stinking straw pallet, staring at the bars, until the turnkeys closed the cells for the night. Then he rolled on his stomach and tried to sleep, bitten by bugs, scratched by the straw, made sick at his stomach by the smell.

In the morning, Werdet came, bringing Balzac's clothes and writing materials, as well as two hundred francs in cash and a terrine of sausage meat of the kind that is sold in Touraine.

"The King of France is trying to kill me," Balzac complained, scratching his bedbug bites. "Be sure that he will not succeed."

He bribed a guard and secured a rough table and chair.

"I may be in prison, but I cannot afford to be idle," he informed Werdet that afternoon, when the publisher returned.

The three hundred odd inmates of the Hôtel des Haricots played cards noisily, fought with one another, sang revolutionary songs or simply shouted in the effort to kill time. By day, the prison was like a madhouse. Balzac stuffed his ears with cotton and settled down to his daily stint.

After the first night, his nose become more or less accustomed to the prison stench, although he complained to Werdet that it was like living in a pissoir.

Sue was discharged after forty-eight hours, but Balzac, because he had evaded three calls for service, was obliged to serve eight days.

"Eight days!" he shouted at Werdet, as if the poor publisher had been president of his Court Martial. "I tell you, this incompetent king is trying to kill off the best writers in France with his idiotic National Guard."

Sarah came to see him, bringing food in a wicker hamper and a bottle of chilled white wine.

"So my lover turns out to be a jailbird," she said, offering Balzac a slice of boiled ham. "I must say, you don't look out of place."

To Sarah, the idea of Balzac in prison was merely funny. She cheered him up and bolstered his mood of haughty defiance. He was filled with bluster and good humor and he told Werdet

414

that he wouldn't mind remaining in the Hôtel des Haricots for the rest of the year, if that was what the king wanted.

"Good place to work," he insisted. "A man can concentrate here and after a while he gets used to the stink. In six months, I could write myself out of debt, if they kept me locked up. I could even pay off what I owe my mother."

He was talking simply to keep up his good spirits, having sense enough to know that if he permitted his confinement to affect his nerves he would become really ill. He was a man who had suffered a full-dress heart attack. Six weeks in prison would have killed him, let alone six months. The prison was damp and draughty, and though by an effort of will he could work, with his ears stuffed with cotton, he could not sleep.

He came out of prison exhausted, suffering from a heavy cold in the chest that was accompanied by a racking, enervating cough. Two days out of prison he found himself involved in a difficult lawsuit.

The opening chapters of THE LILY OF THE VALLEY, a book for which Balzac naturally had a good deal of affection, since it was in essence the story of his love for Madame de Berny, had been sent to the Paris *Review,* a magazine that was to publish it as a serial. For Balzac, the first proofs of a book were always subject to almost maniacal revision. He had intended to put the opening chapters in order when the manuscript copy was finished.

When he came out of jail, he found a letter from Eve on his desk at the rue des Batailles, informing him that the unfinished version of THE LILY OF THE VALLEY had already appeared in the Saint Petersburg *Foreign Gazette,* a French language periodical published in the Russian capital.

Balzac was furious.

"I wish I knew how to use a pistol," he said to Sarah. "I would challenge Buloz to a duel and kill him."

Buloz was editor of the Paris *Review* and one of the most powerful literary figures in Paris.

"Does it really matter?" Sarah asked mildly. "After all, Russia seems so far away."

"Of course it matters," said Balzac harshly. "It would matter if it were Timbuctoo. The thing involves principle, you see. Author's rights."

415

He went to call on Buloz, filled with the fires of righteous wrath. Buloz laughed in his face.

"Balzac, you are a professional writer," the editor said. "Stop behaving like Lord Byron. Go home and finish your novel, so that we can get on with publication in the Paris *Review.*"

Balzac drew himself up and tapped on the editor's desk with his cane.

"Buloz, I am an artist," he said, with enormous pride. "An artist has rights that a man like you will find it dangerous to tamper with."

Buloz laughed.

"My dear chap," he said in a patronizing tone. "You sound like that lady novelist in trousers. What is her name? George Sand?"

Balzac's cane came down with a crash and Buloz flinched.

"Buloz, I put you on notice," he said. "I forbid you to publish one line of my novel in your filthy little sheet. Those are plain words. Plain enough so that even an editor ought to be able to understand them."

Buloz stood up impatiently, putting a pince-nez on his nose. He looked at Balzac with the vicious eyes of a hanging judge. He had a hideous squint.

"Balzac, I am a busy man," he said. "I have no time to listen to your childish ravings. Your book has been bought and paid for. To me it is merchandise. It will be published when I see fit, where I see fit, in whatever form I see fit."

Balzac felt a twinge in his damaged heart. He steadied himself on his cane, fought for breath, then said in a calm and dangerous voice, "I refuse to deliver the rest of my novel. You will never publish it."

"Let us see what the courts have to say about that," said the editor blandly. "And now, Balzac, if you will excuse me, I have a magazine to get ready for the press."

Balzac went out of the editor's office, filled with a calm cold rage. He was determined to fight for what he took to be his rights, and incidentally, for the rights of other men who made a living, or tried to, with pen, ink, and blank paper.

Balzac wrote a formal letter to the Paris *Review,* forbidding publication of THE LILY OF THE VALLEY. Buloz promptly started suit against him for breach of contract, demanding damages of ten thousand francs.

416

Balzac employed counsel, but he wrote the brief himself, and quickly became deeply involved in the intricacies of the case.

The lawsuit created several problems for Balzac. The Paris *Review* and the *Review of Two Worlds,* both controlled by Buloz, exercised enormous power over the writers of France. Because of the influence of the two journals, Buloz for years had been able to crack the whip. Balzac's crisis with THE LILY OF THE VALLEY had simply brought to a head a long history of grievances against Buloz and his papers.

"We should have our own magazine," Balzac insisted to Sarah. "A publication run by the people who write for it, not by leeches like Buloz, who merely get fat on our labor."

It is an idea that persistently inflicts itself upon the imaginations of writers, always with unhappy results.

Balzac cast his eye about in the back alleys of Paris publishing and found that he could have for a song the controlling interest in a derelict literary magazine called the Paris *Chronicle,* currently owned by one William Duckett, an obscure and not too savory member of the confraternity of editors.

Balzac was determined to buy the paper and convinced that with himself as editor it would quickly put Buloz out of business. Besides, it would give him a platform from which to defend himself against the slanders Buloz had started to run in the columns of the Paris *Review.*

As usual, Balzac had no money.

To help raise the cash he needed in order to buy the Paris *Chronicle,* he sold the rights to half a dozen of the potboilers he had written in the early twenties and published under various pseudonyms. They were to be summarily revised and published under his own name.

Both his sister and Zulma Carraud warned him that he would damage his reputation and begged him not to exhume the bones of his dead pseudonymous past.

"My reputation will take care of itself," he said confidently. "Besides, I am willing to risk a good deal in order to get my hands on the magazine."

For the rights to his old potboilers, Balzac got ten thousand francs. Buisson, his tailor, put up five thousand. So did Sarah Visconti. Balzac bought the controlling interest in Duckett's paper, giving his note for the minority share.

"Now to round up a staff," he said gleefully to Sarah, rubbing his hands with anticipation of the defeat of Buloz. "We must have the best men in Paris. Young fellows with plenty of spirit, fellows who aren't afraid of a fight."

One of the men who joined Balzac was Théophile Gautier, a novelist and critic who was ten years younger than Balzac and a firm admirer though not a disciple. Gautier had recently attracted attention with a daring novel called MADEMOISELLE DE MAUPIN, and his name had the currency Balzac wanted.

The two men quickly became friends, and friendship with Gautier was perhaps worth the time, energy and cash that Balzac was to put into his venture with the Paris *Chronicle*.

Gautier was handsome, brilliant, paradoxical, and passionately honest. He was Balzac's first recruit and the most important of the lot.

"We are probably writing our death warrants by pissing in Buloz's face," he said. "But it is a face that invites such use, and I am the kind of man who always tries to do the appropriate thing."

"It's his death warrant we're writing," said Balzac courageously. "Have no fear, my boy. We will slit Buloz's throat as easily as if he were a rabbit or a rat."

To get things going, Balzac gave a dinner for the new staff of the *Chronicle*. His best silver was in the pawn shop. Sarah sent a complete service from her house in the Champs-Élysées, fantastic stuff from England, beautifully forged and engraved, the spoons and dessert forks washed with gold. She also sent two of her own footmen to help Auguste with the service.

"If you like, I will come and sleep with the most important members of the staff," she said. "We must keep them happy, after all."

"You would only distract them," Balzac decided. "This may be a dinner party, but it is a matter of business just the same."

Balzac gave his new associates an impressive meal—little oysters from the Breton coast, lobster, quail under glass bells, a magnificently roasted saddle of venison sent up from Saché by Monsieur de Margonne, who had killed the deer with his own rifle.

In addition to young Gautier, the dinner was attended by Charles Bernard, from Bésançon, by the critic, Gustave Planche, stolen from the staff of the Paris *Review,* by Jules Sandeau, not long since cast off as a lover by George Sand. There were others.

There was also Caroline Marbouty, a dark-eyed would-be writer from the south, snapping with impudence and sex.

Marbouty had come with Sandeau, but her real interest was in Balzac. He found it amusing, then annoying.

"She is like a bitch in heat, Jules," he complained to Sandeau. "Can't you get her into bed and calm her down?"

Sandeau shrugged indifferently.

"She is in heat, that is true, 'Noré," he said. "But not for a minor writer. She craves dalliance with the great."

"Become famous, Jules, I beg of you," Balzac said.

When the editorial meal had been eaten, Balzac prepared a large pot of his famous coffee and outlined his ideas to the group.

"We writers do all the work and we get a pittance for our labor," he said. "Why? Because we have allowed canaille like Buloz to acquire power, and in France today the only thing that counts is power. Acquire power and people will pay attention to you. We must make publishers and printers dependent on us, not the other way around. Public opinion in Paris today is controlled by a clique of hacks and parasites. We are going to smash them, you and I, and we are going to do it with the Paris *Chronicle*."

There was a round of applause and Caroline Marbouty cried "Bravo!"

Then Gautier said, "Honoré, will the big guns get behind us, the heavy artillery of literature—Hugo, Dumas, Sue, Janin, Sainte-Beuve?"

"How can you doubt it, Théo?" Balzac said. "They are writers, not shopkeepers. Every one of the men you mentioned has been asked to testify in my behalf, when the matter with Buloz comes into court in a few weeks time. The trial will show us which side of the fence the writers of France are on."

Balzac had faith in his fellow writers, even in men he disliked, such as Dumas and Sue and Sainte-Beuve. He could not believe that they would fail to make common cause in defense of the artist's rights.

Balzac's dispute with Buloz quickly became the talk of literary Paris. Buloz began to print vicious articles about Balzac, deriding his talent, ridiculing his taste in dress, sneering at his personal habits, impugning his patriotism. Gleefully, the Paris *Review* exposed the amount of Balzac's debts, made fun of his love affairs,

419

chortled over the secret exits in his living quarters. Balzac was portrayed as a rather dishonest, amorous clown, of no literary consequence, and the Buloz papers hammered away without mercy.

In the columns of the *Chronicle,* Balzac fought back, but he fought back like a gentleman, never stooping to personal attack on Buloz or his henchmen.

The big battalions, from the first, were on the side of Buloz. Buloz had the power. Balzac's friends advised him to give up the fight. They warned him that he could expect no mercy from the powerful editor, who could damage his prestige and even turn the booksellers against him.

Balzac ignored the advice of his friends. He felt that what was at stake was his integrity as a writer and here he would not compromise.

"What is the point of being a writer, if you give up your autonomy?" he demanded. "A writer who is not his own man is nothing. He is worse than a pimp."

The trial was held before three learned judges in an impressive chamber in the Palais de Justice.

Buloz had employed a crafty lawyer. His opening move was to attack THE LILY OF THE VALLEY as a book, reading passages aloud, sneering at them. The novel was a love story and it was a simple matter to take lines out of context and make them sound absurd.

Balzac protested. He was overruled.

He was overruled too when his character was attacked and his honesty called into question.

He fought with dogged persistence.

His great shock came when the men he had been sure would stand behind him, one by one testified for Buloz, putting the fraternity of letters after their fear of the editor's power.

Alexandre Dumas took the stand, dressed in a coat with gold braid that resembled a military uniform. He raised his arrogant head, dusted his nostrils with a scrap of lace, and then smiled smugly at the court.

"What Buloz has done in the case of Balzac's so-called novel is perfectly normal procedure," he informed the court, in response to a question from the Buloz lawyer.

"Balzac is completely in the wrong here," said his old prison

420

mate, Eugène Sue, unfolding his lorgnette and looking at Balzac with distaste.

Sainte-Beuve, Janin, a dozen others, bore witness against their comrade-in-letters. Balzac listened, hardly able to believe that he heard correctly.

When Victor Hugo took the stand, Balzac's heart sank. It rose again in a few seconds, when Hugo began to speak, in a level voice, filled with great authority.

"I know Honoré Balzac well," said the Prince of Poets. "He is a writer of great talent and absolute integrity. To my mind, he was absolutely in the right in this case."

Hugo was followed by George Sand, who had left off her trousers and put on a skirt, out of deference to the dignity of French justice. In her high clear voice, she spoke with some passion in Balzac's defense and in defense of the rights of artists. The judges smiled at her and bowed when she stepped down.

Balzac shook Hugo's hand and kissed frère George on the cheek.

"Thank you both and God bless you," he said.

As Dumas left the courtroom, he stopped beside Balzac. He was wearing a pungent scent that Balzac found offensive.

"Nothing personal in all this, Balzac," he said rather stiffly. "Buloz is our bread and butter, or at least he's the butter on our bread. A man with good sense knows enough not to bite the hand that feeds him."

"Even when the crust he gives is always followed by a slap, Alexandre?"

"Even then," said Dumas, twirling his cane. "If a man doesn't eat, he starves."

As is not unusual with lawsuits, the question passed on by the learned judges was not precisely the one in contention. The learned judges in Balzac's case reduced the question to whether or not a writer could be compelled to complete and deliver a work of the imagination, merely because he had agreed to do so before the work was actually written.

With extraordinary good sense, the judges decided that the human imagination could not be regarded as a commodity to be bought and sold like sugar. They made their decision in Balzac's favor and Buloz was ordered to pay the costs of Balzac's defense against the suit.

The staff of the Paris *Chronicle* cheered the verdict and carried Balzac on their shoulders from the court to the Café de Paris. Everyone drank a toast to the victory in the best champagne. Gautier was delighted. Caroline Marbouty insisted on sitting on Balzac's lap and nibbling at his ears like a puppy, in order to show her enthusiasm.

The decision was a basic defense of authors' rights, and of great future importance. For Balzac, it was a tasteless victory. He had exhausted himself and strained his heart to a point that worried Nacquart. He had made a bitter enemy of Buloz and of the jackals who surrounded him. He had fought in public with most of the popular writers of France.

And it was not finished.

Buloz and his crew of literary assassins were determined to smash the Paris *Chronicle* in which Balzac had placed his hopes and a good deal of borrowed money.

Buloz had cash, power, and influence.

A new publication is always a tender and shallow-rooted plant. Deprived of sun and rain, it dies quickly. Buloz meant to deny the *Chronicle* the sun of contributions and the rain of public notice.

Balzac fought back.

His magazine was a good one, not as polished as the Buloz papers, but meatier, and vibrant with youth and vigor, alive with a sense of the future. It should have succeeded. But for Buloz and Company, it would have succeeded.

Buloz was shrewd and utterly without mercy or scruple. He let it be known that the columns of the Paris *Review* and the *Review of Two Worlds* would be closed forever to any writer who published so much as a rhymed couplet in Balzac's paper. He threatened newsdealers with reprisals if they offered the Paris *Chronicle* for sale. "Sell the Paris *Chronicle* if you like," the newsdealers were told. "But if you do, don't expect to get your copies of the Paris *Review*."

In the cafés, henchmen of Buloz spread lies, gossip and scandal about the *Chronicle* and its staff. Balzac and Gautier were homosexual. Caroline Marbouty had been a famous prostitute in Marseilles and her ill-gotten gains backed the paper. The *Chronicle,* in fact, was an organ of the British espionage service, which omnipresent organization worked through Balzac's English mistress, the so-called Contessa Guidoboni-Visconti, who was quite possibly an actual officer of the British army, moving about Paris in skillful disguise.

Balzac continued to fight. He and Gautier served as editors and made up the paper, going to the printers each week to stand over the composing stone. When there were not enough contributions to fill the space, Balzac wrote them himself. In a single night he wrote all of THE ATHEIST'S MASS. He dashed off articles on politics, reviewed books, criticized plays, even invented three-line fillers. He was tireless, passionate and determined.

Meanwhile, trouble appeared on another quadrant of Balzac's literary horizon.

Under his old contract with the Widow Bechet, he owed the Widow two books, which were to round out the series he had called STUDIES IN XIXTH CENTURY MANNERS. The Widow herself had more or less given up the effort to extract the books from Balzac, but shortly after the Buloz lawsuit, she had the good fortune to marry a young and vigorous man of business who at once took over management of her affairs. He succeeded in getting a court order instructing Balzac to deliver the books in twenty-four days, and to pay a fine of fifty francs for every day he was in default.

Balzac could have appealed the decision of the provincial court, but he had just been through the ordeal of defending himself against the Buloz suit. The prospect of more time wasted in courtrooms did not appeal to him. He decided to give the Widow her books, within the two weeks' deadline, and to be done with her forever.

"I am going to fulfill the contract, but I am also going to turn out two first-class books," he told Sarah. "After Buloz's slanders, I cannot afford to publish anything that is less than brilliant."

He went down to Saché and locked himself in the corner room that the Margonnes kept in readiness for him. He wrote for fifteen hours a day, living on black coffee and bread. He finished LOST ILLUSIONS and A YOUNG PROVINCIAL IN PARIS, two brilliant and pivotal books, one a study of literary life in Paris, the other an examination of the career of a master printer in the Provinces.

He kept the promise he had made to Sarah. He gave the Widow her two pounds of flesh and produced work of the highest standard. He also very nearly killed himself.

Two days after he came back from Touraine, with the manuscripts in his carpet bag, he collapsed with something that resembled an apoplectic stroke. For several days, one side of his body was paralyzed. He was in bed for three weeks, at the end of which time Nacquart ordered him to get out of Paris, away from the pressures of running the *Chronicle* and from the harassment of bill collectors, bailiffs and representatives of the National Guard, who had not yet given up their efforts to make him perform the service demanded by the King of France.

"I cannot go," said Balzac flatly. "There is the *Chronicle* to be looked after. I have a book to write. Besides, as usual, I have no money."

"You must go," said Nacquart bluntly. "Young Gautier can look after your magazine. As for the money, beg, borrow or steal it, but get it."

Sarah Visconti found a way to get Balzac out of Paris. Not long before, her husband's mother had died in Italy, leaving an inconclusive will over which scores of Visconti relatives were fighting. Count Emilio was disinclined to tear himself away from his music and his pharmacy in order to represent his branch of the family.

"Besides, I am terrified of legal things, as you know," he said to Sarah. "I never understand them."

Someone, however, had to go to Milan to represent the Guidoboni-Visconti interests.

"Why not de Balzac?" Sarah asked. "To send an ordinary lawyer in a family matter would be considered rude. Nevertheless, one prefers to be capably represented. Balzac does not practice law, it is true, but he does have a law degree. He is a friend of the family, and a famous man, whose name is certain to command respect."

"The very person," agreed Count Emilio, delighted that his wife had removed the matter from his hands. "Please make all the arrangements."

"He will need authorization," said Sarah. "And a Rothschild letter of credit to cover his expenses."

"Have them prepared at once and I will sign them," answered the docile descendent of the Condottieri.

Balzac was enthusiastic about going to Italy, but he did not want to go alone.

"Take that little bitch Marbouty," Sarah suggested. "She's been sniffing at your heels for months now."

"If I take Marbouty to Italy with me it will start all kinds of gossip," Balzac objected.

"She's got a figure like a boy's," said Sarah. "Put her into a pair of trousers and pass her off as your secretary."

The idea was just absurd enough to appeal to Balzac's sense of humor. He sent a note to Marbouty and asked her to come to see him in the rue des Batailles. An hour later she knocked at his door, bright-eyed and eager. Balzac looked at her critically. Sarah is right, he decided. Marbouty was slim-hipped and her breasts were not too large. She had the clean-limbed figure of a boy.

"How would you like to come to Italy with me, all expenses paid?" he said.

"You don't have to ask me a second time," Marbouty answered pertly. "When do we leave?"

"As soon as my tailor, Buisson, can make you a pair of pants," said Balzac.

"Pants? I don't wear pants," she said, lifting her skirt and petticoats, displaying a rump innocent of covering. "I am an emancipated woman."

"Trousers then," Balzac said. "You are going to travel disguised as a boy."

"People will think you are some kind of pansy," she said. She rubbed her hands over her breasts and buttocks, then added, "And I don't think I'll make a very convincing boy."

"That is a risk we will have to take," said Balzac genially. He slapped her on the backside. "Come along, kitten, we will see what Buisson can do to turn you into a bright young man, suitable to be secretary to a famous author."

Buisson was the shrewdest tailor in France and he loved intrigue. He cut a coat so artfully that Marbouty's figure was concealed. With her hair cut short she made quite a plausible boy— until she walked.

"No boy ever moved his rear end quite like that," Balzac objected.

He imitated Marbouty's lascivious walk, making her squeal with delight.

"I will practice," she promised.

Before he left for Italy, Balzac gave instructions to Gautier concerning the Paris *Chronicle*. He took Gautier to lunch at the Café

425

de Paris and became very fatherly over the second bottle of wine.

"You are a good writer, Théo," he said. "MADEMOISELLE DE MAUPIN is first class. I should be glad to have written it myself."

Gautier was pleased and said so. He had a fierce respect for Balzac and was one of the few men who understood the staunch brave artist's heart sometimes concealed by Balzac's clownishness.

"One thing though," said Balzac. "You are a young fellow, Théo, and handsome. The women will be after you. Watch out for them. A writer ought not to get too much involved with women, you know. They make him lose too much time."

Coming from Balzac, this sententiousness made Gautier smile politely.

"Still, women must have been put into the world for some purpose or other, 'Noré," he suggested mildly. "What sort of relations do you think it is permissible to have with them?"

"One should write them letters," Balzac declared. "It helps to improve the style. There is nothing more difficult to compose than a good love letter."

Gautier laughed and said, "Honoré, you are a marvel. You even believe your own humbug when it suits you."

"And why not?" Balzac demanded. "It is the best humbug in France, is it not?"

Having already drawn a substantial sum against Count Emilio's letter of credit, Balzac insisted on paying the bill. The two friends drove back to the rue des Batailles. They found Caroline Marbouty in the Turkish boudoir, posing in front of the full length mirror, wearing nothing but the skin-tight trousers that had been fitted to her by Buisson. It was an obscene tableau, suggesting all sorts of bizarre perversions. Gautier laughed.

"Well, my celibate writer," he said, clapping Balzac on the shoulder. "This is one of your correspondents, no doubt?"

Marbouty squealed and hastily put on some kind of shirt. Balzac roared with laughter.

"Marbouty is not a woman," he said. "What you see before you, my friend Gautier, is an exceptionally well developed boy."

426

Chapter 41

BALZAC'S LETTER

of credit was limited only by his discretion. Since he knew that money was a matter of small concern to Count Emilio, and feeling that the representative of the Guidoboni-Visconti family should make a good impression on the Italians, he hired a private carriage for the journey over the Alps. He asked the stable to send him O'Donohue as driver but he was disappointed. The versatile Irishman had gone back to his native island on some kind of revolutionary mission. Instead of his favorite Patrick, he got a taciturn Alsatian who disapproved of Marbouty.

Marbouty wore the suit Buisson had made for her and carried a leather portfolio with Balzac's initials stamped on it. She answered to the name of Marcel. She was enchanted with the idea of going to Italy and mightily thrilled by the prospect of having the great Balzac himself as a lover.

Balzac was bored with her by the time they reached Lyons. She was a chatterbox and one of those people who find it impossible to sit without appearing to be in motion.

"Here I am on my way to what everyone calls the country of love," he said to himself. "Why am I taking this creature in trousers with me?"

Brooding, as the carriage lumbered over the tree-lined highway, Balzac suddenly slapped his thigh and gave a short burst of laughter. He remembered the light in Sarah's eye when she had suggested that he take Marbouty to Italy with him.

"What a clever wench she is," he thought. "Marbouty is no one for Sarah to be jealous of, and with Marbouty along it will be difficult for me to become involved with the proud Italian beauties, who might be real competition."

Marbouty's disguise was adequate for casual innkeepers along the route, who, indeed, would have made no objection had she been wearing a grass skirt, but when they reached the Monastery of the Grande Chartreuse and asked the good monks for shelter, the masquerade failed. A red faced friar looked critically at Marbouty's inadequately disguised breasts and shook his head firmly.

"This is a House of God," he declared. "That creature may not enter."

There was a pleasant mountain stream nearby, crystal clear, spring fed water that was warmed by the sun. Under a hospitable tree, in full view of the monastery, Balzac and his companion ate a picnic lunch before taking up the journey again. When she had eaten, Marbouty stretched herself like a cat and made a sign of obeisance to the sun.

"I should like to bathe," she announced.

"There is water," said Balzac. "In my bag you will find soap and a towel."

Managing to make the performance intolerably suggestive, Marbouty stripped off her shirt and trousers. She stood naked in a shaft of sunlight, playing with her small, well rounded breasts, sticking out a bright red tongue at the indignant monks. Then she plunged into the water. In the sunlight she made quite an attractive picture. Balzac discovered that he was aroused. When they stopped for the night at a country inn, he got into bed with her.

He found it amusing.

"After all, it is therapeutic," he said to himself.

He decided to relax and enjoy himself. Marbouty was light-minded but she had a pleasant figure and she made love with noisy enthusiasm, squealing with delight, nibbling at his ears, admiring his prowess as a lover.

When they reached Milan, Balzac took a suite of rooms for himself and his secretary. There were two bed chambers and a sitting room that might have been designed by a maker of wedding cakes. The ceiling was painted to resemble a sky populated with fluffy clouds on which cherubs were at play, the whole thing surrounded by an ornate gilt cornice, like an enormous picture frame. There was a quantity of crimson plush and white plaster, and enough gilt so that the sitting room suggested the royal box at the opera.

Balzac was enchanted with it. He was enchanted with Italy, enchanted with Milan.

Here, as in Vienna, Balzac was offered homage as one of the

greatest of living writers. Every distinguished family in Milan asked him to call. A carriage and horses from the royal stables were placed at his disposal.

Like Byron, Goethe and Stendahl before him, Balzac fell in love with Italy.

"These people are free!" he exclaimed with delight. "Here the Renaissance is still alive."

Milan meant music. Milan meant La Scala, magnificent and baroque, the largest theater in Europe except for the San Carlo in Naples. Night after night, Balzac sat in the gilded horseshoe, enchanted by the art of Italian opera, beguiled by the grace of Italian ballet.

"At La Scala, a woman's reputation is made or broken," Stendahl had told Balzac. "It is made when she is escorted into her box by her lover, broken when she is accompanied by her husband."

The Italian women fascinated Balzac.

"They are the most feminine women in the world," he wrote to Gautier. "But don't tell Sarah I have said this."

Balzac went to parties and dances, to receptions given in his honor. Marbouty continued to wear her trousers and to pass as his secretary, though the sharp Italian eyes quickly saw through her disguise.

A few months earlier, George Sand and her lover Alfred de Musset had passed through Italy. Everyone in Milan knew that Balzac's famous colleague wore her hair short as a man's, smoked cigars, wore trousers instead of a skirt, and changed her lovers as often as she changed her drawers. Within a few days after Balzac arrived, everyone accepted the idea that his traveling companion was George Sand. This was an error that Marbouty encouraged rather than attempted to correct. It brought her a good deal of attention from the young Italians, and this more or less made up for the fact that Balzac was becoming indifferent to the demands of her flesh, which were of the kind that required frequent satisfaction.

"Smoke a cigar," Balzac suggested. "Then no one will doubt that you are frère George."

Marbouty laid in a supply of tough black Italian cigars and took to smoking them in restaurants. Balzac, who hated the smell, forbade her to light one in the hotel.

429

Balzac quickly became used to the grunts, groans, and squeals of delight that issued from Marbouty's bedroom when she was giving some young Italian the pleasure and prestige of going to bed with the famous George Sand.

He was glad to have her off his hands. It gave him time to devour Milan. He rambled through the streets, walked on the broad Corso, visited churches, looked at paintings. He was an inveterate sightseer, even in Paris, which was almost his native city. He steeped himself in the air of Italy and it was good for his soul.

He gazed at Leonardo's Last Supper with considerable awe. Correggio delighted him. So did the smaller pieces by painters whose names were unknown.

He wanted to immerse himself in the Italian atmosphere. Since he could not read Italian, he thought that Latin would be the next best thing. He found a second-hand copy of Tacitus, and formed the habit of reading a few pages each night before he dropped off to sleep.

Count Emilio's business moved slowly. Balzac enjoyed himself. It was marvelous to have nothing to do, and to be able to obtain money when he needed it, simply by scribbling his initials at the bottom of the count's letter of credit.

The Guidoboni-Visconti possessions in contest were not all in Milan. Balzac found himself obliged to go to Turin, Venice, Rome and Genoa, in behalf of Count Emilio's interests. He returned to Paris, reported progress to the count, got rid of Caroline Marbouty, and some months later set out on a tour of Italy, all expenses paid.

Rome disappointed him.

He was enraptured by Venice.

He reached Genoa in high spirits, and found himself pulled up short. The city had been stricken by an epidemic of typhoid fever. Along with other tourists and travelers, Balzac was quarantined for two weeks in a vile-smelling hospital.

He was depressed until he discovered that the Italian in the next bed, a merchant named Giuseppe Pezzi, had once made a trip to the wild, savage island of Sardinia. Reading his Latin history, Balzac had come across references to the attempts of Imperial Rome to exploit the silver and lead deposits on the island. Always on the alert for a chance to make a fortune, Balzac had been struck with the idea that there must be quantities of silver

430

left in the ore that had been excavated centuries ago by the Roman miners.

Pezzi was an undersized, shrewd-eyed businessman who seemed indifferent to Balzac's questions about Sardinia until Balzac mentioned the silver mines. Then his beady little eyes flashed with excitement.

"Of course the signor is probably right," he said. "The slag heaps are there. I have seen them with my own eyes. But it never occurred to me that there must be a fortune in them just laying on the ground."

"Are there roads on the island?" Balzac demanded.

"Of a sort," Pezzi told him. "They are not what one would call boulevards, I promise you that."

"Still, the Romans must have managed somehow," Balzac said. "Even if the roads are rough, it should be possible to get the ore out on sledges."

Balzac was beside himself with excitement at the prospect of becoming a millionaire by taking out the Sardinian silver the Romans had dug from the ground and left behind them. He plied Pezzi with claret from the hospital canteen, had sumptuous meals sent in from a first-class restaurant, and pumped the little merchant about the mysterious island.

When his quarantine was up, he pledged Pezzi to secrecy, and promised to write to him as soon as he got back to France.

"God has blessed you with good fortune, my friend," he told Pezzi. "I am going to give you a share of the profits."

Pezzi borrowed a thousand francs on the strength of the millions that were to be made, swore undying loyalty to Balzac, and promised that not a word would pass his lips.

"If the thing gets out, all is lost," Balzac warned him.

"You have the word of an Italian," Pezzi assured him. "I am silent as a thousand tombs. Torture could not pry it from me."

Balzac hurried back to Milan and brought Count Emilio's business to a close. Sarah had not been altogether cavalier in persuading the count to send Balzac as emissary. Balzac negotiated shrewdly and the count's fortunes came off well. In the long run, the letter of credit that Balzac used so enthusiastically proved to have been a very profitable investment for the amateur pharmacist in Paris.

Balzac set out for France, traveling over the Simplon Pass.

There was snow on the mountains, rising to fifteen feet in the Saint-Gothard, obscuring the tall stone posts that marked the road. He crossed the summit at one o'clock in the morning, by sublime, timeless moonlight. The scene was like nothing on this earth. Balzac had a sense of eternity.

He waited on the summit until dawn, watching the sunrise on the snow-capped peaks.

When Balzac reached the rue des Batailles, he found several hundred letters waiting for him, stacked on his writing table, the bills carefully culled by Auguste and put into a pile of their own. In excellent spirits, Balzac sat down and began to go through his mail. Suddenly, he had a conviction of disaster, though he had not not as yet opened a single letter.

"Something is wrong," he told himself. "I can feel it."

He went through the letters quickly. Halfway through the pile, he came to an envelope of heavy vellum, marked with a black border. His heart stopped dead for a moment, then recovered and raced madly, giving him pain.

He turned the letter over, reading the sender's name and address: A. de Berny, la Bouleaunaire, Nemours.

For several minutes, he sat in his chair as if he had been the victim of a stroke. Then he opened the letter and read it.

Madame de Berny was dead.

"She asked for you constantly at the last," wrote her son to Balzac. "She died in her sleep, without pain."

Balzac looked at the date on Alexandre de Berny's letter. July 27th.

"Where was I on July 27th?" he asked himself. "What was I doing in those hours when she was asking for me, with her last breath?"

He stared at a corner of the rug.

Was I sleeping with some little bitch in Italy? Or gorging myself in some restaurant in Milan? Or sitting in a box at La Scala, listening to Rossini's music, watching the girls in their white tutus, moving on the stage like white birds?

He got up and went to the window, his heart like lead in his breast. His first love was dead and buried, cold in the ground and already rotting. He had not seen her for more than a year, though she had begged him to come.

432

It was a betrayal.

He knew that he would never in his life quite get over the guilt.

Why did I not go to her at La Bouleaunaire? he demanded of himself. I meant to go. I wanted to go. Once I was even already packed.

But something had always come up to keep him in Paris. It had been a year of disasters, this one, what with going to jail, the law suit with Buloz, the Widow Bechet's court order, and that damned attack of apoplexy that had put him on his back for three weeks.

In all logic, he was not to blame.

Yet he was to blame.

She had given herself to him when she was needed, given without stint. When he was needed, he had failed her. It was a moral crime. Balzac cursed himself, clenched his fists and struck at the muscles of his chest. Then he dropped heavily into his red armchair and covered his face with his hands. He wanted to weep, but the tears refused to come.

Night fell. Balzac remained in his red chair. He sat there, not moving, through the night, as if he sat in watch over the dead. When dawn showed at the tall windows, he got up and crossed the room, looking down at the Seine, then at the gilt dome of the Invalides, touched with pale sweet pink. In the promising, rationed light of the dawn, the beauty of Paris was heartbreaking. Balzac was unmoved. He turned back into his room, looking around him. He was overtaken by disgust, almost by nausea.

He loathed the room.

He had the urge to flee, as if he could run away from the black bordered parchment that lay on his writing table with its envelope beside it.

"I must go," he said aloud, striking the palm of his hand with a fist. "I must go."

His affairs in Paris were demanding. There was the magazine to see to. He must make a report to Count Emilio. There were publishers to be seen, proofs to be read.

He could not bear the idea of doing any of these things. He wanted to get away at once, to get out of Paris, to go somewhere and be treated with the respect shown a child who has lost his mother.

The Carrauds were at Frapesle, where they had gone when the major had at last retired from the army. It was a quiet old house

433

that had belonged to Zulma's father. They were quiet, good people.

Balzac struck both hands together, making a sharp sound in the deathlike silence of his room.

He sat down and wrote a note to Gautier, asking him to make things right with Sarah. Then he rang for Auguste.

"Pack a bag, Auguste, I am going away," he said.

"But, Monsieur de Balzac, you have just come home," the servant protested. "You should rest."

"I have no home, my dear Auguste," said Balzac heavily. "I am the Wandering Jew of Thought. Something always pursues me. I used to think I would escape it, but now I think it pursues me to the grave."

The little château of Frapesle was near Issoudun, in the verdant province of Berry. The gardens had always been magnificent and Zulma had made them superlative. Balzac's room at the back of the house had a window that looked down on one of the finest rose arbors in France. The room was sweet with the perfume of the swelling blooms.

For three days, Balzac slept, recouping the energy expended during his Italian expedition. It was a habit with him, when life became too much to cope with—simply to give way to sleep for days at a time, taking no food and scarcely any water.

The Carrauds left him to himself. Of all the people on earth who knew him, perhaps only Zulma Carraud and his sister Laure had any conception of the void in his life created by the death of Madame de Berny.

It was a part of himself which had died, and Zulma understood that. When he arrived, exhausted, pale as a ghost, his eyes vacant and sad, she had the good sense to say nothing to him at all, but simply to take his hand and lead him up the stairs to his bed. She kissed him on the forehead, touched his cheek, then turned and went out of the room, leaving him alone with his grief and his exhaustion.

The long sleep did its work.

When he woke up on the third day, Balzac understood that he had recovered sufficient strength to master the reality he faced. Madame de Berny was dead, and when she had died a part of him had died. The rest of him had remained alive and was obliged

434

to go on living. He shaved himself, changed his clothes, and went downstairs to join the Carrauds for dinner.

Zulma's oldest child, Ivan, was old enough to eat with the family now, so there were four of them at table. Ivan was a fine looking lad, destined for Saint-Cyr and the army. He was shy with Balzac at first, then fascinated by him and eager to know everything about Paris and the world beyond Frapesle.

Major Carraud had aged. His hair was white as paper and his shoulders were beginning to be stooped. His hands were gnarled and the veins showed like the tracks of moles. Yet he still looked like what he was—an officer and a gentleman, the only real passion of whose life had been to serve his country, the opportunity for which had, ironically, mostly been denied him.

The food was superb. There was a serving of some fresh water fish, hardly larger than minnows, breaded, then fried in deep fat, eaten whole. There was consommé, clear as topaz, fragrant with chopped fresh parsley. There was a clod of tender veal, larded with pork strips that had been put to soak in the best brandy. There was a refreshing pink wine from the Valley of the Rhone. There was, in Balzac's honor, a gateau Saint-Honoré—a ring of pastry filled with whipped cream tinted with cognac, the ring topped by a dozen puff paste balls coated with syrup.

Balzac had scarcely eaten since the day he had read Alexandre de Berny's letter. Now he made up for the meals he had lost. He tasted the food and enjoyed it; before this, it had turned to ashes in his mouth.

"I hope you haven't forgotten how to play billiards, Honoré," Major Carraud said, while they were eating the sweet dessert.

"I think I can manage to hold a cue," answered Balzac, his mouth full of whipped cream. "I also am certain that I can defeat Madame Carraud at the frustrating game called backgammon."

Over coffee, Balzac entertained the Carrauds with stories of Italy. Major Carraud brightened up. He had fought there with Napoleon, and he plied Balzac with questions.

It did Balzac good to talk. When they had finished coffee, he and the major played a game or two of billiards, with young Ivan keeping score. Balzac was outmatched. The major played the game like an artist. Finally Balzac shook his head.

"I am simply not in your class, monsieur," he said. "You are a master."

435

"It is a small accomplishment for a man who set out to be a Marshal of France," the major said. He looked at his son. "Perhaps this lad will get the baton. Who knows?"

Balzac and Zulma played backgammon. Young Ivan went upstairs to do his preparation. The major fell asleep in his favorite chair, his gouty leg propped up on a hassock. It was a familiar tableau—the drowsing major, Zulma and Balzac, the backgammon board between them, the modest fire burning on the hearth.

Zulma reached across the board and took Balzac's hand.

"Well, my friend, you have come to a turning point in your life, have you not?" she said.

Balzac nodded.

For several minutes he sat without moving, making no sound. Then he got up, knelt beside Zulma's chair, put his head on her lap and cried. She held him like a mother. It was the first time in years that he had wept the tears of honest grief.

The raw wound made by Madame de Berny's death and by his own sense of guilt, healed over at Frapesle. Sleep, kindness, good simple food, the rich, somnolent air of Berry, the sense of health drawn up from the generous fields of the nearby farms, all these did their work.

The scar and the void in the soul, these were things he would never get rid of, Balzac understood, but the emotional paralysis was gone. He was like a man who has lost a leg and must now get used to walking without it.

He remained in a curious state of suspension, out of touch with the current of his life.

He had not written a line for more than three months, and it worried him. It was the first time in nearly eighteen years that he had neglected his work for more than a few weeks at a time. Even at the height of his passion in Vienna, he had obliged himself to produce a daily offering of words. Even at Aix-les-Bains, where the Duchesse de Castries had driven him nearly out of his mind with frustration, he had kept up his literary stint.

In Italy, he had written nothing, except for a few letters to Eve, and they had been shallow letters, padded out with lies.

The lost time made him feel guilty and uneasy, yet he was not quite ready to begin a book. He was distracted. He could not get out of his mind the conversations with Signor Pezzi in the quarantine lazzaretto in Genoa. He was haunted by the conviction that a fortune in silver slumbered unnoticed in the forgotten Sardinian mountains.

Suddenly, damning himself for a fool, he remembered that Major Carraud had been educated at the Polytechnique and qualified as an engineer before he became a gunner. All his life, Carraud had been interested in science. He dabbled with astronomy and chemistry. He kept up with the scientific journals. Certainly his opinion would be worth having.

That night, after dinner, Balzac told the major about the old Sardinian mines. The major came to life as if Balzac had touched him with an electric current.

"My dear boy, I had no idea you were interested in these things," he said.

"Candidly, what interests me is the prospect of making some money," Balzac said honestly. "As a writer, I've worked for twenty years, and worked like a slave, if I say it myself. I am not without talent, or the popular touch. My books have sold by the thousands. My name is known all over Europe, in England, even, they tell me, in the forests of America. And what is my reward? A half a million francs of debt, give or take a hundred thousand. The bailiffs swarm around me like flies. An old woman could feed herself, selling my dunning letters for waste paper. If there is silver in Sardinia, I mean to get it out."

Carraud promised to look up the Roman methods of silver mining and to find out what he could from his books about the quality of the Sardinian ore. A few days later, he was as enthusiastic as Balzac.

"If the ore is the way the Romans left it, there must be a fortune in those hills," he told Balzac. "Of course, there is only one way to make sure."

"What is that?" asked Balzac.

"Get samples of the ore and have them assayed by a good metallurgist," the major said. "That way, one would be absolutely certain of how much silver and lead the Romans left behind them."

Balzac saw his fortune made. He and the Carrauds would both be rich. As soon as he returned to Paris, he wrote to Signor Pezzi and asked the little merchant to undertake to obtain samples from the Sardinian slag heaps. Again, he cautioned Pezzi to silence.

A month passed, two months, and there was no word from Pezzi. At the end of three months, Balzac concluded that Pezzi had failed to get his letter.

"The Italian mails are unreliable," he told Sarah. "There is no help for it. I must go to Sardinia in person."

"Honoré, you are absurd," his mistress said good-naturedly. "Sardinia is filled with mosquitoes and bandits. What is there to attract a writer?"

"I am not going as a writer, but as a prospector," Balzac said haughtily.

She laughed at him for a fool; he did not mind. She was one of the few people who could laugh at him without hurting his feelings.

Chapter 42

WITH HIS EXPE-
dition to Sardinia, the comic opera side of Balzac's temperament
reached its full expression.

His reason abandoned him, to be replaced by frenetic enthusiasm. He formed the Sardinian Exploitation Company, and raised
money from those of his friends and acquaintances who were solvent—Buisson, the tailor, Dr. Nacquart, Sarah Visconti, a few
others.

"These funds are simply to cover the cost of the preliminary
survey, you understand," he explained to the fortunate investors.
"Once the slag has been assayed, you can be sure that every bank
in Paris will be fighting for the privilege of underwriting our
company."

Balzac considered approaching the Baron de Rothschild and
getting the Baron to lay the ground plans for a huge stock company. He decided to put that off until he returned from the island
with the assurance of victory in his hands. He bought a geologist's
hammer and chisel and a little handbook on mining. Buisson made
him an explorer's costume, copied from an illustration Balzac
found in an adventure book—breeches that laced below the knee,
the insides lined with chamois, and a kind of bush jacket, a loose-
fitting arrangement supplied with a variety of pockets and pleats.
He found a broadbrimmed hat and a pair of gauntlets with stiff
cuffs.

Balzac was not absolutely certain of how one got to Sardinia,
or of the precise political status enjoyed by the long-neglected
island.

"One must go to Marseilles, that much is clear," he decided.

He went down the Rhone Valley by stagecoach. It was his first
visit to Roman France and he was obliged to see the monuments
of Provence. He went to Avignon and admired the Palace of the

439

Popes. He went to Chateauneuf-du-Pape and drank the aristocratic wine. He went to Arles to see the Coliseum. He admired the famous Grecian carriage of the sandaled Provençal women.

After several delays en route, he reached the wicked seaport of Marseilles, the old Phoenician settlement that had never quite surrendered to the softer ways of France. He put up at a hotel in the rue Sainte, on the edge of a slum, for it occurred to him now that he should try to keep his expenses down. He was roused in the night by a knife-fight in the alley underneath his window. He saw the loser dead on the cobbles, the victor streaking into the darkness like a sinister and accomplished cat. This vicarious touch of murder whetted his own zest for the adventure. He felt like an intrepid explorer, going alone to the badlands, armed with courage and unafraid.

The next morning, dressed in his explorer's jacket, he went down to the waterfront and made inquiries about booking passage to Sardinia.

"Nobody goes to Sardinia," a grizzled old fisherman told him. "Why in hell would anyone want to go there?"

Balzac wandered along the quays, where hundreds of stout-nosed fishing boats were tied up, gunwhale to gunwhale. The smells of the sea—salt water, tar and cordage, quickened his pulse.

After half a dozen tries, he found a merchantman's mate who told him that it was possible to get to Sardinia from the French owned island of Corsica.

"No use trying to go direct," the sailor told him. "You might hang around Marseilles for a month."

A few days later, Balzac got deck passage on a vessel bound for Ajaccio, on the Corsican coast. Before they cleared the Marseilles breakwater, Balzac was seasick. He was no sailor, certainly. This was his first voyage by sea and he was in misery, retching by the hour, praying for merciful death that would deliver him from the hideous pitching and rolling of the boat.

An hour after he landed, he was in the best of spirits. If he had been enchanted with Italy, he was enraptured by Corsica. The little port was picturesque and charming. The fishing boats had bright-colored sails. The fishermen themselves were brownly handsome, half-naked, looking enormously capable. The nutbrown blackhaired girls wore skirts that were bright as flags and carried themselves with stately Mediterranean pride.

440

After eating his first solid meal in several days, Balzac set out to explore Ajaccio on foot. As a lifelong admirer of Bonaparte, one of his first objectives was the house in which the Emperor had been born, not quite seventy years ago.

He was shocked.

The house had been abandoned for at least a generation. It was a ruin. The roof had collapsed and one of the walls had fallen in. A sad tree grew in the ragged garden. Chickens and runty filthy pigs browsed through the rooms in which Napoleon had played as a small boy.

Tears came to Balzac's eyes.

He closed his eyes, standing in the roofless corpse of a house. He could hear the shouts of the crowds in the Tuileries Gardens, as he had heard them when he was a boy.

"Vive la France! Vive l'Empereur!"

Seventy years ago, he murmured, opening his eyes and touching a segment of crumbling wall. The lifetime of a man, so the Bible has it, yet Bonaparte had been dead and buried nearly twenty of those years.

Balzac dabbed at his eyes with his handkerchief, remembering the day in the rue Cassini, when he had scribbled on a piece of paper: "What he began with the sword, I shall finish with the pen."

Bonaparte's bones were dust. His birthplace was a leaning ruin. Balzac had written sixty books and made something of a reputation, but he felt that he had scarcely approached the gates of the Empire of Letters he had set out to conquer or to create, he did not know quite which.

He sat down on a low wall, overgrown with vine, affected by a profound sense of loneliness. He had a hollow awareness that he was homeless, and a longing for some place where he could come to a full stop, and where there would be people to whom he belonged, not as de Balzac, the writer, but as a simple Frenchman, with a strain of goodness in his heart.

He felt sorry for himself and for the Emperor Napoleon, both of them exiles, homeless men, outcast because they had clutched at the stars.

The mood passed.

While he waited for a fishing boat to take him to Sardinia, Balzac hired a cart and driver and explored Corsica. The country reminded him of Switzerland, except that there were no lakes. It was a rich island, dramatically underpopulated, with three hundred thousand people living in an area that could with ease have supported five million. Balzac made notes, intending to communicate his ideas to the French government when he returned to Paris. After all, by that time he would have obtained the rights to silver deposits worth millions of francs. Those inky clerks who ran the country always listened to a man with money, whether he talked sense or not, and Balzac intended to be one rich man who would talk nothing but sense.

Balzac made the voyage to Sardinia in an open boat, rowed by a pair of stalwart Corsican fishermen who sang at their oars and frequently refreshed themselves with wine from a basket-covered bottle. Halfway across the channel between the islands, they rested oars, put out a kind of crude sea anchor, and had lunch—sandwiches made of garlicky sausage and coarse grey bread made from the whole kernel of the wheat, washed down with wine from a second basket-covered bottle. The wine was tart and had the aftertaste of cold bronze. The sausage warmed the stomach.

Fortunately for Balzac, the sea was calm as a millpond. He enjoyed the good simple food and the taste of the southern sun on his face. As they approached Sardinia, there was a light offshore breeze, carrying the perfume of the island, a redolence of earth and grass, mixed with the smell of the salt sea.

Balzac landed at Sassari and paid his boatmen the few coppers they asked him for. On the crude wooden quay, brownskinned naked children stared at him solemnly, then squealed and ran away.

Corsica had been primitive.

Sardinia was savage.

The town of Sassari consisted of a few crooked, unpaved streets, lined with huts made of crumbling plaster. Here and there was a wooden building, the boards unpainted and weathered to a silvery grey. The people in the streets were gaunt, barefoot, most of them weakened by the malarial fever that was the island's curse.

No one spoke French.

Using a kind of rudimentary Latin, salted with a few words of Italian, Balzac found that he was able to make himself understood, if what he wanted to say was simple. Understanding the natives was another matter.

442

He found the chief of police, a big fellow, wearing a ragged cotton uniform, equipped with a sword and a varnished hat with wings.

"You are a French subject?" the policeman asked skeptically.

"Evidently, signor," said Balzac pleasantly, offering his passport.

The policeman studied the document with some care, scratching himself behind the ear. Not for several seconds did Balzac realize that he was holding the paper upside down. He suppressed a smile and waited patiently until the policeman had finished pretending to read.

"And why do you come to Sardinia, signor?" the man asked.

"I am a simple tourist, your excellency," Balzac replied, having decided beforehand that it would be unwise to disclose the true nature of his business. "I have come to your beautiful island to see what there is to see."

"It is not my beautiful island," the policeman told him. "I am from Genoa. As for Sardinia, unless one is fond of the sea and sky, there is not much to look at. Nice hunting, up in the hills, if you enjoy hunting."

"I will try it," said Balzac, thinking that hunting would be as good an excuse as any for the expedition he planned to make into the hills.

"Is it possible to hire a wagon and driver?" he asked.

"A wagon, signor?" the policeman said, shaking his head. "There are a few wagons, here in Sassari, and in Cagliari, but elsewhere on the island a wagon would not be much use to you, I'm afraid. You see there are no roads on Sardinia."

"No roads?"

"There were roads once, a long time ago, when the Romans were here," the policeman told him. "But they've all been overgrown. Sometimes one sees traces of them, in the hill country."

"How does one travel?" inquired Balzac.

The policeman shrugged and touched his patent leather hat.

"Along the coast, one goes by boat," he said. "In the hill country, on foot or on horseback. I myself do not travel, except to Genoa once a year when I get my annual leave."

Balzac asked for a place to stay in Sassari, while he arranged for a horse and supplies. The policeman recommended a *pensione*. Balzac picked up his bag.

443

"By the way," said the policeman, as if he had just remembered something. "There are other Frenchmen here on the island. They came about a month ago."

"Other Frenchmen?" said Balzac. "What are they doing?"

"Same as you," said the policeman. "Just looking around at nothing."

He turned away to contemplate a brownskinned child making water in the dusty street. Both child and policeman seemed fascinated by the erratic course sought out by the little stream.

Balzac moved off through the dirty little town. The streets reeked of garbage, excrement and urine. Half-starved mongrel dogs barked shrilly and nipped at his heels. The stunted people, starved as their dogs, stood in their doorways and stared at Balzac as if he were a man from another planet. The poverty and attendant filth were omnipresent and unrelieved. The street was a gutter between rows of pathetic houses.

Balzac had a sense of dread. He passed a church, a miserable shack, doors opened. It was crowded with black-shawled women, on their knees, intoning prayers. A barefoot priest in a rusty cassock looked hostilely at Balzac.

"Bon giorno, padre," said Balzac, touching the brim of his absurd hat.

The priest grunted a reply. His expression did not change. His face was unrelenting, his eyes something out of the Inquisition. Balzac had a precise impression that he was in enemy territory. He was not so much frightened as aware of unease, and of being an intruder.

It was the same at the *pensione,* a mudwalled house with a broken lantern over the doorway. They gave him a bare, cool room with a stone floor and a bed made of coarse rope.

He asked for food.

"There ain't no food," he was told. "Only the soup we eat ourselves."

"That will do nicely if you can spare a bowl, said Balzac, smiling at the stone-faced woman.

The soup was made of mutton stock, heavily flavored with garlic. Floating in the greasy broth were limp, unidentifiable greens. It was not inviting but it was hot, and with it they gave him a wedge of tough black bread.

In Frapesle, Major Carraud had provided Balzac with an old

444

ordinance map of Sardinia. While he spooned up the soup, Balzac studied the map. He and the major had agreed that the Nurra range would be the best place to explore, for it was in these hills that the Romans had had their most important mines, as far as the major had been able to discover.

Sketchy roads leading nowhere were indicated on the map, but Balzac guessed that the policeman was probably more accurate than the map, which was far from new, and which in any case might very well have been worked up in the War Department in Paris from some old Roman maps.

A few days later, mounted on the back of a short-legged mountain pony that he immediately nicknamed Louis-Philippe, Balzac set out from Sassari to look for his Eldorado.

Sardinia has been called the Sleeping Princess of the Mediterranean. It is a wild, rough and beautiful island, with rocky coasts and a mysterious interior. At various times, the Sardinian coasts had been occupied by Carthaginians, Greeks, Romans, Arabs, Pisans, Genoese and Spaniards, and all of these had left traces of themselves in the coastal towns. None of them had succeeded in making permanent settlements in the interior. For thousands of years, the Sardinian soil had ripened in the hot silence of the mountain ranges behind the rocky coasts. There were no roads, as the policeman had promised, only a rough mountain track that the specially bred, mule-like ponies were able to negotiate at a slow, monotonous pace.

Balzac had never been much of a horseman. When he had ridden at Saint-Cyr, his mounts had been well-mannered army horses, chosen for gentleness by Carraud. Louis-Philippe had personality but not much breeding. Within an hour, Balzac's haunches were bruised and the insides of his legs and thighs were rubbed raw, in spite of his explorer's breeches.

In the morning, he was riding into the sun, and by noontime his face was badly sunburnt. His back ached. The journey into the interior was one to try the temper and stamina of a hardened soldier. For a man whose life had been passed at a writing table in Paris, the expedition was madness. Yet Balzac refused to turn back. All his life he had wanted a fortune, and there his fortune was waiting for him, in the beckoning, violet hills of the Nurra Range.

Along the flat malarial plain, there were stunted palm trees and Arab-looking houses. The island impressed Balzac as a place outside of time and history, forgotten, or ignored by both.

As he progressed inland, toward the southeast, he passed through tiny greystone hamlets, and began to encounter peasants dressed in traditional costumes. These people were healthier looking than the town folk he had met in Sassari, and they were clean. The women wore wide skirts of geranium scarlet, with tight-fitting boleros of emerald green and purple, over full-sleeved blouses made of bleached linen. Half a dozen of these girls together were like a cluster of bright poppies.

The men wore black and white—white linen pantaloons, cut full, short black jackets, black stocking caps. The physical types were curiously unfamiliar, looking neither French nor Italian, men with broad, flat faces and dark, unlighted eyes. Yet in some way, they were familiar. Balzac searched his memory, and finally recalled having seen faces like these in a book of engravings made of scenes in the arctic. They were Eskimo faces, clearly, here on this Mediterranean island.

The girls were brisk and defiant. There was no Italian tenderness about them, no flirtatious play-acting. The men were fierce, wild and proud, clearly men, capable, Balzac judged, of hot, dark, unquestioning love, and of swift, intransigeant punishments. The role of the sexes was here defined almost with the clarity of a savage puberty rite. Men were men, women were women. Idly, Balzac wondered what was the fate of the Sardinian unfortunate enough to be born a pederast.

Balzac passed the first night in a naked stone village that sheltered on the hillside behind a gathering of windy trees. He slept on the bare dungeon floor, covering the stones with a thick, leathery blanket he had bought in Sassari. His host was a silent peasant with the face of a red Indian chieftain.

In the morning, Balzac was given goat's milk and coarse black bread. He offered money. It was refused.

The second day, Balzac climbed through heath and scrub oak, breast high and thick. The trail was narrow and overgrown, difficult to follow, but the little horse moved on. There were hazel thickets, and occasionally a quite tall hazel tree. The night was cold, higher in the hills. The peasants wore black sheepskin tunics, with the hair on the outside, giving them a prehistoric, almost an animal look.

Balzac woke to a sharp morning.

Beneath him, as he stood on the hillside, was the valley through which he had ridden. From the height, he could see cleared land, cultivated like a tapestry. On the hillsides, short-legged black cattle grazed industriously. They were like the stunted, sturdy cows he had seen in Brittany.

He rode on, through wild, moor-like hills, studded with grey outcroppings of sun-sweetened rock. From the doorways of stone cottages, the Sardinian hill men stared at him. The young girls would gaze at him firmly, then turn suddenly and flash into the houses, bright and quick as birds.

The next day was Sunday.

Balzac rested in Nuoro town, which he planned to use as a headquarters since it was nearly in the center of the island and in the heart of the ancient mining country.

This was the true Sardinia, here in Nuoro, for centuries almost entirely untouched by any outside influence. The town was hilly, with narrow streets and stone stairways, paved with ancient, slick-worn stone. Clear water ran in the gutters. There was no dust, no sense of filth.

The morning light was bright, with an intense mountain clearness. Balzac wandered through the town, which centered on the spire of an ancient stone church. Ahead of him, a peasant procession moved toward the church, scarlet, white and black, moving slowly against the greyish ochre of the buildings. These were peasants from outlying farms in the hills, come into town to go to mass. As the long, bright-colored queue inched toward the church, the people chanted, the men uttering staccato prayers, the low rustle of the women's voices making the responses.

Balzac moved behind the procession. He could not understand the language in which the people were praying. It seemed altogether unrelated to French or to Italian.

In front of the church was a life-sized, seated image of Saint Anthony of Padua, a crude, powerful, polychrome figure, the lips of the saint oddly effeminate, mulberry red. As the procession passed the statue, people bowed and crossed themselves.

Balzac stood in the back of the church. There were no pews. The worshippers stood and knelt on the bare stone floor. Morning sunlight through the high windows turned the ochre walls to gold.

At the altar was a priest, clad in white vestments, richly embroidered with gold wire. It was a Roman Catholic mass, but beneath the ritual he had known since childhood, Balzac sensed the presence of a wild, ancient, pagan religion, older and harsher than Christianity. It was non-European, Christian only on the surface. There was an undertow that drew the souls of the people back to the Mysteries of Greece. It was atavistic and troublesome, suggestive of old gods and of blood sacrifice.

When Mass was over, Balzac moved out of the church and walked slowly through the empty Sunday streets to his *pensione*. Part of his task as a novelist was to make things and people less obscure and secret by finding relationships between them that he could put on paper. Sardinia baffled him. He could create a Frenchman to the life, a passable Englishman, an Italian, a German, even, if pressed, a Russian. He thought that he would hesitate to make a fictional Sardinian for whom he would be willing to vouch.

At his *pensione* they gave him a bed made of leather thongs, wide enough for a family of six, a regular battlefield of a bed. He slept soundly. In the morning, after coffee made of roasted acorns, he set out to look for his silver mines.

Two hours ride from Nuoro, he came to his first slag heap, a dull grey hillock that he recognized at once. He dismounted, rubbing his saddle-sore buttocks, and got out his geologist's hammer. He chipped off samples of the slag, feeling profoundly scientific, and examined them in the sunlight. There were bright colored crystals and veins of what looked like lead. He put the samples and hammer into his saddlebag, got back on his pony, and rode along through the ancient diggings, pausing from time to time to chip off a bit of dull grey slag.

The imperfectly worked ore had weathered until it looked like volcanic rock, but it was not light and spongy, the way lava is. It was heavy, and Balzac was certain that it was heavy with silver and lead.

The Nurra diggings covered miles of rough hill country, rocky summits sparsely grown with weatherbeaten bushes. Balzac traveled for three days, taking samples as he went along. His saddlebags were heavy. His mood was good, in spite of the blisters on his backside, which gave him no relief.

448

He grew quite fond of his rugged little horse, who carried without protest the heavy, sagging saddlebags. At night, he camped in the open, living on dried boar meat he had bought in Nuoro, brewing coffe in a tin mug over a little fire made from twigs.

"It is an odd thing, your majesty," he said to Louis-Philippe one night when he was camped on the open range, sitting in front of his fire. "I am tired. My backside hurts. I haven't had a proper meal or a decent glass of wine for weeks, and yet in a strange sort of way, I'm happy."

Louis-Philippe gave an equine grunt and nibbled at the short, tough grass. He had the shrewd, ironic face of an old non-commissioned officer. Balzac laughed at him and rolled under his leathery blanket.

On the fifth day out from Nuoro, at noontime, Balzac rode toward a large slag heap. As he drew near, he saw that men were moving about the base of the big grey mound. There were half a dozen horses and four pack mules, tethered behind a grove of hazel trees.

Balzac moved forward, kicking his horse in the flanks. In a few minutes he could hear the voices of the men. They were speaking French. Not pidgin-French, of a kind the Sardinians attempted, but the rapid, arrogant French of Marseilles.

Balzac dismounted and went forward on foot, leading his horse. Four men labored on the slag heap, breaking off chunks with sledge hammers, feeding them into a wooden breaker box that had been set up nearby. Balzac read the words painted on the box: LAMARTINE ET FILS, ASSAYERS, GEOLOGISTS, MINING ENGINEERS—MARSEILLE, FRANCE.

A fifth man, wearing a tweed jacket, watched the others work. He seemed to be in charge. Balzac touched his hat and told him good day, then expressed his curiosity.

"Oh, we're assaying these old slag heaps that the Romans left," the man explained. "You see, our firm in Marseilles bought the rights to exploit every old slag heap on this Godforsaken island."

For a few seconds, Balzac was numb. Then he asked, with a dry mouth, "How did you find out about them?"

The engineer grinned.

"A smart little macaroni named Pezzi came to us with the rights in his pocket. Said he got them from Turin. We thought he was

449

a crook at first, but by all the saints in heaven, he was right. The ore is rich."

"What does it assay?" Balzac asked, trying to control his voice.

"Ten percent lead, eight to ten silver, what we've done so far," the man from Marseilles told him. "There ought to be a hundred million francs in that dirty grey hill right there." He looked at Balzac curiously, then said, "You a geologist, by any chance?"

Balzac shook his head.

"No, I am a writer by trade, he said. "A novelist."

"At any rate, you are French," said the engineer, as if not quite certain what a novelist was. "We are about to have lunch and you are welcome to join us."

Balzac was famished, but he declined. He climbed into the saddle and followed a trail that led downhill, toward the seacoast. When he was out of sight of his compatriots, he fished in his saddlebag for a chunk of dried boar meat. He chewed on this, walking the pony.

"Ten percent lead, eight percent silver," he said to the uncommunicative horse. "At any rate, we were right about it, old Carraud and myself. There is a fortune in those ash heaps, for Pezzi and that crew from Marseilles."

It was like all of Balzac's schemes—the idea sound, even touched with genius, the execution wildly incompetent.

He shrugged it off, or tried to, and headed the horse for Sassari. The Sardinian comedy was over.

Chapter 43

SO YOU SEE, THE idea was sound," Balzac explained to Sarah. "Impeccable. It was simply the fact that Pezzi, the scoundrel, staked his claim before I did."

"I don't understand a single word, but I am sure that you are right," she told him sweetly. "After all, matters of intelligence, planning, business affairs—those are in your department, my dear. I am simply a woman."

"Are you making fun of me?" Balzac demanded.

"Of course not," she said demurely.

They were having dinner at the Grand Véfour. Balzac had been back in Paris for a week, after an absence of three months. He was brown as a North American trapper and his muscles were hard. He looked fit and very attractive.

His affairs were in gross disorder.

While he had been in Sardinia, Werdet had gone bankrupt, holding, among other things, certain notes that Balzac had endorsed. Werdet's creditors were pressing Balzac to make good on his signature. His own creditors, as usual, were encamped on both his doorsteps. To complete the area of harassment, the National Guard had summoned him again and the sergeant-major dentist was on his trail.

A sensible man would have packed up and fled to America or the colonies. Balzac refused to believe that God did not intend to save him, as he had done in the past. He sat in the rich, handsome restaurant, facing his rich, handsome mistress, and enjoyed himself.

By an oddity of the law concerning debt, summonses and writs could not be served during the hours of darkness which were defined by the Civil Code as those between sunrise and sunset, as given in standard almanacs.

After two weeks of dodging process servers, Balzac decided not

451

to appear on the streets of Paris except during these hours of immunity.

"What an idiotic law," Sarah said. "Surely you've got it wrong, my darling."

"Never," said Balzac. "I am a lawyer, you must remember." He frowned and attempted to look like an advocate. "There was a case, let me see, involving a certain Major Castrata, whose predicament was not unlike mine, except, of course, he had no talent. Well, this Castrata was arrested ten minutes before sunrise, according to the almanac. There had been a typographical error, you see, and a sharp-witted bailiff took advantage of it."

"And what happened, pray?" asked Sarah.

"Oh, the good Castrata sued the publishers of the almanac for damages and won his case. He collected a handsome sum."

Sarah laughed in the indulgent way the British laugh at certain oddities of the French.

Balzac bought an almanac and measured his comings and goings by the tables. During this period he was to be met at three or four or five in the morning, striding along the banks of the Seine, taking his constitutional. Sometimes bailiffs trailed him, watches in their hands. He always managed to disappear a few minutes before the expiration of his astronomical period of grace.

For a time all this amused him. Then it became frustrating. Both the rue Cassini and the rue des Batailles were torture chambers for Balzac because of the coporal's guard of pursuers always holding the houses in siege. It was impossible to work, impossible to rest, impossible to think.

"I survived Sardinia, but I don't think I can survive Paris," Balzac complained. "I have a scheme that will get me out of this mess I'm in, but I need time and some peace of mind in order to work out the details."

"Move into our house in the Champs Elysées," said Sarah promptly. "They won't look for you there, at least not right away. And you will be comfortable."

"But your husband?" Balzac asked. "Certainly his generosity doesn't extend that far."

"Emilio won't mind," she promised. "He may try to get you to listen to him while he saws away on his fiddle, but that's a risk you must take."

"Prepare for a guest!" said Balzac.

452

That night he moved into an enormous back room in the Guidoboni-Visconti mansion. There was a huge gilded bedstead with a billowy satin tent above it. The sheets were silk. The mattress was stuffed with the best down. Balzac tested it with his fingers and decided that it felt like an enormous breast.

Balzac relaxed and enjoyed the life of the rich. A cute little maid in a starched apron brought his breakfast in the morning. Count Emilio's valet took his clothes away in the night, while he slept, bringing them back brushed and ironed. Sarah ordered a barber for him. He bathed in a huge marble tub, the warm water made aromatic with a handful of perfumed salts from Cologne.

He was not cut off from the outside world. Publishers, editors and others obliged to see him were told to masquerade as tradesmen and call at the service entrance.

For several weeks it was the perfect hideaway. Balzac settled down to his work.

Then one morning a polite young lawyer's clerk called at the front door and asked for Monsieur de Balzac. The servants had been instructed to inform Sarah when this happened. She faced the caller with a fine show of British arrogance.

"This is the residence of the Count Emilio Guidoboni-Visconti," she said disdainfully. "What persuades you to ask here for Monsieur de Balzac?"

"We have tried everywhere else, Madame la Contessa," replied the man deferentially. He fingered a fat envelope. "It is a pity that he can't be found, for my firm is trying to make delivery of six thousand francs that belong to him."

"I will take them for him," said Sarah promptly.

The man shook his head.

"To my regret, Madame la Contessa, I am obliged to hand this personally to Monsieur de Balzac," he said. "It is a matter of law, you see."

Sarah knew how desperately Balzac needed six thousand francs. The man did not look like a bailiff to her inexperienced eye. She decided to take the risk.

"Come into the house," she said. "I will send for Monsieur de Balzac."

Balzac came down the grand staircase, dressed in his monkish white robe, paper shears swinging from his waist.

"Well, my good man, let me have the money," he said briskly, impatient because he had been disturbed at his work.

"Monsieur Honoré de Balzac, the novelist, publisher of the *Paris Chronicle?*" asked the man.

"I am de Balzac," was the answer. "There is only one."

The man opened his envelope, took out a paper, and put it into Balzac's hand.

"I represent William Duckett," he said, in a tone no longer deferential. "That is an arrest warrant for a debt of five thousand francs. You were once a lawyer, Monsieur de Balzac. I think you will not contest the fact that the paper has been legally served."

"An arrest warrant," said Balzac, glancing at the document in his hand. "So Duckett has stooped to this, has he?"

"What does it mean?" asked Sarah, who had no understanding of the laws concerning debt.

"It means that unless I hand this agent of Duckett's five thousand francs at once, he will take me to the Debtors' Prison at Clichy, with the aid of two policemen, undoubtedly in the street waiting his orders."

"Now?" said Sarah. "At this instant?"

"Now," said Balzac. "At this instant."

"That is the law," said Duckett's agent.

Sarah blazed with splendid anger.

"Monsieur de Balzac, go back to your work," she said. She turned to the agent imperiously, "As for you, my good man, you shall have the five thousand francs you have come for. Be good enough to go around to the service entrance at the rear of the house. The money will be handed to you by my butler."

The agent hesitated, his eyes on Balzac.

"Do you want your money?" Sarah demanded. "Then please to follow my instructions."

The agent bowed and said, "Very well, Madame la Contessa."

He went out the front door. Balzac went back upstairs to his room and took up writing where he had left off. Sarah went looking for her husband, found him in his private pharmacy, and asked him for five thousand francs.

When Balzac told Sarah Visconti that he had a master plan that would get him out of his predicament, he had not been altogether pipe-dreaming. He remembered having heard from Madame Récamier that when the great Chateaubriand had been overwhelmed by debt, he had sold his pen to a syndicate, making over future profits on his books in return for cash in the hand.

"It was a way of buying time," Madame Récamier had explained. "It gave him peace of mind."

Through his good friend, Delphine de Girardin, Balzac had put himself in touch with Victor Bohain, the literary entrepreneur who had organized the syndicate for Chateaubriand.

Bohain had agreed to do a similar service for Balzac. The stumbling block was in the fact that Werdet held the rights to a number of Balzac's most important works, and the prospective investors insisted that these books be free and clear, as part of the security to be held in the name of the syndicate.

Werdet was willing to give up the rights, but his affairs were in hopeless tangle. Night after night, Balzac sat in the room the Viscontis had given him, pouring over contracts and law books, seeking loopholes by means of which he could be repossessed of his novels.

At last, after months of maneuvering, he succeeded in giving Bohain most of what was needed. An agreement was drawn up between Balzac and the faceless investors. In return for making over his royalties on a series of books yet to be written, Balzac was to receive fifty thousand francs in cash. During the first year of the contract, he was to be paid a stipend of fifteen hundred francs a month, and this salary was to be doubled in the second year if the agreement was renewed.

Balzac regarded the arrangement almost as an Act of God. It was the kind of deliverance he had dreamed of, and he regarded Bohain both as a genius and an angel of mercy, in spite of the fact that to Bohain the matter was a straightforward affair of business, for the negotiation of which he collected a handsome fee.

Balzac was a free man again. It was no longer necessary to hide like a thief in the home of his mistress. He moved back into his rooms in the rue des Batailles, and once again began to frequent his favorite cafés and restaurants.

It was a relief to be able to go out for a walk without consulting the almanac, but Balzac realized that the respite was only a temporary one. He had bought off the leaders of the pack that bayed on his doorstep, but soon other creditors would appear, demanding money for miscellaneous debts that he had himself long since forgotten.

Besides, there was always the danger of being apprehended by the National Guard and again thrown into a cell in the Hôtel des Haricots. The doughty dentist in a cocked hat regarded the capture of Balzac as a matter of personal honor and he had sworn to bring him in.

"I understand that only residents of Paris are obliged to serve in this weekend army," Sarah told him. "Why don't you move to the country, or at least to the suburbs, and be free of the dentist once and for all?"

"The idea has occurred to me more than once," Balzac admitted. "The trouble is that up until now I simply haven't had the cash or the credit. With this syndicate behind me, of course, all that is changed. I have the backing of powerful people, big men in the financial world. It might just be managed, if I could find the right place."

"We will look for a place together," decided Sarah. "I adore inspecting houses."

The weather was benign, ideal for excursions into the country. In the Guidoboni-Visconti barouche, drawn by a handsome pair of chestnut geldings, served by a liveried coachman and footman, Balzac and his gallant English mistress explored the countryside around Paris.

The elegant horses and equipage and the elegant woman at Balzac's side impressed dozens of estate agents. Balzac and his Sarah wandered through scores of châteaux, hunting lodges, mansions and what not, offered for sale or rent.

At last, after weeks of looking, Balzac decided to settle down in the Valley of Sèvres, south of Paris. The landscape was delightfully unspoilt, fresh, green and innocent.

The Versailles-Paris railroad line was being surveyed, and Balzac learned that there was to be a station at Sèvres. This decided him.

"You see, with the railroad in operation, it will be a simple matter to get back and forth from Paris, should business demand one's presence in that inferno," he told Sarah.

Now that he was moving to the country, Paris was a hell-hole, vile with filth, noisy, odoriferous, a place that no decent man would live in unless he had to.

Balzac found the place he wanted at Ville d'Avray, near Sèvres. It was the little estate of Les Jardies, a plot of sloping land, with what the real estate agent called a "mansionette." From the high

456

land in front of the house, one had a view of the Seine and the soft, poetic hills of Sèvres.

"I have bought a humble cottage for a song," Balzac wrote enthusiastically to Eve de Hanska, when he had signed the contract for the purchase of Les Jardies. "From now on I reject Paris in favor of a simple life in the country."

The "song" was four thousand francs, a sum well within Balzac's means, had he indeed been content to lead a simple life in the country. Unfortunately, once in possession of Les Jardies, he saw its possibilities.

It is quite in order for a writer or artist to yearn on occasion for a vine-covered cottage or mountain retreat, far from the marketplace, where he can create in rustic peace untroubled by metropolitan cares and free of the fratricidal warfare that attends the marketing of artistic matter.

For most men, the country cottage is a harmless conceit, and often affords some happy years of life in the arms of nature.

Balzac, however, did not have the temperament for simple, rustic living.

Once he acquired Les Jardies he decided to become a country gentleman, the literary squire of Ville d'Avray. The mansionette that came with the property certainly would not do, except as an auxiliary to something more ambitious. The rooms were too small for Balzac, the whole aspect of the place too cramped.

"It reeks of petit bourgeois timidity," he announced to Sarah. "Everything must be changed. There must be a sense of space. Even on a small estate it is possible to be gracious, if one understands these things."

His first idea was to remodel and possibly to enlarge the mansionette. After deliberation, he concluded that this would be a waste of money.

"It will never be anything but what it is," he said. "A house without imagination. I must start from scratch and build what I want."

He provided himself with an architect's kit—T-Square, triangle, drawing board, tracing paper and sharp pencils—and sat down to design his house. When the plans were finished he turned them over to a building contractor in Ville d'Avray.

"I want these plans followed to the letter," were his instructions. "There are to be no changes."

457

"It is your house and your money," the contractor said dispassionately, having demanded and been paid half of his fee in advance.

While the carpenters, masons and plasterers were putting up his house, Balzac turned his attention to the grounds. The land was on a steep slope, consisting of a series of terraces supported by stone retaining walls. For most of the day these terraces enjoyed full sun, a fact that inspired Balzac to one of his most original conceptions.

"You know, we French are very backward when it comes to intensive cultivation of the land," he explained to Théophile Gautier. "In that field we are for surpassed by the humble Japanese farmer, who gets as much from one acre as we get from twenty acres of the richest land in Berry."

"My God, 'Noré, you are not going to try to become a farmer on a few square yards of dirt in Sèvres?" Gautier protested.

"In a highly specialized way," Balzac confided. "The other day at Les Halles I had occasion to purchase a pineapple. Have you any idea what the robbers charged me?"

"Not the vaguest," Gautier confessed. "It is not a vegetable I buy very often, in the ordinary course of events."

"It is a fruit," Balzac corrected. "The price was a Louis. A gold Louis! For a simple pineapple, that one bathes in kirsch and serves as a dessert! You see, they are not grown in France. That makes necessary the absurd price."

Balzac pointed with his stick at a hillside in the sun.

"On that slope that you see before you, I intend to grow pineapples under glass," he announced portentously. "With so much sun, very little artificial heat will be needed to approximate tropical conditions. I shall be able to produce pineapples at five francs a piece."

"Truly?" said Gautier.

"Naturally the demand will be enormous," Balzac went on. "That hillside alone should bring in a hundred thousand francs a year, once it begins to produce pineapples."

"You are mad," Gautier said with affection. "You don't belong at Sèvres but at Charenton."

"On the contrary," argued Balzac, taking no offense at being called mad. "I have taken all this up with competent authorities at the Botanical Gardens. These gentlemen—experts, mind you—

458

assure me that the scheme is practical. It simply has not been thought of before. Our French farmers are too unimaginative."

The two friends strolled across Balzac's land. From the house came the din of hammer and saw and the chatter of busy workmen.

There was a tiny green meadow at the edge of the property, watered by a pretty but reluctant stream. Balzac bent down and pulled a tuft of grass from the earth. He smelt it, then chewed on a blade, offering the clod to Gautier.

"The grass of the Sèvres Valley is famous," Balzac said. "I intend to invest in a small herd of Rambouillet cows, which, as you know, are the most famous milch cows in the world. I will supply milk and cream of the highest quality to the hordes of rich people who will flock into the district as soon as the Paris-Versailles railroad is in operation."

"Honoré, that little patch of grass won't feed a goat, let alone one full-grown cow," said Gautier.

"Land can be bought," said Balzac grandly. "In the Sèvres Valley, land is no problem at all. There are acres for sale at a song."

With difficulty, Gautier persuaded Balzac to put off buying a shop on the Sèvres road that was vacant, from which he intended to sell the pineapples of Les Jardies.

When the contractor was finished, Balzac inspected his house. The first floor satisfied him. It was exactly as he had laid it out on paper with his T-Square and triangle. There was a big drawing room, uncluttered by pillars and posts, just the way he wanted it. The dining room and kitchen were perfect. He complimented the builder and looked around him, in search of the stairway to the floor above, that should contain the bedrooms and his study.

"Where are the stairs?" he demanded.

"No stairs," the builder said, puffing on a rank pipe.

"What do you mean, no stairs?" Balzac said.

"No stairs called for," the builder told him.

He produced the plans that Balzac had given him with orders that they were to be followed to the last i-dot and comma. The man was right. Balzac had forgotten to put in a staircase.

"We been using a ladder to get up and down," the builder advised him. "If you want to, I guess we can build you a staircase on the outside of the house."

"A splendid idea," said Balzac. "It's what I had in mind. Begin it at once."

While the staircase was being built, Balzac laid out an arrangement of asphalt walks, placing benches in places from which a good view was to be had. In almost every direction, the outlook from Les Jardies was impressive. From the front of the house, looking south, one saw the well-bred Forest of Versailles. From the other side, on clear days, could be seen the Plain of Montrouge and, like a slender ribbon, the road to Tours.

The sloping land, together with the fact that the soil was slippery, made landscaping Les Jardies a very sporting proposition. Balzac attempted to control the intractable, shale-like soil by means of various walls. He had a dozen stone masons busy for weeks on these battlements, which kept falling down with a loud crash.

"There are the Walls of Thebes and Troy. There are the Walls of Rome and Carthage. There is the Great Wall of China. And there is the Wall of Les Jardies," Gautier said. "Of them all, perhaps in the end the wall at Les Jardies will prove to have been the most expensive."

When the outside staircase was finished, Balzac moved his furniture and his collection of several thousand books from the rue des Batailles to Sèvres. Some instinct toward self-preservation prompted him to have most of his belongings stored in the mansionette, which he intended eventually to have remodeled as a guest house, with the idea that Sarah and her husband could use it from time to time. Meanwhile, it held his books and the furniture and ornamentation he had collected over the years.

For the decoration of the new house he had ambitious plans. It gave him enormous pleasure to explain these to anyone who happened to be visiting him. He took Gautier through the house a few weeks after he had moved in. The walls and floors were bare. The windows were without curtains. The fresh plaster was still curing, so that the air was chill and dank.

Balzac was in high spirits.

It didn't matter that a paragrapher in the Paris *Review* had made fun of his scheme to grow pineapples, or that another rascal had described his new house as a birdcage. When the decorations were completed, Les Jardies would be a triumph, one of the finest small estates in France. He was sure of it.

460

With a bit of charcoal in his hand, he led Gautier through the house. In the first floor salon, he approached the fireplace breast.

"Here, of course, I intend to have a facing of Pharos marble. It is the only thing possible."

With the charcoal stump, he wrote the words: PHAROS MARBLE on the spotless, innocent plaster.

At one end of the big room were to be a series of columns carved from cedar. With his charcoal, Balzac wrote: STYBOLATE, LEBANON CEDAR.

They went on through the house, Balzac lecturing on the decor and marking up the walls. The principal ceiling was to be adorned with a painting by Eugene Delacroix. One wall was to be covered with a Gobelin tapestry. The upstairs fireplace, of green striated cipolin marble, was to be carved by a famous Italian sculptor whose name was unknown to Gautier. Between two rooms on the upper floor were to be doors in the Trianon style. Here there was to be a mosaic parquet, made of rare island woods.

"What do you think of my plans?" Balzac demanded enthusiastically, when the tour had been completed.

"You have forgotten something," said Gautier.

He took the charcoal from Balzac's hand and drew a large picture frame on the most dominant wall. Inside the frame he lettered the words: HERE A PAINTING BY RAPHAEL, PRICELESS, AND SUCH AS NO ONE HAS EVER SEEN.

Balzac laughed and took back the charcoal.

"Of course!" he exclaimed. "The pictures."

On the second wall, he drew another frame, HERE A LANDSCAPE BY WATTEAU.

They went through the house again, hanging mythical works of art by great French and Italian masters.

"The collection will be small, but very choice," Gautier decided. "And very expensive."

Balzac clapped him on the shoulder.

"Théo, I am hungry," he said. "Let us go and eat."

They went to an inn on the Sèvres road and ate a hearty meal, sitting for a long time over coffee, talking about literature.

Balzac did not permit Les Jardies to interfere with his work. He went on writing, first in the rue Cassini, while he kept it, then in a little room over the shop of his faithful tailor, Buisson. He wrote a masterpiece, CÉSAR BIROTTEAU, a score of first-class short pieces, and the opening volume of his massive study of immorality in France: SPLENDORS AND MISERIES OF THE COURTESANS.

He continued to edit the Paris *Chronicle* and to publish it from time to time, until at last the pressure of Buloz made it impossible to go on and the gallant but unhappy magazine expired.

On his fortieth birthday, he was more or less permanently installed at Les Jardies, though the house was still almost unfurnished, lack of funds having prevented him from carrying out his extravagant plans.

The mansionette had been remodelled and furnished with Balzac's things from the rue des Batailles and the rue Cassini which Balzac had finally given up.

During the summer and early autumn, Sarah Visconti and her husband passed some time in the mansionette. Sarah continued to be Balzac's mistress, though the fires burned more slowly, and Balzac suspected that she was experimenting elsewhere.

Their friendship was unchanged.

"You are a good friend, Sarah," Balzac told her.

"I am your friend always," she told him. "And your mistress when it pleases you."

Balzac was very fond of her. She was one of the few women in his life with whom he felt no constraint. He enjoyed being with her. He could let down his guard, wear his emotional slippers, as it were. Yet he would not have married her, even if Count Emilio did not exist. He was committed to his grand passion and to *adoremus in aeternum*.

Chapter 44

BALZAC'S GRAND
passion remained in the Polish Ukraine, with the Faraway Princess
to whom he had pledged his heart and soul. Eve de Hanska, in her
absence, became to Balzac the very idea of love; she was the bright
promise that made life worth living.

The Ukraine is a long way from France, but not so far that
gossip from Paris did not sometimes penetrate even the forests
of Wierzchownia, where the waiting princess smouldered in her
tower, captive of God, the Tsar and the astonishing disinclination
to die displayed by her chronically invalid husband.

Eve de Hanska's relatives deplored her relationship with Balzac,
who was regarded by them variously as a parvenu, a fortune
hunter, a libertine, a pornographer whose works were proscribed
by the Pope, an atheist, a notorious glutton, a reckless gambler,
and a writer of very little importance, since, as Eve's brother Adam
was fond of pointing out, he had not been elevated to the Academy,
whither were consigned all French writers of respectable fame.

Leading the Slavic pack was Eve's old Aunt, Rosalie Rzewuska,
who had disliked Balzac from the moment she met him, in Vienna,
where she lived and absorbed Austrian culture. Between Vienna
and Paris, there was a constant interchange of gossip, and Aunt
Rosalie collected it all, sorting out items that concerned Balzac
and passing them on to Poland.

French gossip, like certain French wines, does not travel well.
It is attuned to the air of Paris, where its meanings are properly
interpreted. Even a short journey destroys its subtlety and wit,
and the amount of distortion is in direct ratio to the distance
traveled.

Paris was always buzzing with stories about Balzac, most of
them stories that no one believed. By the time they had been passed
through Eve de Hanska's Austrian listening post, they often had
suffered dangerous change:

Balzac was married to an English woman.

He was dead.

He had become homosexual.

He had built a palace in the suburbs, larger than the one at Versailles.

He had joined the numberless army of George Sand's lovers.

He had lost a million francs at roulette.

He had become a drunkard, an addict of hashish.

He was in prison for high treason.

A stream of letters issued from Poland, bearing these accusations and others. For his sake, Eve de Hanska reminded Balzac, she had committed mortal sin, sentenced herself to the flames of hell. Was this the way he showed his gratitude?

The comparatively innocent Balzac composed conciliatory replies and poured out his heart in burning letters that protested his undying love.

There was, of course, a shred of truth or at least of inspiration, in each one of the rumors.

Balzac had not married an English woman, but his name had become firmly attached to that of the Contessa Guidoboni-Visconti.

He was not dead, but he had suffered another heart attack, lain alone and unconscious for most of the night on the floor at Les Jardies, and been confined to his bed for three months.

He was not homosexual, but for a few weeks he had employed as his secretary a willowy and suspect young aristocrat known to have been the companion of various properous pederasts.

He had, it was true, spent enough on his house at Les Jardies, if one included the retaining walls, to have built a modest palace somewhere in Touraine.

He had tried his luck at the gaming tables at the Palais-Royal, and lost five hundred francs, which sum he had borrowed from Leon Gozlan, one of his new publishers.

He had not become George Sand's lover, but he had been to visit frère George, at her retreat at Nohant.

That had been in the autumn, after he had passed a week at Frapesle with Zulma Carraud and her family.

Frère George had changed somewhat since the days when Jules Sandeau had been her lover and Balzac had fed them in the rue Cassini, then made them both half-drunk with his conversation and his special blend of powerful coffee.

464

For one thing, frère George was now quite famous. Not as famous as Balzac, but famous enough so that everyone except Balzac had read her books.

She was also notorious.

Even if rumor were subdivided, she had gone through a staggering number of lovers since discarding Jules Sandeau. That Balzac was not among their number was altogether a matter of his own choice.

He arrived at Nohant unannounced and surprised frère George in her dressing gown. She was smoking an after dinner cigar in a silent, baronial room, heavy with Persian carpets and hangings. Beneath her dressing gown she wore bright red silk trousers. Her feet were covered with Oriental slippers made of saffron colored kidskin, the toes pointed and bearing bells, like a jester's cap.

Loverless at the moment (she was resting between affairs) George was delighted to see Balzac, even though he had taken Sandeau's side at the time of her break with "Little Jules" as the sympathetic Balzac had called him.

"Well, my dear Balzac," she said, "I am told that you and I traveled through northern Italy together. Never have I gotten less pleasure or more notoriety out of a love affair."

Balzac laughed and kissed her cheek.

"So you have heard of l'Affaire Marbouty, have you?" he said. "That was one of Balzac's mistakes. A dreadful girl, Marbouty. I am told she is writing a book about me. Promise that you won't believe a word of it."

George gave Balzac a Persian pouf to sit on, then ordered coffee, made strong the way he liked it.

"Bring me my hookah, if you please, and a jar of the best latakia," she told the servant.

"You are Oriental with a vengeance," said Balzac. "The next step, one presumes, is a harem of young male Turks."

"I find that latakia, smoked through a waterpipe, stimulates my literary glands," she said earnestly.

Balzac watched with some interest while George prepared the hookah, an elaborate affair with a cutglass water bowl and four flexible tubes with mouthpieces. It was a communal hookah, of the kind used in Oriental coffee houses.

Balzac was a confirmed non-smoker. He had written articles denouncing tobacco and he would not employ a servant who refused to give up smoking. Nevertheless, the rich black stuff that frère

465

George was feeding into the bowl of the hookah had a fragrance that appealed to him, a voluptuous Oriental aroma that he found seductive.

Frère George put a glowing fragment of charcoal on top of the moist tobacco, then drew heartily through one of the tubes. The charcoal burned intensely, igniting the tobacco, releasing a little cloud of smoke that smelled delightful. When the tobacco was burning well, she offered a tube to Balzac. Fascinated, he took it.

"Draw the smoke into your lungs, like this," frère George told him.

Balzac drew.

The taste was cool and pleasant, not at all what he had expected. It was rather like inhaling a good full-bodied red wine.

"You say it helps you to write?" he asked.

She shook her head.

"It helps with ideas. It puts one into a certain mood."

The coffee and the rich tobacco had an effect that Balzac found delightful. He was relaxed, filled with a sense of well-being. George Sand seemed especially brilliant and bewitching. He knew that nothing would please her more than to have him join the roster of her distinguished lovers, and under the influence of the strong latakia he was tempted. Yet he resisted the impulse.

Looking at George, then drawing deep on the waterpipe, he asked himself why he was not inspired to sample what other men had tried and pronounced delicious. He was not the libertine described in Aunt Rosalie's letters to Poland, but, on the other hand, he had never been the man to turn away from an affair that looked promising.

It was not simply pride that held him back, the disinclination to become a private in the rear rank of her lovers, though that was a factor, certainly.

It was something else.

In spite of the poetic beauty that Eugène Delocroix admired and loved to put on canvas, to Balzac, George Sand was not quite a woman. The trousers and masculine hat she wore were not simply affectations, or the expression of rebellion against the restraint that society imposed on the female sex, though both of these were involved.

There was something else, the lack of some feminine ingredient.

It was not that there was anything lesbian about George, not even the crypto-lesbianism often encountered among women of

466

the aristocracy, the self-infatuated women of the Faubourg Saint-Germain.

No, it was another thing altogether.

George was an artist, great-hearted, devoted, generous, and temperamentally chaste. Her promiscuity was a fraud.

Men of parts, especially artists, want to love all mankind.

A woman, in the deep truth of her nature, wants to love one man.

Looking at George through the blue haze of fragrant smoke, Balzac asked himself whether it was possible for a woman to become an artist without first giving up the kernel of her womanhood. It was the kind of question he could answer, but the answer always took the form of a book.

He put down the tube of the waterpipe, feeling a trifle guilty. In that instant he had realized that he intended to write a book in which George Sand would be a character.

The novel was BEATRIX and it was one of Balzac's masterpieces. It was also a great best-seller, though not because of its literary quality. BEATRIX was read as the report of a famous scandal, a literal rendering of the love lives of George Sand, Franz Liszt, and the daring Countess d'Agoult, alias Daniel Stern. All of these were people very much in the fashionable eye, and Paris buzzed with gossip.

Balzac had dedicated BEATRIX to "Sarah." This brought a blistering letter from Eve, filled with accusations and denunciations.

Balzac decided to try a new tack. Instead of inventing excuses and explaining away Eve's accusations, he admitted everything.

"Yes, Sarah is the Contessa Guidoboni-Visconti, a good friend if I ever had one. Yes, Mademoiselle des Touches is George Sand. Yes, Beatrix is Madame d'Agoult. Yes, the story, apart from a few changes in detail, is true."

For several months, nothing but silence emerged from the snow-covered Polish wastes. Balzac was afraid that he had gone too far. Then, suddenly, Eve wrote a charming, gossipy letter, acting as though nothing had happened. The episode of BEATRIX and its dedication was put aside.

Balzac's life at Les Jardies provided lots of material for the gossip-mongers of the boulevard press in Paris, literary hucksters and pimps who made a living by retailing scandal at so much a line.

467

For the most part, Balzac ignored the attacks.

"A whore can't help her profession, it seeks her out," he said to his friends when they urged him to deny the gossip. "It is the same with these fellows. They are beneath contempt."

When the *Journal des Ecoles* published a cartoon with a few lines of text that implied he had been in Clichy Prison for debt, however, Balzac lost his temper. Through the Author's League he pressed for an apology and retraction and he got it.

That he had not occupied a cell at Clichy was a matter of perpetual astonishment to his friends, enemies and acquaintances. By the spring of 1840, he owed, as nearly as he could reckon the figure, something over two hundred and fifty thousand francs, which, in terms of present-day purchasing power, was roughly a million dollars.

Balzac's debts were famous. They were part of the Balzac legend, along with tales of his fabulous energy, his coffee-drinking, his real and apocryphal love affairs, his clothes, his gluttony, his canes and his genius.

When he was at his writing table, dressed in his Carmelite robe, Balzac believed in himself and his work and in nothing else. He told the truth as he had seen it, without regard to the prejudices or the sensibilities of his readers. He was not out to shock for the sake of sensation, but he despised Dumas and his followers because they catered to the public taste for sugar-coated history and perfumed life.

Nowadays, in writing a book, Balzac catered to no one, not even to himself. He was an artist, staunch and honest, committed to the truth, warts and all.

Selling a book after it had been written, printed and bound—that was another matter and had nothing to do with art.

Balzac believed in the power of publicity.

If people read BEATRIX because they thought he had been George Sand's lover and heard the story between George Sand's sheets, what did it matter, so long as BEATRIX was bought and read?

"An author without readers is nothing, a literary masturbator, no matter how great his gifts," he insisted to Gautier, who thought that Balzac sometimes went too far in order to attract attention to his books.

"The public is fickle, tasteless, stupid and stingy," Balzac de-

468

clared. "It is, nevertheless, the public. It is the second heart that pumps blood into the author's creative veins. It must be bullied, cajoled, coaxed, flattered, frightened, dragooned, conscripted, blackmailed, fooled, threatened, in order to make it read books and keep on reading them."

Balzac had a thousand schemes for advancing the cause of the working writer.

"We should be organized," he insisted.

At Les Jardies, in the dead of winter, he gave a dinner party for a group of young writers and editors who were more or less in his camp.

There was Gautier, of course, and the publisher, Leon Gozlan. There was Laurant Jan, and the painter Béranger, whose portrait of Balzac had hung in the Salon. There were Louis Desnoyers and half a dozen others.

When the meal had been eaten and the coffee served, Balzac ceased to be the host and became the chairman of a meeting.

"I've got you here for a purpose," he said. "I want to form a society."

"I am leaving," said Gautier, pretending to rise from his chair. "For authors to form into groups is like soldiers on the battle-field getting too close together. The enemy gets them en masse, with a single cannon ball, and is saved the trouble of picking them off one by one."

"Théo, sit down!" Balzac commanded. "This society is going to be different. Instead of being shot at, we will do the shooting."

Gautier sat down. The others leaned forward in their chairs.

"Writers should help one another," Balzac said. "During the Restoration, there was a group of men who called themselves the Company of the Knife and Fork. Each man swore on his mother's honor that if ever he became a member of the French Academy, he would use every influence to help his comrades to become members. After a certain number of years, inevitably, every member of the Company of the Knife and Fork became a member of the French Academy."

"When did this yearning to become one of the Immortals strike you, 'Noré?" asked Gautier innocently.

Balzac flushed. The French Academy had been established by Cardinal Richelieu and the members, the so-called "Forty Immortals" had been instructed to devote their energies to the perfection of the French language. In other epochs its membership had included the elite of French letters. Today it was moribund, a receptacle for official mediocrity.

"I don't care anything about the Academy," Balzac said, not altogether truthfully. "If they elect me, I won't refuse. If not, that's quite all right with de Balzac."

"Why the society then?" asked Gozlan.

"Times have changed since the days of the Company of the Knife and Fork," said Balzac. "We writers have a new enemy. Its name is journalism. It is a blind force, powerful, wicked, amoral, traditionless, dangerous."

"What do you propose, a St. Bartholomew's Eve for journalists?" Théo asked. "A general massacre?"

"No. I propose that we use this terrible machine of journalism for our own purposes," said Balzac.

"Ha, ha!" said Gautier.

"Don't laugh," said Balzac. "First we must organize. And then we must see to it that there is a member of our Society on the staff of every important paper in Paris."

"Where will you find journalists you can trust?" someone wanted to know.

"When we've shown our teeth, they will coöperate," Balzac promised.

"Journalists as a class are not ambitious," Gozlan objected. "They are quite satisfied with things as they are."

"You are mistaken," Balzac insisted. "They pretend to be indifferent, cynical and so on. It is a veneer. At heart they are ambitious as tomcats on the prowl. The fellow who writes the gossip column would like to be writing the serial. The one who does the serial wishes he could do the leading political article and so on. They can be maneuvered, these fellows, I promise you that."

When Balzac had an idea, there was no putting him down. He was convinced that a secret society of authors could break the power that the newspapers held over novelists and playwrights. After arguing for half the night, he more or less succeeded in convincing the others that he was right.

"Is our society to have dinners?" Gozan asked.

"Most certainly," said Balzac. "Once a week."

The conspirators had arranged to meet on a Sunday afternoon

at the main entrance to the Jardin des Plantes. Balzac thought it was appropriate that a little mystery be attached to the formation of his secret society. When the others had collected, he led them from the Jardin des Plantes along the Quay of the Wine Market. Between the rue des Fosses St. Bernard and the rue de Poissy, he stopped, raised a hand in the air, and announced, "Gentlemen, we are here!"

The others blinked. There was no sign of a restaurant or café, but only the dingy entrance to what might have been a grog shop in some mean suburb. A faded sign hung at an angle over the repellent doorway. Balzac pointed. In the greasy light of the alley, the others saw, painted on the sign, an enormous red cart horse, standing on its hind legs, and under the hoofs the words, Au Cheval Rouge.

"Look carefully at that sign," Balzac warned his companions. "From it, we take our name. From this moment, we are The Society of the Red Horse."

The Restaurant of the Red Horse occupied a shed between a disused well and a storehouse used for wine barrels. There were rough board tables and sawdust on the floor. The patrons were almost exclusively porters from the Wine Market, husky fellows in leather aprons, with great bare arms and powerful necks.

"It will appear to be just as it was in François Villon's day, even to the smell," said Gautier.

The air in the place was vile. There were the odors of stale wine, cheap food, and the unwashed bodies of the wine porters, all blended into the native dankness of the old shed.

"Balzac, why are we here?" Gozlan complained, holding his nose.

"Secrecy," explained Balzac. "Who would suspect that a group of writers would be meeting in a place like this one?"

They trooped into the dining room and were seated at a great round table. Wine barrels served as chairs. The patron was unenthusiastic. The regular customers were clearly hostile. Balzac ignored all this, as he ignored the smell and the tepid esprit of his companions.

The food was better than what one expected, coarse, but plentiful and well-cooked. The table wine was good and unbelievably cheap.

Only one journalist of importance had been seduced into coming to the first meeting. That was J. T. Merle, editor of *La Quotidienne*, the paper in which Balzac had run his agony column notices to Eve de Hanska. Merle was older than the others, a hawknosed but gentle cynic who believed that he lived in the tradition of Voltaire.

"I will help you as much as I can," Merle told Balzac. "But I beg of you, don't do anything for me. I can't afford it."

Balzac had drawn up a constitution for the society and this was read after dinner. The members pledged themselves not only to help one another, but to be on the lookout for new recruits.

"People who can be trusted," said Balzac. "Men like ourselves."

The Order of the Red Horse did not achieve many of its objectives, but it had one important effect on Balzac. He began to take an interest in the Authors' League—the Société des Gens de Lettres, which heretofore he had ignored.

He attended meetings, made speeches, entered protests, seconded motions, and eventually, somewhat to his surprise, was elected president, succeeding Villemain, his old professor at the Sorbonne.

For years Balzac had carried on a one-man crusade for authors' rights. However ineffectual he might have been in other affairs of business, when it came to making a contract with a publisher he was acknowledged to be one of the shrewdest and most dangerous men in France.

Now that he had a platform he began to agitate for reform.

The greatest injustice suffered by Balzac and his colleagues was the wholesale piracy of their books. There was no international copyright law, and only a loose one at home, so that as soon as a book appeared in France, editions were brought out in neighboring countries and even in the French provinces, for which the author was paid nothing. Sometimes these counterfeit editions did not even bear the author's name. Often they were brutally edited to suit the caprice of the pirates.

For French writers, the greatest offenders were the Belgian pirates in Brussels, whose counterfeits were published in the French language and often smuggled into France by the thousands, to turn up on the bookstalls at half price, beside the legitimate editions. It was bad enough to have one's work stolen in a foreign language; to be pirated in French was insufferable.

One evening, Balzac arrived at the monthly meeting of the Authors' League, carrying a large bundle of books. He took his place on the rostrum, the books on a table beside him. When the meeting had been opened, Balzac pointed to the little tower of books.

"A small library," he said. "Best Brussels craftsmanship."

He took a book from the top of the pile, glanced at the title page, and dropped the book to the floor with a thud, then stamped on it with his heel.

"CÉSAR BIROTTEAU, by de Balzac," he said.

He picked up the second book and made the same gesture.

"CÉSAR BIROTTEAU, author unknown," he said.

He went through the pile in this way. When he had finished, he leaned on the dais, his forearms crossed. The books were on the floor at his feet.

"If you lost count, gentlemen, there are twenty-five," he said. "Twenty-five counterfeit editions of CÉSAR BIROTTEAU, published in French, in Brussels alone. How many in Germany, in Holland, in England, in America? God only knows. What is certain is the fact that you and I are being robbed in wholesale fashion."

"What is to be done, Balzac?" Henri Soulié said wearily.

"We must fight," said Balzac. "Write laws. Get them passed. Press for international agreements. Simply because a man is an artist instead of a peddler of women's drawers doesn't mean that every Tom, Dick, and Harry in Brussels has the right to rob him."

Throughout his term as president of the Authors' League, Balzac hammered away at the need for a uniform copyright law. It was not passed while he was in office, but he made it the central question for every authors' organization all over the world.

At the end of a year, Balzac's term expired and he was replaced by Victor Hugo. As a parting gift to the Authors' League, Balzac wrote the draft of a copyright law that was a masterpiece to be placed beside the Declaration of the Rights of Man.

The following year, as a result of Balzac's agitation, a special commission of the French Chamber of Deputies was appointed to investigate the whole question of authors' rights, the first official notice any government had taken of the fact that authors possibly had rights, like those of other property holders.

"Eventually, we will get a copyright law, and authors as yet unborn will thank you," Victor Hugo told Balzac, shaking his hand.

It was ironic that Balzac, the Lone Wolf, a man who had always been at bitter war with literary cliques and claques, should have made the greatest single contribution of his day to the communal welfare of his fellow writers.

Not long after Balzac stepped down as president of the Authors' League, Victor Hugo paid him a visit at Les Jardies.

Hugo was the one writer in France whose fame and influence perhaps exceeded Balzac's. They were almost of an age, these two titans. In France, they were the opposite numbers of Dickens and Thackeray. They were the giants of the century, and neither man was unaware of the fact.

Hugo's bohemian days were behind him. He lived as befitted an aristocratic member of the French Academy, and dressed in a black frock coat.

During his country gentleman period, Balzac's dandyism was in abeyance. At Les Jardies he wore old clothes and often went without shaving, with mud on his boots, burrs on his breeches.

Gautier suggested that it might be a good idea to shave for Victor Hugo. Balzac brushed this aside as bourgeois nonsense.

"Hugo is a great man," he said. "What do appearances matter to greatness?"

He received Hugo looking like a peasant just in from the fields, a three-day beard on his face, his clothes ragged and spattered with mud. If Hugo was offended, he managed to conceal it. He greeted Balzac with affection and embraced him.

The two men stood on the asphalt terrace in front of Les Jardies. Both of them had changed since the day they had first met in Charles Nodier's rooms in the old Arsenal Library.

Hugo had been clean-shaven then, marvelously, unbelievably young. Now he wore a blunt, greying beard. He was heavier, and slightly stooped. Balzac could not suppress a twinge of envy when he noticed the scarlet rosette in his buttonhole, the badge of an officer of the Legion of Honor.

"Before we dine, Victor, I want you to see my place," he said offering Hugo his arm. "It is not much of an estate, but it's mine."

Arm in arm, Balzac and Hugo made a circuit of the grounds. Gautier and Gozlan followed, a few paces behind. Balzac pointed out the famous chestnut tree of Les Jardies.

"That is the tree that was supposed to make me rich," he said with a laugh.

474

"From chestnuts?" Hugo asked.

"Oh no, from manure," said Balzac.

He explained that by feudal custom, the populace of Ville d'Avray were obliged to empty the contents of their privies at the base of the tree.

"No inhabitant of the neighborhood has the right to refuse this service if I demand it," said Balzac proudly. "Imagine the quantity of this municipal manure which I will have, with the right to sell to farmers, vine-growers and market gardeners of the vicinity."

Hugo laughed good naturedly. He had no way of knowing that a few months earlier Balzac had taken quite seriously this project of selling human excrement as manure and had even made representations at the City Hall of Ville d'Avray.

When the estate had been inspected and admired, the party passed into the house for lunch. Balzac had neglected his appearance, but he had not neglected the luncheon menu. There were six superb courses and three good wines.

Hugo did justice to the meal. Over coffee, on the terrace, he and Balzac talked. Gautier and Gozlan sat by and listened.

"As for me, I have reached the conclusion that the only place that a writer can make any money is by writing plays," Hugo said. "Aside from manure, of course."

Balzac's ears came up sharply.

"Truly, Victor?" he said.

"It has been my own experience," Hugo told him. "There is no real money in novels."

Balzac frowned. He was a novelist by temperament, a novelist to the bone. His only play was the disastrous Cromwell of his youth. He sometimes enjoyed going to the theater, but for the playwrights of the day he had little respect, regarding them as mere entertainers. Still, if there is money in it. . . .

"How much can a man make from a play?" he asked.

Hugo shrugged. He was peeling an apple carefully, using a little pearl handled knife he had taken from his pocket.

"Enormous sums, actually," he said, squinting at the apple. "One gets royalties, you see. Sometimes as much as five hundred francs for a single performance. There are earnings from the provincial productions. Then there are revivals. Oh, it can be a profitable thing, writing plays."

As Victor Hugo talked, Balzac saw a diamond mine opening

at his feet. Everyone knew that Hugo lived in first-class style, keeping his wife like a queen, his mistress, Julie Drouet, like a princess. If all this came from playwriting, then the theater was a thing that he, Balzac, could not afford to overlook.

The conversation passed to other matters. Soon it was time for Hugo to go. He and Balzac walked down the path to the driveway together. It was coming on dusk. Hugo mentioned the Academy.

"There will be a vacancy soon," he said. "You should have the seat."

Balzac shook his head.

"They will never elect me," he said. "I have stepped on too many toes."

"Perhaps. Perhaps not," said Hugo. "In any case, I want you to know that you can count on my vote."

"Thank you," said Balzac.

Each great writer is an island to himself. It is always difficult for giants to be intimate friends. Hugo and Balzac, twin giants of their generation, were never intimate friends, but between them there was a fierce loyalty that derived from mutual respect.

The two men stood in the fading light in front of Balzac's absurd house and looked at each other calmly. They clasped hands, saying nothing. Balzac turned and walked back to Les Jardies.

Chapter 45

F<small>OR</small> SEVERAL
weeks after Hugo's visit, Balzac talked of nothing but the theater.
He could not get Hugo's glowing descriptions of dramatists' profits
out of his mind. Hugo was in the Academy, a member of the Legion
of Honor, prosperous, with both a wife and a mistress, and all
of this, Balzac persuaded himself, had come from the writing of
plays.

Balzac dragged Sarah from one theatrical café to another, watching actors and managers, listening to them, picking up theatrical
gossip. He went to plays, read plays, constructed a theory of
dramaturgy. Hugo had opened his eyes to a gold mine. Always
on the lookout for a scheme to get rich quick, Balzac was determined to become a successful dramatist without further delay.

"It's what I should have done years ago," he said to Sarah. "You
see, with a play, one gets royalties. Then there are provincial rights
and revivals. It is the only way for a literary man to make any
money."

Sarah frowned doubtfully.

"Surely it can't be as simple as all that, or every idiot in France
would be a successful playwright," she said.

"You forget that I am a trained novelist," said Balzac. "Dramatism is child's play beside the writing of a novel. In a play, the
actors do two thirds of the work. One invents a story and writes
a little dialogue. What could be simpler?"

Except as a means of making money, Balzac had no respect for
the theater. He was a novelist to the bone, a chemist of the human
emotions. In his books he dealt with gradual, subtle changes of
character. When he turned his back on potboiling, he had turned
his back on the fast scene and the glib solution, things that he
thought must be essentials for the stage.

He knew that Dumas and others hired "ghosts"—men who

477

worked up plots for them, did research, even wrote scenes in rough draft. To have sought such help in the writing of a novel Balzac would have considered contemptible, if not actually immoral. For Balzac, writing a novel was a form of witchcraft, a thing carried on in secret, alone, preferably in the dead of night.

He had no such feeling about the writing of plays. If there was a way to make dramatism easier and quicker, well then, he intended to use it.

Without bothering very much about his qualifications, Balzac hired a ghost, a young man name Charles Lassailly who had tried his hand at journalism and at verse. If Balzac had deliberately set out to find an incompetent, he could not have succeeded better. It was as if he knew in advance that no ghost was going to suit him.

Lassailly was a neurotic bohemian with a long nose and a mane of lank, greasy hair. His clothes seemed always to be damp. He radiated melancholy. In three years, he had not eaten a square meal. He had a slow, tortuous, Teutonic mind. As a collaborator for Balzac, he was the most improbable choice one could imagine.

However, he was available and Gozlan had told Balzac that he needed work. He was employed.

Balzac installed him in a bedroom at Les Jardies, fed him for three days, then gave him a batch of play outlines that were twenty years old, things he had roughed out in his garret in the rue Lesdiguières and put away.

"See what you can do with these, my boy," he cheerfully told the hapless Lassailly. "Lift what's worth lifting. A scene here, a scene there."

Living with Balzac, Lassailly, perforce, was obliged to adjust himself to Balzac's peculiar work routine.

"In bed by six in the evening, my boy. Up at midnight," Balzac explained. "That way we work when we are sure that no one will disturb us."

Lassailly labored over Balzac's moth-eaten outlines. He chewed on his nails and tried to invent plots of his own. He made a hundred false starts. He produced nothing.

Three or four times a night, Balzac would knock on his ghost's door, rousing Lassailly from a sound sleep, on the chance that the dramatic muse might have crept into Lassailly's bed while he slept.

"Anything yet?" he would bellow. "Any ideas? Any plots?"

Lassailly would rub his eyes and mutter some excuse.

478

"Keep trying, my lad," Balzac would tell him. "You will think of something in the end."

Lassailly stood it for three weeks. He was eating as he had not eaten since he left his mother's kitchen. He had a good bed to sleep in. His socks and shirts were clean for the first time in years. He was gaining weight. He should have been utterly content, except for the fact that Balzac was driving him mad.

One morning at three A.M., when Balzac was busy at his writing table, Lassailly decided that he could bear no more. He dressed himself in the dark and crept out of Les Jardies, walking all the way from Sèvres to Paris.

A few days later, Leon Gozlan met him, slouching along the rue Lafitte. Lassailly's shirt was filthy. He needed a shave. He was gaunt with hunger. He was shivering with cold. He was content.

"Well, Charles, so you have left Les Jardies," said Gozlan cheerfully. "Didn't Balzac treat you well?"

"Very well indeed," said Lassailly. "The house is charming. The scenery is delightful. We had meat twice a day, any amount of dessert, and the most marvelous coffee in France."

"Why did you leave?" Gozlan demanded.

Lassailly turned his eyes to heaven.

"Balzac is insane," he said. "I tell you, Gozlan, a million francs would not persuade me to set foot in Les Jardies again."

"Clearly, ghosts are no good," Balzac told Gautier. "It is evidently necessary to do the thing oneself."

"Evidently," Gautier agreed.

Balzac always worked best when he had a deadline to face. He liked to be committed to a project for which he had been paid some money in advance. He decided that the thing to do was to obligate himself to a manager. That way he would have no choice but to get a play written.

Gautier suggested that the best way to a manager might be through a well-known actor.

"I will find the best," Balzac announced.

The best-known actor in France was Frédérick Lemaître, and by a stroke of luck Lemaître happened to be a passionate admirer of Balzac's novels. He had written to Balzac, a long letter, praising PÈRE GORIOT and Balzac had found the letter among his things.

He wrote to Lemaître and asked him to lunch at the Café de Paris. Lemaître was delighted to accept.

The actor was a man of forty, slim, aristocratic looking, immaculate and highly intelligent.

"I shall consider it an absolute honor to appear in a play by de Balzac," he said without hesitation. "You may consider me committed."

"Which producer do you think is best?" Balzac asked.

"Harel," said Lemaître promptly. "He is the most imaginative producer in France, and the most intelligent."

Harel was manager of the Theater Porte-Saint-Martin, a well-known eccentric. In his own way, he had the reputation of being as independent as Balzac.

"Harel is afraid of nothing," Lemaître said. "Once when he was short of money, he tried to borrow thirty thousand francs from the King."

"Did he get it?" Balzac asked.

Lemaître shook his head.

"From that tightwad?" he said. "The King simply looked at Harel and said, 'Why monsieur, that's very odd. I was just going to ask you for the same sum.'"

The two men parted in front of the Café de Paris. Lemaître was off to a rehearsal, Balzac on his way to see Harel.

As he turned the corner, swinging his stick, Balzac bumped into the expatriate German, Heinrich Heine, a man for whom he had some affection.

"Well Heinrich, congratulate me," he said. "I am about to become rich."

Heine smiled benevolently.

"What is it this time, Honoré? Another Sardinian adventure?" he said in his atrocious French.

"I am writing a play for Frédérick Lemaître," Balzac announced proudly. "With Frédérick in the leading role and Harel as producer, no play can fail, least of all a play from the pen of Honoré de Balzac."

"Ah yes, the theater," Heine said wearily. "The writer's El Dorado. Still, 'Noré, I think you may be making a mistake."

"Mistake?" said Balzac, looking at Heine as if the German were mad. "This is a sure thing, Heinrich. A sure thing."

Heine shook his head.

"When a man gets used to one prison, it's not easy to change

480

to another," he said. "You are used to the novelist's prison. You may not like the smell of a strange jail."

"Ah, Heinrich, exile depresses you," Balzac said, clapping Heine on the shoulder. "At any rate, you must promise me that you will come to my play on opening night."

"I will be there," Heine promised.

Balzac walked across Paris to the Theater Porte-Saint-Martin, twirling his stick like a Scottish bandsman. He was walking on heady theatrical air. In the time it took him to cover the distance, he roughed out in his mind the plot of a five act drama to be called VAUTRIN, using one of the characters from PÈRE GORIOT as its central figure.

By the time he reached the theater, Balzac was dancing with enthusiasm, persuading himself that the play was already written, in his head.

"All that remains is to put it down on paper," he said to himself. "How simple! How remarkably simple!"

He sent in his name to the manager and Harel did not keep him waiting. An old man in a faded blue smock led him through a narrow, brick-walled alley, then through the working part of the theater, under a maze of ropes, to Harel's tiny office.

Balzac had never been backstage. He was susceptible as a yearning girl to the musty smell of old scenery, the odd sepulchral echo of the empty house, an odd, imperative awareness of the ghosts of old plays lurking in the dusty wings.

He found Harel very much to his liking, as he had found Lemaître. He decided at once that these working people of the theater were princes.

Harel was a solid, dark Frenchman with a southern accent and brilliant eyes. There was nothing of the charlatan or hack about him. He radiated competence and energy.

"You say that Frédérick Lemaître has agreed?" he asked, when Balzac had outlined the plot of his drama, VAUTRIN.

"With enthusiasm," Balzac assured the manager. "It was Frédérick who sent me to you."

"A combination of Lemaître and Balzac would seem certain of success," the manager said. "How soon will the final draft of the play be ready?"

"Give me three weeks," said Balzac. "There is a certain amount of polishing to be done."

"Take four," said Harel.

So Balzac's unwritten play was placed on the schedule of the Theater Porte-Saint-Martin. Balzac agreed to take the token advance of two thousand francs—a grain of sand as compared with the millions VAUTRIN was sure to make. He walked out of Harel's office a happy man.

Halfway across the empty stage, Balzac stopped and looked out at the ocean of empty seats in the darkened auditorium. He felt an ancient thrill, then struck an attitude, one hand on his bosom, the other raised in the air like the arm of a marble Caesar.

"Take up thy banners, France! My native lair!
And while avenging me, hear thou my prayer!"

He spoke the lines with some force and they were returned to him from the rows of empty seats. They were lines from his old Cromwell that had somehow stuck in his mind.

"Monsieur is leaving?" said a voice at his side.

It was the old stage door porter. Balzac flushed and muttered something, then followed the man through the narrow alley and found himself on the street.

In front of the theater, he met Henri Monnier, a gifted young actor of his acquaintance. Eager to share his good fortune, he caught Monnier's arm.

"Come and drink with me to the success of VAUTRIN," he commanded.

"VAUTRIN?" asked Monnier.

"My new play," said Balzac proudly.

Monnier groaned and said, "Oh no, Balzac! Not you too!"

They sat down at a marble topped table in a tiny actors' café just outside the Palais-Royal.

"With Frédérick Lemaître in the cast, we are sure to have a run of at least one hundred and fifty nights," Balzac confided to Monnier. "That makes a total of seven hundred and fifty thousand francs, do you see? On a royalty of twelve per cent, I will net at least sixty thousand francs. Then there are the author's free tickets. They should bring in another five thousand francs. Then there will be the sale of the printed book—say, ten thousand copies at two francs a copy, another twenty thousand right there."

Monnier raised his glass in a mock toast. He looked at Balzac importantly, a smile on his handsome, cynical face.

482

"Suppose you let me have the loan of five francs, on the strength of these great expectations," he said.

Balzac laughed.

Neither Monnier nor Heinrich Heine could dampen his astringent good spirits. He was a playwright by announcement. He took for granted that he was a success.

Balzac understood that if publicity was important to the success of a novel, it was the heart's blood of a play. Immediately, he began the task of making Paris aware of VAUTRIN, a play in five acts by H. de Balzac, featuring the popular Frédérick Lemaître. Before the curtain went up on opening night, Balzac intended that every bootblack and pastry girl on the banks of the Seine should be familiar with VAUTRIN.

It was not a thing that could be done from Les Jardies. To publicize a play, one had to be in the midst of Paris. Balzac moved into a second floor room in Buisson's house, which was only a few minutes walk from the Theater Porte-Saint-Martin, and close enough to the theatrical cafés.

"You see, I intend to be present at every rehearsal," he explained to the faithful tailor. "It gives the actors confidence when the author shows an interest in their work."

Balzac gave Harel a cast of characters, with descriptions and a synopsis of the plot. The producer ordered scenery and engaged actors to support Lemaître.

Meanwhile, Balzac launched a full dress press campaign. He wrote notices and mailed them to the newspapers and magazines. He buttonholed critics and gossip writers. He organized his friends into a claque to talk up VAUTRIN.

A week passed. Two weeks. A month.

Harel's actors were waiting, and some of them were impatient, threatening to take other assignments. The producer demanded copy.

"My God, I have forgotten to write the play!" Balzac confessed to Buisson.

He sent a note to the theater, promising Harel that he would have a script within twenty-four hours. When the note was on its way, he commandeered Buisson's apprentice and sent the boy to round up Gautier, and four other members of the defunct Society of the Red Horse.

Buisson let Balzac have glasses and a bottle of first class Burgundy, the gift of a delighted client. When his friends arrived, Balzac gave them chairs and wine. He stood before them, dressed in his monk's robe.

"Well, my friends," he said disarmingly. "Tomorrow, at ten in the morning, I must read a five act play to Harel, at the Theater Porte-Saint-Martin."

Gautier settled into his chair, glass in his hand.

"So you want our opinion before you brave Harel, is that it?" Théo asked.

"The play isn't written yet," Balzac said innocently.

"Then what are we here for?" Gautier asked. "Your play won't be ready to read for at least six weeks."

"You are mistaken," said Balzac smoothly. "The play will be ready for Harel in the morning."

"Impossible!" said Laurent Jan, one of the Red Horses Balzac had sent for.

"Not at all," said Balzac. "You, Théo, will write Act One. Laurent Jan will do Act Two. Ourliac, Act Three. De Belloy, Act Four. I will do Act Five myself, and pull the whole thing together. Tomorrow at ten, I will read it to Harel, as I have promised."

"Balzac, you are mad," grumbled Laurent Jan.

"We are all professional writers," Balzac said. "There are only four or five hundred lines in each act of a play. That is nothing to a professional—five hundred lines of dialogue. A few hours' work."

Gautier suggested that it might be helpful if the collaborators were to be given some idea of the plot.

"My God, if I have to stand here and tell you the plot we will never be finished on time," Balzac said impatiently. "You all have a good idea of the story. Just write what comes into your heads. I will put it all together."

In the end, of course, Balzac wrote VAUTRIN himself, in a little less than three days time. It was a patchwork, and a bad one, and Harel had advertised a masterpiece by the author of PÈRE GORIOT.

"We will pull it together in the theater," Balzac explained to Harel. "It is the best method. Victor Hugo assures me that his plays are practically rewritten on stage."

484

Harel refused to be depressed. He had two great names to put on his notices and God only knew what could happen to a play, once it was on the stage. Together, he and Balzac tried to whip VAUTRIN into shape for opening night, which had been set for the middle of March.

Balzac knew that the journalists, led by Buloz and the Paris *Review,* would do their best to assassinate his play, and he had an idea that the partisans of Alexandre Dumas would do the same. He tried to control the sale of first night tickets, and to pack the theater with his friends.

He had done his publicity too well.

The advance demand for tickets was enormous. Everyone, it seemed, wanted to see VAUTRIN. Large blocks of seats passed into the hands of speculators, who sold them for ten, twenty and thirty times their face value.

Since Victor Hugo's HERNANI, no Paris theatrical opening had attracted so much attention. Reporters were on their way from London, Rome and Berlin, and from cities in provincial France. For days before the opening night, people talked of nothing but VAUTRIN.

Balzac was uneasy.

He knew the play was bad, but Harel and Lamaître and others assured him that bad plays succeeded more often than good ones.

"Besides which, 'Noré, until a play is performed in front of an audience, nobody knows whether it's good or bad," Lemaître insisted. "There is an odd chemistry in the theatre, and the audience is an important ingredient. So are the actors." He put a hand on Balzac's arm and winked. "I am not an amateur, 'Noré," he said. "I may have a trick or two up my sleeve that will pop out on opening night."

Balzac was not convinced. Ordinarily the soul of self-confidence about his own work, he had a premonition of disaster about VAUTRIN. When he sent a ticket to Alphonse Lamartine, his old friend and fellow writer, he sent along a note that said, "You will see a failure, I'm afraid. As a playwright, I am a good midwife. *Morituri te salutant Caesar!*"

Chapter 46

As THE OPENING night of VAUTRIN approached, Balzac's enemies sharpened their knives. Buloz had a long memory, and his camp followers had their instructions to work against Balzac's play.

It was whispered in the cafés, and with some truth, that the Royal Censors did not altogether approve of the production. Lines had been deleted and so on. There were rumors that Lemaître was leaving the cast, that Harel was going to sue Balzac. It was hinted by Buloz's agents that the play would never open.

Meanwhile, the traffic in tickets went on. By opening night, two thirds of the seats were in the hands of people hostile to Balzac. Buloz distributed batches of seats in the gallery to thugs from the Paris slums, many of whom had never before been inside the doors of a theater.

"Stop worrying," said Lemaître. "They may come in on the side of Buloz. They will leave the theater cheering for Balzac, Lemaître and VAUTRIN. Vautrin is a crook, isn't he? Well then, he should appeal to the canaille that Buloz has rounded up."

Sarah Visconti was in England on opening night. Balzac came to the theater alone, wearing a high silk hat and a flowing cape that Buisson had designed for the occasion. He went to Lemaître's dressing room to shake hands with Frédérick, then stood in the rear of the house, behind the last row in the pit.

The Porte-Saint-Martin theater had recently been outfitted with gas lighting. The auditorium was dazzling. The intensely white light pointed up the gilt of the boxes and the jewels of the women who sat in them.

Balzac saw Buloz in the front row of an important box, a diamond flashing on his shirt front, a supercilious smile on his face, looking at the audience through a jeweled lorgnette.

Dumas was in another box, wearing a bottle green coat, his latest mistress beside him.

486

Moodily, Victor Hugo sat alone, arms folded across his chest.

In the cheap seats, Buloz's thugs chewed on garlic sausage and swigged wine from bottles they had brought with them.

There was a flurry of excitement and a general rising as the Duke of Orléans, eldest son of Louis-Philippe, entered the theater with his duchess, and took his place in the Royal box. The duke was a connoisseur of art and letters, but very much under the thumb of his father.

Balzac was as nervous as a child bride on her wedding night. His palms were sweating through his white gloves. His mouth was dry. He had a curious, prophetic pain in the heart. He wished he had never written the play.

There was a flourish of music.

The curtain rose.

The opening scenes were played out. Frédérick Lemaître made his entrance and gathered a round of courteous applause with only a few catcalls. Balzac began to relax. His lines did not seem quite as bad as they had sounded at the dress rehearsal. Perhaps Lemaître could bring it off.

The audience received the first three acts with indifference. Balzac scanned the theater, not knowing quite what to expect. The ill-feeling was there. He sensed it, a kind of sullenness, but it seemed hesitant, as if it were gathering force, waiting for the proper moment to explode.

The moment came in the fourth act.

Lemaître made his entrance, dressed in the costume of a Mexican general. Balzac gasped. So did the audience. In some way, and with an artful change of carriage, Lemaître had altered the costume so that he was a grotesque and unmistakable caricature of His Majesty Louis-Philippe, the sovereign ruler of the French.

For a few seconds, the audience found itself caught off balance. There was an interval of shocked silence. Lemaître took this for approval. He smiled at the audience and made a bow, flourishing his headdress, which was decorated with the plume of a bird of paradise. The gesture was unmistakably that of Louis-Philippe, a gesture that was familiar to everyone who sat in the theater.

In one of the first tier boxes, a woman tittered loudly. Someone else laughed. Angrily, the King's son got to his feet, glared at Lemaître, and left the theater, followed by his duchess and entourage.

487

Then the audience exploded. Buloz was on his feet, shouting, "For shame! For shame!"

Dumas was roaring with laughter.

Someone in a box cried, "Treason to the Crown! *Lèse Majesté!*"

The ruffians in the cheap seats began to throw rotten fruit and vegetables at the stage, shouting, "Down with Balzac! Down with Vautrin!"

When they began to throw wine bottles, Harel rang down the curtain to prevent the actors from being injured.

Balzac trembled with rage and fear. Then Gautier was at his side, grasping his arm.

"Come, Honoré, get out of sight before these ruffians see you," Théo said nervously. "In a moment this so-called audience is going to become a mob."

The two friends hurried out of the theater, leaving the bedlam behind them. They went into a café directly across the street. Balzac gulped a glass of brandy and ordered another, watching the entrance to the theater. A crowd was gathering in the street, attracted by the shouting inside. A mounted policeman wearing white crossbelts, trotted up and drew his sword.

"In the Name of God, what possessed Frédérick?" Gautier asked.

"Frédérick is an actor," Balzac said. "The audience was bored with the play, and Frédérick decided to liven them up."

"He certainly succeeded," Gautier said, swabbing his forehead with a handkerchief.

At this moment, the ruffians who had been hired by Buloz burst into the street. They were a mob, out of control. At once, as if by instinct, they began to tear paving blocks from the street and to hurl them at the theater. They shouted what Buloz had told them to shout.

"Down with Balzac!"

"Hang the traitor!"

"Where is his English whore?"

"Balzac, Balzac, pay your debts!"

There was a clatter of hoofbeats on the cobbles. A squadron of mounted municipal police charged into the crowd, using the flat sides of their sabres. They were tough, professional troops, with brass helmets and breastplates, hated by the people.

Immediately, the wrath of the crowd abandoned VAUTRIN and

488

turned in its fury on the detested mounted police. A big workman, wearing a red stocking cap, climbed on top of a wagon, a paving stone in his hand.

"Down with the King!" he shouted gleefully, heaving the stone at a policeman.

Balzac laughed.

"Poor Vautrin is forgotten," he said. "They are after Louis-Philippe."

He took Gautier's arm. "Come, Théo, let us see if there is a back way out of this place."

Frédérick Lemaître's buffoonery very nearly turned VAUTRIN into a commercial success. The press was merciless, but on the strength of the riot, the public queued to buy tickets, eager to see what kind of play it was that had brought the police into the streets.

Unfortunately, the King was informed by his son of Lemaître's impudence. A few minutes before curtain time on the second night, a captain of the Municipal Police served Harel with a notice from the Ministry of the Interior. By royal decree, further performances of the play VAUTRIN, by one de Balzac, were prohibited in the interests of public safety.

Balzac appealed the following day. His appeal was refused. In the name of the French Academy, Victor Hugo attempted to persuade the Minister to lift the ban, pointing out that there was nothing disloyal in the text of the play, that Lemaître's fourth act costume would be changed, that Balzac would be happy to submit the script to the Ministry for revision.

"You don't seem to understand, Monsieur Hugo," the Minister said gently. "The objection to VAUTRIN did not originate with me, but higher. Much higher. There is nothing to be done, I'm afraid."

Harel refunded the money that had been paid for tickets. The cast was dismissed. The sets were struck. The Theater Porte-Saint-Martin was dark. VAUTRIN was finished, after one performance and a riot.

Commentary in the press continued, even though the play was closed. The play was called immoral, incompetent, a joke, an insult to the French public.

"Is Monsieur de Balzac really the author of this piece of barbarism and ineptitude?" asked the most influential critic in Paris.

489

Ordinarily, Balzac regarded himself as immune to commercial criticism. This time he was crushed. In most of the reviews there was an undercurrent of real hatred, deep-going and vicious, far more relentless than what one expected in the ordinary give and take of literary feuding.

"Why do they hate me?" he asked Hugo, who called and tried to console him.

"They can't help themselves," said Hugo. "They cannot stand an original mind."

Chapter 47

T<small>WO WEEKS AFTER</small>
V<small>AUTRIN</small> was closed, the Minister of Fine Arts sent for Balzac. He
was a genial, over-fed official of the kind who prides himself on
getting along with everyone. In his buttonhole was the inevitable
red rosette. There was a thick rug in his office. On the walls were
innocuous landscapes, framed in gilt, bought by the Crown from
various well-behaved artists.

"His Majesty has no desire to be harsh, Monsieur de Balzac,"
the minister said. "Unfortunately, from the point of view of public
safety, it was necessary to close your play. We are aware of what
this means to you, in terms of lost revenue, and the government is
prepared to compensate you with a free grant of five thousand
francs."

Balzac very much needed five thousand francs. On the strength
of V<small>AUTRIN</small>, he had borrowed ten thousand from Sarah and five
from a moneylender, at exorbitant interest. He was actually short
of ready cash, and would be obliged to borrow small sums in order
to pay his grocer's bill.

Yet he did not hesitate. He felt that in honor he must refuse
the crust offered him by Louis-Philippe.

"I am a writer, not a beggar," he said proudly. "I am not in
the habit of accepting alms, even from the King of France."

The Minister was unimpressed by Balzac's gesture. He con-
templated the polish on his fingernails, shrugged his nicely tailored
shoulders, and said, "As you wish, monsieur. It is not our policy
to force money on those who do not want it."

Balzac went back to Les Jardies to lick his wounds. He was
exhausted. For three months he had been occupied with V<small>AUTRIN</small>
and the strain had been too much for his heart. When he attempted
to take up his work again, he collapsed. Gautier sent for Nacquart,
who ordered a month in bed, to be followed by three months on
an invalid's régime.

"I cannot live as an invalid," Balzac complained. "I don't have the temperament for it."

"Then perhaps you will not live at all," Nacquart warned him.

Within two weeks, Balzac was back at his baize-covered table, working on a five act drama that he called MERCADET. His answer to misfortune was always work. This time he was determined to write a play that would eventually be included in the permanent repertoire of the official theater of France, the Comédie Française.

The catastrophe with VAUTRIN had been murderous financially. Balzac could not meet his notes, and the familiar squadrons of bill collectors invaded the peaceful Valley of Sèvres, brandishing writs and court orders.

Balzac was worried for fear one of his creditors would distrain the furniture and books hidden in the remodeled mansionette. He ordered a sign-painter to make a notice and nailed it to the front door of the little house:

CONTENTS OF THIS BUILDING ARE

THE PROPERTY OF

HIS EXCELLENCY

COUNT EMILIO GUIDOBONI-VISCONTI

DO NOT DISTURB

Balzac thus outwitted the bailiffs and prevented them from carting off his most precious belongings. The unfortunate Count Emilio, however, was charged with "having brought part of the chattels of Monsieur de Balzac to a place of concealment, and having been concerned with the removal of the aforesaid chattels from the property known as Les Jardies. Furthermore, he has been a party to the act of depriving the creditors of Monsieur de Balzac of objects of considerable value, and which represented security for their claims, thereby causing them a loss which he must make good."

492

Count Emilio had not the faintest idea of what he was charged with, but he cheerfully paid what was demanded. It was a story that delighted the gossipmongers of Paris.

Balzac borrowed small sums here and there and for a time managed to exist, but in the end he was obliged to face the truth. His dream of a "humble cottage in the country" had come to an end. In two years, Les Jardies had cost him more than a hundred thousand francs, a sum for which he might have purchased a house in the most fashionable section of Paris.

"Clearly, Les Jardies must be sold," he said to Sarah.

"Turn the whole thing over to a good lawyer and clear out," she advised him.

His love affair with Sarah was coming to an end, but the friendship between them remained firm. She found a lawyer who agreed to dispose of Les Jardies, and advanced him money with which to pay the rent on a house in Paris.

He found what he wanted in the outlying section of Passy, on the western flank of Paris. It was a modest stone house that had two entrances, one on the rue Basse, the other, a basement entrance, on the rue du Roc. Balzac employed a carpenter to build a trapdoor and a pair of secret stairs, leading to the entrance on the lower level, so that he could make a quick exit if he found himself pursued. From the basement entrance, the street led quickly to the banks of the Seine, an excellent route of escape.

Furnished with the articles that had been stored in the mansionette at Les Jardies, the house at 19, rue Basse was comfortable from the first. In a few weeks, Balzac was asking himself by what aberration of the mind he had ever persuaded himself to live in the country.

He suffered a personal blow shortly after the move from Sèvres to Passy was made. His old retainer, Auguste, at last left Balzac's service, to marry a widow with a competence that included a little shop in one of the working class districts of Paris. Auguste wept when he said goodbye.

"I don't like to leave you, monsieur, but you know, I am getting on," he said. "A man doesn't fancy being alone, once he's had a glimpse of old age."

"I don't blame you, my old friend, although I shall miss you, you know that," Balzac said. He put a hand on the servant's shoulder. "A shop you say. What kind of shop is it?"

"Alimentation," said Auguste. "General store, really. It's a small place, but the house is snug."

"And the widow?" Balzac asked.

Auguste smiled sheepishly, scratching an ear.

"Well, sir, she's no beauty, that is for certain," he said. "But she's quiet and she cooks well and she's fond of me, you see. That counts for a lot."

Balzac looked at his valet, a man who had passed his life waiting on people, absorbed abuse as a sponge absorbs water.

"Do you know, Auguste," he said, without affectation, "I envy you. Quite honestly, I envy you your widow who's fond of you and your little shop."

Nacquart insisted that Balzac must not attempt to live alone, when Balzac announced his intention of doing without a servant altogether, in order to save money.

"A heart like yours is a tricky thing," Nacquart told him. "When you have an attack, it is very important that you get treatment without delay. It may mean the difference between living and dying, you see. No, Honoré, I insist on it. There must be someone in the house."

When Nacquart had gone, Balzac wandered through the house. It was lonely, no question about that. He was going to miss Auguste. Not to be able, in the middle of the night, to bellow, "Auguste! My coffee machine!" and know that the servant would come trotting a few minutes later, that was going to be hard to get used to.

Balzac stood at one of his windows, moodily watching the Seine, which at this point made a pretty curve. He had a sudden, chill sense of lonely, vacant old age, though he was really scarcely over the threshold of his middle years.

The affair with Sarah was petering out, not breaking up so much as dissolving. At the moment, there was no one else in Paris to whom he was attached, except in the most casual way. He yearned for a kind of emotional anchor, for some element in his life that would give it form and stability. In youth, his work had served as the magnetic center of his existence. It was still the center, but it was not enough.

If only Hanski would die! he thought. Why does he persist in living? He crossed himself, without thinking, and begged the par-

494

don of God for having permitted the hideous question to take form in his mind.

Yet he yearned to see Eve, to hold her in his arms, to tell her that he loved her.

He wrote that night, begging her to persuade her husband to make a journey to Italy or Spain, or to invent some excuse for traveling to the west alone.

"If you only knew how empty my life is without you, you would find some way," he wrote.

There were tear stains on the letter he sent to Poland. He spoke from the depths of his heart. He was refused.

"What you ask is impossible," she said curtly. "You forget that I am not free, as you are, but a woman with many obligations and a position in life that must be maintained."

He wrote again. She did not answer. Months passed without a letter. Half in jest, half in earnest, Balzac wrote to Zulma Carraud and asked her to find a wife for him.

"She must be young, of course—not more than twenty-five—beautiful if possible, and rich, the richer the better. Intelligent, but not too intelligent. Of good family and strong character."

Needless to say, Zulma did not find this paragon in Frapesle. Nor did Balzac find her in Paris. He stayed on alone in Passy, after trying a dozen slatternly country girls who could neither cook, serve, nor keep quiet. For a time, at Nacquart's suggestion, Gautier stayed with him, but it was not ideal for two writers to live together. Balzac knew that he must make some kind of permanent arrangement, if not to satisfy Nacquart, then simply for the sake of hearing another footstep in the house.

One evening he went to dine with the novelist, Frédéric Soulié. His companion at the dinner table was Louise Breugniot, a good-looking, brown-haired woman of about his own age. Balzac had known her casually for a number of years. Tonight he was impressed by her calm intelligence and her sense of self-possession. She had very clean, capable looking hands and a low-pitched voice that was reassuring. She was almost like a good nursing sister— the kind of woman who would find it difficult to give way to an assault of bad temper.

"One hears that you have lost Les Jardies, monsieur," she said, making conversation with him.

"Yes, I rattle around in Passy, in an empty house," he said. "I'm on the lookout for a housekeeper, someone who will manage things for me, without driving me mad. Do you happen to know of a woman? Someone competent and trustworthy? Not too young. I've had enough of idiot girls."

Louise Breugniot looked at Balzac studiously for a few seconds. He was being inspected, but she did it so calmly that he did not mind.

"Yes, I know of a woman," she said quietly.

"What is her name? When can I see her?" Balzac demanded. "I have no more clean plates. My dirty laundry makes a pile that is up to my shoulder. I tell you, Louise, I am desperate."

"I was thinking of myself," she said.

"You're not serious!" he exclaimed.

"I am honest and competent, not too young and I need a job," she said.

"But it would be awkward," said Balzac. "We have friends in common. Soulié here. Lamartine. And you are simply not a servant."

She shrugged and gave him a little smile.

"I will be if you employ me," she said. "I am quite serious, you know."

"It is settled!" said Balzac.

She was a godsend to Balzac, the dream servant that women are forever talking about. She put his house in Passy in order, without disrupting his work. She placated the tradesmen who supplied his table. She lied to bailiffs and bill collectors. She sponged the spots from his clothes and ironed his shirts. When his hair was shaggy, she trimmed it, expertly as any barber. She was a woman of education and some literary experience. She helped with his proofs and very quickly began to attend to minor details of his business with publishers and printers. She was housekeeper, cook, laundress, serving girl, literary agent, secretary, night watchman, nurse, companion, hostess and confidante.

One night, a few months after she moved into her top floor room in the house in Passy, she became Balzac's mistress. It was a thing that happened naturally as a shower of warm rain in the summer. She came to his bedroom to bring him the tepid milk that Nacquart advised as an encouragement to sleep.

"Stay for a moment," he said. "Don't go."

She sat on the edge of his bed while he sipped the warm sweet milk. It was four o'clock in the morning. The sleeping city was silent, beyond the bedroom windows. Balzac was tired, after a night of work. He stretched himself, then handed Louise the empty cup. She put it on his night table, looking at him calmly with her grave brown eyes. He kissed her. She drew his head to her breast and held it. Her body was warm and smelled vaguely of the kitchen. He was aware of her heartbeat, steady as the movement of a good clock. He moved his head, so that his cheek touched the soft skin of her breast. She blew out the candle, stood up and slipped out of her flannel robe, then got into the bed beside him. Balzac sighed in the warm darkness, then took her in his arms.

She was no tigress like Sarah Visconti, but Balzac was a man in his forties with a heart valve that was unreliable. She was gentle and affectionate. She made love like a good wife. A sensible man would have married her, despite the fact that she hadn't a penny.

Balzac was a genius, but he was not a sensible man. He would not give up his Faraway Princess, though she neglected to write to him and was almost indifferent when she did write. He was an incurable romantic. In Vienna, he and Eve had pledged *adoremus in aeternum*. He clung to the motto and to the lofty idea of his love.

Now that his affair with Sarah Visconti had passed from passion to simple friendship, Balzac had time on his hands. Partly out of boredom, partly because he felt the need for stimulation, he began to go out into society again, making new friendships and picking up the threads of old ones.

Balzac called on Madame Récamier at the Abbaye-aux-Bois. She told him that he was a genius and that it was intolerable that he had not been elected to the French Academy, but that she disliked his work.

"I am an old woman now, Honoré," she told him. "I can afford to say what I please. You are a genius and you will live, but for me your meat is too tough fibered and too highly seasoned. For me, things must be disguised a little."

During the season, Balzac formed the habit of making an appearance at Delphine de Girardin's salon. It amused him to be lionized and he had always liked Delphine.

One evening at Delphine's he found himself in a corner of the great room, talking with the Marquis de Belloy, who had just returned from Italy and was bubbling about Dante and the DIVINE COMEDY.

"I don't know," said Balzac. "I am a Frenchman, a Touragneau. It is my nature to prefer the human comedy to the divine."

"The human comedy," de Belloy repeated. "Of course, my dear Balzac, it is what you write. Your subject matter, in substance, is the comedy of human life."

"Excuse me," Balzac said abruptly, almost rudely. "I must go."

He hurried out of the house and went alone to a café. He ordered coffee and sat for an hour behind windows that were thick with winter steam. Then he went home to Passy, the words burnt into his mind.

"The Human Comedy!"
"The Comedy of Human Life."
"La Comédie Humaine!"

It was the title inevitable for the structure he had been erecting since the day he put his name to the title page of THE LAST CHOUAN. It was a title that summed up the whole and drew everything together. It was simple, solid as the Bible, magnificent, filled with power and assurance.

When he reached his house he was in a state of agitation. He rang for Louise and demanded coffee, then stripped off his clothes and got into his white robe. He sat at his writing table and headed the page LA COMÉDIE HUMAINE.

Then he began to outline the structure of his life's work. When it was finished, he realized, it would be nothing less than a social history of the first half of the nineteenth century in France, covering every phase of human life, peering into every corner of the human heart.

Balzac broke his HUMAN COMEDY into major divisions: *Scenes of Provincial Life, Scenes of Military Life, Scenes from Private Life,* and so on. Under each sub-heading, he wrote the titles of the books that were already written, then the tentative titles of those that remained to be done.

When the first rough outline was completed, Balzac experienced a profound sense of exhilaration, close to what a man feels when he has fallen desperately in love. Then came a purring, throbbing sense of self-confidence, the sense of greatness.

He had a roof over his house at last.

Ever since he had written the STUDIES IN XIXTH CENTURY MANNERS for the Widow Bechet, he had been groping toward this kind of grand conception, the majesty of which now left him slightly stunned.

The Comedy of Human Life!

There was nothing like it in all of French literature. To find a conception as mighty, one must turn to Shakespeare, and even Shakespeare had not planned a building with quite so many rooms.

Balzac leaned back in his chair and reread what he had written. His edifice was far from finished. There were gaps in the walls, whole wings to be erected, empty chambers to be furnished. Bare patches marred the garden and there were holes in the roof.

For the ordinary writer, what remained to be done would have provided the work of a lifetime, and his own lifetime, Balzac realized, was more than half used up. But he was not the ordinary writer. He was Balzac. The Great Balzac.

The next day, Nacquart came to listen to Balzac's heart, a big, gold turnip of a watch in his hand. When Nacquart had finished his examination, Balzac said to him straightforwardly, "Tell me, Nacquart, in your best medical judgment, how many years of life do you give me?"

Balzac asked this question calmly, as if he were asking the time of day. It is the kind of query that doctors always dislike. Nacquart shrugged, looked heavenward at Balzac's ceiling, and offered the standard medical reply.

"Such matters are not determined by physicians, Honoré, but by higher authority," he said.

"My dear Nacquart, I am a good Catholic, as you know," said Balzac. "I will make proper inquiries of the Deity. But this is important. I need sixteen years. Will I get them?"

Nacquart wound his watch, then uttered a profound sigh.

"With luck, and proper respect for your heart, I see no reason why you shouldn't live for twice sixteen years," he said.

"Sixteen will be enough," said Balzac cheerfully.

Nacquart put a hand on Balzac's shoulder. He was not a

499

demonstrative man, but he felt powerful affection for Balzac, and it was revealed.

"Don't overdo it, Honoré," he said. "As a doctor, as a friend, as a kind of godfather, I implore you. Don't overdo it!"

Nacquart opened his black bag and took out a bottle of small white pills.

"If you get an attack, and can manage it, try to swallow one of these," he said, handing the bottle to Balzac.

Balzac looked at the pills and said, "What are they?"

"Digitalis," Nacquart told him. "They are made from the leaves of the foxglove. A useful drug for a heart like yours, but dangerous. Don't take more than one."

Balzac looked at the pills and smiled.

"Death in a small packet?" he said. "A useful thing to have in the house."

"Joke all you like," said Nacquart. "But take care of yourself, my boy, if you want to live for six months, let alone for sixteen years."

The unfinished sections of THE HUMAN COMEDY henceforth were the calendar of Balzac's life.

Sixteen years.

Sixteen years, four months, and eighteen days, according to the schedule he had drawn up. He was in a race with time and death, a race with fame, a race with Almighty God Himself.

He approached the battle with sublime self-confidence. He went to Notre-Dame, as he had promised Nacquart, and prayed God for the time he needed. Then he went to work. Everything else was thrust aside. THE HUMAN COMEDY became the hub upon which Balzac's life was centered.

He had his house in Passy.

He had Nacquart to look after his heart.

He had his pills made from foxglove, to intervene if his heart protested.

He had Louise Breugniot to take care of his general needs and to serve as a wife when he needed her.

He had one good friend for companionship—Théophile Gautier.

He was consecrated and he was happy, filled with healthy pride. He might have been satisfied to have remained in his work room

500

in Passy, collecting his sixteen years, four months and eighteen days, writing the books that were in his soul.

He was not given the chance.

One morning in January of the year 1842, a bomb came in the mail from Poland.

Balzac finished his night's work a few hours after dawn. Louise drew back the heavy curtains, letting in the light, then served Balzac his breakfast and brought him his mail. Balzac sipped his coffee and munched on a sweetened roll, sorting through the batch of letters. He came to one with a black border, addressed in the familiar hand.

He turned it over and ran his thumb across the blob of coal black wax that sealed it. His heart was racing dangerously. He opened the letter and read it quickly.

Count Hanski was dead.

Eve was a widow.

Balzac's life had been turned upside down.

Chapter 48

Balzac was prepared to make a dash for the snows of Russia the moment Eve gave him the word. He was wild with anticipation and discussed with Buisson the possibility of having an overcoat made with mink on the outside. THE HUMAN COMEDY was forgotten. Nacquart's predictions of death were thrust aside. The Faraway Princess was free at last and the White Knight must rush to her side.

The next letter from Russia brought Balzac to a full stop. He must be out of his mind, said Eve, to think that she could permit him to join her. She was in mourning. There was the estate to be settled. He must be patient.

"Patient!" he roared to the faithful Louise. "Does she think that I am made of stone? I have waited for seven years. Now she tells me I must be patient."

"You are forgetting your Bible, monsieur," Louise said with a slow smile. "Jacob served seven years for Rachel, then served seven more."

"I am no long-suffering Hebrew," Balzac roared. "I am a Frenchman, and I have waited long enough."

Roaring at his housekeeper eased Balzac's temper, but it had no effect on his light of love, who remained curiously indifferent to the fact that the man to whom she had promised herself was two thousand miles away. Another man would have taken her indifference as dismissal. Not Balzac. To Balzac, Eve was an obsession. He would not rest until they were married.

For eighteen months Balzac laid siege to Madame de Hanska, bombarding her with letters. At last he produced a breach in her defenses. She wrote to him from Saint Petersburg, where she was engaged in a bitter lawsuit over the de Hanski estate, and gave him permission to come in July. There was no mention of marriage, no hint even that he would be granted the favors first bestowed in Geneva, but Balzac was satisfied.

"Once I am in the room with her, I will break her down quickly enough," he promised Gautier.

Gautier sighed.

"I suppose it is useless to remind you that you don't do badly in Paris," he said.

"Wait until you see her!" Balzac exclaimed. "Then you will understand why I have waited for all these years."

Gautier glanced at the painting of Eve that hung over the fireplace in Balzac's study.

"She is beautiful," he admitted.

"The picture is nothing," Balzac insisted. "She is a dream, I tell you. One of the truly great beauties of the world. And rich, Théo. She is fantastically rich."

It was the middle of June. Paris was sweltering in a pre-summer heat wave. The air was like moist, warm cotton. A sullen summer haze obscured the sun, but seemed to offer no relief from the merciless heat.

Balzac rushed about Paris, bathed in sweat, exhausting himself in the effort to acquire a wardrobe sufficiently splendid to impress the Russian capital, and perchance the Imperial Court.

"Certainly it is possible that the Tsar may command me to appear at the Summer Palace," he told Théo. "After all, there has always been an affinity between the Russians and the French where literature is concerned."

Buisson made Balzac three dress coats, one of an astonishing plum color, one of grey, a third of vivid blue. The famous gold buttons made by Gosselan were attached to the new blue coat. Balzac ordered six new waistcoats, an assortment of cravats, and three dozen pairs of the best quality white silk stockings.

"After all, in Russia people will regard me as a representative of France," he said to his tailor. "I cannot afford to be badly dressed."

The long-suffering Buisson sighed and pulled a basting thread from one of Balzac's new coats.

"The fact is, my old friend, you can't afford to be dressed at all," he said. "But I suppose one cannot permit you to wander about the world in the nude."

Balzac laughed. He had no idea of how much money he owed the good Buisson. In recent years, he had formed the habit of making some mention of Buisson in a magazine article from time

503

to time. This appealed to the tailor's vanity and brought him a quantity of business from customers who actually settled their accounts at the end of the year. The arrangement seemed to satisfy Buisson and it kept Balzac supplied with clothes.

Now he smiled at the tailor and touched a sleeve of his new coat. "In a few months, Buisson, debt will be a thing of the past to me," he said. "I am going to Russia to make a rich marriage."

He took it for granted that he and Eve would be married quickly and that together they would spend Count Hanski's Slavic fortune.

The early heat sapped Balzac's energy and before his new clothes were finished he was obliged to take to his bed for the day in order to recoup his strength. Nacquart warned him that the journey to Russia might very well cost him his life.

"It's true that you're only forty-three, 'Noré," he admitted. "But you have the arteries of a man of sixty and your heart is about as reliable as an Italian grenadier."

"For me, Nacquart, Saint Petersburg is the fountain of youth," said Balzac earnestly. "All this strain that you keep telling me is so bad for my heart—it will be over and done with the minute I get to Russia."

He brushed Nacquart's warnings aside, putting his faith in the predictions of Balthazar, the fortune teller. During the last year, Balzac had comforted himself and sustained his courage by resorting to regular sessions with the famous somnambulist.

"You have never loved as you love this woman," Balthazar assured Balzac. "For you, no other love is possible in this life."

Again and again in the darkened atelier where Balthazar probed into the mists of the future, Balzac heard reassuring words. Balthazar's mystic certainties fortified his will against the advice of his friends and his physician.

Now, on the eve of his journey to Russia, Balzac again consulted the celebrated seer.

"Your destiny is clearly in the East," Balthazar told him. "Your star is an eastern star."

It was enough for Balzac. He was unimpressed when Gautier reminded him that Balthazar had been thrown into prison for performing abortions, an enterprise he pursued as a sideline to telling fortunes.

504

"What have abortions to do with the truth?" Balzac demanded. "I tell you, Balthazar is an authentic mystic."

Gautier threw up his hands. Nacquart admitted defeat and contented himself with warning Balzac against over-exertion. Louise was heartbroken and managed to hide it from Balzac.

A few days before he sailed, some impulse, imprecise but powerful, prompted Balzac to visit his mother, who was living in a modest house on the outskirts of Paris. They were on bad terms, as usual. On the surface, the issue was the old one—money—but underneath it was still the ancient war that had started when Balzac was in his cradle.

Anne-Charlotte was sixty-one.

A lifetime of self-concern had made its effect. The deep, throbbing sexuality was gone, but the beauty remained, the beauty of a nurtured, hothouse plant that has been coddled into living far beyond its span. Her waist was slim. Her breasts were firm. Her skin was clear and without wrinkles. Her hands were still a matter of pride.

Her hair had gone stark white, and she made the most of its dramatic quality. Though she complained bitterly about the size of the allowance Balzac made her, she continued to go to the best bottiers and dressmakers in Paris, and her clothes were modish. She wore black nowadays, almost exclusively, because of the effective contrast the color made with her hair.

Today she wore black taffeta, the bodice fitted with whalebone stays, the full skirt revealing just a hint of vermilion petticoat when she moved quickly across the room. She wore the chypre perfume he remembered from childhood.

The sitting room of her little house was furnished with things that had been at Villeparisis, even, some of them, at Tours. There was a sofa that had been recovered, a chair that his father had always liked, a wonderfully mellowed Aubusson carpet. In their glass case, the door still locked, were the cups of eggshell china from Limoges.

There was nothing in the room for a man to be afraid of. It was an old woman's room. Even his mother was harmless now.

Yet Balzac felt puerile fear as he sat down across from his mother and was handed one of her second-best cups, filled with rather pallid tea.

"I am going to Russia," he announced calmly, expecting that he dropped a bombshell.

His mother sniffed.

"Everyone in France by this time knows that the Great Balzac is going to Russia," she said contemptuously. "Another fool's errand, like your Sardinian adventure."

He shook his head.

"This time you are wrong, mother," he insisted. "When I return from Russia, I will be a married man. And a rich one."

"You talk like a schoolboy," she said harshly. "In a man of your age, with grey hairs and something of a paunch, maturity would be more appropriate."

"The grey hairs were honestly acquired," he said mildly, touching the hair near his temples. He patted his stomach. "As for the embonpoint. Well, when one leads a sedentary life, it must be expected."

She looked at him with the inveterate scorn of the slim person for the not so slim.

"You eat too much," she said bluntly. "You indulge yourself, in food as in everything else."

Balzac looked at his mother, trying to dredge up out of the swamp of childhood and youth, one word of affection or kindness. He encountered none.

"It is your family that suffers because of your improvidence and neglect," she said bitterly. "I live in a hovel, fit for the widow of some clerk. Your sister Laure is ill and in financial difficulty. What do you give her? Good advice."

"I offered something more than advice," said Balzac. "It was refused."

This was true. When de Surville had lost his post and Laure had been desperate with worry, Balzac had offered money, or at least he had offered to try to get the money. What had intervened had been Laure's pride in her husband.

"I suppose a mother doesn't matter," Anne-Charlotte said mournfully.

"Is it nothing to you that you are the mother of the greatest writer in France?" Balzac said calmly.

"Your monstrous ego!" she said.

"Posterity will agree with my judgment," he said. "Balzac will be one of the great names of the century. When my HUMAN COMEDY is finished. . . ."

506

"Human Comedy!" she exploded. "Your whole life is a human comedy. When will you realize that people are laughing at you?"

Balzac remembered the words of his father, offered twenty years ago, in one of the old man's rare unguarded moments: "My boy, you will never in this life have a worse enemy than your mother."

He put down his teacup and rose to his feet. Crossing the room, he stood in front of the china cabinet, looking bemusedly at the cups and saucers sheltering behind the polished glass, resisting a powerful impulse to smash the glass with the toe of his boot and to trample the fragile cups underfoot.

"Do you know that I drank from one of these cups, years ago, at Villeparisis?" he said speculatively.

"You are a liar!" Anne-Charlotte spat out the words. "That cabinet has never been opened by anyone except myself. Those cups have never been used. Never!"

She was furious. The color rose in her cheeks and her hands were clenched into tiny fists. Balzac laughed softly and went back to his chair. He leaned forward, forearms resting on his thighs, looking at his mother intently.

"I am going to Russia to take a wife," he said. "You are my mother. I am your son. I have come for your blessing. Are you going to send me away without it?"

She did not answer him. He sighed deeply, then slapped his thighs with his palms, making a sharp, realistic sound. He had behaved like an idiot, yet some urge toward the respectable and proper had prompted him to come. He got up, kissed his mother's hand, and went out of the room without saying anything more. As he passed through his mother's garden gate, there were tears in his eyes, but he did not turn back to look at the house.

Balzac made the voyage to Russia aboard a British ship—the steam packet *Devonshire*, sailing from Le Havre. By some miracle the channel and the North Sea were calm and Balzac was able to enjoy a few pleasant days on deck. The English food astonished him—beef that appeared to have been boiled in lye, pudding made of sweetened glue, slabs of stewed fat and oat soup for breakfast. So did the English passengers astonish him. They were of an altogether different breed from the Britishers he had known in Paris.

"The women are like two-legged horses," he said to a fellow Frenchman on board. "As for the men. *Mon Dieu!*"

When the *Devonshire* passed through the Cattegat and entered

507

the Baltic Sea, she encountered thematic summer storms. For the rest of the voyage, Balzac remained in his tiny, airless cabin, begging for death, prevented from throwing himself into the sea by a long-suffering cockney steward who offered atrocious remedies.

When the *Devonshire* reached Saint Petersburg, Balzac was in frightful condition. He remained aboard ship overnight in order to gather his strength before facing up to the fateful meeting with the woman he loved.

A night's sleep put him nearly right. He dressed in the tiny cabin, taking special pains with his toilet. He inspected himself in the dim mirror bolted to the washstand, looking for traces of age and illness. Certainly he had changed in the eight years that had passed since he and Eve had pledged their love in Vienna. He persuaded himself that the years had contributed to his face a look of distinction as well as age.

Driving away from the quayside in a droshky, he was aware of the odd effect that Russia traditionally works on the visitor from the west—a mixture of fear and excitement, combined with a sense of mystery, the feeling that one has left Europe and is entering what is not so much a country as a vast, cryptic private domain. Even here in the capital, a western city, built to order, there was the suggestion of Asia, an awareness of the Tartar wastes beyond the horizon, reaching toward the interminable, inscrutable east.

The droshky driver spoke no French, nor could he read his own language. After a frustrating interchange, the driver summoned an exceedingly military looking policeman who spoke enough French to negotiate for Balzac and to send him on his way.

The driver went down the Nevsky Prospekt, a fine broad boulevard lined with trees, with shops and cafés just coming to life. Then he turned into a street of splendid private houses, bringing the horses to a stop in front of an impressive mansion made of grey-pink granite. He turned in his seat and looked at Balzac suspiciously, as if he wondered what possible business an outlandish character like this one might have at such a house. He shrugged and climbed down from his box, unloading Balzac's luggage.

Before he touched the brass bellpull, Balzac looked up at the façade of the big house. He had not expected to find Eve living in a third class pension, but he was unprepared for a mansion that was larger than the Castellane Palace. As the droshky turned in the street and moved off, Balzac took a deep breath. Then he tugged on the bellpull.

A pretty maid came to the door, wearing a blue serge uniform, protected by a starched white apron. She was impossibly blonde. Her grey-blue eyes were limpid.

"De Balzac," Balzac said importantly.

"Monsieur is expected," the servant answered, in quite good French. "Please to come in."

The house smelled pleasantly of sandalwood and tea and it was cool after the warmth of the sun. The furnishings were heavy and rich, the stone floors covered with priceless Persian rugs. Balzac had a sharp, awkward memory of the day he first went to call on the Duchesse de Castries, and a gnawing awareness that when he had stepped through the door behind him he had stepped into a world where he did not belong.

He was not kept waiting, as he had been at the Castellane Palace. In a few minutes, the pretty maid led him up a grand staircase hung with tapestries, down a corridor to the door to Eve's sitting room.

The sitting room was blue, a pale, silken blue. The curtains had been drawn back and the morning light touched the leaded windows with pink. Beyond the windows, as he crossed the room, Balzac caught a glimpse of the Neva and the spires of the Church of Saints Peter and Paul.

In the center of the room, demure as a waiting schoolgirl, stood Eve with her hands clasped behind her. He stood still, frozen for a moment, missing a heartbeat and a breath.

"She has not changed!" he assured himself.

In that light, to his ardent eye, she looked precisely as she had looked eight years ago in Vienna.

For several seconds, neither of them moved. Then Eve raised her arms, a gesture that was at the same time romantic and maternal. He moved toward her across the rich rug, in the poetic morning light. They embraced. In the blue, silent room, for Balzac, the years dissolved. He was choked with emotion.

After a few seconds they drew apart, as if from a long kiss, although their lips had not actually met. Eve looked nervously at Balzac, as if trying to guess what was his reaction to her, after eight years. There was a question in her eyes.

"You are more beautiful than ever," he said. "It is astonishing."

"You haven't changed," said Eve.

Neither statement was the truth, and Eve knew that hers was a lie. To Balzac, blinded by the force of his love, Eve in truth seemed not to have changed.

Eve sat down on a blue sofa. Balzac made as if to take the place beside her, but she shook her head.

"No, Honoré, we must talk," she said. She nodded to a chair. "Sit there."

He sat in the straight chair. They were close together, facing each other. Her perfume was in his nostrils. He was as madly in love as he had been at Neuchâtel. His obsession did not matter now, nor did Eve's money or title or social power. At this moment, Balzac was in love with a face and a voice and glittering hair, with moist lips and a clear translucent skin. Had Eve been a washerwoman, he would have loved her.

"I adore you," he said, and profoundly meant it.

She looked at him with mournful Slavic eyes, then turned away, looking toward the great bank of windows that faced the Neva.

"You must give me time," she murmured.

"A lifetime," he said. "The rest of our lives."

He held up his hand to display the ring she had given him in Vienna, that held a lock of her hair in the secret compartment.

"Do you remember our motto?" he asked.

"Adoremus in Aeternum," she answered.

He got up, kissed her cheek, took her hand and again made as if to sit beside her. She shook her head. He returned to his chair.

"I am glad you have come," she said. "I need you. I need help. My brother has turned his back on me and I have no one upon whom I can depend."

"I am yours to command," said Balzac.

"You are French," she said. "You have no idea what it means to be a Pole, a woman and a Roman Catholic, and at the same time to be a subject of Tsar Nicholas the First."

Balzac drew from his pocket a packet of documents he had brought with him from Paris.

"In twenty-four hours time you can become French and place yourself under the protection of the French Crown," he said. "These papers authorize the French Consul-General to marry us at once, in a civil ceremony. The church wedding can be performed in France, whenever you like."

She sighed.

510

"Ah, my dear Honoré, if only it were so simple," she said.

"What could be more simple?" asked Balzac. "We marry and that is the end of it."

"We are not in France, but in Saint Petersburg," said Eve. "For a Russian subject to marry a foreigner without the Tsar's permission means that all Russian property is forfeited to the Imperial treasury. If I married you tomorrow, I should be a pauper by sundown."

"Incredible!" said Balzac.

"For myself, I don't mind," Eve said. "But I must think of my child, do you understand? I have no right to destroy Anna's inheritance."

"We must apply to the Tsar for permission to marry," said Balzac. "That much is clear. There must be a standard procedure, and after all, I am not unknown."

"It will be difficult," she told him. "Powerful forces have been working against us at court. Why do you think I have put off having you come, until I could bear it no longer?"

"Who opposes us?" asked Balzac.

"My brother, for one," answered Eve. "My aunt, of course. And my husband's uncle, who has been trying to steal the estate at Wierzchownia from myself and my child."

When she spoke of the child, Eve's voice took on a note of passion and sincerity. Whatever else she loved or did not love, her child she adored, with passion and conviction.

"If it weren't for Anna, I think I should have given up and let them have what they wanted," she said bitterly. "Think of it! To steal from a child! They are like jackals."

"Remember, Eve, I am a lawyer," Balzac said. "Perhaps I can be of some service here."

"We are in Holy Russia," said Eve, uttering the words with some bitterness. "You will find that a knowledge of the French Civil Code is not much use in these Russian courts."

"Lawyers are lawyers," said Balzac. "French, Russian, Hottentot. It is a type of human mentality."

Because of the lawsuit that was before the courts involving the estate at Wierzchownia, it was inadvisable for Balzac to stay at the de Hanski house.

"The slightest breath of scandal would prejudice the court in favor of my husband's uncle," said Eve. "There is too much at stake. My child's future. Her whole life."

Balzac put up at a residence hotel not too far from Eve's house. He got a comfortable room with a big bed and they brought him an impressive breakfast in the morning.

With Eve, he found himself in the position of an ardent and welcomed suitor. He wooed Eve as if she were a young virgin. He sent her flowers, perfume, chocolates. He went with her when she ordered clothes, casting a critical Parisian eye on what the Saint Petersburg designers offered, giving shrewd advice. He played the courtier. He was always on call, always ready to jump to Eve's service.

Eve de Hanska was a vain woman.

She was flattered by Balzac's attention, and she found it reassuring to have someone beside her who, without question, argument or equivocation, took her side in the family quarrel. And she was pleased by the fact that Balzac seemed to get on well with the child, Anna.

"She likes you," Eve said, as if she were rather surprised. "I am glad. She has never really had a father."

Had Anna been a two-headed monster, Balzac would have pretended that he found her enchanting. Actually, it was unnecessary to pretend. Anna was bewitching, a grave, soft-voiced girl, just blooming into life, with eyes like her mother's and soft hair worn in braids.

"If I weren't madly in love with you, my dear, I would marry Anna like a shot," said Balzac one afternoon, when he had just passed an hour with Eve's daughter.

It was the wrong pleasantry. Eve's face darkened with anger and she glared at Balzac.

"Please do not be grotesque," she said.

Balzac apologized. It was passed over. But he began to realize that he had a rival in Anna. Certainly, there was no hope that Eve would marry him until Anna's future was assured. She made that clear. Balzac accepted this fatalistically, and resolved to keep a weather eye open for the right young man.

Still, there was something troubling, almost unnatural, in Eve's preoccupation with her daughter. She insisted on brushing the child's hair, though there was a maid to do it. She selected her clothes in the morning, supervised the details of her education,

512

took the child into her room at night if Anna was frightened or slightly ill. Any of these things, by themselves, might have been perfectly normal in an attentive mother; it was the fiercely possessive way in which Eve did them that sometimes troubled Balzac.

Still, he reasoned, Anna should not be a problem for long. In a little while, she would marry, and then he would have his Eve to himself.

Like many a Frenchman before him, Balzac was quickly infatuated with Russia. He was the first French writer of consequence to visit Saint Petersburg since the days of Catherine the Great. To the intelligentsia, he was an object of awe. The mighty line of Russian novelists were men in their twenties, yet to be published. Pushkin, recently dead, was the local literary god, but here in flesh and blood was an almost legendary figure from the west, a writer from dangerous, brilliant and forbidden France.

At the University, students mobbed Balzac, kissed his hand, offered him flowers, asked him to sign his name on various bits of paper.

It was Vienna and Milan all over again.

He basked in it.

He enjoyed it.

"Do you know, it has occurred to me that I might remain here," he said to Eve. "I could open a school for writers interested in French literature. Perhaps I could start a magazine."

"If you remain in Russia it will be without me," said Eve flatly. "I am a Pole. This is not my home."

It was a thing he encountered again and again in Eve—her fierce Polish pride. Though she was accepted by the Russian court and the nobility, she would not relinquish a deep-going Polish patriotism and a refusal to accept in her heart the authority of the Russian Tsar.

To the aristocracy of Saint Petersburg, Balzac was not a demi-god as he was to the students and intellectuals, but he was an object of curiosity and some celebrity. Everyone had read his books. At least they had read his naughtier pieces, and those aristocrats who remained in the city were eager to meet him.

Most of the great houses were closed, the leaders of Petersburg society having opened their *dachas,* or summer villas, but Eve and Balzac were invited to the few mansions that were open.

In spite of the insufferable heat of July and August, Balzac was enjoying himself. He was in a city where his fame was openly hailed. There were no creditors on his doorstep. He had a certain confidence in the future, and he was becoming reconciled to the idea that his marriage must be postponed for a time.

He and Eve had not yet resumed the intimacy established at Geneva, but Balzac, somewhat to his own surprise, found that he was content to wait until it suited Eve to receive him completely.

"My God, I am truly older," he said to himself one night, in his hotel room. "Five years ago, I would have been straining at the leash. Now I find it almost enough to sit with her and hold her hand."

Through the summer, he and Eve were drawn closer and closer together. They did not quarrel, as they had done in Vienna. They spoke frankly of the future, of money, of the child, even of Hanski and of Madame de Berny, of whom Eve, with a woman's precision, had always nourished a lingering jealousy.

"She was an angel," Balzac said soberly. "I should like to think that in loving her, I was really anticipating my love for you, and that you, indeed, possess all those noble qualities of hers that softened my character and made me a better man than I was."

He spoke from the heart; there were tears in his eyes. Usually, such emotional candor was reserved for his writing table, and did not involve himself, but some invented character.

Perhaps because she needed his emotional support that summer in Saint Petersburg, Eve revealed to Balzac the most tender side of her nature. Her love for Anna was a touching thing. Balzac enjoyed seeing mother and daughter together in intimate moments, as he was more and more permitted to do, during July and August, when, in the sweltering capital, the formalities of life were somewhat forgotten.

During the hot months in the semi-deserted capital, they became a kind of temporary family, Balzac, Eve and Anna. Lirette Borel, Anna's Swiss nurse, continued to regard Balzac with suspicion and fear, but Anna laughed at Lirette for a little Protestant bluestocking.

Together, Balzac and the mother and child went for long drives in the country, taking a picnic lunch in a hamper, eating under the trees on the shores of Lake Ladoga. Balzac played pater familias and enjoyed the role.

514

Anna found him captivating. He was the story-book uncle, who was never cross. He told her stories of the old regime in France, gorgeous tales of Versailles. When he told her the story of poor doomed Marie Antoinette he brought tears to her eyes. He told her tales of the Roman legions and of the Knights of Burgundy.

One afternoon, sitting on a grassy bank above the broad calm waters of Lake Ladoga, he told her the whole of THE LAST OF THE MOHICANS. She swept for the noble savage. When he learnt that she had never read Sir Walter Scott, he scoured the second-hand bookshops of Saint Petersburg until he found French translations of IVANHOE and QUENTIN DURWARD. He read these books aloud to Anna, acting out the great scenes, standing up and moving his arms like an actor until he had both Anna and her mother bursting into applause.

"Honoré, you are astonishing," Eve told him. "You have lived as a bachelor all your life, but when you are with Anna, one would think you had reared a dozen children."

"Ah, there are things about de Balzac that not everyone understands," he said. He took her hand. "You are still a young woman, Evalina. I am not exactly a patriarch. We must have children, you and I."

She withdrew her hand abruptly and turned away from him. He had touched the wrong nerve again.

"I have not been very lucky with childbearing," she said bitterly. "I don't think I could be persuaded to try again."

It was a thing she did not care to discuss. In her youth, Eva had carried seven children. Only Anna had survived. The others had been miscarried, or been stillborn, or died a few days after birth. It was this that made Eve almost pathologically concerned with Anna and her future.

Though he had never made the suggestion, Balzac was firmly convinced that the cause of the difficulty had been Hanski. Sometimes he was even disloyal enough to wonder whether Anna was actually Hanski's child, or the product of some long-forgotten love affair. He knew nothing of Eve's past, really, he thought, while she seemed to know everything about him, from the time he had been a child in Tours.

Balzac's compelling physical vitality was not a thing that a normally passionate woman in daily contact with him could ignore

515

or resist for very long. Illness had not dimmed his throbbing sexual potency; there was a sense of the virile about him that was partly pure animal and partly related in some way to the bursting creative energy of the artist, the interior vigor that contributed even to his slightest work a compelling sense of life.

Eve was a passionate woman—more so than Balzac knew. She had had an affair with Franz Liszt, George Sand's old lover, when Liszt had come to Russia armed with a letter of introduction from Balzac.

During the year in which Balzac had received only two or three letters from her, she had been involved in a frantic affair with a swaggering, pig-sticking officer of the Imperial Household Cavalry. It had been an equestrian, outdoor romance that had involved a good deal of al fresco lovemaking in hayricks and overnight adventures in country inns. The officer had been handsome, virile and stupid. When he killed himself by falling off a horse during an army steeplechase, Eve had already become so bored with him that it did not much matter.

Since the guardsman, she had been chaste, except for the few weeks with Liszt, not from choice or because of her conscience, but from caution and the lack of opportunity. During the last two years she had been very much on guard where her conduct was concerned, knowing that any whiff of scandal would be ammunition for the greedy Hanskis, who were trying to steal from her half the fortune that her husband had left.

Eve was a long way from being the constant angel of Balzac's imagination. If he had not lived up to the motto of Vienna, then neither had she. She had sent for him this year because she was bored and lonely and because she knew that his presence would give her a certain cachet in Saint Petersburg, among these Russians that she despised, and to whom she was, after all, merely a member of the Polish provincial nobility, with a pretty daughter to marry off, a daughter who might or might not be wealthy, according to the way in which the Imperial courts finally disposed of Wierzchownia.

She had sent for Balzac for selfish reasons. She had not intended to take him back as a lover, and she certainly did not regard herself as bound by the promises made in Geneva. She was an aristocrat and was accustomed to using people quite as cynically as the Duchesse de Castries. At bottom, Balzac meant nothing to her.

No one meant anything to her, except herself and her daughter Anna. Balzac was useful only so far as he served her ego and gave her a sense of self-importance.

In her planning, however, Eve had underestimated two things. One was her own strong sexual need, a profoundly Slavic hunger for love. The other was Balzac himself. She had forgotten the intensity of passion that had swept her into bed in Geneva, against her better judgment.

Also, there was the weather.

Summer in Saint Petersburg has itself something of the character of brief, illicit love. The heat comes quickly after the cold, and it is intense, relentless and demanding. Those who can do so, escape the city from mid-July through late August. Those who must stay, as did Eve because of her legal involvements, live through these weeks as one lives through a sea voyage in the tropics, isolated, drawn together by the common denominator of the moist, erotic heat. The streets, even the parks, are intolerable in the daytime. The damp air caresses the skin with a warm, seductive touch. There is a shocking, tropical awareness of the flesh.

Restlessly, the young girls toss in their damp and virginal beds. There is a sense of physical urgency and even the most circumspect are prompted to throw caution and custom aside. Fathers keep their daughters at home if they can, during the long, hot northern nights. The young men gather in the parks, which, for these few weeks, are like scented tropical gardens.

For a northern and snowbound people, the short stabbing summer can be a very demoralizing thing. The dangerous glands are in possession. The armor of chastity melts away in the hot suggestive evenings.

In the middle of August, Eve de Hanska's reconstituted chastity dissolved. In the hot twilight after dinner one evening, she fell into Balzac's arms, defenseless as a ripe orchid.

Her bedroom faced the Neva. The tall French windows were open and pale net curtains floated in the tepid breeze like the gauze dresses of dancers. From a little park some distance away came the hint of music. Bandsmen from the Winter Palace were playing summer waltzes for proletarian lovers who took their ease on the Tsar's warm grass.

Balzac and his Eve made love softly on Eve's blue silk sheets that were embroidered with the de Hanski coat-of-arms. She gave

517

herself to him as freely as if she had been a Polynesian maiden with a flower in her hair, instead of the mistress of Wierzchownia and the rich widow of a Polish feudal landlord.

For Balzac, it was the culmination of a thousand dreams. He loved with heart, soul and body. He loved with a full consciousness of being the Great Balzac. He was tender, he was fierce. He was delicate as a moth, ardent as a stallion. He was worthy of his own great scenes. It was hot, tropical Hebraic love, the Song of Solomon, the taste of pomegranate, the limp, honey-sweet exhaustion.

Such are the marvels that can be produced by continence, followed by propinquity, with the aid of a bottle of French wine and the perfumed warmth of a northern summer.

Balzac was intoxicated with love. He bathed in Eve's caresses. He was happy.

She sent him away before dawn.

"We must think of Anna," she whispered. "At her age she is easily shocked. And poor Lirette would never recover."

He kissed her breast. Her flesh tasted faintly of salt. It was pleasant.

"You are right," he agreed regretfully.

He got out of bed and dressed in the dark, and crept silently out of the house. While he was dressing, Eve fell asleep. He was careful not to waken her.

It was cool, in the early morning, but the smell of the heat remained in the air. Balzac stood on the bank of the Neva, surrounded by the sleeping city, aware of mysterious and not so holy Russia. He was conscious of the delectable languor that follows prolonged and successful love, but he was not in the least sleepy. The prospect of sitting in his hotel room, wide awake and alone, did not appeal to him. He decided to walk through the early morning.

"One doesn't know a city or a woman until he has seen them wake up in the morning," he said to himself cheerfully, deciding to remain in the streets until Saint Petersburg had come to life.

He walked slowly along the eastern bank of the Neva. Families of river barges, crude things beside French barges, were tied up for the night along shore. In the frugal, pre-dawn light, the landscape was monochromatic, steel grey, with dense black shadows. There was the last of a yellow moon, the color of a cat's malev-

518

olent eye, backed by a remnant of torn cloud—an unhealthy kind of sky, with intimations of death in it.

Under the Neva's bridges slept the shapeless poor, as they did in Paris under the bridges of a better river.

Balzac stumbled over the body of an unconscious drunkard. He recovered his footing, then knelt beside the man to see whether he was dead or alive. He was alive. He reeked of vodka and of sour straw. Balzac shook his head, looking at the shocking face. He opened his purse and found a fifty kopek piece, tucking it into the derelict's pocket.

He moved on beside the river. He met a lonely policeman on patrol who saluted and said good morning politely. Balzac had the pleasant sense of proprietorship that sometimes imposes itself on a man in love, a sense of being blessed with so much good fortune that there must be plenty to spare for all, in smaller, more appropriate quantities. There must be a portion of good luck in the world, even for the foul-smelling drunkard on the pavement, even for the lonely, footsore policeman. Balzac had the urge to rush back, to embrace the policeman, kiss his cheek, in some way to show delight in the fact that they were both alive at the same instant, while the heartless planet spun.

He resisted the impulse, swung his cane in an arc, and turned into the Nevsky Prospekt. At this hour the great broad thoroughfare was empty, faced on either side with implacable iron shutters, giving an effect of total desertion, as if the inhabitants had gone into hiding from a rapacious invading army. Balzac's heels and the ferule of his stick rang on the hollow slates of the pavement. He felt like a solitary conqueror, so dreaded that everyone disappeared while he inspected the prostrate, surrendered city.

Then he remembered the complex fact that no one conquers Russia. Charles the Twelfth and Napoleon had broken their blades in the ice and snow. Russia simply absorbed her invaders; they died in the swamps or the snowdrifts, or they remained when their armies had gone and simply became Russian.

Balzac stood on a handsome bridge and watched the intensely orange sun come up out of the Gulf of Ladoga. All over Saint Petersburg, the church bells were ringing to welcome the dawn. The city stirred and came slowly awake. Porters and serving girls, still half-drugged with sleep, sloshed the pavements in front of shops with water, then scrubbed the slate with witches brooms made of coarse twigs. At the first café that was open, Balzac stopped and ordered tea. It was hot fragrant tea, and he had learned to drink it from a glass, a lump of sugar held in his teeth, straining the hot liquid through it. It was a trick that Anna had taught him.

He went into a church and stood through the curious Orthodox Mass, feeling profoundly religious, as one feels when he is in love.

"As soon as I get back to Paris I will make my peace with the Church," he promised himself. "It may be all right for a bachelor to be casual about his religious obligations. For a married man it is another matter."

He came out of the church into bright fierce sunlight. Already one could feel the heat. His coat was too heavy and he began to sweat. He made his way back to his hotel, guessing at the turnings, and stripped himself. A maid brought him his grotesque Russian breakfast—eggs, meat, little cakes made from potatoes, a gallon of vigorous tea in a copper samovar. He ate it all, hungry from his walk.

Then he stretched out on his bed and dozed, tickled by little rivers of sweat that formed on his body, though he did not move, and ran in a trickle down his chest and neck.

He was happy. He had been blessed by God. His Eve had surrendered and now it was simply a question of time until they were married.

Balzac, analyst of women, failed in his attempt to read the secret heart of his Eve. The fact that she had again become Balzac's mistress and enjoyed it, did not for an instant mean that she had at last decided to marry him. As a lover, Balzac was one thing, as a husband he would be quite another. Eve could be voluptuous after dark; in the daytime, she was not the woman who forgot to count the cost.

A few days after she had surrendered to Balzac, Eve's Aunt Rosalie arrived in Saint Petersburg, determined to prevent her niece from falling into the Gallic clutches of this fortune hunter from Paris.

Aunt Rosalie was formidable. She had not yet thrown in her lot with the family bloc that opposed Eve in court, and Eve wanted her support; besides, although Aunt Rosalie was a sour old maid, in Eve's judgment, she was no fool.

"How can you think of marriage with this miserable scribbler?"

520

Aunt Rosalie demanded. "You, Eve de Hanska, the Countess Rzewuska, with the proudest blood of Poland in your veins. No doubt you sleep with him—" A veined and bony hand went up as Eve began to protest—"Don't deny it, I know all the signs. It doesn't matter. To sleep with Balzac is one thing. But to marry him! That is unthinkable!"

"My mind is not made up," said Eve, stating the flat truth.

"You know nothing about him," insisted her aunt. "Are you aware for instance that he is in debt to the tune of more than two million French francs? This is not rumor, my dear Eve. I have had the facts investigated by an official of the Imperial Embassy in Paris. Discreetly, mind you, but nevertheless, with efficiency."

Eve frowned. She knew that Balzac was in debt. She had not imagined that he was in debt for the sum of two million francs.

"Who is to pay for his extravagance?" Aunt Rosalie demanded. "You, my foolish widow, if you are misguided enough to marry him. He will bleed you white."

Aunt Rosalie painted the picture of an unprincipled libertine, a jailbird, a reckless adventurer. It was a picture difficult to reconcile with the attentive and well-behaved Balzac Eve saw almost every day, but Eve was cautious and self-centered.

After Aunt Rosalie went back to Vienna, and Balzac was able to spend more time in Eve's house, he pressed her for permission to make his petition to the Tsar.

"The thing takes time," he said. "We should start it now. I have been to the French Embassy and they tell me that for a man in my position it is not improbable that the Tsar will see fit to grant a personal audience."

The idea of being presented to the Tsar of All the Russias, perhaps in some kind of uniform that might be approved by the French Embassy, was one that appealed to Balzac's imagination.

Eve would not hear of his making any approach to the Tsar.

"Not a move must be made until my appeal in the Superior Court has been decided," she told him. "There is too much at stake and my lawyers tell me that one wrong move could ruin everything."

Balzac agreed to wait.

A few days later, cautiously, Eve sounded out Balzac on the subject of his debts.

"Marriage is more than a romantic affair," she said. "There is the matter of money, property, settlements. Are you sure that you are in a position to marry?"

"In a position to marry?" he said. "I don't understand you."

"I have been told that you are deeply in debt," she said.

"Ahhh! Aunt Rosalie!" Balzac said.

"Does it matter?" said Eve.

They were in the main sitting room of Eve's Koutaizoff Mansion. Above the chimney piece was a portrait of some ancestor of Eve's, a massive Pole with a square jaw, wearing a tall fur hat ornamented with a jeweled badge. The eyes were an intense, impossible, blue, blue encountered only in porcelain, the pupils highlighted in such a way that Eve's forebear looked down on Balzac with a fierce and disapproving stare. Balzac stared back boldly, then wrinkled his nose at the portrait.

"I don't deny that I am in debt," he said soberly. "It is the price of devotion to literature. All my life I have been swindled by editors and publishers, because I have been too concerned with creating to attend to my mundane affairs. It's not that I lack shrewdness. If I had been a wholesale grocer, for example, I should be a rich man today."

"If you were a grocer, you would not be here," said Eve briskly. "The point is, how can you think of marrying, when you are so compromised by debt?"

"What does money matter!" he exclaimed angrily.

"It matters," said Eve, the two words like shots from a pistol.

Balzac promised that his debts would be paid—the greater share of them at least—before the marriage was celebrated. How this was to be done, he had no idea, but he was determined to marry if it meant turning highway robber.

"The attitude of my family might be changed somewhat if you were a member of the French Academy," Eve suggested, a little later. "My brother says that important French writers are elected as a matter of course."

She had touched a sensitive nerve. Balzac raised his eyebrows.

"Tell your brother to put his mind at rest," he said coldly. "It is a certainty that I will be made officially immortal when the next vacancy occurs. I have the word of Victor Hugo for that, and he is a power in the French Academy."

This was stretching the truth, but Balzac felt that he was justified. After all, Hugo had said many times that Balzac *ought* to be in the Academy. Hugo had even gone so far as to say that a French Academy without Balzac was absurd.

"There is also the matter of the Legion of Honor," Eve went on mercilessly. "Aunt Rosalie says that you have been excluded because of your loose way of life and your indifference to public opinion."

"Public opinion!" Balzac said. "Tell your aunt that the Legion of Honor is a haven for druggists and former mayors. Red rosettes are becoming as common as were red cockades in the revolution, and not much more meaningful."

He pretended to be indifferent to the fact that he had been passed over by the Academy and the Legion of Honor. It was not so. He was bitterly resentful, and as he sat here in Eve's Russian drawing room, he made up his mind to take both citadels of prestige by storm when he returned to France.

Though Eve evaded every effort that Balzac made to extract a definite promise of marriage, as his mistress she denied him nothing. At night they were like young lovers. They whispered pet names in the dark. They had a private language, almost lewd, which enabled them to refer in public to the most intimate contacts enjoyed between Eve's blue silk sheets.

The effect on Balzac was tonic. He had told Nacquart that for him the fountain of youth was in Saint Petersburg, and it seemed to be true. He felt young and vigorous, capable of anything. Intimations of illness or death were absurd.

He adored his Eve, and during this Russian summer of passion he was blind to all her faults. His love became the central fact of his life, a true obsession now, abnormal and not to be controlled.

He left Saint Petersburg in October, having extracted from Eve a conditional agreement. If the lawsuit were settled in her favor, so that Wierzchownia was saved, if Anna were safely engaged to be married, if Balzac's debts were paid and his life put in order, if the Tsar gave his permission—then, possibly, a marriage might be considered.

Balzac returned to France by the overland route, unwilling to risk a second encounter with the Baltic Sea. He was satisfied, filled with confidence in the future. His powers of self-deception were as marvelous as his powers of creation. He had a promise in his pocket. There were conditions, it was true, but it did not occur to him to doubt Eve's good faith.

523

Chapter 49

WHEN THE COURTS in Saint Petersburg decided the appeal in Eve's favor and she was the unchallenged mistress of Wierzchownia, Balzac saw a break in the clouds. One obstacle, at least, had been removed. There remained Anna and his debts.

"I am going to Dresden for a holiday," Eve wrote him cheerfully. "This legal warfare has been exhausting and I feel the need to relax in surroundings more diverting than those at Wierzchownia."

Balzac joined her in Dresden. The fear of scandal was behind her now, and he moved into the hotel suite in which she was living. She was generous to him, passionate, entirely agreeable, until the subject of marriage was mentioned.

"Why are you not satisfied with what you have?" she asked bluntly one day. "Why do you insist on marriage?"

Balzac considered the question for a moment, then answered simply, "I want a home. I have never had a home, even as a child."

Eve laughed at him.

"At heart you are bourgeois as any grocer, my dear Balzac," she said. "When you speak of a home, the tone you use calls up visions of carpet slippers before the fire and interminable family meals at a round table in a dining room with dreadful decor."

Balzac flushed. In Dresden, Eve had acquired a brittle manner that disturbed him. From his point of view, Dresden was a poor meeting place. The town was filled with Poles and Russians, wealthy aristocrats who sought in Saxony a breath of the freedom denied them at home. They were people Eve had known since childhood. Some of them were relatives, some family friends. All were amused by Eve's affair with Balzac, indulgent so long as Balzac was merely her lover, but appalled by the idea of marriage.

In any case, there was Anna, sixteen, nearly seventeen, and

524

without a suitor who met with Eve's approval. When Balzac suggested that Eve set standards no young man alive could meet, he was told to attend to his own concerns.

"I am not trying to marry off a mud-faced girl from Tours, with a dowry of ten thousand francs," Eve said angrily. "Anna will be a rich woman. I do not intend to give her to the first good-looking guardsman who puts his face in the door."

"You keep me living like a bird on a branch," Balzac complained.

"Have you paid your debts?" Eve demanded accusingly. "There was more than one side to the bargain, you know."

Balzac returned to Paris.

Eve went from Dresden to Kannstadt, from Kannstadt to Strasbourg. Balzac followed her, though he could not afford it and in spite of Nacquart's disapproval. So ardently did Balzac pursue Eve across central Europe that his good friend Delphine de Girardin called him "the coachman of love."

For months Balzac tried to persuade Eve to come to France with her daughter. He thought that once she had seen Paris, and the glories of French civilization, her resistance would be dissolved.

"The air of France will persuade her," he told Gautier.

But the Tsar had forbidden his subjects to travel in France, a country that he regarded as alive with dangerous ideas and underlayered with red revolution. Eve was unwilling to take the risk of incurring the Tsar's displeasure.

"You forget my responsibilities," she told him. "If I were to defy the Tsar, he is quite capable of confiscating all my property."

Finally, Balzac hit on an idea. He had French passports issued in the names of his sister Laure and one of Laure's children. Eve and her daughter crossed the French frontier as *"Madame de Surville et fille."*

Balzac wanted to show them Paris, but Eve was afraid.

"There are as many Poles in Paris as there are in Warsaw," she said. "We cannot take the risk."

They went to Fontainebleau, to Orléans, to Bourges. Balzac was like a happy child, showing his presents. Eve was unimpressed, and she complained about the accommodations. It was Anna who saved the day. Anna was delighted with everything. She exclaimed over the food. She wept over Joan of Arc, when they stood in the square in Orléans. She was perfect.

"Would you like to see the prison house where I went to school?" he asked her.

"I would like to see everything!" she said. "I love France!"

They went to Vendôme and paid a visit to the college.

"You have read LOUIS LAMBERT," Balzac told Eve. "Now you will see the desk at which the actual Louis Lambert sat, the stocks in which he was punished."

To Balzac's astonishment, Monsieur Mareschal was still alive and still in command at the Collège de Vendôme. He was white haired now and feeble, walking with the aid of a stick. It amused Balzac to observe that he was an officer of the Legion of Honor.

"It gives us pride to welcome our most distinguished former student," Monsieur Mareschel said deferentially.

One would have thought that Balzac had passed through Vendôme with the highest honors, instead of having been carted away by Nacquart, speechless and in disgrace.

With Eve and Anna at his side, Balzac passed through the dank corridors, populated by dozens of little boys who wore the hated uniform of prickly grey cloth. The boys looked just like the boys who had been there in Balzac's day. There were the same runny noses, the same chillblained knees. The smell was the same.

Balzac hesitated at the door of his old classroom, then took a deep breath and entered. The room was empty. The battered forms and benches were there and so was the fat little stove in which had been burnt Balzac's treatise of the human will. He sat down for a moment in his old place, forgetting his companions. From the courtyard outside came the shouts and cries of boys at play. Balzac closed his eyes. He half expected to hear the voice of Father Haugoult:

"Balzac! You are doing nothing!"

It was all here, the scene of his childhood misery, yet he felt very little. For him, the Collège de Vendôme and most of its tortures had been laid to rest years ago in the pages of LOUIS LAMBERT. That was at least one advantage offered by the thorny trade of writing, he thought. One's ghosts could be laid to rest. Once he had been written about, Father Haugoult had ceased to possess the power to inspire terror. It had been the same with the Duchesse de Castries.

"Monsieur, the smell in this place is appalling!" said Eve with some asperity.

The sound of her voice brought Balzac out of his revery. He got up and apologized and they passed through the gates of the school, into the bright sunlight.

"Are they bad little boys in that school?" asked Anna.

"No worse than most," said Balzac.

"Then why are they being punished?" the young girl wanted to know. "It is a prison, is it not?"

Balzac laughed softly.

They went through the Valley of the Loire. At the sight of the great châteaux, Eve's spirits brightened. These were things she understood, these palaces of the rich.

At Tours, Eve announced that they must go to Brussels.

"Why to that dull town?" Balzac asked.

"We are meeting a young man there who may just do for Anna," Eve said thoughtfully.

"Are you serious?" said Balzac.

His heart pounded with excitement. If a husband were found for Anna, the only thing in the way of marriage would be the Tsar of Russia . . . and his own debts.

"Quite serious," Eve said. "Of course there is nothing definite. Nothing has been settled."

The suitor who waited in Brussels was Count George Mniszech, a mild and pleasant young Polish nobleman, with an innocuous talent for drawing and an absolute passion for entomology. One of the trunks that went with him on his travels contained a collection of insects, mounted on velvet-covered boards, catalogued and labeled.

"My God, he is another Count Hanski," Balzac said to himself. "A bug-watcher, this one, instead of a bird-watcher."

Balzac was genuinely fond of Anna and though it was in his own interest to see her safely married, he could not prevent himself from suggesting that young Count Mniszech, as a lover, might leave something to be desired.

"I know. You would like to see her married to a handsome cavalry officer without a penny to his name," Eve said. "Count Mniszech has virtues that do not appear on the surface."

Count Mniszech's virtues were his tractability and a million-odd acres of good rich Polish soil. He was heir to an estate even larger than the Hanski domain at Wierzchownia.

Young Count Mniszech joined Eve and her daughter for a period of probation. Balzac went along, and they traveled to Genoa, to Geneva, to Basle, to Heidelburg, crisscrossing over Europe, rich people on a holiday. They went to Rome. Though his best books had been condemned by the church and would find their way to the *Index Librorum Prohibitorum,* Balzac went to the Vatican with Eve, stood in the patient queue, and when his turn came, dutifully kissed the Pope's satin slipper.

They went on to Switzerland.

At Soleure, in the high Alps, Eve stood with Balzac one evening on a hotel balcony, facing the improbable mountains that were bathed in pink evening light. She seemed preoccupied. He took her hand and held it. She looked at him with unusual tenderness, then bent toward him and whispered.

"I am pregnant," she said. "I am with child."

Balzac was wild with delight, certain that his troubles were over at last.

"We must be married at once," he said. "The child must be born in wedlock."

"It would be preferable, I admit," she said. "Still, I cannot marry until Anna and George are safely wed. It would be unseemly for the mother to marry before the daughter."

A few weeks later, Anna was married in a barn-like church at Wiesbaden. Balzac served as one of the witnesses. He stood behind the bridal couple, listening to the nuptial Latin, certain that the last great obstacle was gone. Even without the Tsar's permission, even if they must be married in secret, he and Eve would be married at last.

Balzac was infatuated with the idea that he was going to become a father. He was the caricature of a man with a pregnant wife, fussing over Eve like a mother hen, giving her advice about diet, making sure she was warmly dressed.

The child of course was to be a boy.

"We will call him Victor-Honoré," Balzac decided. "Then he will have the names of the two greatest French writers of the century."

"And if *he* is a girl?" said Eve.

528

Balzac ignored her.

"Victor-Honoré de Balzac!" he said. "It has a powerful sound!"

Eve seemed disinterested in the child and in Balzac. Now that Anna was married, she was eager to get back to Wierzchownia, to see to the affairs of the estate, and the intervention of pregnancy was a delay that merely annoyed her.

She agreed to be married before the child was born if Balzac could find a mayor or prefect who would perform the ceremony and agree to keep it a secret. She preferred giving birth to a bastard to running the risk of arousing the wrath of Nicholas the First. She had met the Tsar and knew his temper; he was not the man to be trifled with and he had a profound suspicion of everything French.

Balzac succeeded in persuading the mayor of the border city of Metz to perform a secret marriage.

"Later on we can be properly married by a priest," he explained to Eve. "But at least Victor-Honoré will be legitimate, no matter what happens."

Eve agreed rather sullenly. She was having a bad pregnancy. From the first month she had been nauseous, and each day she became more irritable, complaining of the difficult lot that the Lord has assigned to womankind, more than ever impatient with various of Balzac's mannerisms that she disliked.

"To be married in a closet by the mayor of a dreary provincial town may be your idea of something important but it isn't mine," she told Balzac. "Count Hanski and I were married in a cathedral, by a bishop."

At the last moment she went back on the agreement.

"It is too risky," she insisted. "How do you know the mayor can be trusted? The Tsar has secret agents everywhere in France."

"Very well, we will go to Paris," said Balzac wearily.

He took Eve to his house in Passy, not knowing where else to take her. For most of the time she was too ill to go out, or too ill-natured to be willing to leave Balzac's bedroom, once she had been established. Her pregnancy became an illness. Balzac was in despair.

She fretted constantly about her estate at Wierzchownia.

"The overseer is a thief," she insisted. "He is in league with

529

Hanski's uncle—the one who tried to rob Anna of her birthright."

When Balzac tried to reassure her, she lashed out at him furiously.

"You know nothing about it!" she shieked. "How dare you contradict me?"

Balzac apologized.

"You have always lived like a Gypsy," she said contemptuously. "You have no conception of what it means to be responsible for a large estate. The serfs are drunkards, sodden oafs. The foremen are thieves. Things go to rack and ruin when the mistress is absent too long."

Nothing satisfied her.

She complained about the size of the rooms in Balzac's house, assuming that all of the rooms in Paris were like those in Passy.

"You live in birdcages here in Paris," she said.

He promised her that when they were married they would live in a house the size of a palace.

She complained of the noise from the streets.

He promised her silence.

She moaned with pain.

He tried to console her.

A man less obsessed than Balzac would have concluded that she was a shrew and that he was fortunate to have escaped being bound to her in matrimony. Not Balzac. He saw virtue in every complaint. He blamed himself that the house was small, the district noisy, the weather not to Eve's liking.

And he persuaded himself that everything would be different, once Victor-Honoré saw the light of the Paris day. A child to nurse, to adore, that would soon take Eve's mind off her troubles and all her complaints would vanish in a sweet pink cloud of maternal love.

Louise Breugniot nursed Eve and put up with her bad temper for Balzac's sake and in return for a gift of money. When she was ill, Nacquart attended her. Balzac was her servant, secretary and whipping boy. She ruled the little house in Passy like a sick and intemperate queen. The table beside Balzac's bed was loaded with ivory toilet articles and a dozen bottles of perfume and cologne. Hours at a time Eve lay in bed, holding a mirror before her face, contemplating her beauty.

530

Out of boredom, she stuffed herself with food and demanded all sorts of odd things to eat, for which Balzac obediently searched in the stalls at Les Halles. At midnight, she wanted a pineapple. He went to the market and bought one for her. She insisted on oysters when there were none in Paris. Balzac sent to Brittany and a small cask of oysters came, packed in wet seaweed. They were not to her taste; she refused them.

Balzac and Louise sat at the kitchen table and ate them. Louise touched Balzac's hand.

"It is not my place to speak," she said quietly. "But the Countess Hanska is not good enough for you."

Balzac was furious. He rose from his chair and stood over Louise with a fist raised in the air.

"How dare you speak?" he demanded. "You are here to be of service, not to give advice."

Louise said nothing. Balzac sat down, staring at the pile of grey blue shells beside his plate. After a little he looked up and said, "I am sorry to have lost my temper, Louise. You meant well, I understand. But you are wrong. She is a sick woman now, and she has suffered a great deal for my sake."

As he spoke, Eve's bell rang out fiercely. Louise got up from the table.

"I will go and see what she wants," she said.

"No. I will go," said Balzac.

As he climbed the stairs to the bedroom, Eve shook the bell again. In the narrow hallway the sound was hideous.

"I am coming," called Balzac. "I am coming."

Early in December, Eve's labor began, late at night.

The midwife was summoned. After an hour she came to the door of Eve's bedroom and shook her head.

"There is something wrong, monsieur," she said. "I think madame should have a doctor."

Louise ran through the night to fetch Nacquart. Balzac held Eve's hand until he arrived. She was in agony, writhing on the bed, biting her lip against the pain.

When Nacquart arrived, Balzac was exiled from the bedchamber. Louise and the midwife boiled water and brought Nacquart dozens of bright clean towels.

Balzac sat in his workroom, feeling utterly useless. For a time he heard Eve's shrieking, the sound muffled by the heavy door. He suffered with her.

Then he heard nothing.

"It must be over," he said to himself. "The child must have been born at last."

He held his breath, listening for the telltale wail that should announce Victor-Honoré's first breath of the air of earth.

He heard nothing.

He tiptoed to the bedroom door and placed an ear against the paneling. He could hear the sounds of movement within, then the sound of water being poured from a kettle into a basin. He had the impulse to open the door and demand to see his son. He controlled himself and went back to his shabby red armchair. For the first time in many years he appealed to the Virgin for help.

An hour later the bedroom door opened slowly. The hinges creaked as if the door were reluctant to open. Balzac got to his feet. In the doorway stood Nacquart. There was blood on his shirt and on his hands and forearms. He was exhausted and his face was grave.

"How is she?" Balzac demanded.

"She is very ill but she will live," Nacquart said.

"And the baby? Victor-Honoré?" Balzac asked.

"The baby is dead," Nacquart told him. "It was born dead."

"No!" Balzac thundered.

Nacquart touched his shoulder. Balzac covered his face with his hands.

"Victor-Honoré," he sobbed.

"It was a girl, 'Noré," said Nacquart gently.

Balzac's head went up. His lip stiffened.

"Of course," he said dully. "A boy would never have deserted his mother."

He started for the bedroom; Nacquart stopped him.

"I've given her something to make her sleep," he said. "Don't disturb her now, 'Noré. She's been through a dreadful ordeal."

"I want to see the child," said Balzac.

"I don't advise it," said Nacquart.

"I insist," said Balzac stubbornly.

"Very well," said Nacquart, sighing.

The shriveled, strangled corpse had been wrapped in a heavy towel. It was grotesque, like a tiny, lacerated pig. Balzac sobbed. Nacquart covered the little body.

532

"It must be baptized," Balzac insisted. "It may have lived, even for a few seconds."

"I will arrange it," Nacquart promised. "Now you must get some rest, Honoré. It will be hours before Madame de Hanska wakes up."

Balzac looked at Eve. She was sleeping heavily, under the influence of Nacquart's drug. She looked calm and unconcerned. For an instant Balzac felt a flash of anger against her for not having given him the child he had wanted. It passed. He bent and kissed her forehead. He and Nacquart went out of the room.

"What happened?" Balzac asked.

Nacquart shrugged.

"It is a malformation of the womb," he said. "To me it is incredible that she has ever given birth to a living child." He put a hand on Balzac's shoulder. "Certainly, my dear chap, she will never have another," he said.

To Balzac, the fact that Eve would never be able to give him a son was prophetic as well as tragic. He took it as a personal reprimand from God. He sat in his study and cursed himself, reviewing the catalogue of his sins. His sense of guilt was so profound that he was unable to pray. He thought that it would be an effrontery for a creature so vile as himself to make an appeal to God.

Eve seemed scarcely affected by the death of the child. She recovered quickly from the ordeal. In a few days she was sitting up and demanding exotic food. In a week, she was out of bed, trying on her clothes before Balzac's full length mirror. Balzac was baffled. She seemed relieved rather than disappointed.

When he mentioned their marriage plans, she laughed.

"Certainly there's no need now for a hurried wedding," she said carelessly. "Before I think of anything else I must get back to Wierzchownia, to see how much those vultures have robbed from my child."

"Always it is Anna," Balzac said. "She will always come first with you, won't she, Eve?"

"Would you have me turn my back on my own flesh and blood?" Eve demanded.

"But she is married. She has a husband to protect her," said Balzac.

533

"A husband!" said Eve scornfully. "She has George Mniszech. He needs protection as much as she. I tell you, I have a duty to perform and it is in Poland not in Paris."

"Let me come with you," Balzac begged. "Perhaps I can be of some service."

Eve shook her head firmly.

"It is out of the question," she said. "If you came to Poland with me now, my position would be weakened. I shall need all my strength and authority."

At this moment Louise knocked, then entered the room, bringing Eve's afternoon tea. Eve watched her cynically while she poured out the tea and served the little cakes. When she had gone, Eve looked at Balzac and smiled.

"Why should you miss me?" she said. "You will have your housekeeper to console you when I am gone."

"What are you suggesting?" Balzac asked, unable to meet her glance.

Eve laughed contemptuously.

"I am not an innocent, my dear de Balzac," she said. "Of course you sleep with her. Probably you have been sleeping with her while I suffered with your child. What does it matter? She is only a servant."

"My God Eve, I love you!" Balzac cried in agony. "Can't you understand that I love you?"

"So you have said many times," Eve said complacently. "There is more to love than pretty words of the kind you put into your novels."

Sometimes she enjoyed putting Balzac on the rack. She had a deep strain of ancient Slavic cruelty in her makeup. Part of her temperament was reconciled to the philosophy of the knout. Against this kind of cruelty, Balzac was powerless, as he had always been without armor to protect himself from the cruelty of his mother.

After a time her mood changed. She became affectionate again. Balzac blamed all of her bitterness on the agonies she had suffered. She promised him that she would send for him as soon as things had been put in order on the estate.

"You understand that I must go alone to prepare the way?" she said. "When they have got used to the idea, then you can come."

"Of course. I understand," he told her.

As soon as she was well enough to travel, Eve made a whirl-wind shopping tour of Paris, buying clothes and jewels and per-fume and new trunks to carry them in. Now that she was on her way to Poland, she was frenetic and gay. She was also filled with recklessness. When Balzac mentioned his investments and his con-nection with Baron de Rothschild, Eve proposed that they estab-lish a joint fund for the future. She gave him fifty thousand francs the day before she set out for Poland by the overland route through Germany.

Balzac was stunned. A few weeks earlier she had seemed to take delight in torturing him. Now she took it for granted that their fortunes were joined. She was unpredictable as the wind. He put it down to the Slavic temperament and asked Rothschild to advise him about investing the money.

"I would suggest that you put the money into shares of the Chemin de Fer du Nord," Rothschild advised him. "From the point of view of growth, railway shares are the best investment."

"I rely on your judgement," Balzac told him, flattered, as al-ways, by his connection with famous banker.

"If you like, you can come into a combine with my associates and myself," Rothschild said. "That way, your fifty thousand francs will control a hundred thousand shares of stock."

"But if the stock goes down?" Balzac asked.

The banker shrugged.

"If the stock goes down, one merely covers the difference with cash," he said.

"Put me down for fifty thousand, in your combine," Balzac said heartily, having no idea where he would get the money to cover his margin, should the shares drop on the Bourse.

He went out of Rothschild's office filled with the heady self-confidence of a man who has made a wise investment.

Alone for the first time in nearly a year, Balzac looked to his own affairs. His work had been shamefully neglected. So had his friends. He was out of touch with the literary world of Paris. As soon as Eve was on the train, he went to the Church of Saint-Ger-main-des-Prés and lit a candle for his dead child. Then he crossed the river to the right bank and went from one literary café to another, looking for Théophile Gautier, one friend he knew would not complain of having been neglected these last months.

535

"Théo, my boy," he told Gautier, when they were dining together that evening in a modest restaurant that Gautier liked. "I wish we had kept the Order of the Red Horse together. I need friends with influence in high places. This year I am determined to pass three milestones. One, I plan to get rid of my debts. Two, I intend to be elected to the French Academy. Three, I plan to be married to the most beautiful woman in Poland."

Gautier smiled and ran a hand through his magnificent, unruly hair.

"If I were rich I would pay your debts," he said good-naturedly. "If I were a member of the French Academy, I would without cease agitate for your election. If I were a priest, I would marry you free of charge. As I am none of these things, the best I can do is to buy your dinner."

Balzac laughed. He had missed Gautier and he had missed his work. He was filled with plans and schemes, with ideas for books, stories and articles.

"I might even try another play," he said self-confidently. "MERCADET is not so bad, you know."

"Stick to books," advised Gautier. "Leave the playwriting to Dumas."

"Dumas!" said Balzac contemptuously. "What he can do, I can do twice as well and in half the time. Why the man is a public fraud. Half of what he publishes is written by hired assistants."

"That sounds like the old Balzac," Gautier said with approval. "Whenever you denounce Dumas with exceptional vigor, I know that you are getting ready to write a first-class novel."

Chapter 50

In all of his complicated dealings with publishers, Balzac had been shrewd enough never to part with his single most valuable literary asset— the right to publish his collected works in a uniform edition. He had always regarded these rights as a kind of trust fund or insurance policy. Now, with marriage to Eve actually in prospect, the time had come to draw on this reserve.

Always, when he began a project, Balzac was as crafty as any banker; it was only later, when he had become intoxicated with his own enthusiasms, that his various schemes went wrong.

With the aid of his friends, Théo Gautier and Laurent Jan, Balzac permitted the publishing world of Paris to discover that he was preparing a uniform edition of his collected works, each title carefully revised and supplied with an author's preface especially written for this edition. Balzac knew that what he had to sell was one of the most valuable literary properties in Europe, and he wanted to place the publishers in a position where they must bid against one another.

Gautier and Laurent Jan talked the thing up in the salons and cafés where publishers gathered. Balzac himself sat on his hands, saying nothing, behaving like a good natured Sphinx, playing the waiting game.

He had settled down to work in Passy, with Louise to look after him. He went out hardly at all, except for his nocturnal walks, and cut himself off from his acquaintances except for Gautier and Jan.

Balzac's friends did their spade work well. At the end of a few weeks, Balzac had a dozen offers from first-class publishers. He decided to take the offer of a syndicate headed by P. J. Hetzel, who suggested a down payment of fifteen thousand francs for the rights to what had been written of THE HUMAN COMEDY, to be issued in sixteen closely printed volumes.

537

Hetzel was a man of some judgment and Balzac got on with him.

"There should be a general introduction," Hetzel said. "Something that will outline the grand design of your work for the ordinary reader."

Balzac agreed and suggested that George Sand be commissioned to write it.

"She is too controversial," Hetzel objected. "And she would not be able to resist the chance to air her own theories of life, love and art."

"Sainte-Beuve would be the right man, but Sainte-Beuve detests me," Balzac said. "What about Gautier? He's brilliant, and he understands my work."

"Not quite strong enough," said Hetzel.

"It is a problem," Balzac admitted. "Most of the well-known critics have had their noses tweaked by me at one time or another. You know I've never played the game with these literary cliques and clacques."

"I think you should write the introduction yourself," said Hetzel thoughtfully. "It is too important to entrust to anyone else."

"Hetzel, you are trying to kill me," Balzac said. "I have three new books on the fire and several hundred sheets of proof to correct."

"Even so," said Hetzel. "No one else really grasps what you have in mind. After all, it is probably the greatest conception in the history of literature."

"Very well, I will write it," agreed Balzac wearily.

The sixteen pages that comprise the standard introduction to THE HUMAN COMEDY cost Balzac as much energy as the composition of a full-length novel, and in his present state of health he knew that every book he wrote almost certainly shortened his life.

In the course of the last twenty years he had published enough for ten writers and given the world at least six books that stood unchallenged as masterpieces. He was exhausted, body and soul, but he could not afford to rest. In front of him were the three mountains he had sworn that he would conquer within the next twelve months—freedom from debt, the Academy, marriage to Eve.

"Be as modest and objective as you can in the introduction,"

538

Hetzel had advised him. "Imagine that you are an old man, looking at yourself down an avenue of the years. Speak like one of your own characters, and you will produce something of indispensable value."

Balzac took up his pen, considering what the publisher had said.

"Speak like one of your own characters," he repeated. "A sound enough idea, but which shall it be? Old Goriot, the prisoner of love? Vautrin, the archcriminal? Young Rastignac, the careerist?"

There were two thousand characters in THE HUMAN COMEDY; eventually there would be five thousand. Balzac was all of them and he was none of them. He dipped his pen in the ink and wrote as Honoré de Balzac, novelist.

"Chance is the greatest of all novelists," he wrote. "In order to be creative, one has only to study it. French society is the real author of THE HUMAN COMEDY. Balzac has merely guided its pen. By taking an inventory of its virtues and vices, selecting the most significant social occurrences and forming types by the combination of similarly constituted characters, perhaps I have managed to write the history of morals for our time, which so many who profess to be historians have forgotten to do."

Putting down on paper what he had done and what he planned to do gave Balzac a grasp on life firmer than what he had had in the past, and filled him with intensity of purpose. Once and for all he was done with the world of the Faubourg Saint-Germain, that shallow, brittle remnant of the past, with which he had for so long been infatuated. People like the Duchesse de Castries had no charms for him now. His friends were literary people—Gautier, George Sand, Laurent Jan.

George Sand was in Paris again with her lover, Frédéric Chopin. Balzac often dined with them, arguing with George, listening to Chopin play the piano.

Frère George's bohemianism was in full flower. Her café au lait sitting room was like a Turkish boudoir. The floor was covered with a red carpet upon which George often sat, puffing away at a long cigarette.

Half in earnest, half as a joke, Balzac one night praised the absolutism of Russia, managing to infuriate the libertarian George, who was moving more and more to the Left and making dire predictions of bloody revolution in France, Germany and Russia.

"When the serfs rise in their misery and march, the heads of your Russian aristocrats will roll in the gutters," promised George. "If you are wise you will persuade your countess to liberate her serfs, sell her lands, and emigrate from Poland."

Balzac laughed.

"If you could see the Tsar, you would find yourself infatuated," he told George.

When the argument grew too bitter, Chopin rose and went to the piano, playing one of his own preludes, ignoring Balzac and George. He did not play with the bravura of Liszt, but Balzac thought he was the most intelligent musician in Europe.

Balzac enjoyed sitting in George Sand's exotic parlor, listening to Chopin play the piano, staring meditatively at George or at one of the handsome Delacroix paintings on the walls.

Nowadays Balzac found such an interlude more rewarding than a dozen evenings passed in the fashionable salons. He sometimes regretted the time and energy he had wasted trying to storm the bastions of the Faubourg Saint-Germain. He often remembered Madame de Berny's warning. Still, he reflected, it was not too late to change his life. He was in the middle of his forties, no longer young, perhaps, but by no means old.

Reason told him that most of his best years should still be before him. He clung to the idea of heredity and thought of the long span that his father had managed. Nevertheless, sometimes in the dead of night he had the sharp premonition of death.

Often, nowadays, he was tired to the point of exhaustion for no reason, and his nervous system declined to respond to the stimulus of caffeine.

"I drown myself in coffee," he complained to Gautier. "I might as well drink hot water for all the good it does."

"Try hashish," Gautier suggested. "Come with me tonight and eat some."

The oriental drug had recently become fashionable in Paris and Gautier had taken it up. Balzac was curious, remembering the latakia he had smoked in George Sand's hookah and the potent effect it had had on his brain.

"I might as well be a dope fiend as a tired old man," he said. "All right, Théo, I'll come with you."

That night they drove halfway across Paris to a damp alley in the Latin Quarter. Gautier led the way down a narrow flight of

540

stone steps to what had once been a wine celler, now a bizarre room decorated with rugs and brasses, furnished with a number of low Turkish couches. There were half a dozen people in the room, men and women. One of them was a gaunt young man with haunted eyes who rose to greet Gautier.

"This is Charles Baudelaire," said Théo. "He is by way of being a poet when he is not eating hashish."

Baudelaire was already under the influence of the drug. He bowed, took Balzac's hand and kissed it, then addressed him as master, and began to praise his books.

"We have come to eat hashish, Charles, not to listen to your literary opinions," said Gautier. Sit down."

Baudelaire returned to his couch. Balzac and Théo sat down and presently an obsequious Algerian appeared, offering them cakes of hashish. The cakes were the size of a walnut, grey green in color. Balzac bit into one and nibbled on it. It was like dried grass. The taste was slightly bitter, but not unpleasant.

"One must eat at least three cakes," Gautier told Balzac.

Obediently, Balzac finished three of the walnut-sized cakes. Then he sat on his couch and waited for the miraculous effects he had been promised.

Gautier, Baudelaire and the others had entered a trance-like state. On one of the couches a boy and girl made shameless love, very slowly. Balzac felt nothing. He tried to relax. He made an effort to encourage the drug to work on his senses.

Nothing happened.

For all he felt he might as well have eaten bread as hashish. If he did not see that his companions were under the influence of the drug, he would have thought that the Algerian had swindled him.

"My brain is too strong for it," he assured Gautier, when they were driving back to Passy, having left young Baudelaire in the cellar, wrapped in the dreams evoked by half a dozen cakes of hashish.

Gautier shook his head briskly and rubbed his temples, trying to throw off the after effects of the drug. He looked at Balzac with curiosity and a certain amount of awe.

"Truly, 'Noré, you felt nothing?" he asked.

Balzac shook his head and answered, "Nothing. Nothing at all."

"You are not human," said Gautier.

"On the contrary," said Balzac. "I am altogether human. The effect of a drug depends on the way in which one has exercised his brain. I have a theory about it."

"Of that much, I'm certain," said Gautier drily.

"Laugh if you like," Balzac said. "History will prove that I am right. There are compartments in the human brain. Some are open, some half open, some not open at all, except in sleep or when we are otherwise unconscious."

Balzac was fascinated by anything that had to do with the working of the human brain. Recently he had been reading a book on madness by the authority, Dr. Moreau. As soon as he finished the sixteen volumes of THE HUMAN COMEDY that he owed Hetzel, he intended to study anatomy and morphology at the medical school. He thought of asking Dr. Moreau to take him as a special student, and to make a study of madness.

He had a thousand ideas. His brain was bubbling like the brain of a young student at the Sorbonne, but more often than not he could not find the energy to exploit what was in his mind. Time after time these days, when Louise came to his bedroom to wake him up at the appointed hour, he found it impossible to rise for an hour or two after he had been called and the candles in his workroom had been lighted. Too often, when he got to his work table, his hand refused to hold the pen, his brain declined to function.

What he felt was not precisely illness, but a lack of life, a difficulty of *being*.

"What is the matter with me, Nacquart?" he demanded desperately. "I am alive but I feel dead."

"You must rest," Nacquart said curtly.

Nacquart warned him again and again. One day, writing a prescription for Balzac's heart, he said brutally, hoping to shock his patient and friend, "You will die!"

Balzac shook his head.

"Oh no," he told Nacquart. "I have a private god of my own, a god stronger than all your diseases."

Nacquart sighed and handed him the prescription.

"I hope that if you marry you will take two years off for rest," he said. "It is not a matter of a week in bed any longer, 'Noré. You need a long rest. Very long."

542

"When I am married I will be happy," Balzac said, as if he repeated a chemical formula. "When I am happy I shall not need rest."

Nacquart threw up his hands, snapped the locks on his bag, and departed.

Aside from Nacquart, only Louise and Gautier knew the truth about Balzac's health. He appeared to be robust as ever. When he went out in public he forced himself to exhibit the vitality for which he was famous, even though the effort expended put him to bed for a day.

He had a dread fear that if gossip started about his health it would somehow reach Wierzchownia. To publishers and casual acquaintances he boasted that he had never been more fit, that he intended to outlive his father, and that he was going to write a hundred novels before he died, novels such as had never been written.

Nacquart and Gautier watched him. Both men loved him, yet there was nothing they could do.

"He is breaking up inside," said Nacquart. "It is not so much a matter of his embarrassed heart. It is the whole machine. He has demanded too much of the flesh, you see."

"Yet he must marry his countess," said Théo. "His heart and soul are set on it."

Balzac took it for granted that THE HUMAN COMEDY would get him into the French Academy. With some justice, he declared that a French Academy that did not include him was an absurdity. Of the forty immortals now ensconced, actually only two were fit to fill his inkwells—Victor Hugo and Alphonse Lamartine. A few of the others were good men, like his old friend Charles Nodier of the Arsenal Library, but they were not men of stature and two-thirds of the seats were filled by nonentities. Balzac was so certain of being elected that he was already counting on the honorarium of two thousand francs.

Regretting that he had not kept the Order of the Red Horse alive, Balzac undertook to lobby in his own behalf when a seat became vacant. Inside the Academy he had the support of Hugo, Lamartine and Nodier.

It was not enough.

The Academicians upon whom he called in search of support

543

received him with stiff formality. All of them were men of substance, men who lived in big houses, kept large staffs of servants, maintained various carriages. A few of them were blunt enough to mention Balzac's famous debts to his face. One man looked through his lorgnette and suggested to Balzac that he change his tailor. The aristocratic and newly elected member, the Duc de Noailles, was reported to have said, "I am afraid that Monsieur de Balzac is too large for our chairs."

When the votes were cast, the vacant seat and the coat with palms went not to Balzac but to a rich nonentity.

Balzac was bitter about it.

"If honest poverty keeps me out now, I shall never apply again, no matter how rich I may become in the future," he said to Gautier.

"Your debts are nothing but an excuse," said Gautier. "The fact is, the timeservers inside the Academy are afraid of you, 'Noré."

Gautier, of course, was right. To keep Balzac out of the Academy was like drawing up a list of French generals and leaving off the name of Napoleon. Yet it was done. The French Academy, like most official bodies of its kind, preferred to avoid the dangerous and the disconcerting, and naturally it was inclined to fight shy of genius, especially in times like these, with Louis-Philippe on the throne and the merchant middle class everywhere in the saddle.

After his first flash of bitter anger, Balzac pretended to be indifferent to his rejection. Actually, the wound was a deep one. He had wanted the honor for himself and because he had promised it to Eve.

And, though it was something he did not care to admit to himself, he wanted it for his mother.

Nowadays, his mother gave him no peace.

She complained incessantly about her lack of money, about his neglect, about the unsettled character of his life. Balzac made her a decent allowance and he knew that she lived in comfort, if not in the lap of luxury.

When she learned that he had been refused by the Academy, she was filled with self-righteousness and took the side of the well-dressed gentlemen who had turned him down.

"Now you see the result of ignoring your obligations," she

544

told him. "All your life you have been in debt. All your life you have been involved in one kind of scandal or another."

"I was sure you would say they refused me because I was thirty-second in Latin at Monsieur Lepître's school," Balzac said wearily.

"You may joke," said his mother. "For your family is it no joke, I assure you."

He looked at the handsome, relentless face, wondering what she would feel toward him now had he stuck to the profession of law, made a comfortable fortune, married a girl she would have selected, presented her with an assortment of grandchildren, perhaps by this time become a judge and worn a flat topped cap in court. He shook his head, looking at the small, perfectly shaped mouth.

Nothing would have satisfied her.

He could have become the King of France and still remained in his mother's eyes an object of contempt.

With part of his being he detested her, yet he yearned for some sign of love. He would never be free of her. The cord was there that runs between the generations, invisible, but stronger than steel.

They were sitting now in Balzac's rooms in Passy. Over the sitting room chimney piece hung a little painting of Eve de Hanska, done for Balzac by the artist, Dafflinger. It was a handsome piece of painting and a good likeness of Eve. To Balzac it had become a kind of icon, the last thing he looked at before he retired, the first to attract his eye in the morning.

His mother looked at it candidly, as a woman will look at the image of another whom she has never seen, searching for faults, looking for a mouth a bit too large, eyes placed a trifle too close together, a telltale sag in the flesh of the neck that the artist has not concealed.

Dafflinger had permitted Eve to display not even the smallest fault.

After a moment, Balzac's mother said innocently, "A beautiful woman. Of course, like the rest of us she grows no younger as the years pass, this rich foreigner of yours. One presumes that the portrait was painted some time ago?"

"She was thirty-three when it was painted," Balzac said. "Last year in Saint Petersburg she looked even younger than she does in the portrait."

"Ah yes, love is blind, as one remembers," his mother said.

She looked at the portrait suspiciously. "In any case, it is apparent that she has led you up the path of her Polish garden."

"We shall be married within the year," said Balzac firmly.

His mother uttered a short, contemptuous laugh.

"You poor fool!" she said viciously. "She will never marry you. Why should a woman of wealth and position, even though she is a foreigner, marry a penniless writer, refused by the Academy, a man who will never be out of debt?"

The muscles of Balzac's arms stiffened with anger and his lip trembled. He felt a stabbing pain in his chest, as if the walls of his heart were determined to burst. He fought for his breath. His eyes bulged in their sockets. His vision failed him. He saw his mother's face in a haze of steam, like the face of a malevolent witch. Then he saw nothing. He shuddered like a stricken ox, clawed at his throat, and fell to the floor with a crash.

When he came to, Nacquart was with him. It was early evening. His mother was gone. Louise Breugnoit stood near the doorway, holding a basin, waiting for Nacquart's instructions. Behind her he saw another figure, dressed in black. At first he took it for a woman. Then he saw that it was a priest dressed in a cassock, a parish priest from Saint-Philippe du Roule. I am dying, he thought. They have sent for a priest. Nacquart has given me up at last.

Gradually, full consciousness returned. Balzac became aware of an odd sensation in his legs. He lifted the covers and looked down. Leeches were drawing the blood from his body. He stared at the creatures, fascinated. His mouth was dry. His tongue felt stiff and hard. With some difficulty, he spoke, asking for his mother.

"I sent her away," said Nacquart briskly, reaching for Balzac's pulse, then glancing at the suckling leeches. "When our little friends have finished dinner you must have absolute rest and peace. That you will never get from your mother. Louise here will look after you."

Louise smiled warmly at Balzac. He raised a hand in a feeble salute. The priest moved forward. He was a young man with a good face.

"I won't be needed after all," he said, smiling at Balzac.

"Not this time, Father," said Nacquart.

He was packing his black bag. He looked at his patient, then at Louise.

546

"He is not to move for at least a month," he said. "Louise, I hold you responsible. Tie him down if you must, but keep him in his bed."

Balzac did not protest this time. He stayed in his bed for the full month that Nacquart had set as the minimum. Louise fetched and carried for him. She bathed him in his bed, read to him, guarded his door against everyone except Nacquart and Gautier.

His mother was forbidden to visit him. She raged and stormed but Nacquart was firm.

At the end of the month when he got up, Balzac was rested and the pressure of blood on his brain had lessened. Nacquart was satisfied with him, and even gave him permission to work for a few hours a day.

Curiously, Balzac, who had turned work into a kind of religious ritual, now had no desire to write. The attack seemed to have killed his ambition. He slept through most of the nights, that had always in the past been devoted to labor. He did not complain of pain or discomfort; he simply did not work.

The days were devoted to searching for a house that he and Eve would live in after they were married and to the acquisition of objects with which to furnish it. Balzac turned to the buying of furniture with the same energy he had formerly put into his work.

Once started as a collector, he became as hopelessly enmeshed as a drug addict or a gambler. In a short time he fancied himself as a connoisseur of fine china, painting and furniture and regarded his purchases as investments on which he and Eve would eventually realize enormous profits.

There was nothing modest about his conceptions.

He owned neither a house nor the land upon which one might be built, but in his search for antiques, paintings, objets d'art, he seemed determined to rival the Louvre, the Hermitage and the Uffizzi Gallery in Florence. He made up his mind that when he brought Eve to Paris as his bride she would inhabit a mansion, the walls of which would be hung with unrivaled examples of the work of Holbein, Raphael, Van Dyck, Rembrandt, Watteau.

At Les Jardies he had merely scribbled the great names on the walls with a stub of charcoal. Now he actually bought pictures and paid good prices for them. Balzac had a warm love for painting and he was capable of enthusiasm, but his knowledge of art

547

was sketchy and intuitive rather than precise. He did not buy wisely for the walls of his castle in the air.

He was filled with an almost simple-minded self-confidence, a kind of sublime faith that whatever he did would turn out to have been the right thing.

Nacquart was inclined to wonder whether his brain might not have been damaged by the cerebral stroke he had suffered.

"We don't know much about it," he confessed to Gautier. "If his brain is damaged, then the damage is permanent, of that much you can be sure. But he doesn't seem to be mad."

"He seems more drunk than mad," said Gautier.

Balzac was perfectly lucid and in total command of his faculties. It was simply that he saw his future through the most improbably optimistic lenses.

"In a year we shall possess one of the most delightful houses in Paris and I shall be not a single sou in debt," he wrote to Eve. "THE HUMAN COMEDY will bring me half a million francs, not counting future royalties, which should come to another half million. So you see, if I live long enough I shall be an excellent catch, with a million francs to my name."

His enthusiasm carried across fifteen hundred miles to Poland. When he asked Eve for money, she ordered her bank in Saint Petersburg to forward a credit of a hundred thousand French francs as her contribution to the furnishing of "one of the most delightful houses in Paris."

With such a sum at his disposal, Balzac's collecting passed to the stage of true mania. It was a malady worse than love, relentless as addiction to alcohol, expensive as habitual gambling.

If Balzac admired a picture, a piece of furniture or bric-a-brac, a Persian rug or a tapestry, he must have it. He had no sleep until the object had passed into his possession.

He haunted the auction rooms and galleries of Paris. THE HUMAN COMEDY, that was to bring him a million francs, was forgotten. Nothing mattered but collecting. In the slums and back alleys of Paris, in the workingmen's cafés, a social revolution was brewing up. The French monarchy was tottering. Workmen talked of barricades and blood. Balzac ignored this prophetic groundswell, that Hugo and Dumas and Lamartine were watching with passionate interest, and in which they saw both danger and the hope for a revitalized France.

548

Balzac had no time to concern himself with revolution; he was furnishing a house that he did not own for a bride who had not yet agreed to accept him.

From all over Europe, packing cases arrived in Paris containing the various objects that Balzac had bought for his house of the future. Germany, Italy, Holland, Spain, even despised Great Britain, gave up their treasures to Balzac, the collector.

Balzac had faith in his own judgement and it did not occur to him to ask why he was having such phenomenal luck at finding bargains. He believed that he was acquiring priceless items at a fraction of their value. His gullibility was exceeded only by his enthusiasm.

He bought an old set of china, a dinner service for eight people, that the dealer assured him had been made to the order of a branch of the British royal family, by the best porcelain makers in China.

"I got it for three hundred francs," he wrote triumphantly to Eve. "Dumas, the ignoramus, gave four thousand for a similar but inferior set. I am assured that mine is worth at least six thousand."

Eventually, the Chinese porcelain turned out to have been made in Holland.

"It is no more Chinese than I am," Balzac admitted ruefully to Théo. "Believe me, collecting bric-a-brac is a science."

Such incidents did not discourage him; they were charged up to experience.

"One must make mistakes in order to learn," he explained to his friends. "Besides, Dutch or not, the dinner service is rather pretty."

He wandered about Paris, picking up one bargain after another:-

"A yellow cup (for five francs; it is worth at least ten!) a marvelous piece of craftsmanship. Secondly, a cup in blue Sèvres, Empire style, which had been offered to Talma. Incredible coloring! A bouquet of flowers that must have cost twenty ducats fee to the artist. (I got it for a mere twenty francs) Thirdly, six armchairs of truly royal workmanship. I shall keep four of them and have the other two made into a settee. The gilding is superb! They will be enough, with a good Persian rug, to furnish a small salon. (Two hundred and fifty francs! No more)."

549

On the same day in another corner of Paris, he found a pair of Sèvres vases.

"They must have cost the original owner between five and six hundred francs. (Don't whisper a word to anyone; I got them for thirty-five!) It is the biggest bargain I have ever struck. The fact is, my dear Eve, people simply do not know their way around Paris. With time, patience, luck and good sense—and a certain amount of knowledge, of course—there is nothing you cannot find here, and cheap to boot."

A few days later he was negotiating for the purchase of a chandelier.

"It once belonged to the King of Prussia and weighs two hundred pounds. It is of solid brass and the metal alone is worth two francs, twenty centimes the kilo. I intend to buy the chandelier for the bare cost of the metal, a mere four hundred and fifty francs, so I shall have the workmanship for nothing. I am ransacking Paris. One must not lose time. The really good things are doubling in price every day."

A few days later he assured Eve that: "You will live like a queen, surrounded by all the princely splendor that the arts can provide, and amid the greatest possible wealth and elegance."

Balzac's most ambitious purchases were a writing table and chest from Italy. Balzac was certain that they had been made by the finest craftsmen in Florence for no less a celebrity than Marie de Medici.

"Certainly they bear the Medici coat-of-arms," he told Gautier. "Heraldry is a subject on which Balzac is not easily fooled. I am astonished to find these pieces on the market. They belong in the Louvre."

Balzac bought the chest and table for thirteen hundred and fifty francs. As soon as he had paid over the money, he decided that he had bought more than mere furniture. He had purchased the key to a romantic question of history.

"I have made a startling discovery," he informed Eve. "Only the chest belonged to Marie de Medici. The escritoire bears the arms of Concini, or the Duc d'Epernon, but it also has two letters 'M' in a charming intertwined border. This proves that there was an intimate relationship between Marie de Medici and one or the other of her favorites. She presented him with her own chest, then, as a gesture of love, had the escritoire made for him."

Balzac decided that in view of the historical interest, the chest alone was worth four thousand francs. He intended to sell it to the King, who would certainly want it for the Sommerard Museum. The desk he intended to keep for himself; it would amuse him to write a book, using a desk that had belonged to a lover of Marie de Medici.

"Even if the King is only willing to pay three thousand, for the chest, I shall be perfectly happy," he announced. "That will give me a profit of sixteen hundred and fifty francs, plus the escritoire."

As a shrewd man of business, Balzac understood that the price would go up if his find was cleverly publicized. In the columns of *The Messenger,* he planted the following notice:

> One of our most famous authors, who is also a great connoisseur of antiques, has by chance brought to light a piece of furniture of supreme historical interest. The article in question is a chest that once adorned the bed-chamber of Marie de Medici. This piece of furniture, one of the most superb works of art it is possible to conceive, is of solid ebony. . . .

Balzac waited for the King to make his overtures. Louis-Philippe refused the bait.

A few dealers, intrigued by the newspaper item, came to inspect the pieces. One of them assured Balzac that if the chest could be authenticated it was worth at least ten thousand francs. Balzac, who considered his own judgment sufficient authentication, was wild with delight. He raised the price of the chest at once and wrote to Eve:

"The piece that we are going to keep is here in my apartment. It is beyond all praise. It is too marvelous and sublime to be described in words."

Balzac announced that he did not intend to keep either piece indefinitely.

"Much as I would like to, I cannot afford it," he explained. "Our best known dealer estimates that the chest is worth sixty thousand. The cabinet maker who renovated the desk says that the workmanship alone is worth twenty-five thousand. The inlaid arabesques are of a quality that Raphael himself would not have been ashamed of. I will see whether the Duke of Sunderland in London, or perhaps Sir Robert Peel, will be willing to offer me three thousand pounds sterling for it. I would let it go at that price.

Meanwhile I will keep it in my rooms and have the joy of seeing it when I wake up in the morning."

For months Balzac was preoccupied with his Florentine treasures. Now it was the banker de Rothschild who was interested. Now the King of Holland.

Balzac hired an artist to make engravings of the pieces, with the idea that they would be published in the *Collector's Journal*. He tried to persuade Gautier to write an article about them.

Nothing happened.

Neither de Rothschild nor the King of Holland was interested to the tune of seventy-five thousand francs, which was now Balzac's asking price.

As Balzac continued to ferret out bargains, his rooms in Passy became crowded with crates, packing cases, boxes and odds and ends of furniture. The hallways and doorways were so jammed that it was difficult to move about in the house. Also Balzac was worried for fear one of his creditors would get a writ of attachment and take possession of his treasures. The time had come to find a house into which everything could be moved, the whole then registered in the name of the Countess Hanska.

"That way my things will be out of reach of these harpies and their bailiffs," he told Gautier.

"But Honoré, you have a house. . . ." Gautier began.

He cut himself off. Nacquart had told him that it was pointless to interfere with Balzac now, or to attempt to advise him.

"The thing must run its course," said the doctor. "It is simply his way of taking a rest from his work, which he knows will kill him."

The house that Balzac wanted must be more than simply a place to live. It must also be an investment, and a good one. It wasn't wise to tie up money unless one was certain the property would appreciate in value. Certainly, he and Eve needed something on the grand scale. They were not going to live like paupers, after they were married. Balzac estimated that he would need forty thousand francs a year, if they were to live in a style approximating what Eve had been used to.

"Not a centime less," he declared firmly. "Victor Hugo spends twenty thousand and he lives no better than a church rat."

This was the same Victor Hugo whose princely style of living had prompted Balzac to become a playwright!

Not far from Balzac's house in Passy there was a mansion offered for sale at a hundred thousand francs. Balzac was convinced that if he could buy it, it would cost only sixty thousand in the end.

"I have secret information," he said to Gautier. "A new road is to be built in Passy, and it must go through the land on which this house stands. The authorities will be forced to buy from me and at my price."

Fortunately, Balzac found it impossible to strike a bargain for the palace in Passy.

He continued the search, deciding to look for a place outside of Paris.

He hired a coach and driver and drove through the Valley of the Loire, searching for a suitable small château, somewhere near his birthplace.

"In the country one lives for nothing," he reminded himself, intoxicated by the beauty of Touraine, determined to find an estate whose vineyards would bring in a profit and provide a life of ease such as Monsieur de Margonne enjoyed at Saché.

He was looking for a large place now.

"The small estates are absurdly expensive, since there are so many people in France with modest fortunes," he concluded. "To do a really profitable stroke of business, one must select a large property."

He negotiated for the purchase of the Château of Saint-Gatien, on whose charming fields and woodlands the present owner, the Chevalier de Custine, had brought himself to bankruptcy. Balzac was certain the secret was in Custine's inefficiency. With Balzac as manager, Saint-Gatien would make money faster than the Bank of France.

The deal fell through; Custine wanted too much cash.

Balzac quit the Valley of the Loire, returned to Paris, and took up again the search for a fashionable town house. At last he found what he wanted, to be had for a down payment that he was able to produce.

It was the Pavillon Beaujon in the rue Fortunée, an impressive eighteenth century mansion, built in pre-revolutionary days by a wealthy tax-collector. The price was fifty thousand francs. Balzac considered it a bargain, and announced that the Pavillon Beaujon

—soon to be the Hôtel de Balzac—was to be his final home on this earth.

He moved his treasures from Passy to the rue Fortunée and put everything in Eve's name.

He kept the rooms in Passy, intending to go back to work, now that his adventures in collecting were over and he had a home that was fit for his bride.

He could not work.

He sat at his green baize table in Passy, in the room where thousands of words had poured from his pen, and could not produce so much as a sentence.

He had sold a novel entitled THE PEASANTS to Eugène de Girardin, for publication as a serial in the columns of *The Press*, leading newspaper of France.

Twice, de Girardin began to print installments of the book, only to have Balzac fail to deliver the next installment when it was needed. Now he refused to publish more until Balzac gave him the completed manuscript.

"I don't mean to be harsh," he told Balzac. "But my God, man, I have my readers to think of. They aren't willing to wait six months in order to get on with the story."

In nearly thirty years of professional writing, Balzac had never left an editor completely in the lurch. When the typesetters were waiting for copy, he had always managed to sit down at his green baize table, strong coffee at his elbow, and grind out something with which to feed the presses.

Now his mind would not respond to his will. For the first time in his life he was obliged to lay down his pen, to face the blank, accusative paper, and to protest to the unresponsive night: "I cannot!"

It was Eve de Hanska who had brought him to this, as much as the overwork that Nacquart had deplored. She had forced him to simmer in a broth of uncertainty, one day loved, the next despised, one day engaged to be married, the next regarded almost as a servant. With her equivocation, her refusal to accept him finally or to give him dismissal, she had caused him to be uncertain almost of his own identity. He was unable to take the simplest decision if it involved anything more serious than the purchase of a pair of gilt sconces.

"I cannot write. I am finished," he told Gautier. "I don't think that I shall be capable of writing another line of fiction until Madame de Hanska relents."

"Love is difficult," Gautier admitted.

Balzac fixed his eyes on his friend. Then he caught Gautier's hand and held it, as if he were a drowning man clinging to a bit of flotsam in the middle of the sea.

"It is no longer simply a matter of love, Théo," he said hoarsely. "It is an obsession."

It was the first time he had used the word to describe the force that enslaved him to Eve de Hanska. The idea was one that crushed him. He sat in his red armchair after Théo Gautier had gone, rigid as a corpse, staring at a corner of the rug with the intensity of a hypnotist staring at his victim.

"My God, I am helpless," he said to himself. "I, de Balzac, I am helpless."

He passed into a mood of despair. If he could not marry, he could not work. If he could not work, he could not live, for his life and his work were the same thing. There was little hope that he would marry. He was doomed.

He got up and went to his cabinet, taking out the bottle of digitalis that Nacquart insisted always be near him. There were forty pills in the bottle, fifty perhaps. Certainly enough to kill him, if he swallowed them at a gulp.

"Death in a small package," he had said to Nacquart, when Nacquart first had given him the bottle. Now he held death in his hand and looked at it calmly. The gesture would be such a simple one. No more to it than swallowing a small crust of bread.

He put the bottle back where he had found it and closed the door of the cabinet firmly. He went to his writing table, sat down, and wrote to Eve, asking her, in a tone that was almost cold, for permission to join her at Wierzchownia.

Chapter 51

BALZAC'S LETTER reached Wierzchownia at a moment when Eve was bored. During the last year she had gone through a dozen young men with blond cavalry moustaches and blond cavalry brains, stupid fellows with brutal thighs who made love with one eye on Eve's money, the other on her vast estate. She had concluded that one might as well go to bed with a healthy serf as with a member of the Polish nobility, and to Eve a Polish serf was halfway between the ape and man.

She had listened to the creaking overtures of half a dozen elderly landowners who were eager to increase the size of their estates. She had danced in Kiev and in Warsaw and passed a month in Moscow.

She found nothing that suited her.

Back at Wierzchownia, she had devoted her energies to putting her lands in order and discovered that she enjoyed the exercise of feudal authority. She had ordered a hundred serfs flogged for misconduct during her absence and in some cases looked on while the flogging was done. She had enjoyed the sight of blood.

Now she was bored. She wanted to be flattered and amused. She wanted to speak French and to hear the gossip from Paris. For all his bad breeding and egotism, Balzac was amusing. He would keep her entertained through the snowbound Polish winter. If he became tiresome, she would simply give him some money and send him back to Paris.

She sat down at her escritoire and scrawled on a bit of her thick notepaper the one word: *"Viens!"*

Balzac wept when he received the message. Perhaps it saved his sanity. For several weeks before it came he had been closer to nervous collapse than Nacquart cared to let him know. He had lived in an agony of impotence and uncertainty, subject to hell-pits of depression, unable to work.

556

Balzac's health did not recommend arduous overland travel and Nacquart would have preferred that Eve come to Paris, but anything must be approved if it meant an end to the separation that threatened to become Balzac's grave. In any case, Balzac would have gone to Russia on a stretcher, Nacquart or no Nacquart.

Nacquart gave Balzac a fresh supply of digitalis.

"If you get a pain in the chest, 'Noré, take one of these," he ordered. "Then, no matter where you are, get into bed for at least three days. Flat on your back. Bottles and bedpans. No getting up, do you understand?"

Balzac looked at his doctor and smiled. Nacquart was seventy-five. He looked fifty, though he worked twelve hours a day and still managed to find time to write monographs on medical subjects.

"You must be a good doctor," said Balzac. "You have such an honest scientific face."

"Medicine is no science," said Nacquart. "At its worst, it is like cookery. At its best, it is like art."

Balzac was worried about his house in the rue Fortunée, where all of his treasures were stored. He had hired two rather stupid servants and started to put the place in order, but a great deal remained to be done. He wanted the house in readiness, because this time he meant to bring Eve back to Paris with him in style, before the whole world.

Certainly the establishment could not be left in charge of the two oafs who were in it now. Louise refused to take over; she was determined to marry as soon as the house in Passy was closed. Balzac needed a responsible person who knew how to deal with servants, someone who would make the two idiots toe the mark and keep things in perfect order.

Gautier might have done, but Gautier was riding a donkey in Spain. Sarah Visconti would have been perfect, but Eve would be sure to hear that he had seen her and that would cause an earthquake in Poland that one would hear in the rue de la Paix.

There was no one, except his mother.

Eve could raise no objection to his mother's presence in the house and certainly his mother would take no nonsense from the servants.

557

He made his peace with the hard old woman, or at least managed to establish a truce. She was relentless now, at seventy, as she had been on the day he was born, but she could not resist the attraction of being placed in charge of valuable property. All her life she had been infatuated with the sense of power that is the reward of management. She would have been a magnificent success at the head of a business or of a school, as the Mother Superior of a busy convent.

"You understand that these things are not my property, of course," he explained to her as he showed her through the house. "As yet I am merely the caretaker. What you see here is almost entirely the property of Countess Hanska."

"Why doesn't she send her mother to look after it then?" Anne-Charlotte asked dryly.

"As her fiancé, I am responsible," Balzac said importantly.

Before quitting Paris, Balzac made his will. He left what he owned to Eve, with the proviso that Eve agree to make his mother an allowance.

"At the moment my estate seems to consist mostly of debts," he confessed to the lawyer who drew up the document. "Actually, the rights to my books will be worth millions in the years to come."

The lawyer made no comment; privately, he decided that Balzac must either be mad or a swindler, to have created such a monstrous pyramid of debt on assets as doubtfully sound as a few dozen novels.

Balzac signed his will, saw it locked in the lawyer's safe, and told his mother that she had been magnificently provided for. In a mood of glorious anticipation, he set out for the steppes of Poland.

The normal traveler wanted fourteen days minimum for the journey between Paris and the estate of Wierzchownia, in eastern Poland. One went by train through Germany, thence by stagecoach across the width of Poland. None of the route was first-class, once the railway had been left behind.

Balzac decided to cover the distance in seven days. He was eager to be with his Eve and he disliked traveling alone. Without pausing to catch his breath, he made a mad dash through Germany, from Paris to Cologne, from Cologne to Hanover, then Berlin and on to Breslau.

Instantly he crossed into Russian Poland he was fascinated. It was Eve's country, unspoilt by the Germans—a land that was dark, mysterious, medieval and potent.

More than half of Poland was uncleared primeval forest. To the eyes of a Frenchman, used to tidiness in agriculture, it seemed to be not a country at all, but a wilderness almost as trackless as the North American forests that provided the setting for the novels of Fenimore Cooper.

As the mailcoach carried him eastward, Balzac became filled with a marvelous sense of adventure, even stronger than what he had felt when he stepped ashore in Saint Petersburg. Poland itself was remote. Eve's part of Poland was almost inaccessible.

Wierzchownia was in the heart of the Government of Volhynia, far to the east, touching Russia. It was a part of the world that God had apparently intended to remain secret, primitive, cut off. On the north, Volhynia was guarded by the Pripet Marshes, the greatest swamp in Europe. To the south rose the peaks of the magnificent Carpathian mountains. Between these two natural barriers, Volhynia slumbered—an area nearly as large as France, where life went on not very much changed from the way it had been in the fifteenth century.

"Poland is not so much a country as it is a state of mind."

So a distinguished Pole in Paris had once told Balzac. Balzac felt it now, moving eastward through the forests. The state of mind, he realized, was feudalism. This was a land of nobles and serfs.

At Radziwilloff, where the stagecoach stopped for inspection at a military post, Balzac got a taste of what autocracy meant. Beside the barrier, he was interviewed by a cavalry officer who spoke to him in perfect French and recognized his name at once.

"Honoré de Balzac? The writer?" he said.

Balzac confessed that he was a writer.

"My dear sir! This is an honor!"

The officer stepped back and saluted, then insisted that Balzac have a drink in his quarters. He gave him vodka and bits of spicy sausage, then brought out a handsomely bound copy of PÈRE GORIOT, which he asked Balzac to sign.

559

"How far are you going, Monsieur de Balzac?" the officer asked, looking fondly at his autographed book.

"To the Countess de Hanska's estate at Wierzchownia," Balzac answered with some pride, pleased to let the officer know that his Polish acquaintanceship was of the highest.

"A man of your importance should not be traveling in the common mailcoach," the officer said. "I will get you a vehicle more suitable to your position."

He went to the door and barked for a sergeant, then spoke to the man in rapid Polish. When the sergeant had gone he said to Balzac, "I have ordered them to provide you with what we call a *kitbitka,* and a Cossack sergeant to drive it. You will find it more comfortable, I think, and a good deal faster than the mailcoach."

Balzac protested that the mailcoach would do.

"Nonsense," the officer declared. "For me this is a privilege and an honor." He held up the signed copy of GORIOT. "And one for which I am being very handsomely paid. You have no idea how this will impress my comrades in the officers' mess."

Balzac bowed and accepted the service; like most writers, he was always reassured when he encountered positive evidence of fame.

The army *kitbitka* was a light low-slung carriage, drawn by a pair of military horses that were in superb condition. The top-heavy mailcoach had lumbered over the rutted Polish roads. Driven by a young and adventurous Cossack N.C.O., the *kitbitka* seemed to fly, touching only the high spots of the road.

Balzac was nervous at first as the light wheels skimmed over the ruts, then he realized that the young cavalry sergeant was an expert and began to enjoy the ride, though he was somewhat alarmed by the quantities of vodka the sergeant consumed whenever they stopped to rest the horses.

"Try some, *barin,*" the sergeant coaxed him. "It is the water of life."

Balzac took a small glass. It was fiery stuff, and an ounce of it brought tears to Balzac's eyes. The young soldier tossed back three or four glasses whenever they stopped at some primitive inn made of weathered wood.

The sergeant spoke almost no French and Balzac knew no Polish, but they managed to communicate and got along quite well during the three days they were on the road to Wierzchownia.

Balzac had been prepared for a large estate, but he had been thinking in terms of the Valley of the Loire, supposing that the Hanski holdings were a more or less glorified version of Saché. Monsieur de Margonne's handsome vineyards would have been lost in a corner of Eve's domain, which was the size of a French department.

When the *kitbitka* passed under a wooden arch, the driver grinned and said, "Wierzchownia!"

Balzac expected that the house would appear beyond the next turning of the road. Instead, they drove across Eve's land for nearly four more hours, past clusters of crude huts and broad fields planted in what Balzac took to be rye. Here and there was a weather-grey, forlorn looking church, made of rough wooden boards, sometimes with the Orthodox cross, sometimes the Roman Catholic.

At last the house came into view, a huge palace as startling at first sight as the Cité of Carcassonne. Balzac climbed down from the *kitbitka*. An enormous serf came forward, a bearded fellow dressed in a high-collared blouse made of rough unbleached linen.

"Barin!"

Balzac expected him to bow. Instead, the giant threw himself prostrate on the ground. He remained there, motionless. Balzac was baffled. The Cossack sergeant grinned and put the heel of his boot on the serf's neck, whereupon the serf rose, bowed low, and began to unload Balzac's luggage.

For a few minutes Balzac stood in the driveway, looking up at the enormous house, black and white stone, with a hundred windows, a dozen towers, a palace in the midst of the wilderness. He offered the Cossack sergeant money. The man refused, stepped back and saluted, then got into the kitbitka and drove away.

Balzac climbed the steps that led to the front door. A maid wearing a bright-colored skirt under her starched white apron led him to Eve's private sitting room, where Eva was having tea alone, behind a glittering samovar.

He surprised her. Thanks to his dash across Germany and the speed of his Cossack driver, he was six days early.

"Honoré!" she cried, startled as if she had seen a ghost.

"It is I," he announced.

She recovered her poise and rose to greet him, moving forward, arms extended.

"Welcome to Wierzchownia."

As she came toward him, mistress of this palace and of all the land around it, she had the proud bearing of a queen. Balzac thought she was magnificent. All at once he understood facets of her character that had baffled him. In this setting, her arrogance suited her as piety suits a priest. Here at Wierzchownia she was a reigning sovereign. What were faults elsewhere, here became virtues.

They embraced and kissed. She looked at him and smiled, then took his hand.

"Come, you shall have tea," she said. "Tea from a real Polish samovar."

Balzac was given a suite of rooms on the second floor of the palace, an apartment that consisted of a salon, a study, a dressing room and bath, and a bedchamber. The bedroom alone was the size of a drawing room in a French town house. The carpets and furniture were superb. The apartment was fitted with every convenience; in this country of vast distances and bad roads, long visits were the rule. A guest might stay for six months or a year.

At the door to Balzac's apartment was a straw pallet, upon which slept his personal serf, close by so that he could give instant response to Balzac's slightest demand. The serf, whose name was Tomash, prostrated himself before Balzac, touched the floor three times with his forehead, then kissed Balzac's feet, first right, then left. Tomash was not a servant, as such things were understood in France. He was a serf, a body-servant in the Oriental sense. No personal service was too menial for him to perform.

Balzac stood in the study room, looking down at the vast park that surrounded the palace, trying to digest the staggering fact of Eve's enormous wealth, which was far beyond even his wildest imaginings, far beyond anything of which he had boasted to his friends in France. It was wealth exceeding anything that could be measured merely in terms of money. Wierzchownia was a little kingdom with more than three thousand subjects—the Hanski serfs, who were bound to the earth, whose children and grandchildren the Hanskis inherited like cattle, despite the fact that the serfs were Christian souls, communicants, many of them, of the Roman Catholic church.

Eve behaved like a queen and she treated Balzac as a royal consort.

562

Her private apartments were on the floor with the rooms that had been assigned to Balzac. The furnishings took Balzac's breath away when he saw them first. There was a Louis XIV sitting room that was like something out of the palace at Versailles. There was a bedroom hung with lace from Alençon, the various poufs and little chairs covered with sky-blue satin. There was a bathroom lined with Italian marble, a boudoir with blue satin walls, a pantry, nearly a kitchen, from which meals could be served.

Eve's bedroom and boudoir were always soaked in the odor of some exotic perfume that Eve did not use when she went abroad, a heavy, suggestive scent that inspired visions of exotic Oriental sexuality, a scent that suggested a harem.

Here at Wierzchownia, Eve herself took on an eastern quality. On her native soil, western reserve and decorum fell away. Sometimes her mood was that of a savage Tartar queen.

Balzac was in the second half of the fourth decade of his life. He was by no means impotent, but by the laws of nature the fires smouldered more than they blazed. He was hard put to it to satisfy Eve's demands.

Often, here in Poland, she drank vodka instead of wine, tossing it down in the way the Cossack sergeant had done. The fiery spirit seemed to have an aphrodisiac effect. After drinking vodka, she became wanton, reckless, experimental, demanding, often insatiable.

Balzac remembered a German saying: "A drunken woman is an angel in bed."

His temperament was not Teutonic. He found the experience exhausting.

When Eve was drunk, her latent strain of sexual cruelty came to the surface and controlled her. If he was incompetent, she taunted him.

"The Great Lover! The Empress Catherine would have had you shot. That's what she did with her lovers when they displeased her, you know."

Fortunately for Balzac, these moods did not appear too often. Most of the time, Eve was delighted to have him at her side. He entertained her, reading to her by the hour, making up stories to please her and acting them out, giving her all the Paris gossip.

When she was pleased with him she clapped her hands in approval like a child.

" 'Noré, you are delightful," she would exclaim. "You are outrageous and delightful."

Balzac did not permit himself to admit what he was beginning to discover—that under the surface Eve was not very intelligent and certainly not profound. All her life she had been exposed to education and culture and this had produced a kind of gloss. At heart she was interested in food, sex, comfort and amusement.

She was enormously vain. In her boudoir was an alcove fitted on three sides with plate glass mirrors. After she had bathed, Eve would stand in this mirrored closet for hours at a time, admiring the repeated reflections of her figure. She adored her body, even though it was beginning to show the effects of her intemperate love for sweets. She gorged herself on chocolates and sometimes could not resist taking two or three pieces of pastry, after having eaten an enormous Polish dinner. She would look wistfully at the tray that the lackey offered her, upon which were arranged tarts, cream puffs, rich éclairs, oversized macaroons and the like, then sigh and say, "But they are all so good, 'Noré. I simply can't make a choice between the cream and the fruit."

"Ma grasse Eve," Balzac would say, smiling at her indulgently. "You are becoming as plump as a Turkish harem girl."

She did not mind that she was slightly fat. Neither did Balzac. Her flesh was soft but not slack. Her skin was delicate, white with a pink underglow, and very smooth. A little fat, she thought, was becoming, and in any case she had no intention of depriving herself of the rich things she liked to eat.

For all her vanity and self-concern, she managed Wierzchownia more ably than ever her husband had done in his day. He had been lax and easygoing, leaving things to his managers, happy when he was permitted to be alone with his bird books and not troubled by everyday affairs. Eve was different. She had an imperious streak and she enjoyed the exercise of power. She insisted that the fields produce to the limit, and showed no mercy to the serf who shirked his duty or tried to withhold grain for his own use.

"The land is mine. The serfs are mine," she said proudly to Balzac. "Even the sun and rain are mine, when they fall on Wierzchownia."

Balzac admired this. All his life he had believed in authoritarianism. The only fault he had ever found with the Bourbons was the lack of intelligence with which they had expressed their power. Otherwise, it seemed to him proper that the ruling class should rule and that the servile class should serve.

Still, there were things that he did not know about the Slavic methods of rule.

One morning, some weeks after he arrived in Poland, Balzac noticed that Eve was unusually animated at breakfast time, when they sat together in her sun-soaked morning room, bright with chintz, the breakfast table between them laden with eggs, hot rolls, sausages, ham, three kinds of honey in silver pots, coffee in a polished silver urn. Her eyes flashed with excitement. She seemed to be tense with anticipation.

"This morning you will see how we keep discipline in Poland," she said to Balzac. "There is a serf to be flogged."

"But surely it is not necessary for you to watch it," said Balzac mildly.

Eve raised her head proudly.

"It is a good thing for discipline, when the master is present at punishments," she said. "My father always made a point of it. Unfortunately, Count Hanski had no stomach for blood and in consequence things have become incredibly slack at Wierzchownia. It is a thing I am trying to correct."

After they had finished breakfast, Balzac and Eve climbed aboard the *troika,* a carriage drawn by three horses, and were driven out to the place of punishment, a good-sized clearing, bare of grass, in front of an enormous log warehouse. To the left were rye fields, to the right, a birch forest. From somewhere deep in the wood came the astringent smell of a charcoal oven. It was a cool autumn morning. The air was invigorating and very clear, so that objects cast sharp clean shadows on the ground. Making a circle at the edge of the clearing were about a hundred serfs, men, women and children. These were neighbors of the culprit, obliged to witness the flogging and expected to take warning from it.

When the mistress of Wierzchownia reached the clearing, the serfs fell to the ground, touching the earth with their foreheads, like a group of Moslems bowing toward Mecca. It was an impressive display of allegiance. Balzac felt a thrill of fear. He glanced at Eve. She was calm, self-possessed.

In the center of the cleared space, a wooden post had been sunk

565

into the ground. It was fitted with leather handcuffs, fastened to the post with chains. The unfortunate serf was led out quickly and his wrists were strapped to the whipping post. He was a man in his late forties, with a gaunt, baffled face. His hair and beard were matted and filthy. His trousers and black smock were shapeless.

A peasant priest, almost as dirty as the serf, wearing a cassock that was patched in a dozen places, touched the culprit's forehead with his fingertip, made the sign of the cross and mumbled a prayer. The watching serfs uttered a long, collective sigh. Never had Balzac seen a group of people whose whole being expressed such total resignation. To them, it was clear, the flogging they were about to see was an act of God, no more to be questioned than fire, birth, death or storm.

"He is to get fifty lashes," Eve said speculatively. "He stole six bushels of grain. The drunken swine all steal grain, you know, and try to make vodka with it."

One of the de Hanski foremen came out of the warehouse, carrying under his arm three knouts, or lashes. He bowed to Eve and offered these for her inspection. Bits of metal had been knotted into the heavy rawhide thongs, which were fastened to short stout handles. Eve touched the rawhide.

"Have they been soaked in milk?" she asked.

"Of course, Mistress, as you have commanded," the foreman answered, touching his cap.

"Why should the thongs be soaked in milk?" Balzac asked curiously.

"It stiffens the leather," Eve answered impatiently.

The foreman was impassive as a hangman. He slit the prisoner's smock with a knife, then ripped it from his body, exposing an emaciated back, atrociously scarred by former whippings. A kind of groan escaped from the lips of the serfs who watched. Eve sat up straight on the cushions of the *troika,* her eyes bright with excitement now, her lips moist and slightly parted.

The first whip was tested in the air. The thongs made a whistling sound. Having been steeped in milk then dried in the sun, the rawhide edges were keen as knife blades.

The foreman turned toward Eve and bowed, indicating that all was ready. Eve raised her hand, making the salute of Imperial Rome, signal that the punishment might begin.

The knout whistled in the air again, came down with force and

566

was laid across the victim's naked back. His scream was inhuman. The crowd gasped. Eve caught Balzac's wrist in a tight grip. Her eyes were fixed on the driblets of blood that now rose through the welt on the sallow skin. She was intoxicated by the sight of the torture. As the knout rose and fell, her breathing quickened, as it did when she made love. Her fingernails bit into the flesh of Balzac's wrist. The touch of her hand was hot. It was impossible to deny the profoundly physical quality of the pleasure she took from watching the serf being beaten.

After a dozen lashes, the culprit's back was a bloody pulp, all skin gone. The foreman tossed the bloodied knout aside and took up a fresh one.

"Why does he do that?" Balzac asked.

"The blood softens the thongs, you fool!" Eve hissed angrily, furious at the interruption.

After two dozen lashes, suddenly, the serf's body went limp. The man hung from the leather handcuffs. The foreman paused, moving the insensible head, which hung like a clod of earth on the flaccid neck. He shrugged, then turned and faced Eve, the knout in his fist, as if asking her for instructions. She raised her hand. The flogging was resumed.

"But the man is dead!" Balzac protested.

"He was awarded fifty lashes," Eve said harshly. "Fifty lashes he shall have, dead or alive."

Balzac's eyes turned back to the bloodied corpse lashed to the whipping post. As the lash rose and fell, the blood pounded in his head. His vision faltered and the scene before him seemed to move out of focus. He was back at the Collège de Vendôme, in Father Haugoult's study, his bared buttocks cold and helpless. He saw the fanatic eyes of the priest, the lash in his hand. His soul revolted. The cry that he had refused to utter forty years ago now burst from his lips.

"No!" he cried. "In the Name of the Virgin, Father Haugoult, no!"

His eyes went black. He retched. Then he fainted. When he came to, Eve held a bottle of smelling salts close to his nostrils. The sharp fumes stabbed the tender membrane of his nose. He shook his head and sat up. Then, as if a ground fog were clearing quickly, his vision returned to normal.

Eve was laughing at him.

567

"You may be a Slavophile," she said. "But you don't have a Slavic stomach."

Balzac rubbed his eyes, then looked at her wonderingly. She was in marvelous good humor, filled with all the complacency of a woman who has just enjoyed a triumphant episode of love.

The murdered serf had been cut down. Beside his body knelt the ragged priest, giving the last rites of the church. Slowly, the audience of serfs turned away from the scene and trudged helplessly back to their labors in the harvest fields.

Balzac and Eve drove back to the palace, where the midday meal was waiting for them. Balzac stared at his soup, almost unable to bring himself to eat.

"You are shocked by our Polish methods," Eve said contemptuously. "How do you expect us to run the country, except with harsh methods?"

Balzac made no reply; he played with his spoon in the thick soup.

"My ancestors governed an estate that was as large as all of France," Eve said proudly. "And they governed it with the knout. On the Mnizsech lands, Anna's husband rules over fifty thousand serfs. Do you expect him to keep the drunken pigs in order by proclaiming an era of sweetness and light?"

Balzac did not argue with her. By a process of reasoning, the flogging of the serf was justified. That he had died was an accident. If one believed in autocracy, he must accept harsh disciplines and absolute intolerance of disobedience. Balzac's mind accepted the bloody corpse as a necessary social fact; it was his soul that shuddered in protest.

The Ukrainian winter began its assault before the autumn was properly finished. Small wild snowstorms formed up in the Carpathian foothills and swept across the fields of Wierzchownia, leaving patches of white on the frozen clods. In early October the serfs had erected hundreds of miles of snow fence along the weather sides of the roads, using sections made of wood that looked like oversized sawhorses. These were pounded into the rich black soil, making a barricade.

Soon the real storms came, day-long, relentless, silent blizzards. By the first of November the drifts were over Balzac's head. A white stillness was imposed on all of Volhynia. Wierz-

568

chownia was almost entirely cut off from the outside world. Travel was possible by sledge, but it was kept to an absolute minimum. The serfs wore sheeplined coats and huddled in their cabins.

Because of its remoteness from any city, Eve's palace offered certain inconsistencies, especially during the winter months. The furniture and appointments were as elegant as anything to be found in Paris. There were cabinets filled with porcelain that belonged in a museum. There was a dinner service for thirty-six people made of solid gold, the value of which was more than the lifetime income of a middle-class family in France. There were linens and laces and velvet hangings. Including the kitchen staff, there were more than fifty servants in the house. In the evenings a string quartet stood by, ready to play if Eve was in the mood for music. In many ways the luxuries of Wierzchownia exceeded anything in Balzac's imagination; the scale was Oriental rather than European.

Yet the yawning stone fireplaces and white porcelain stoves were stoked with faggots of rye straw, so that the house was always filled with faintly yellow, acrid smoke. There were charcoal briquets for the kitchen stove, but none for other purposes. There was only one oil lamp. The palace was lighted with hundreds of candles.

On the other hand, the household staff included a barber, a bootmaker, a furrier and a first-class tailor. For Balzac, Eve ordered Russian snow boots and a magnificent greatcoat, lined with Siberian sable.

On clear, bright nights, he and Eve would sometimes ride over the countryside, wrapped in their furs, comfortable in a sleigh pulled by four horses, specially shod with shoes that gave them footing in the snow and ice. A contingent of Cossacks on cavalry horses, bearing pitchpine torches, lighted their way home if the moon had set.

Balzac enjoyed himself. He had never seen real winter before, except briefly in the Swiss Alps. He came to understand its virtues. The sense of isolation imposed by the snow had the effect of a benign drug, after the first wave of depression had passed. One lost track of the days and weeks, became unconcerned with time, accepting the cloister of the snow. It was calming to the nerves and to the spirit.

Eve and Balzac were like fairy tale lovers imprisoned in the Faraway Palace. Once a week, more or less, depending on the state of the roads, the postman's sledge brought the mail. It was the only connection with the outside world.

On Sundays, Eve and Balzac went to Mass in the de Hanski private chapel, a little fieldstone church that had been built a short distance from the house. In winter, the pathway from the house to the chapel was roofed over. The church was simple and very small. There were two rose windows of stained glass that Hanski's grandfather had ordered from Paris. The furniture of the altar had come from Rome, the gold chalice beautifully jeweled. The priest was a young man with a passionate Ukrainian face, high cheekbones, stern jaw. He uttered his Latin phrases in a low-pitched, resonant voice. He was manifestly devout.

"Do you never have him to dinner?" Balzac asked.

He was thinking of the provincial clergy in France, who are from time to time asked to dine in the great châteaux. Eve shook her head.

"Never," she said. "His father was a mujik—a government peasant, do you understand. His grandfather was a Hanski serf."

"But he is a priest, not a serf," said Balzac.

"It would not do," said Eve firmly.

She would not sit down to her dinner with the priest, because he was the son of a government peasant and the grandson of a serf, yet to him she confessed her sins and from him she received absolution. In the same way she accepted the love of Balzac's body, soul, mind, and heart, received him into her own body, and sometimes at the same instant looked upon him with contempt, as her God-ordained inferior.

She was a web of contradictions.

There was more evil in her than good, more cruelty than kindness, more meanness of spirit than affection.

Yet Balzac loved her, or at least was mortally committed to the idea that he loved her, and this in its way was worse, for he was an artist, and he had the artist's stubborn faith in his own conceptions.

Balzac had intended to remain at Wierzchownia at least until the following spring, but in January he found himself obliged to return to Paris. The Baron de Rothschild wrote to him on a sheet of deckled vellum. Shares in the Northern Railway were falling. If he hoped to avoid bankruptcy he must return to Paris at once and put his affairs in order. He would need cash, Rothschild warned him, in order to cover the shares, so as not to lose them altogether.

Most of the money he had invested in the Northern Railway Company had come originally from Eve. Now Balzac was obliged to explain his predicament to her and to ask for a loan.

"Rothschild!" she exclaimed bitterly. "You were a fool to trust a Jew. We know them better here in Poland, let me tell you. Sometimes it is impossible to prevent the peasants from cutting their throats in batches."

She went on, expressing regret that the Baron de Rothschild had not met his fate in a Polish pogrom. She questioned Balzac's intelligence and implied that he was dishonest. But she gave him the money, a draft for fifty thousand francs. Money was something she had and to spare. Her ego fed on Balzac's pathetic begging.

In the dead of the Polish winter, huddled in his Siberian overcoat, a charcoal stove on the floor of the sledge at his feet, Balzac set out to cross Europe, en route to Paris.

It was twenty below zero, the air so astringent that it was almost impossible to breathe. The roads were simply gullies in the snow, frozen slick in patches, so that the going was dangerous. The two mujiks who drove the sledge kept themselves warm with vodka, swinging their arms in the air and bellowing folksongs at the horses in alcoholic Polish. Their beards were frozen solid but they were drunk and happy.

Balzac was miserable. The journey from Wierzchownia to the railhead at Cracow, in winter, was enough to test the strength of a young and healthy peasant, used to living in the out-of-doors. Balzac undertook the journey at the risk of his life, and he knew it before a day had passed. Yet he would not turn back and he had made up his mind that he would not die.

Eve had given him two stone bottles of vodka, flavored with sour-grass. He used the spirit as medicine, taking a mouthful at a time. It burnt his lips and made him gag, but it kept him alive—it and his will power, that had seen him through other crises of mind and body.

In the middle of February, exhausted and running a dangerous

571

fever, he reached his house in the rue Fortunée, where his mother had been left in charge of the treasures that he had bought for Eve. As he entered the main hall he heard the sound of rifle fire, coming from central Paris. He stopped, waited, and heard another fusillade.

"What is that?" he demanded, his voice hoarse with fever.

"That is the revolution," his mother said drily. "The people in the streets have finally agreed with you that Louis-Philippe must go."

Chapter 52

THE FIRING THAT
Balzac heard came from the rifles of the National Guardsmen, who
had been shooting over the heads of the mob in the Place de la
Concorde, in an effort to force the people to disperse.

A week later the rifles were lowered, the National Guardsmen
aimed and fired and once again the blood of the people ran in
the ancient gutters of Paris. The Revolution of 1848 had begun,
and the echoes of the cannon in the Tuileries Gardens could be
heard by the common people all over Europe. The sound of the
guns even reached Saint Petersburg and Moscow and Kiev, heart-
ening the land-bound serfs, continuing a libertarian cycle that
Frenchmen had started half a century ago. It was the beginning
of the death struggle of the ancient system that Eve enjoyed at
Wierzchownia.

Balzac was ill and belonged in bed but he did not intend to
miss the revolution.

Wearing his sable overcoat and a high fur hat in the Russian
style, he went into the streets of Paris. There were soldiers everywhere. Thousands of regular army troops had been called into
the city from garrisons all over France. Even the cadets from
Saint-Cyr had been ordered to active duty. Louis-Philippe was
making an effort to save his monarchy with a show of military
force.

The time for that was past.

All over Paris, republican meetings were being held. Crowds
were singing the "Marseillaise," waving tricolored flags. Street
vendors offered reproductions of the Gallic cock, defiant rooster
that was a traditional French symbol of liberty. Workmen pinned
red cockades to their caps.

The day was warm for February and the mood of the crowd in
the Champs Elysées was gay, almost the mood of a carnival. The
shops were closed, with shutters drawn, but most of the cafés were
open and filled with people.

It was not a carnival, however. Over the voices of the crowd,

573

Balzac could hear the hobnailed boots of a regiment being moved into position. On a side street off the Champs Elysées, he saw a battery of artillery, gun carriages and caissons unlimbered and ready for action.

He shouldered his way through the crowd. It was a working-class crowd, the men wearing denim blouses, and his furlined overcoat inspired some comment, but he was not molested, or even recognized, until he came to the Place de la Madeleine.

As he rounded the church, a big workman stepped into his path and blocked the way. He was a powerful fellow with intelligent eyes, now slightly bleary with drink. He wore a scarlet cockade in his hat.

"Citizen Balzac?"

Balzac stiffened and his hand closed around the knob of his cane.

"I am Monsieur de Balzac, a subject of the King of France," he replied evenly. "Stand aside and let me pass."

The man caught his arm in a fierce grip.

"Not until I show you what a good writer looks like," he said. He spun Balzac around and pointed. "Take a look, Balzac, at Citizen Lamartine. He's a writer and a good one, who is not ashamed to be on the side of the people."

Balzac tore his arm free. It was indeed Lamartine who stood on a crude wooden platform, making a speech to the crowd. Beside the platform stood a boy holding a tricolored flag.

Balzac made his way toward Lamartine.

"Alphonse!" he called, when Lamartine was obliged to pause for breath. "Alphonse Lamartine!"

"Balzac!"

Lamartine grinned down at him and waved. Then he went on with his speech, urging the people to keep discipline, but to stand fast for their rights. When he finished the crowd roared with approval. Men tossed their hats in the air. Clearly, thought Balzac, Lamartine is the idol of the mob.

Lamartine climbed down from his platform and shook hands with Balzac. A young workman took his place and began to make a speech.

"Let us find a café," said Lamartine. "My throat is dry with too much speech making."

"I'm not sure it shouldn't be cut," said Balzac. "Why do you encourage the rabble?"

574

"That rabble, as you call it, is the French people," said Lamartine calmly.

"It is the duty of the people to do as they are told," said Balzac, with some irritation.

"The revolution is a fact. Nothing can stop it," Lamartine told him. "The people need leadership. They must have it."

They found a café behind the Madeleine and sat down at a little table, ordering brandy and strong coffee. The proprietor served them nervously, glancing through his windows at the crowds, which were gathering strength.

"What will it be this time, if the King must go?" asked Balzac.

"A republic," said Lamartine flatly. "As certainly as that Greek temple there is the sanctified Church of the Madeleine, France will become a republic within a few weeks time."

Balzac groaned. "Not another!" he said.

Lamartine leaned forward, arms on the table, one hand encircling his coffee cup. He was a lean, handsome man, ten years older than Balzac, with a mass of strong iron grey hair in disorderly ringlets. He looked rather like a French Hamlet, but his sincerity and intelligence prevented the effect from being objectionably theatrical.

"Face the facts, Honoré," he said persuasively. "You have been backing the wrong horse for years, ever since the old days when we met at Nodier's, in the Arsenal. The Bourbons are finished. So is the House of Orléans. The King is a fool. He will take advice from no one. In his own mind he has confused himself with Louis XVI and he will be very lucky indeed to escape Louis' fate."

"Revolutions gain nothing," said Balzac. "We have had them before in France."

"This one will gain electoral reform, at least," Lamartine insisted. "We are supposed to be living in the nineteenth century, under a constitutional monarchy. If it weren't such a scandal, it would be a joke. There are thirty-five million people in France, Honoré. How many of them do you suppose can vote?"

Balzac shrugged his shoulders.

"Two hundred thousand. No more," said Lamartine. "And nearly half of those who vote are employed by the government. The King appoints the House of Peers. He virtually appoints the Deputies. There is no Loyal Opposition, as one finds it in England. The common people have no voice at all, except for that voice that you hear outside in the Place de la Madeleine."

"It is a voice my ears find unpleasant," said Balzac.

"Get used to the sound," Lamartine advised him. "It is the voice of the future."

At this moment the window pane behind them was shattered by a bullet. The two writers ducked to the floor, showered with splinters of glass. Lamartine stood up, shaking bits of glass from his coat. His cheek was cut and bleeding.

"Municipal Guards," he said. "The National Guard has gone over to the side of the people."

Balzac stood up and looked through the broken window. Lamartine was right. The crowd was being dispersed by mounted policemen wearing brass helmets with horse tail plumes and glittering brass breastplates. They were members of the hated Garde Municipale, elite troops detested by the people, who regarded the conscript National Guardsmen as their friends. The Municipal Guards were professionals, ruthless, impassive, and efficient.

There was no more shooting.

The troopers were using the flats of their sabres and the rumps of their specially trained horses, moving the crowd back into the half dozen side streets that feed into the Place de la Madeleine.

"They order these things better in Russia," Balzac said, half in earnest.

Lamartine shook his head, dabbing at the cut on his cheek, dipping his handkerchief into the brandy.

"This is France, Honoré, not Russia," he said. "Come over to the side of the future, where a writer belongs."

"I prefer the past," said Balzac.

"Your books betray you," said Lamartine. "Your best books are on the side of the future. They cry for change."

The following day, the revolutionary crowds threw up barricades in the most densely populated parts of Paris. Workmen in denim smocks tore up the paving blocks from the streets. Wagons, carts, even old items of furniture were used to block the narrow thoroughfares. In pairs and fours, the Municipal Guards trotted through the city on patrol. One after another, whole companies of National Guardsmen went over to the side of the revolution.

Balzac wandered through the city.

In front of the official residence of Monsieur Guizot, the King's Minister for Foreign Affairs, a mob of several thousand had gathered, most of them working men and women from the Fau-

576

bourg Saint-Antoine, a quarter that Balzac had haunted during his apprentice years in the rue Lesdiguières. Here and there among the crowd he recognized a face out of his past, a washerwoman, a blacksmith, a man who kept a cheap café where he had often stopped for a cup of black, bitter coffee.

From a little distance off, standing on a stone railing, Balzac watched the crowd, seeing at the same time a mob, with one personality, and a group of Paris workingmen and their wives, individuals, some of whom he knew and had once called by name. It was possible to feel the mob growing in cohesiveness, individuals called Jacques or Jean or Paul or Marie or Yvette, giving up their identities, becoming simply human items in a faceless mob.

For some time, nothing happened. A cordon of troopers with drawn sabres defended the minister's house. The high, indifferent sun glinted on their polished helmets and on the broad blades of their swords. The horses were nervous and difficult to control. The troopers reined them in sharply, jerking savagely at the bit when an animal moved forward.

"Down with Guizot!" the crowd chanted, stamping their feet on the cobbles.

The day was colder than yesterday; steam came from the mouths of the people and from the nostrils of the horses.

"Down with Guizot!"

"Down with the King!"

"Vive la République!"

Suddenly an officer's horse charged forward and reared up, his forelegs frantically pawing the air. A woman was thrown to the ground and trampled. Further down the line, another horse was out of control. There was a sudden, high-pitched scream, then the shrill cry of a horse in terror.

The crowd, in that instant, ceased altogether to be a gathering of workingmen and women from the Faubourg Saint-Antoine. It became a mob, with a single face and a single heartbeat, losing even the instinct for self preservation. It moved toward the file of Municipal Guards, inflamed with collective anger, determined to pull the troopers from their saddles.

Balzac heard the barked commands and the horses were edged back. Then the sabres crashed into their scabbards. The troopers drew their carbines and fired into the crowd.

An instant later they fired again.

The mob staggered, like a wounded elephant, stood firm for a

577

moment, then fell back. The troopers fired a third volley. A horse snorted angrily. Another reared his head in the air and uttered a terrifying scream.

A hundred people lay on the cobbles as the crowd drew back. Fifty of them were dead. The crowd was silent, shocked, watching the blood form into pools, blood that was the same color as the cockades they wore on their caps.

Balzac vomited, tasting the stomach bile in his mouth. He sat down on the stone railing, feeling dizzy and quite sick.

The crowd moved up two-wheeled carts of the kind used by market men. Into these the dead were piled like so much cordwood. On top of one cart was the body of a young woman, skirts up, legs spread obscenely, the dead flesh spattered with blood.

"Cover her!" someone cried.

"No! Leave her as she is. Let the bastards see what they have done."

The girl's body was left uncovered, a shocking and cruel sight. All day long the workingmen drew the carts through the streets of Paris.

"Lamartine was right about one thing," Balzac reflected, walking home. "The King has lost his reason. There is no saving him now."

Still, Balzac was not persuaded to lend his support to the revolutionists. If he were asked to serve a new government when it was formed, well and good. He had no intention of climbing up on a packing box beside Lamartine, to make speeches to the mob.

While the crowds roamed the streets, displaying their dead and singing revolutionary songs, in the Tuileries, Louis-Philippe sat in council with his ministers and the Queen.

"Perhaps I should resign the crown," the King said nervously. "I want to do what is right for France."

"You cannot abdicate, mon ami," his Queen said. "France needs you. Let Monsieur Guizot resign. That will satisfy the mob."

Guizot resigned.

Thiers became first minister.

The King and the royal family remained in the Tuileries, terrified, afraid to show themselves.

Guizot had resigned too late. The mobs in the streets were not going to be satisfied with a scapegoat. They demanded the fall of

578

the King himself, and they had the power in their hands. There were barricades all over Paris. The National Guard and various regiments of the regular army had turned their backs on the régime. They gave their rifles to the mobs and threw away their uniforms.

A mob of workmen with appropriated rifles took possession of the École Militaire. Another mob sacked the Palais-Royal, which was the private property of the King. Everywhere, men chanted their demands for the King's head.

The next day, Louis-Philippe abdicated in favor of his grandson, the little Comte de Paris, announcing, with tears in his eyes, "This child is now your King."

As soon as the King and Queen had left the palace, with an escort of tough, loyal dragoon guards, a mob from the streets poured into the gorgeous halls.

Balzac was with them.

The mob looted the official files in the administrative offices of the palace, making confetti of state papers, throwing them from the high windows into the historic gardens. From a palace window streamed a length of pink gauze, found in the boudoir of some lady in waiting. After a little, objects of furniture, gilt chairs, mirrors, delicate footstools, were hurled from the windows into the flower beds below.

Balzac, half-dazed, drifted through the marble halls of the palace. The scenes were bizarre. In one of the Royal bedchambers, a workman in wooden shoes was rubbing scented pomade into his hair, grinning idiotically at his reflection, then smelling his calloused palms with delight. Another workman poured perfume on himself from gold and crystal bottles. A third scrubbed at the blackened stumps of his teeth with a brush that royalty had used that morning.

In one of the gilt and crystal reception rooms, a big man in a drayman's blouse sat at a mother of pearl piano, stamping out the "Marseillaise," which for many years had been a forbidden tune in Paris.

At the top of the grand staircase stood two National Guardsmen, wearing white cross belts, bowing to the mob: "Enter, ladies and gentlemen! Enter!"

In the King's bed, three workmen were smoking cigars.

On the silk sheets of the Queen's bed, a rawboned Paris whore lifted her skirts and offered to take on all comers, free of charge.

A street urchin, wearing one of the Queen's headdresses with a bird of paradise plume, went from one room to another, methodically slashing the faces from the royal portraits that hung on the walls. Balzac raised a hand to stop him, then thought better of it. Until the mob grew tired of destroying things, there was no point in appealing to reason.

In one of the young Prince's bedrooms, Balzac picked up some exercise books, containing royal Latin lessons. With these, and a strip of gold embroidered velvet cut from the throne of Louis-Philippe, he shouldered his way against the crowd, down the grand staircase, passing into the Tuileries Gardens, which were now a shambles of smashed furniture, clothing, broken bottles and pots of cosmetics.

Around one of the iron lampposts, a humorist had laced a pink corset. The silk straps fluttered in a light breeze. Old women in black shawls prowled moodily through the flower beds, looking for objects of value.

That night in the Place du Carrousel, the mobs lighted a bonfire and burnt the fairy tale carriages that had been hauled out of the royal stables. A triumphant cheer rose from the crowd when Louis-Philippe's state coach, in which he had ridden on the day of his coronation, was fed to the flames. All night long, the fires burned and the crowd watched, singing and dancing by the firelight, unmindful of the acrid smell made by the burning varnish and upholstery.

The next morning the entire working-class population of Paris seemed to be in the streets. There was a semblance of revolutionary order and purpose that had been lacking earlier. From the tricolored flags on public buildings, revolutionary committeemen cut the blue and white strips, leaving only the red. Others, with tarpots and brushes, went through the city, systematically effacing the royal arms wherever they appeared.

The city became preternaturally quiet.

No vehicles passed through the streets, for the paving blocks had been torn up to make barricades. Shops and cafés were closed, shutters tightly drawn. The troops that had seemed to be everywhere, now mysteriously disappeared.

Late in the afternoon, at Harfleur, an obscure seaport town,

580

Mr. and Mrs. William Smith embarked on an English steamer. They were the former King and Queen of France, going into exile in Great Britain.

The first phase of the revolution had been completed. Now came the problem of putting the pieces of France together.

In the rue Fortunée, Balzac sat in his red armchair and brooded over what had happened, still shocked and shaken by some of the sights he had seen.

He had never admired Louis-Philippe. Even less did he admire the republican mob that was lionizing his colleague, Alphonse Lamartine. He wondered quite seriously whether there would be a place for a man like himself in the egalitarian France that Lamartine and others seemed determined to bring into being, even at the cost of more blood. Perhaps he should return to Poland, with the idea of remaining there and becoming a subject of the Tsar.

Rothschild changed his mind.

"The so-called Republic is only a phase," the banker told Balzac. "It is doomed. Men of influence are privately supporting Louis-Napoleon. When he takes power, he will know how to deal with the rabble in the streets."

"And in the meantime?" Balzac asked.

The banker shrugged. He was a financier, who always took the long view. The meantime was something he was always prepared to deal with and to wait out.

"In the meantime of course, things will be difficult," he said. "Money will be very tight." He pursed his lips, then said, "If you need cash, for immediate expenses, perhaps I can help you."

During the last few weeks, hard money had almost disappeared from Paris. Gold and silver could be obtained only by standing for hours in the queues that formed in front of the mairies, and then in strictly limited amounts, for specific purposes. Yet tradesmen and others refused to take anything but metal. Balzac was pleased to accept five thousand francs in gold from Rothschild, who took the money from his safe and gave it to Balzac in a canvas bag of the kind that banks use.

Balzac left Rothschild's mansion in a mood that was much improved. The financier had assured him that his railway shares, in the long run, were as sound as the soil of France itself.

"Buy more while they are low," Rothschild had advised. "The

intelligent man can make money, even out of a revolution. It is all a matter of knowing in advance which way the wind is going to blow."

Balzac at once wrote to Eve, urging her to forward money to be invested in the crippled shares of the Chemin de Fer du Nord. He wrote to her every day, but no replies were forthcoming.

"It is the mails," he insisted to his mother. "Almost nothing is getting through because of Lamartine's revolution."

"Letters that are not written are seldom delivered," said his mother sarcastically.

She had never set eyes on Eve, but she loathed her, principally because Eve had shown no sign of admitting that Balzac's mother existed. The old woman was growing intensely bitter. She had put Balzac's house in order, guarded his chattels like a hired servant, tried to teach his servants their jobs, and she realized that if at last he did marry Eve, there would be no place for her in this ambitious household. She did not even expect to be permitted to welcome the newlyweds on the threshold, when her son brought back his bride from Poland. To forestall the possibility of such an insult, she insisted that Balzac employ a competent servant to replace her, if he intended to return to Wierzchownia.

Because of the revolution, it was difficult to find servants. Balzac interviewed three dozen butlers before he employed François Munsch, an Alsatian who had for some years been a soldier in the regular army. Munsch had curious, wild eyes and Balzac suspected that he drank, but he was impressed by the man's military bearing.

"He will look magnificent in livery," he told his mother. "After all, appearance is an important matter in a butler."

"I have a son who employs butlers," she said bitterly. "Yet I cannot take the omnibus to Surésnes to visit my daughter because I haven't the fare."

Balzac handed her ten francs, knowing perfectly well that she had plenty of money tucked away in her handbag and more upstairs in her room.

Since the sacking of the Tuileries, Balzac had not concerned himself very much with the revolution, but in the middle of April the revolution came to him, in the shape of an invitation to stand for election to the Chamber of Deputies as the candidate of the Club of Universal Fraternity.

Properly speaking, there were no political parties in France. Candidates were offered to the voters in the name of one or another of the hastily formed and hastily named political clubs like this one.

The group that approached Balzac was a collaboration of young, more or less literary men. He was flattered and he knew that if he said the things that the young men wanted to hear, he would almost certainly become a deputy. Once seated in the chamber, he was absolutely certain to become a minister in one government or another.

It was an old dream with Balzac.

Ten years ago he would not have hesitated to have cut his political cloth to fit the situation. In those days, to get elected, he might have persuaded himself that almost any program suited him. Today, he was nearly fifty years of age. It seemed important to him to say precisely what he felt about France, though he knew that he probably forfeited any chance of being nominated.

The young men of the Club of Universal Fraternity wanted to hear ringing words of promise, bright words of defiance, brave slogans flung to the wind.

Balzac had no bright words to give them. To him, stability was the key to the future.

"What France needs is order, self-discipline," he told the delegation that waited on him. "From 1789 to 1848, France—or Paris, if you like—has changed the constitution of its government about once in every fifteen years. Don't you think it is time for us to find a durable form, so that our prosperity, our commerce and art, our credit, our national fame, shall not be periodically called into question? I hope that the new republic will be wise and strong. We need a government that can sign a lease for longer than fifteen or eighteen years."

The young men were disappointed. They thanked Balzac, took themselves off, and looked elsewhere for a candidate. Balzac had thrown away the one real chance he would ever have of becoming a member of the French government.

He turned his back on politics and busied himself with his personal concerns. Rothschild assured him that his railway shares were safe. His new servant, François Munsch, seemed to be capable of running the establishment in the rue Fortunée, provided his mother kept an eye on him. There was nothing to hold him in Paris. As soon as the intense heat of summer had passed, he once again set out for Poland.

Chapter 53

Nicholas the First, Tsar of All the Russias, was a Romanoff autocrat to the bone. There was no generosity in him. For the subject Polish nobility he had both hatred and contempt. Republican France he regarded with fear and detestation. Like the other absolute monarchs of Europe, he had trembled during the winter and spring of 1848, when the rebel mobs were in the streets of Paris, and he had responded to his fear by strengthening the hand of the dreaded Imperial Secret Police.

When he was presented with the petition of a Frenchman named de Balzac, who, it seemed, had the effrontery to contemplate marriage with a landed Russian subject, Nicholas did not deliberate before reaching a decision.

"The petition is refused," he said harshly. "And this Balzac is to be informed by the secret police that in Russia laws are not made to be broken, as they seem to be in France."

Balzac's petition, with various recommendations attached, was returned to the French Embassy in Saint Petersburg, through which it had been forwarded to the Winter Palace.

When the Tsar's refusal reached Wierzchownia, Balzac was in bed, attended by two German physicians, the Doctors Knothe, father and son. He had been in bed for nearly a year, in Eve's Ukrainian palace.

He was a dying man and in his heart he knew it, but the superb will that had commanded his energies through the writing of more than a hundred books fought against the admission. He listened to the officer of the secret police who brought him the Tsar's warning, propped himself up in the bed, smiled and said, "Surely the omnipotent Little Father is not afraid of a mere writer?"

584

The policeman looked at him contemptuously, drew on a pair of white gloves, turned on his heel and departed. Balzac sighed and went back to sleep.

They had made him comfortable at Wierzchownia and the two Germans subjected him to various radical treatments, clucking their Teutonic tongues in unison over the backwardness of medicine in France.

For a time Balzac seemed to improve. In March, after a bedridden winter, he was able to get out of bed for a few hours each day.

On the first day when he got up, he made his way to the carved walnut clothespress in his room. Hanging inside was the monk's robe of white cashmere, uniform of his working life. His hand reached out and touched the cloth. He began to take down the robe with the idea of putting it on. Then he changed his mind. He chose a silk dressing gown and went into his study, sitting beside the porcelain stove. He felt old and hopelessly depressed. He had the sense that the monk's white robe with its dangling shears had been put aside forever.

"My God, I am only fifty," he said to himself, inching closer to the glistening stove, which gave off a little heat. "I am only fifty. It is monstrous."

He had no hope that Eve would marry him now. If ever he might have expected her to defy the Tsar, that time was past. Here in Poland, she was rich, respected, powerful. Why should she exchange this for marriage with an invalid who offered nothing but debts and for life in a faraway country where the mob was in the saddle?

"What have I to offer?" he asked himself. "I can scarcely catch my breath."

Even to talk was an effort for him. For a whole year he had not written a line or earned a penny. Love-making was out of the question. He was weak as a child. Eve de Hanska was now his nurse instead of his mistress, his "wife of love" as he had once proudly called her. In common justice, he thought, I must free her of this obligation.

"I must return to Paris as soon as I am fit to travel," he told her that night, when she came to his rooms with the servant who brought him his supper.

"You shall not go alone," she said quietly. "I shall go with you, as your wife."

Balzac was stunned. He could not believe that he had heard correctly.

"But the estate?" he said. "If you marry without the Tsar's permission, Wierzchownia will be confiscated."

She shook her head.

"The Tsar believes that we Poles are creatures of inferior intelligence," she said. "He is wrong. I have given Wierchownia to my son-in-law, Count Mniszech, in return for which he has agreed to make me an annual allowance. We are free to marry in spite of the Tsar."

Balzac wept like a child, permitting the tears to run down his cheeks unchecked. Eve dabbed at them with a handkerchief.

"An hour ago I was a dying man," Balzac said. "You have made it possible for me to live, and I shall live."

Eve de Hanska's decision to marry Balzac at last had not been made on the spur of the moment. Except where her daughter Anna was concerned, Eve was not given to impulsive gestures. She had determined to marry Balzac with as much cold-blooded self-interest as, in the past, had prompted her various refusals.

She was fed up with Poland and tired of the responsibility of running Wierzchownia. What had been an exciting novelty at first was now a demanding chore. She wanted to live in a great city where various enjoyments would be at her doorstep, not fifteen hundred miles away. Saint Petersburg did not attract her. She detested Moscow and its pretensions. Kiev was an overgrown provincial town. Warsaw was a mud-soaked morgue.

For a woman like Eve, Paris was the place to live, Paris, the City of Light.

But if she went to Paris as Eve de Hanska she would simply be another Polish émigré with a title, not as rich as some, not as poor as others, in substance, a nonentity. She remembered Vienna, Geneva, the warmth of the fame that had been reflected from Balzac. As Eve de Balzac, widow of the famous French novelist, she would have guaranteed importance, entree to the great houses. As owner of Balzac's books and his literary executor, she would be an important person in the literary world of Paris. To be Balzac's wife

586

was one thing, and not very desirable. To be his widow would be quite another.

That she would become Balzac's widow soon after she became his wife was a circumstance the German doctors did not encourage her to doubt. Within six months, a year at the very most, he would be dead and in his grave. It was not much of a price to pay for Balzac's name and control of the rights to THE HUMAN COMEDY.

As for Balzac, now that his dream of seventeen years promised to become a reality, he had no intention of dying. His mood was that of a criminal whose sentence of death has been reprieved. He bullied his doctors and ordered them to make him well.

"How can I get married if I can't breathe?" he demanded of the elder Knothe, who consulted with his learned son and prescribed massive doses of hot lemon juice, in an effort to break up the congestion in Balzac's chest.

Balzac's heart disease had been compromised by an attack of the mild malaria that was endemic in the Polish Ukraine—the so-called "Moldavian Fever." The lemon treatments made him vomit. He shook with malarial chills and fever. His heart faltered and struggled like an exhausted horse.

"He is doomed," the younger German said conclusively to Eve. "No man can survive the malaria with his heart."

Balzac was doomed but he was determined to astonish the Teutonic mind, if nothing else. He made a kind of recovery. During the first week in March, he dressed himself and came downstairs to dinner, shaking, pale, breathing with difficulty, but standing erect on his own feet.

"It is a miracle," whispered the servants, crossing themselves.

"It is the lemons," said the elder Knothe, stroking his beard sagaciously.

"It is Balzac!" said the author of LA COMÉDIE HUMAINE, signalling to the servant for another helping of the stringy Polish beef he disliked.

Two weeks later—nearly seventeen years after they had pledged their love at Neuchâtel—Balzac and his Eve were married in the parish church of Saint Barbara, in the mud-splashed, dreary Ukrainian town of Berdicheff.

In his dreams of other years, Balzac had planned to be married in a cathedral and by a bishop, but he was not disappointed. He was happy, gloriously happy. The pain of his mortal illness was submerged in his happiness.

Before the ceremony was performed, both Eve and Balzac availed themselves of the Holy Sacrament of Penance.

Kneeling in the humble wooden church, Balzac had a sharp awareness of the Infinite Mercy of God. With all his heart, with every fibre of his being, with tears in his eyes, he made a passionate Act of Contrition.

From the dark box, through the grilled window, the words of the priest fell on Balzac's soul like a warm rain of mercy.

"May Our Lord Jesus Christ absolve thee, and I by His authority absolve thee from every bond of excommunication, and so my son I absolve thee from thy sins, in the name of the Father, and of the Son, and of the Holy Ghost. Amen. May the Passion of Our Lord Jesus Christ, the Merits of the Blessed Mary ever Virgin, whatever good thou hast done and whatever evil thou hast borne, be for thee unto the remission of sins, the increase of grace, and the reward of everlasting life. Amen."

It was seven in the morning.

The day was grey.

When they came out of the church, a slow cold drizzle of rain had started. The sky was low and dark, unpropitious. Eve stared at her husband. A gust of wind blew the rain in her face. The first sharp stab of regret pierced her heart.

By the time they reached Wierzchownia, the drizzle had turned into a relentless, depressing spring rain. Eve was struck with dissatisfaction, certain that she had made a mistake. She went straight to her rooms, stripped off her wet things, and locked the door.

Balzac was happy. He wrote to his old friend Zulma Carraud, who had been shamefully neglected these last years.

"I have been married at last to the only woman I have ever loved. This marriage, I believe, is the reward that God has kept in reserve for me. My childhood was not happy. My young manhood was not exactly decked with flowers. But now it seems that I shall enjoy a radiant summer of life and the most delightful of autumns."

Poor Balzac!

He thought of nothing but his Eve. He wrote to his mother, giving her instructions to prepare the house in the rue Fortunée for himself and his bride. There were to be flowers, masses of them, in every room. François Munsch was to see to it that every lamp and candelabrum in the house was lighted as soon as darkness fell, from a date three weeks hence, and this was to be done, without fail, every night until the triumphant arrival from Poland.

As soon as the highways were partially cleared of snow, Balzac insisted on starting out for Paris, refusing to wait for the warmer weather that would have been kinder to his health.

It was a punishing journey.

In Poland the roads were like bogs. Again and again the heavy carriage was mired. Once it was overturned and Balzac was injured. He insisted that they go on. It took them a month to reach Dresden, instead of the normal eight days. By the time they entered Saxony, Balzac was exhausted and his eyesight was failing. He lay on his bed in the hotel room, struggling for breath, writhing with the pain in his chest.

"But the gentleman is very ill," said the hotel porter to Eve. "He should have a doctor. A good German doctor."

"He has already had a good German doctor," said Eve harshly. "Concern yourself with the luggage and not with the state of my husband's health."

"Ja, ja!"

The porter touched his cap and brought up the rest of the bags. Eve left Balzac alone. She dined in the hotel restaurant, a big meal, then went shopping. In a charming little boutique she found a perfectly delightful pearl necklace that she could not resist buying.

Mercifully, Balzac was so wracked by pain and so close to delirium that he did not become aware of the fact that his wife despised him and cared not at all whether he suffered, lived or died.

It was not quite time for him to die, and in any case, he refused the idea of dying on German soil. He made a recovery and the journey was resumed.

As they approached the French frontier, the weather became warmer and Balzac was somewhat improved. He began to admire the landscape, gazing fondly at the orderly allées of poplars along the roads in northern France. Then he began to praise the house that was waiting for them in the rue Fortunée. Eve cut him off bluntly.

"It cost me enough," she said harshly. "I assume that it is fit to live in."

Balzac said no more. He burrowed into his overcoat, shaking with a malarial chill.

Darkness had fallen when they passed through the Porte de la Villette. By the time they reached the rue Fortunée, it was pitch black. Every window of the house blazed with light.

"Perhaps your mother is giving a ball," Eve said sarcastically.

"My mother is certainly not here," said Balzac.

Painfully, he got down from the carriage and with some difficulty, using his stick, he made his way to the front door. He tugged at the brass bellpull. The sound of the bell could be heard through the door.

No one answered the summons. Balzac tugged on the bellpull again. Then he pounded on the door with his stick.

With her rings, Eve rapped angrily on the carriage window. "Please to hurry, monsieur!" she called. "It is freezing here and I am tired."

Balzac beat on the door with his stick and kicked at it with the toe of his boot. He tried to shout. All he managed to produce was a croak.

"François! Open the door! It is I! Monsieur de Balzac! Open the door!"

From inside the house came a peal of maniacal laughter, an unearthly, terrifying sound.

Balzac turned and faced the carriage, leaning heavily on his stick. He was faint and dizzy and scarcely able to see.

"I don't understand," he said helplessly. "There is something wrong."

"Are you taking up the art of understatement in your old age?" shrieked Eve. "Get that door opened at once. I am cold and I am tired."

By this time a little crowd had been attracted by the commotion. Three men made an effort to force the door with their shoulders. It would not budge.

"There is a locksmith in the Impasse Brie," one of the neighbors remembered. "Perhaps he can be persuaded to come."

590

"Impasse Brie?" Balzac said.

He took a step, staggered, and would have fallen had not the man beside him caught his arm and steadied him.

"You are ill, monsieur!" the man cried, his face filled with concern.

"Merely tired," Balzac insisted. "We have been traveling, you see. From Poland. It is my wife's country."

"I will get the locksmith," the man promised.

The locksmith appeared, wearing a nightcap, muttering objections to being awakened. He picked the lock with a long tool.

When the door swung open there was revealed a macabre tableau. The marble floor of the main hall was strewn with thousands of wilted flowers. The stale perfume was overpowering. Lights and candles blazed everywhere. In the center of the hall, holding aloft a three-branched candelabrum, stood Balzac's servant, François Munsch. He was naked and his body was smeared with blood. One look at his eyes revealed that he had gone stark raving mad. He put down the candelabrum and sank to the floor, covering Balzac's feet with kisses.

"Master, master!" he cried. "I have carried out your instructions. The flowers are here. The candles have been lighted. All is in readiness for your bride."

When the others tried to pull him to his feet, Munsch fought like a wounded tiger, clawing and biting at the men who tried to contain him. At last he was overpowered and dragged away to a madhouse, wrapped in an old coat of Balzac's.

Scarcely able to stand, shaken by the experience, Balzac led his bride across the threshold of her new home.

Eve de Balzac had no intention of acting as her husband's nurse, when all of Paris, in springtime, was outside the door. She put him to bed that night; in the morning, Balzac's mother was sent for.

They met in the elegant drawing room in the rue Fortunée, the old Frenchwoman and the Pole, Balzac's mother and Balzac's wife, neither of whom had ever loved him. Upstairs, on his deathbed, Balzac lay half-conscious, struggling for a fragment of breath. Outside, the city of Paris was bright in the May sunshine. The house was silent. One of Balzac's antique clocks ticked nervously on the mantelpiece.

"It is not that I intend to shirk my duty, madame," Eve said

591

coldly. "It is simply that I have had no training in these matters."

"One does not expect a princess to concern herself with the mundane," Balzac's mother said contemptuously.

"I am not a princess," Eve said lightly. "Only a countess."

Balzac's mother shrugged, then looked coldly at her daughter-in-law, in an instant confirming the judgments she had made over the last few years.

"I will undertake to care for my son," she said. "It is apparent that I have no choice."

From the first the two women detested one another. Neither made any real effort to conceal what she felt. They maintained on the surface an icy formality, but that was all.

Balzac's mother moved into a small room near his bedchamber. Eve was established in what had been planned as the master suite, a large bedroom, sitting room and dressing room, richly curtained and furnished.

Eve lost no time in setting out to conquer Paris. She had scores of friends in the French capital, and she quickly made a place for herself in the colony of fashionable Russo-Polish émigrés, as well as with the diplomatic set.

Always infatuated with personal adornment, she haunted the most expensive dressmaking salons and jewelers' shops, buying lavishly for herself and for her daughter Anna. She ordered dozens of evening dresses, daringly cut, and scores of stylish hats. She bought a brougham and English horses and employed a driver.

For the sake of appearance she visited the sick room at least once each day. She was cruelly indifferent to Balzac's suffering. She was waiting for him to die, and she took very little pains to conceal her callous lack of concern.

Nacquart was in daily attendance. He had forbidden Balzac the slightest exertion. For a time, Balzac was not even permitted to speak. His eyes had failed almost completely, so that most of the time he was merely able to distinguish light from darkness. His hand could scarcely hold a pen. He dictated a letter to Gautier, then raised himself painfully in the bed and demanded the quill. He scrawled at the bottom of the page, forced to pause between each letter: "I am no longer able to read or write."

These were the only words that were written by the author of LA COMÉDIE HUMAINE in the house where he had planned to finish the great books that were in his mind.

Nacquart was unwilling to trust his own judgment. He called in

592

a collaboration of specialists. All were agreed that Balzac was finished. No miracle could save him.

"The only thing we can do is to administer palliatives when he is in pain, and stimulants, from time to time," Nacquart advised Eve, when the other doctors had confirmed his opinion.

"You must be the judge of such matters, Monsieur Nacquart," said Eve indifferently, drawing on a pair of long white gloves. "After all, you are the doctor."

Looking at her with distaste, Nacquart watched her leave the house and step into her glistening carriage. Recently, she had begun to omit her duty visits to Balzac's bedside. She had started a love affair with the painter, Jean Gigoux, who, as an old acquaintance of Balzac, was able to call at the house, under the pretext of visiting the sick man. During June, Gigoux and Eve were constantly together, driving in the park in Eve's new brougham, dining in restaurants where Balzac was well-known, even going to the Comédie Française and the Italian Opera, ignoring the fact that they created gossip.

Mercifully, Balzac was too ill to know what was going on. Sometimes he was too ill to know whether or not Eve came to see him.

Everyone except Balzac himself accepted the fact that he was mortally stricken. During his interludes of strength, Balzac brushed death aside and insisted that in two months he would be back at work in the study he had created for himself in this house of his dreams.

"I shall live to be eighty, like my father," he said to Victor Hugo, who came to see him one day in July. "You know, I come from strong stock."

Hugo nodded and patted his hand, brushing a tear from his eye.

Balzac found it humiliating to have his intimate requirements attended to by his mother. He insisted that Nacquart erect an arrangement of ropes and straps above the bed, so that when it was necessary he could heave himself up and make his way across the room.

Late in July, using the straps, he slipped and fell heavily against a carved table leg, gashing his calf almost to the bone. The wound became infected almost at once; Balzac's body had no strength with which to fight the poison.

Nacquart lanced the abcess, but it refused to drain. The poison spread through Balzac's system. His leg, then most of his side became streaked with violent colors, yellow, blue and purple. Nacquart gave him morphine, against the hideous pain.

Still, he did not quite die.

His sister came. He could hardly see her. With his fingers, he touched her face, tracing the outline of her mouth, her nose, her chin. She knelt by his bed and they embraced. He managed to utter her name: "Laure."

She wept.

Through the early days of August, Balzac's life was going fast. He lay in the heat, almost senseless. Then, in the middle of the month, he had a sudden resurgence of strength. His eyes were bright. He was able to speak, though his voice was cracked and unfamiliar.

Nacquart, at his bedside, recognized it for the curious portion of energy that is sometimes the prelude to the end.

"I must finish THE HUMAN COMEDY," Balzac said quite firmly. "Will I live long enough to do it?"

Nacquart shrugged.

"I insist that you tell me," Balzac said.

"How long will it take you?" Nacquart asked.

"Six months," Balzac replied.

The old physician shook his head; he did not intend to lie to Balzac. Too much had passed between them for that.

"What? You can't give me six months?" said Balzac. "Well then, can you give me six weeks?"

Again Nacquart shook his head.

"Tell me what I can hope for," said Balzac. "I suppose you can give me six days. I will outline the books that remain to be done. My friends will finish them for me. Hugo. Gautier."

Nacquart again shook his head.

"How long will I live?" Balzac asked.

Nacquart touched his hand.

"My dear boy, I have known you since the day you were born," he said. "I cannot lie to you, 'Noré. You will scarcely last out the night."

"Not even six hours then?" Balzac said feebly.

His head sank back to the pillow; his eyes were turned to the wall. His hands went limp, as if they relinquished their grip on life.

594

"He is done for, madame," said Nacquart quietly to Balzac's mother. "You must send for a priest, and at once."

The stern old woman stood up, smoothing her skirt.

"Very well," she said. She looked at her son, then said, "I think he would like Victor Hugo to be here. And his sister. He was always fond of his sister."

She went out of the room, dispatching servants to call for the priest, for Hugo and for Laure.

A servant was sent to fetch Eve. He knocked at the door of her bedroom. There was no answer. He knocked again. Eve's voice came through the door, filled with Slavic fury.

"Do not disturb me, you lout!"

The servant retreated.

Victor Hugo was at dinner when the message reached him. He left the table and ordered his coachman to take him to the rue Fortunée. He rang the bell. The moon was shining through a mass of cloud. The street was empty. No one answered the bell. He rang a second time. The door was opened. A maid appeared, holding a candle.

She was weeping. Hugo followed her along a passage, ascended the staircase that was covered with red carpet, and went down the corridor to Balzac's room. As he approached the door, he heard a loud, ominous, rattling sound. He stepped into the room. The odor of putrefaction was heavy. Balzac lay with his head supported by a mass of pillows. His face was purple, almost black. He was unshaven. His hair was grey and cut short, his eyes open and staring. As Hugo saw him in that light, in profile, he was struck by a strong resemblance between Balzac and the Emperor Napoleon.

Balzac could not speak. Hugo went to his bedside, lifted the covers, and clasped his hand. In a corner of the room, Balzac's mother sighed.

"He will die at dawn," she said.

Hugo looked down upon the face of the author of THE HUMAN COMEDY. He was moved by a strong feeling of comradeship. He bent down and kissed the damp forehead, then turned quickly and went out of the house.

The priest came and administered extreme unction. Laure came and held her brother's hand.

Still, Eve had not appeared.

Balzac's mother stood straight as a trooper, staring at her son. Then she turned and marched through the corridor to Eve's bedroom. She rapped commandingly on the panel. There was no reply. She turned the knob and pushed. The door swung wide. In her arrogance, Eve had not troubled to turn the latch.

The room was lighted by a single candle. On the night table were glasses and a champagne bottle in a silver cooler. On Eve's bed lay Jean Gigoux, his legs bare, his breast exposed, his hands clasped behind his head.

Eve, clad in a filmy dressing gown, lurched toward the door. Her hair was tumbled over her shoulders, black as ink. Her breasts were exposed.

"How dare you!" she cried, drawing the robe tightly about her, her eyes flashing with anger.

"Madame, your husband is dying," Balzac's mother said. "Your presence is required."

Eve hesitated for a moment, then surrendered. She followed the old woman down the hall to Balzac's bedside. Together, they stood in the yellow light, amid the odors of decay and death.

Balzac's head was turned to the wall. He died a few hours later.

During his last days, Balzac had insisted to his mother that he wanted a third-class funeral. Eve saw no reason to question his wishes, so that after his death he was permitted to practice the kind of bourgeois economy that had always eluded him in life.

The Requiem service was held in the simple parish church of Saint-Philippe du Roule. The young priest who officiated was the one who had been called to Balzac's bedside some years earlier.

When the funeral service was finished, the corpse of Balzac began its last journey, to a place he had loved all his life, the cemetery of Père-Lachaise, on the hill, high over Paris.

In death, old enmities were forgotten. Balzac's pallbearers were Victor Hugo, Alexandre Dumas, the critic, Sainte-Beuve, and a Monsieur Baroche, Minister of the Interior, representing the French Republic. Behind the hearse walked representatives of the French Academy, the Sorbonne, the Legion of Honor.

It was pouring rain and the stones of Paris gleamed wet in the greyish-yellow light. Passersby stopped in the rain and touched their hats to the creaking hearse.

Monsieur Baroche, the Minister of the Interior, had been instructed to attend the funeral as an official duty. He was soaked and uncomfortable. He turned to Victor Hugo, who walked beside him in the rain, and said curiously, "Monsieur de Balzac was a somewhat distinguished man, I believe?"

Hugo turned his noble head and looked with contempt at the politician.

"He was a genius, sir!" he said.

There was water at the bottom of the new grave in Père-Lachaise. Four workmen lowered the coffin into the earth with ropes. A hundred people stood in the rain. The clouds were low and densely grey, moving fast, with white scud showing here and there.

Eve looked charming in her new widow's weeds. Balzac's mother stood with her thin face turned to the rain. His sister wept.

Victor Hugo stepped forward and began to speak in a great voice. There was a wind that carried away some of his words into the rain. One sentence rang out clearly when there was a lull in the wind:

"Without knowing it, and whether he will it or no, the author of these tremendous works belongs to the strong race of revolutionary writers."

As Hugo finished speaking the clods of damp earth began to fall on the coffin. The people turned away, Balzac's friends and enemies, his false wife and his old mother, who at last was weeping for him, her tears mixed with the sweet rain.

Toward evening the rain stopped.

The sun came out all over Paris.

In Père-Lachaise the great wet stones bore single names: MOLIERE, FONTAINE, silently waiting for the new one that would read: BALZAC.

The End

Author's Note

Wine of Life is a novel, based on incidents from Balzac's life, selected with an eye to their narrative importance. Most of the dialogue and a few of the scenes are imaginary, but there has been no significant deviation from the truth.

Readers who desire standard biographies are referred to André Billy's two volume work in French, *Vie de Balzac* (Flammarion, 1943) and to *Honoré de Balzac* by Herbert J. Hunt (University of London, The Athlone Press, 1957.)